Announcing ...

The Journey of Scott Haldeman

D.C., Ph.D., M.D., FRCP(C), FAAN, FCCS(C)

As a leading supporter of the chiropractic profession, NCMIC is proud to have underwritten the biography of Dr. Haldeman, one of chiropractic's most influential individuals in recent years.

The book, written by Reed Phillips, D.C., M.S.C.M., Ph.D., details not only Dr. Haldeman's involvement in the profession, it reveals the human side of his fascinating life journey.

We hope you enjoy Dr. Haldeman's captivating story.

NCMIC
We Take Care of Our Own

The Journey of
Scott Haldeman

The Journey of
SCOTT HALDEMAN
DC, PhD, MD, FRCP(C), FAAN, FCCS(C)

Spine Care Specialist
& Researcher

Forging International
Interdisciplinary Cooperation

WITHDRAWN

By Reed B. Phillips, DC, MSCM, PhD

The Journey of Scott Haldeman
Spine Care Specialist & Researcher

ISBN 10: 1-880759-90-X
ISBN 13: 978-1-880759-90-5

*This book is dedicated to the future of spine care
and to all those who will collaborate
to provide that future, based on evidence.*

*This was Scott Haldeman's professional **Journey**.*

*This will be his **Legacy**.*

Acknowledgements

The enormous task of writing the life history of someone as complex as Scott Haldeman was Herculean, and required teamwork, patience, and perseverance.

Had Scott and Joan not lived as they did, there would be no story to write, or at best, a different one. They have been indefatigable in helping me pursue details, filling in missing gaps of information, ensuring accuracy, and providing support and encouragement. Besides the expected innumerable phone calls and countless e-mails, I spent time under their Southern California roof and three weeks in their shadow, exploring their homeland in South Africa.

Providing additional back-up information and family insights were Wyn, Scott's mother, and Lynne, Scott's sister. Interviews with Reeve and Stephanie, and Keatly and Megan—Scott and Joan's two boys and their spouses—gave expanded Haldeman perspective.

The following individuals shared personal stories about their experiences with Scott. They are listed in alphabetical order by last name. Each contribution is noted in the substance of the book, the best form of thanks that I could provide: Willem Boshoff, DC; Doug Branvold, DC; Alan Breen, DC, PhD; David Chapman Smith, LLB; Simon Dagenais, DC, PhD; Reg Engelbrecht, DC; Lynton Giles, DC, PhD; Alan Goldman, MD; Allan Gotlib, DC; Adrian Grice, DC; Eric Hurwitz, DC, PhD; Don Nixdorf, DC; Mary Reilly-Tully, DC; Robin Mateski; Sidney, DC, Phd, and Tammy Rubenstein, DC; Louise Taché-Piette; Daniel St-Germain, DC; John Triano, DC, PhD; Henry West, Jr., DC; Jim Wooley, DC.

While most of the photos in the text and the material contained on the DVD came from Scott's personal files, certain individuals also offered assistance and valuable material for the visual side of his story: Margaret Butkovic, MLS, provided access to the photo archives of the Canadian Memorial Chiropractic College and helped identify Josh Haldeman and others in several group pictures; Carl Cleveland, DC, provided his video interview with Scott at no expense to the project; Barry Lewis, DC, provided some excellent photos at the WHO/WFC conference in Beijing; and Glenda Wise, MLS, allowed access to archival material and photos from the collection in the Palmer College of Chiropractic Library in Davenport. She also helped clarify some facts regarding Scott's experience at Palmer.

In addition to Scott's keen memory, others such as Andries Kleynhans, DC, were interviewed for their perspective on details of events regarding Scott's impact in Australia; David Chapman-Smith, LLB, regarding the World Federation of Chiropractic; Attorney George P. McAndrews & his legal assistant, Andrew Sunaitis, regarding the details of the Wilk suit; Don Petersen on issues related to the Mercy Conference; and Aubrey Swartz, MD, on the history of the American Back Society.

My technical team created a polished, professional product. Chris Grasso was responsible for the cover art; Niel Townsend produced the DVD; and Bryan Crockett handled the book layout and printing.

To the team members who corrected my grammar, changed my sentence structure, eliminated redundancies, and brought deserved life to a story already full of excitement are the two editors who read and manipulated the text at least three times from cover to cover. Anne Phillips (daughter-in-law), and Sandra Phillips (wife), made the book a pleasure to read. Fortunately, my spouse found some fulfillment in refining her husband through his writing.

The National Chiropractic Mutual Insurance Corporation and its President, Louis Sportelli, DC, provided the necessary financial support to bring a project they felt was historically significant to a conclusion. Dr. Sportelli read each chapter as it was completed and encouraged me at every juncture in the process.

Foreword

Louis Sportelli, DC

I have been asked to do many things which have been extremely meaningful and memorable in my lifetime. Writing a few words as the foreword of this book is a very high privilege and honor for me.

The last 50 years of the 20th century, I am certain we can all agree, have been the most tumultuous decades of positive advancement for the chiropractic profession. Systematic accomplishment and enormous success were achieved by various organizations and individual visionary leaders all looking to advance the profession, each from their unique sphere of influence.

You are about to read a story of an individual who has had more than his share of struggles and strife, successes and stardom, all while enduring the complexities of simple survival in a professional world that oftentimes neither encouraged nor embraced him.

If by chance you are one of those individuals who are tempted to either skim this book or read ahead to the last chapter, you will miss a fascinating tale of unadulterated desire and determination in every facet of his complex journey, from his legacy as the son of a charismatic chiropractor from South Africa, to his journey in multiple countries obtaining multiple professional degrees. He broke the "glass ceiling" on what was considered unthinkable organizational affiliations and rose to lead those groups.

For those who know Scott Haldeman it will be no surprise to learn that he accomplished all he set his mind to do. As the book will reveal, his extended family, wife, and children, as well as friends and colleagues, believed in him as much as he believed in himself. Knowing the personal anguish he endured throughout his training and since, one could easily understand that he might become pessimistic about life or his career. However, nothing could be further from the truth. This interesting and in-depth story will show the triumphs of hardship and challenge met by dedication and supported by love. It's the anticipation of a dream to make a difference that becomes a reality.

This authorized biography written in vivid detail with intimate knowledge of the life of Scott Haldeman will take the reader on a journey much like the safaris of South Africa, where thirsty roots of his early life were first planted.

The excursion will take you from his childhood through his adult career, to discover the complexity of this individual in eloquence and simplicity. Whether you know Scott Haldeman or not, you will be both captivated and awed by the seemingly impossible accomplishments of this dedicated, driven, and passionately unwavering individual as he achieved his vision for a profession in conflict.

Table of Contents

SECTION I
Background, Upbringing and Education

Section IV
The Future

INTRODUCTION

By Reed B. Phillips, DC, MSCM, PhD

The reconstruction of a person's life is no simple task—even when records are complete, programs and mementos saved, photos preserved, and most importantly, the person is still available and capable of participating in the reconstruction process.

Getting the facts straight is the first step. Having an archival record of events requires thorough review to ensure accuracy of chronological ordering. But typically, no single life event is seminal. Rather it is the intermeshing of each single event with the thoughts and plans preceding and following it that require more than a simple chronicling.

Facts provide framework—a skeletal structure upon which personal thought and emotion can be attached. Determination of where to attach personal thought and emotion, that is, understanding the inner person in the context of a factual event is open to interpretation. Even a person's own memories are influenced by emotion beyond the facts themselves.

Finally, the actual happenings must all be couched within a social construct that is historically accurate and contextually relevant. Only then can the reader of the reconstructed life have confidence that the story is real rather than fictional—the difference between a biography and a novel.

Reconstructing the life of Scott Haldeman was no simple task, but it was an enjoyable one. Being his contemporary (we are close in age), his professional colleague (we are both chiropractors), and having similar passions and ambitions (we have both been involved in research), established a kinship beginning. Such a relationship was requisite before Scott could open his files, his photos, and his personal life to my interpretation and scrutiny. I can even claim to have uncovered skeletons in his closet—those related to his studies and his work—not skeletons of disrepute.

While I did work with Scott on various projects through the Foundation for Chiropractic Education and Research (FCER), never did I have the privilege of daily interactions with him like so many others about whom you will read. It was a Saturday afternoon conversation with him in his back yard in Santa Ana in 1977 that helped influence my decision to pursue further graduate education beyond my DC degree. This was a time when the number of chiropractors boasting an additional graduate degree was less than five.

It was Scott who received the first Fellowship support from FCER—definitely a new concept for the Foundation. Being the recipient of the second FCER Fellowship, I express gratitude for Scott's precedent example.

It was Scott who weakened the barriers that prevented chiropractors from publishing in scientific journals and textbooks. Having personally been denied the right to publish in a scientific (medical) journal because of the DC letters behind my name, I greatly appreciated the fact that Scott broke the professional glass ceiling on the credit of his PhD or MD degrees or both. Eventually, through Scott's influence, scientific medical journals began to publish articles with chiropractors as authors, first by not listing anybody's degrees, and finally giving full acknowledgment. His *Modern Developments in the Principles and Practice of Chiropractic* set the stage for others to publish textbooks pertinent to, and greatly needed in, the chiropractic profession.

It was Scott who chaired the membership committee of the North American Spine Society (NASS) when I applied for membership. I was the second chiropractor ever to do so. Scott was the first. Not wanting to demean the organization by allowing chiropractors to join, there was opposition in their leadership to my membership, but Scott prevailed. I was granted membership on the strength of my PhD, a tactic Scott used to open the door for many other chiropractors to join. Nowadays, being a DC is a non-issue for membership in NASS.

As formidable an influence as Scott can be, both in physical stature and intellect, he was not always successful in breaking barriers. For example, when Scott was serving as president of the North America Academy of Manipulative Medicine, I pursued membership and was flatly denied. Scott lobbied hard, but policy only softened enough to allow me attendance at a meeting when I was requested to provide assistance to Dr. Kirkaldy-Willis, their keynote speaker.

Through my role as the research director at FCER in the early 1980s, Scott and I worked together on the Low Back Pain Clinical Trial, the New York Academy of Sciences conference proposal, the Chiropractic Research Commission, the FCER grant review committee, and various other research-related activities. Always a gentleman to work with and full of activity and ideas, Scott was an asset who FCER called upon often.

Later, at the end of the 1980s when I served as the research director at the Los Angeles College of Chiropractic (LACC), and during the two decades following as president of LACC, which was transitioning to become Southern California University of Health Sciences (SCUHS), Scott and I shared a common pathway on numerous occasions. A frequent guest in our Visiting Scholar's program, a mentor to several of our graduates, an advisor on a randomized controlled clinical trial, a graduation speaker, as co-members of the Research Council of the World Federation of Chiropractic, speaking on joint venues, and as a personal friend, we had many opportunities to share ideas, discuss issues, and prognosticate on the future of chiropractic and manipulative therapy. Never contentious, but assertive when convinced of the correctness of his position, Scott was always a delightful colleague filled to the brim with workaholic drive. It is little wonder that he was called upon by so many organizations to serve on their boards and in leadership capacities.

These many interactions caused me to believe I knew Scott Haldeman well. When I was invited to reconstruct his life in an authorized biography, I was honored. Only after a year's worth of research, plowing through 30+ file boxes (1,500 lbs of paper), hundreds of photos and slides, numerous interviews, three-weeks touring South Africa (the country of Scott's youth) with him and Joan and other friends, living with him and Joan in their home for days at a time, and spending another six months actually writing and editing the work created did I come to realize more fully the true nature of the man. He has done more to break down barriers and create opportunities for the chiropractic profession than any other person in the last score of years in the 20th century.

With all the accolades he has attained, and having gotten to know him almost as well as his family—to whom Scott gives great credit for his success—the description of Scott that repeatedly comes to mind is this ability to build bridges. Some have accused him of being either a fence sitter—not defining himself as either a chiropractor or a medical doctor—or as a traitor to one or the other profession. Never did I find evidence that he was either. He stood with his feet confidently and firmly planted in both professions. He was always a highlight at any speaking venue—for he spoke the facts and made them relevant to the audience. His research was continually focused on the good of the patient, and his practice associates report that his patients thought highly of him.

He never hid the fact from his medical colleagues that he was a chiropractor and, in time, was respected for his honesty. He never boastfully used his PhD or his MD credentials among his chiropractic colleagues but always presented himself as one of "us"—for in his heart and by his lineage and upbringing he truly was. A committed husband and father, and now grandfather, his legacy has been established but has not ended. Scott will continue to expand his legacy—not in boastful pride, but because his inner-self compels him to do so.

It has been my privilege to help others become familiar with the *Journey of Scott Haldeman*.

Reed Phillips, Scott Haldeman, Joan Haldeman circa 1988

Prologue

Why spend a lifetime studying spinal disorders?

By Scott Haldeman

The spine, in my opinion, is the single most interesting and fascinating organ in the body. There is no other organ that encompasses as many tissues and potential pathologies. Spinal disorders are more universal in their impact on society than any other health care concern, with the possible exception of tooth decay and the common cold. They are associated with an extremely high level of disability and expense, and the burden on society is increasing in both cost and disability. The educational challenges, intellectual search for scientific understanding of the mechanisms underlying spinal disorders, the political stimulation of working with multiple professions and their organizations, and the ability to influence public and professional policy to advance the care of patients have been the prime motivators for my ongoing interest in this field. I will attempt to outline in this brief introduction the reason for my continuing enthusiasm for the study of spinal disorders.

Epidemiological studies demonstrate that 80-90% of people will develop back and/or neck pain at some point in their life. Multiple studies have shown that at any one point in time, 30-40% of the population will have back pain or neck pain. No one is immune from back pain. The statistics are similar from adolescent to the elderly years with a slight peak between the ages of 30-50. It affects all races and both men and women.

In a 2002 U.S. government survey, low back pain was considered the most common cause of lost work days while motor vehicle crashes, that usually include neck injuries, was the third most common cause of lost work days in adults. A 2009 study in the *Archives of Internal Medicine* notes that the prevalence of chronic low back pain that impairs function has climbed to more than 10% of the population. Neck pain that inhibits the ability to function has been shown to be present in 5% of the population at any point in time. A major concern is that the number of people impaired by low back pain has increased from 4% to 10% over a 14-year interval from 1982 through 1996. It has been estimated that 150 million days of work are lost each year because of low back pain.

In the United States the cost of treatment, disability, and lost productivity due to low back pain could be as high as $600 billion per year. Treatment costs alone may be as high as $90 billion each year. We do not know how much neck pain costs society, but the amount of money paid for whiplash related disorders from motor vehicle crashes exceeds $8.5 billion a year.

A study published in the *Journal of the American Medical Association* (JAMA) in 2008 reported that in a major national survey, those patients with spinal problems had medical expenditure of more than $6,000 compared with $3,500 amongst those who did not have any treatment for spine problems. This article described an explosion of both the types and number of treatments being used for the treatment of the problem. The total estimated expenditures for the treatment of low back and neck pain increased by 65%, adjusted for inflation, from 1997 to 2005. This was accompanied by an increase in physical functioning limitations from 20.7% to 24.7% in the same time period—a frightening observation that indicates that spending more money is not solving the problem.

TREATMENT OPTIONS FOR SPINAL PAIN

The patient with back or neck pain has always had a very difficult choice when trying to select a treatment approach. In a recent paper, I identified more than 200 potential treatment options which are widely offered by clinicians or advertised in the professional and public media. In order to illustrate the extent of the problem I suggested that these treatment approaches could be divided into aisles similar to those in a supermarket.

In Aisle 1, one could picture more than sixty pharmacological products or medications that are currently being offered to patients with chronic low back pain. In Aisle 2, there are thirty-two different manual therapies, while in Aisle 3, there are twenty different exercise programs. In Aisle 4, I identified twenty-six different passive physical modalities, while in Aisle 5 there are nine educational and psychological therapies. Aisle 6 has twenty different injection therapies, and Aisle 7 contains ten minimally invasive surgical techniques. Aisle 8 has twenty-five different surgical procedures.

This does not include the various lifestyle therapies, including ergonomic aids such as body casts, belts and braces, or foot orthotics, mattresses, chairs and massage instruments. Furthermore there are multiple so-called alternative and complimentary therapies including the various forms of acupuncture, meditation, faith healing, Tai Chi, Yoga, nutritional supplements, and herbal and homeopathic medications.

This supermarket of back or neck pain options has made it extraordinarily difficult for patients, clinicians, and payers of health care to make decisions about which treatments should be reasonably considered. Patients living with chronic pain must often make a choice of treatment approach with insufficient or incorrect information and without adequate understanding of the potential benefits, risks and costs of the various treatment methods. They then have to face the unknown consequences of their choice. Clinicians must recommend treatment but in general have limited information and experience regarding those treatment approaches that they have not learned about through their training or practice. Third party insurance payers and policy makers tend to be lay persons who are overwhelmed by the number of treatment options that make it almost impossible for them to make rational reimbursement decisions.

THE SPINE CARE CLINICIANS

The prevalence of incapacitating spinal pain, the huge costs to society, and the complexity of the treatment options being offered to patients has led to the establishment of multiple different professions and subspecialties who offer care to patients with spinal disorders. A patient with back or neck pain may elect to see their family physician or chiropractor. They may be referred to or demand to see a neurologist, neurosurgeon, orthopedic surgeon, osteopathic physician, physical medicine and rehabilitation specialist, rheumatologist, psychiatrist, or anesthesiologist. The specialist may in turn recommend that the patient see a massage therapist, a physical therapist, occupational therapist, or psychologist. If the patient does not wish to follow routine medical care, they might elect to see an acupuncturist, faith healer, homeopath, naprapath, or naturopath directly.

Irrespective of their training, all of these professionals, who in my experience are dedicated and committed to offer the best care that they can, have noted that a percentage of patients with back and/or neck pain seem to improve while under their care. These observations have tended to reinforce the impression that the treatment they offer is beneficial. However, the majority of patients with back and neck pain are likely to improve without any care and a number of patients seem not to improve irrespective of the care they receive. Patients in this last category often wander from one clinician to another trying out one treatment and then another for years, at considerable cost and without relief. In many cases the patients may actually find that the treatments they are receiving have significant complications or have the potential to make the problem worse. This has often reinforced the opinion of the next clinician they consult that treatments offered by others do not work and may have negative consequences. The problem, both in the past and the present, is that no well-defined criteria have been developed to assist a patient in choosing a particular profession or specialty for the management of their back or neck pain. Most clinicians who treat back pain have become very skilled in the procedures they offer (i.e., surgery, manipulation, exercise or medication). However, the educational programs of the major spine care clinical professionals have tended not to spend time covering treatment options outside of their specialty and even today educational and research conferences of the different professions have little or no presentations on treatments that may be considered alternatives to the skilled procedures offered by most members of that profession. To date, there is no single profession or specialty that has demonstrated the ability to understand and offer all treatment options for the management of back pain. We do not have a "spine specialist" who has the same overall comprehension of their field as for example a cardiologist in heart disease or an oncologist for cancer.

FAILURE OF INTERPROFESSIONAL COMMUNICATION

One of the factors that have led to the confusion over the management of spinal disorders is the historical unwillingness or inability of the healthcare professionals to communicate with each other, conduct adequate research to assess the value of their own procedures, compare it with other alternative treatments, and establish uniform treatment protocols.

This failure of communication was particularly evident between chiropractors (and early on osteopathic physicians) and the different medical specialties prior to the mid-1980s. Often the disagreements were quite vicious and derogatory. The medical profession until the mid-1980s often referred to chiropractors, osteopaths, acupuncturists, and others as "quacks" or "charlatans" and made it unethical for a medical practitioner to cooperate with other licensed health care physicians who did not have a medical degree. They often referred to nonmedical practitioners as "unscientific" despite the fact that at that time, virtually no medical or surgical procedure for the management of spinal pain had been established by scientific clinical trials as effective. The cause of most spinal pain is still not known.

At the same time chiropractors, acupuncturists and other professionals outside the mainstream medical community would make claims of success for conditions based solely on anecdotal observations and theory without conducting the necessary research to justify their claims. They would also attack organized medicine as "monopolistic," "ignorant," and "biased." Elaborate theories were developed in an attempt to differentiate these professions from each other and from mainstream medicine.

THE CHALLENGES OF THE SPINE CARE WORLD

The decision to focus on the spine and the nervous system came from my heritage in chiropractic. The first challenge was to obtain the education necessary to understand the spine and nervous system. My education in chiropractic at Palmer College gave me the knowledge and skills to take care of patients but left a number of questions on how the spine and nervous system worked unanswered. A master's degree then appeared to be necessary to study the basic premise of chiropractic at the time, namely nerve compression. The PhD convinced me that I was only beginning to become educated, and I do not believe I ever felt more ignorant of the spine and nervous system than after I completed my doctorate degree. It also became evident that greater understanding of the clinical sciences was necessary if I was going to advance my comprehension of the spine and nervous system and be allowed to conduct research into spinal disorders. This led to the medical degree followed by an internship in internal medicine and a residency in neurology. The fellowship in electrodiagnosis at the Long Beach Veteran's Medical Center followed by a few years of research at that center gave me the tools and experience to continue my research interest. My education has continued through participation in numerous research projects and interaction with some of the top scientists and clinicians active in this field.

The second, and in some ways most difficult challenge, was to focus research on the issues that I felt were important, namely nerve compression, sensory and pain physiology, clinical electrophysiology, clinical trials, and evidence-based guidelines. At many stages of my career I was encouraged to follow alternative research or professional interests. Often the resources for the type of research I was hoping to do had to be found outside of the department or institution where I was studying or extrapolated from research in other areas. I am fortunate that, at each stage of my career, I had mentors who were supportive of my interest in spinal disorders and encouraged me to continue in this field.

My third challenge came in the necessity of breaking down barriers between the spine care professions. It was obvious very early that no one profession or scientific discipline had the answers to the cause or management of spinal disorders. The only chance of addressing this problem was to combine the resources of all the professions and scientists with an interest in the topic. The fact that my education crossed borders between professions and between the basic and clinical sciences gave me the comfort to work in many different arenas.

The final and most important challenge in my career has been maintaining a family and interests outside the professional world. The ability to achieve this goal has been due almost exclusively to my wife, who has made everything that I have accomplished possible. The journey through my career has truly been a team effort between Joan and I, and could not have happened without her full support. This book is as much a testimony of her hard work as it is mine.

SECTION I

BACKGROUND, UPBRINGING AND EDUCATION

Chapter 1

HERITAGE SETS THE STAGE

FREEDOM OF BIRTHRIGHT

Scott Haldeman's father, Joshua Norman Haldeman, is reported to have repeatedly said that "the problem with children is that they are too much like their parents." His own child was no exception. However, far from proving problematic, the similarities that Scott Haldeman shared with his progenitors provided a standard of excellence that characterized his entire life. What becomes clear upon reviewing Scott's career and personal motivation is that he did not suddenly appear out of a vacuum. In fact, Scott Haldeman is an exceptional product of his heritage and family experiences. By exploring his family history and background, we can gain some insight as to what motivated Scott to hunger for higher education, to find answers through tireless research to questions that were not evident from his training, what drove him to maintain an interest in the advance of natural health and spine care and to travel throughout the world to promote his ideas, always seeking out unique adventures.

There are four family members in particular who have had a major impact on his life's decisions. Scott's grandmother, his father, his mother, and his wife influenced him to pursue his career, and they provided the inspiration and support without which he very likely would have taken a different path.

ALMEDA JANE HALDEMAN LAYS THE FOUNDATION

Almeda Jane Haldeman (ne Norman), Scott's grandmother, has a special place in this story.[1] She is the individual who brought chiropractic into the Haldeman family by entering the health care field, studying nursing and chiropractic, and looking for natural means to care for her husband, John Elon Haldeman, and her children. She is credited as being the first chiropractor to practice in Canada and is the third woman documented to practice chiropractic anywhere in the world. For a young woman of her era, Almeda demonstrated an amazing independence and adventurous spirit that undoubtedly influenced her family to think beyond the culture and beliefs of the time. She also provided a moral code of conduct and emphasized the importance of faith which served as a guiding principle for the family.

The fifth of eight children, Almeda Jane Norman was born to Joshua and Almeda Melissa (ne Densmore) Norman. Even in the first moments of life, Almeda Jane had to develop a strong determination to survive:

> Her premature birth on March 19, 1877 was attributed to her
> mother's pneumonia and [she] was wrapped in cotton batting and
> placed in an oven to keep her warm. She was too weak to suck and
> so her mother had to drop milk into her mouth to feed her.[2]

Eventually, Almeda grew stronger, though, proving each day that she was the newest member of a long line of determined individuals.

Her father, Joshua Norman, was the son of English immigrants Thomas Norman[3] and Mary Ann Harker.[4] Thomas and Mary Ann married in England probably near their home in Potto, Yorkshire, England, about 1822. Mary Ann was the daughter of one of the Nor-

---

[1] See Appendix A for a complete family pedigree chart.
[2] Scott Haldeman, "Almeda Haldeman, Canada's First Chiropractor: Pioneering The Prairie Provinces, 1907-1917," Association for the History of Chiropractic (1983): PG #65-68. Almeda Jane's grandson, Scott, researched her background and published an article on her life in 1983. These extracts are from that article with additional information that was subsequently uncovered.
[3] Born 1792 in Yorkshire, England. Died 27 June 1871 in Essex County, New York.
[4] Born 1802 in Yorkshire, England.

man family servants, and the social differences between her family and Thomas's family was said to have caused the couple such difficulty that they decided to come to America in about 1829—landing first at La Prairie, Canada, then later relocating to Peru, NY, then Lewis, NY. It was there in the log cabin they built on Wells Hill that Joshua and seven more children were born to Mary Ann and Thomas.

Joshua Norman was born October 8 [or 10], 1835 in Franklin Falls, New York. Evidently (before 1860), Joshua and his brothers bought farmland near Bloomingdale, NY, that became known as "Norman Ridge" for its location on a ridge—surrounded by the Adirondack Mountains—in the heart of lumbering country. Joshua also served as a private in the 118th Infantry Co. C of New York during the Civil War. He married Almeda Melissa Densmore[5] on 20 August 1862, and following the marriage and the birth of their first child, James Edward, Joshua and Almeda decided to leave New York and migrate to Minnesota. Upon reaching Minnesota, they first settled in Rock Dell Township in Olmstead County where their second child, Mary Ann "Minnie" was born. From Rock Dell they relocated to Rosewood Township[6] in 1872 where they would have another six children, one of which was Scott Haldeman's grandmother, Almeda Jane. Joshua and his family thrived in Rosewood Township. He enjoyed success on his farm and respect within the community. The editor of the *Montevideo Leader* praised Joshua's farming methods and described him as an upright and industrious citizen, a man of strong character and positive views and as true as steel to his convictions of right and duty. A report in the *Montevideo Leader* says that Joshua Norman, George Knight, and Wm. Bradley purchased "one of Pearson's best fur robes and a lap robe and presented it to Rev. JJ Edwards," because, "they don't propose to let a man suffer that braves the storm to preach for them."[7] Another article in the *Leader* portrays him as a man with a sense of humor and able to laugh at himself. During a trip to New York State, Joshua wrote a letter to the Leader informing them that he

---

[5] Born 10 August 1837 or April 1839 in Lewis (Franklin Falls), New York.
[6] The original Rosewood Methodist Church was built on a corner acre of their land purchased for $1.00.
[7] Published 12 Dec 1890

was "well and hearty...having a good time up among the mountains and in the wild woods of old York State, but doesn't forget his Minnesota friends." The letter further said that while hunting deer, tracking them in about two inches of snow, he was trying to climb over a steep and slippery place and suddenly got lost—that is he lost his foothold and his balance and "fetched up about ten rods below." He then found that he had also lost the seat of his pants and that "wound up the hunting trip."[8]

Almeda's mother, Almeda Melissa, matched her husband in strength of character and strength of will. The farm life must have been very difficult for Almeda Melissa, since she was reported to be a great sufferer from asthma—which evidently contributed to her early death at the age of 64.[9] Despite her difficulties, however, she successfully raised her large family on the home farm in Rosewood Township and was adored by her children and husband. In fact, all of their eight children appear to have settled close to home as adults.

Almeda Jane (ne Haldeman) Wilson

Almeda Jane was raised in a family devoted to hard work and honorable living. As she grew into adulthood, she put into practice the persistence she had been taught at home. Scott Haldeman described his grandmother's fateful decision to pursue an education:

Almeda Haldeman was a woman with great determination and drive and eventually convinced her father to allow her to go to high school. He was opposed to girls getting an education. She graduated from Windom Institute in 1898. A publication at that time reported on her graduation that "the last essay

---

[8] Published 27 Nov 1908
[9] Personal communication with the Haldeman family. Almeda Melissa died 5 Aug 1903.

Windom Institute Class of 1898—Almeda believed to be second from the right, standing

and one of the best was by Miss Almeda Norman and was entitled, "Woman's Work". It was an earnest, thoughtful and well-worded plea for an enlarged field of study and work for young women, and for such professional training as will fit them for self support and enable them to put their talents to the best possible use."

Her son, Josh, always stated that she had some nursing experience although the exact nature of this experience is not clear. It is, however, compatible with her ongoing interest in health matters. She married John Elon Haldeman in August, 1900. They had two children, Joshua Norman and Almeda. John Elon subsequently contracted diabetes in 1904 and was given six months to live. Almeda took him to E.W. Lynch, DC, of the Chiropractic School and Cure in Minnesota. When it was decided to move to Canada to find a drier climate for John's health, Dr. Lynch taught Almeda the adjustments she would need to care for him. Dr. Lynch subsequently issued a diploma to Almeda on 20 January 1905.

> How extensive Almeda practiced as a chiropractor in Minnesota and later in Saskatchewan is unclear, but her children all remember getting regular adjustments. John was inspector of schools and while out on a cold night he caught pneumonia and died in 1909,

5

Almeda Haldeman's Diploma from the Chiropractic School & Cure issued January 20, 1905

nine years after his marriage to Almeda. She remarried in 1915 to Heseltine Wilson and they had two children, Annie Madge (b. Feb. 12, 1916) and Nelbert Elizabeth (b July.4 1918). Their offspring continue to own large and successful farms in Saskatchewan.

Scott concludes his remarks about Almeda by stating,

...she was very active in her community in such fields as the women's vote, the Temperance Movement, and church activities. She was the driving force behind her husband's participation in politics. She was an extremely moral woman of very strong convictions—no one was ever allowed to drink, smoke, use improper language, or tell shady stories in her house. Playing cards was prohibited. While dedicated to chiropractic she never refused medical care when it was duly indicated.[10]

[10] Personal comments added by Scott Haldeman in addition to the article he wrote: Haldeman, Scott. "Almeda Haldeman, Canada's First Chiropractor: Pioneering The Prairie Provinces, 1907-1917. Association for the History of Chiropractic, 1983, p. 65-68. The information on the Windom Commencement was taken from a newspaper clipping held in the Haldeman Family files, no date or indication of where it was printed was preserved. Circa 1898.

No one can predict the legacy of their descendants. All we can do is teach the correct principles and offer an example of living a "good life." Almeda did both. She loved chiropractic and transferred that love to her son and he then taught it to his son. As they lived the life she exemplified, they achieved heights she likely never could have conceived.

Heseltine and Almeda Jane (ne Haldeman) Wilson. March 2, 1915

JOSHUA NORMAN HALDEMAN SETS THE EXAMPLE

Almeda Jane set an example for her family as a remarkable, persevering individual, but her son Joshua Norman, the man who would become Scott Haldeman's father, was an amazing person in his own right. His sense of duty, his political skills, and his experience had a large impact on the chiropractic profession in two countries. His belief that anything could be achieved by his children, coupled with his positive attitude towards the future served as an example for Scott and his siblings. His flying adventures and his search for the Lost City of the Kalahari Desert served as an unbelievable training ground that allowed Scott to feel he could go anywhere and do what was necessary to achieve his goals.

Joshua Norman's adventurous life began on November 25th, 1902, when he was born to Almeda Jane and John Elon Haldeman in a small log cabin in Pequot, MN. The family would eventually leave the place of his birth for Canada in order to find a drier climate for his father's failing health. According to family speculation, John's life was extended an additional five years beyond medical expectation due to the move and also the chiropractic care he received at the hands of his wife; however, he eventually succumbed to his poor health and died in August of 1909. At the age of seven, Joshua Norman had lost his father. Despite the tragedy, Joshua was able to learn early in life to adapt and make the best out of new circumstances. His mother eventually married Heseltine Wilson, the local Reeve of Excelsior Municipality, who maintained a very large farm.

It was on his stepfather's farm that young Joshua Norman grew up, becoming quite skilled in bronco horseback riding, boxing, wrestling, and exhibition rope spinning. With two parents trained as professional teachers, however, it is not likely that his education was left unattended.

In addition to ranch skills and activities, Joshua was also able to attend several schools and colleges. However, he did not earn a degree until an unfortunate schoolyard injury would turn his educational and future career path in a fateful direction.

Joshua received a severe blow to the head that left him with damaged eye sight. Being raised in a home predominated by healthy living, it was no surprise when Joshua's mother decided to seek chiropractic care for her son's condition. She wrote the Palmer School of Chiropractic to see if they could be of any help. They responded in the affirmative and extended an invitation for Joshua to come to the school for treatment and also to enroll as a student at the same time. Not only did Joshua experience a complete remission of his eye problems while at the Palmer School from 1922 to 1926, but he was also able to obtain his Doctor of Chiropractic degree.

These were stormy years at the Palmer School, with many objecting to BJ Palmer's business tactics related to the acquiring of the Neurocalometer (NCM), an instrument used to detect spinal subluxations. Despite the school being rife with conflict and opposition, Joshua was able to maintain a close friendship with BJ Palmer throughout his professional career as well as with several of his college professors who were violently opposed to Palmer—so much so that they broke away to form the Lincoln College of Chiropractic in 1926, the same year Joshua graduated from Palmer. Again Joshua demonstrated his ability to adapt and thrive in challenging circumstances.

Joshua practiced for only a couple of years after graduation (circa 1926-28) before he decided to return to farming. However, in the following six years, the devastating Dust Bowl conditions that plagued the region, along with Joshua's overextended credit, led to the complete loss of his farm. This crushing loss of his livelihood left him adrift and with a sour taste in his mouth for financial institutions that lasted the rest of his life. With nothing left for him on the farm, Joshua took to the road. He "...traveled extensively in Canada...by freight and passenger coal tender...lived with homesteaders in the bush country, trappers in the lower Peace River...was a stowaway on an ocean-going boat, and lived in the hobo jungles."[11]

It was during this period that he married Wanda Eve Peters on December 23, 1927 and they had a son, Joshua Jerry Noel Haldeman. However, difficult times eventually led them to separate and finally divorce in 1941.[12]

From 1934 to 1936 Joshua settled in Assiniboia, Saskatchewan, and served as the Chairman of the Assiniboia Federal Constituency for Cooperative Commonwealth Federation, which later became the Government of Saskatchewan. In 1942, the decision to take a ballroom dancing lesson from a pretty teacher earned him not only some new dance steps, but a new wife, Winifred. He also started to practice chiropractic again, first in Assiniboia and then he moved his office to Regina where he practiced until 1950.

While remaining true to his training roots—a Palmer "straight" chiropractor who limits practice to non-medical procedures—Joshua also sought additional education in 1935 from the National College of Chiropractic, a rival school in thought and practice to Palmer. Atypical to the notion of being a "straight" chiropractor, Joshua prided himself in having taken courses in such things as physiotherapy, colonic therapy, dissection, laboratory diagnosis, gynecology, first aid, and minor surgery. He received a certificate of membership in the National Chiropractic Association's (NCA) National Council of Chiropractic Roentgenologists in 1938.

---

[11] A man well qualified to serve Prince Albert. The Canadian Social Crediter. May, 1945, p. 1.
[12] Born 12 December 1934. Jerry went on to be a bush pilot and establish a company that, at one time, had over 20 aircraft that served loggers in northern British Columbia.

Joshua's prominence in the chiropractic community continued to grow. By 1943 he found himself deep in chiropractic politics. He was instrumental in the drafting and eventual passing of the Saskatchewan Chiropractic Act of 1943. He recalls the experience in his own words:

> Saskatchewan had a Chiropractic Act of 1929 under which the chiropractors at that time were licensed, but no one was ever licensed afterwards. I was very active in politics and although opposed to the Provincial Government, one of the frontbenchers was a friend of mine. While discussing with him the possibility of a new Chiropractic Act, he said "Why not try it?" He offered to help so we had a good chance.
>
> I drew up the Act in my office, got in touch with the other members of our Provincial Council; we all agreed on the terms and the main points. Then I wired Mr. John Burton, [Dominion Council for Canadian Chiropractors, Executive Director and legal counsel] whom I knew was attending the chiropractic meeting in Winnipeg, to stop over in Regina and help us put the Chiropractic Act through.
>
> When he saw me in Regina, he was quite disgusted that I had bothered him. He told me that he received the telegram while he was addressing a banquet of the Manitoba chiropractors. He read my telegram over and could not believe it; read it again and held it up so the others could see and said, "This crazy man, Haldeman, wants me to stop over in Regina and help put a Chiropractic Act through the legislature. After all the money and work that had been spent on trying to get acts through, now Haldeman says he wants me to stop in Regina to put an act through just like that!"
>
> Mr. Burton changed some of the legal phraseology, but most of it had been copied from other acts. It so happened that the act was presented to the Legislature at the end of the last session, before election. There was no opposition, as the Medical Association did not realize a Chiropractic Act was going to be considered until after it was passed. As I remember, it cost our association $230.00 dollars for expenses.[13]

[13] Haldeman, J.N., "The Flying Haldeman's". Unpublished family manuscript written by J.N. Haldeman.

After the passage of the Chiropractic Act, Joshua was appointed to a number of important positions within the Canadian Chiropractic community: he became a member of the first Examining Board and the first Executive Board of the Saskatchewan Chiropractor's Association. The Dominion Council for Canadian Chiropractors (DCCC—later the Canadian Chiropractic Association) inaugural meeting in 1943 welcomed him as the Saskatchewan representative. He and Dr. Walter Sturdy held meetings with the Canadian Defense Minister to obtain recognition for chiropractic in Canada's armed forces. Though he was unsuccessful in his bid with the armed forces, as part of the DCCC he was the force behind the creation of a chiropractic school in Canada. Joshua was on the original committee established to look into the possibility of starting a school and continued to serve on the committee as it evolved into a formal proposal. Moving forward with the formation of a school was a contentious effort with disputes over the scope of

Joshua Norman Haldeman circa 1945

chiropractic to be taught, the length of the curriculum, whether to make it a non-profit organization, and the degree of control to be exerted over the school by the DCCC.[14] Joshua pushed for DCCC control of the college but was overruled. A separate body called the Canadian Association of Chiropractors became the charter organization of the Canadian Memorial Chiropractic College (CMCC), located in Toronto, Canada, which opened its doors to students in September 1945. Joshua was appointed to the first Board of Governors of the new college.

[14] Joshua was in favor of including, within the curriculum, the subjects of diagnosis and laboratory work, but was stern on the limitation of therapeutic methods to only chiropractic. Physiotherapy was initially allowed only as a postgraduate course, to appease those who had the right to practice physiotherapy, but was later voted in as part of the regular curriculum, against Joshua's wishes for he felt physiotherapy was not chiropractic.

Throughout the rest of the decade, Joshua's career continued to build momentum. He was elected to serve as the vice president of the DCCC in 1947 and became the DCCC representative to the International Chiropractic Association's Board of Control in 1948. In 1949, when a government-sponsored study in Quebec came out with a negative opinion about chiropractic, Joshua wrote a scathing rebuke to Quebec's Royal Commission to Study Chiropractic, pointing out discrepancies and evidence of the "hand of the medical profession" in their final adverse decision. Just some thirty years later, Joshua's son Scott, would actually appear and become a key expert witness in another Royal Commission on Chiropractic in New Zealand, only this time the commission would render a far more favorable opinion.

While attaining prominence in the chiropractic community, Joshua Haldeman was also making a name for himself politically. From 1935 to 1941, he became involved with an international group that advocated economic reform through changes in the monetary system. He became the leader of the Canadian branch of Technocracy but resigned in 1941 when it pledged collaboration with Stalinist-led Russia. After a brief effort to organize his own political party in Saskatchewan, he redirected his efforts in support of the Social Credit Party (SCP). As World War II was winding down in 1945, Joshua had elevated himself to vice president

Joshua Norman Haldeman Social Credit Party Member

and provincial secretary of the Social Credit Party in Saskatchewan and ran for the Prince Albert Federal Constituency. Despite losing the race, he remained active with this party until 1950.

Josh proved to be as health conscious as he was socially conscious. He incorporated the philosophy of health he had learned from his mother and at Palmer College when helping his own family. Smoking was not permitted in their home. Coffee and alcohol were for adults only. Whole wheat breads and cereals and unrefined flour and sugar were the staples of the family diet. Josh had a strong opposition to Coca-Cola which, in his early years, contained cocaine. In fact, he actively campaigned against its consumption and never allowed it in his home. While in Canada a friend and supporter of his campaign against Coca-Cola fell out of a window and died under mysterious conditions. Josh always believed it was foul play. He claimed that he was told that he would meet the same fate if he did not back down on his campaign. He never retreated from his stand on Coca-Cola but threats didn't materialize.

Regardless of any danger or opposition he faced, Joshua never compromised his values. He was not a cursing man nor did he allow cursing in the home. He was an avid student of the Bible and believed in Christianity but rarely went to church stating that he could interpret the Bible as well as any minister. He did, however, insist that the children attend Sunday School to learn Christian standards. In his stories about flying, Josh exposed his religious foundation when he talked about a guardian angel being with him and Wyn on their many adventures, and the family continues to feel the presence of a protective force.

After 24 years of active involvement in politics and chiropractic practice, the Haldmans decided on a drastic change of location in 1950. There are probably many reasons why they pulled up their Canadian roots and moved to South Africa. The rapid increase of a controlling government over individual rights, a declining moral value in Canadian society or just Joshua's adventuresome spirit alone could have contributed to their relocation. Josh relates an experience with a "medium" [spiritualist] in 1936 who told him he must practice in Regina for fourteen years and then, "...move to a city in a far away place." He said he had tried to leave Regina several times but was never able to make things work out until the fourteen years had passed and then everything fell into place. After speaking with an Anglican Minister from South Africa at an International Trade Fair in Toronto, Joshua became convinced that South Africa was that "far away place."

Whether it was as an outspoken advocate of his profession, a spirited politician, or a man intrigued by adventure, Joshua Haldeman's example and influence as a father was pronounced and positive. Eccentric by some standards, he provided well for his family, taught and lived good principles in the home, practiced his health beliefs by example and exortation, and left a posterity that honors his name to this day.

WINNIFRED HALDEMAN PROVIDES THE BASE

Winnifred Josephine Haldeman (ne Fletcher), Scott's mother, provided the love and stability that allowed him to achieve his goals to the best of his ability. She provided the security of knowing that things would always be okay at home. Her faith that the family would do the right thing was a basic principle that her children accepted as fact. Her willingness to travel around the world in a single engine airplane with her husband and take her five children into the remote, off-road regions of the Kalahari Desert in order to be part of her husband's life required a strength that very few people are able to find. Her eventful life brought her a wide array of experiences and left her with a variety of skills. Among other things, she became South Africa's woman's pistol champion. Her artistic talents, first as a dancing instructor and then as an accomplished artist, remain an inspiration to her family.

Perhaps her remarkable resourcefulness as she moved from place to place can be attributed to her unique heritage. Winifred was the daughter of Harold Fletcher,[15] who, at 16, left his home in England for Canada. Her mother, Edith Reeve Angel[16], was an English born immigrant who had a father with the blood of an aristocratic and a mother with the blood of a gypsy. Their marriage, and the conflict of class that came with it, had engendered so much strife from their parents

---

[15] Born 22 October 1884 in Lincolnshire, England
[16] Born in Surrey, England in 1883

that Edith's father was completely disowned by his aristocratic Angel side of the family. However, Edith always took pride in the gypsy side of her family and attributed certain of her own characteristics to her gypsy ancestry.

Harold and Edith's daughter, Wyn, or Winnie, as she was often called, was born March 10, 1914 in Moose Jaw, Saskatchewan, Canada. She grew into a talented and hard-working woman; she took stenographer training in high school and eventually got a job working for a local newspaper, which she maintained for ten years. It was a demanding job, as she worked the ads department and was always under pressure to meet deadlines.

Winnifred (Wyn) Josephine Haldeman

Winnifred also honed her creative side by traveling to various dance schools to further her dance skills. Each year she received a free rail ticket and a month's vacation which enabled her to go to places such as Banff, Chicago, Toronto, Vancouver, and New York to work on her dancing. She was also deeply involved in drama and produced religious programs for Zion's Church at Christmas and Easter. Musicals and plays were her passion. She became part of a semi-professional traveling entertainment group and had a wonderful time.

In addition to her drama activities, she also received a formal degree (by correspondence) from the Trinity College of Music in London, and an elementary certificate in ballet from the Royal Academy of Dance in England. All of her achievements eventually allowed her to form her own small ballet company in Regina.

One night in 1942, a man came to the studio, introducing himself as Joshua Haldeman. Joshua had been without a companion since 1937 when he had first separated from his former wife, and he was feeling down, so he decided to take up ballroom dancing lessons. When he inquired about lessons, Wyn informed him that she was booked until 9:00 pm. Rather than being discouraged, he informed her he would return at that time for his first lesson. Return he did, and after six months of lessons he asked his teacher when she would marry him. She boldly responded, "Tomorrow." After some consideration, however, they decided to give themselves more than a few hours to plan the event. When the big day finally came, Joshua provided a diamond ring for the wedding and noted that it was a very handsome diamond but was best seen with a magnifying glass. And in return, Wyn, who had learned from Josh's secretary that he had some outstanding bills in need of payment, paid the outstanding balance on his false teeth.

At the time that he was taking dancing lessons, Josh was nearly broke and living at the YMCA. He and Wyn could not afford much, especially not a lavish honeymoon. So they spent their honeymoon in a straw patch on his parent's farm and then moved into Wyn's six-by-eleven foot trailer. Their first son, Scott, slept in an apple box hung on a side of the wall. When daughter Lynne arrived, bigger quarters were needed. Fortunately, by that time Josh had established a successful practice and was able to purchase a three-story, twenty-room house providing space for Scott and his three younger sisters, Wyn's dance studio, and her parents.

Because his other duties required a significant amount of travel, Joshua decided to take up flying at the age of 45. Even though he was afraid of heights, and both he and Wyn were subject to severe motion sickness even on the train, they signed up for lessons and soon became convinced that travel by air was cheaper, safer, and more practical than other modes of transportation. With only a few hours of instruction (not yet qualified to fly on their own), they purchased a plane in Calgary while traveling through the area. Wyn took the train to Regina while Josh flew home in his new plane along with the former owner who offered to ferry it home for them.

Josh and Wyn next to their 1948 Bellanca Cruisaire

Their first plane was a single engine Luscombe but was expensive to maintain, slow in flight, and was only designed to carry two people, so they upgraded to a 1948 Bellanca Cruisaire. Joshua had the name Winnie painted on the side. Having a plane forced Wyn and Josh to continue their pilot training. Wyn stopped taking flying lessons when she delivered the twins, Maye and Kaye. She never obtained her pilot's license, but she was always there as the navigator for her husband on his excursions in the air.

While taken on initially as a convenience to expedite travel, flying soon became a major family activity. Soon the "Flying Haldemans" became celebrities at the many events to which they traveled by air, most notably the Palmer School of Chiropractic homecomings, convocations, and ICA meetings in Davenport.

When the family moved to South Africa, the plane moved with them. After flying for three years in Canada and the U.S. (1947 – 1950) Joshua dismantled and shipped it to its new home.

In 1952 Wyn flew with Joshua completely around Africa and Europe, up to Scotland and Norway to speak at the ECU Convention held in Oslo, and then back home. He wrote about this trip in his July 5, 1952 Clinic Bulletin:

> 57 countries or territories were crossed, 22,000 miles flown on this trip. We collected 74 government stamps in our passport books and 90 in our log-book. We had 91 air maps, most of them on the scale of one to one million. Our fuel and oil bill was about £250. We have never had a forced landing, but were prepared with first aid supplies, water, food and other emergency equipment for jungles, deserts and water crossings.[17]

In 1954 Josh and Wyn made a 30,000 mile trip up the coast of Africa, across the southern Middle East and Asian coast to Australia, around Australia, and back to South Africa. The family is not aware of anyone else who has attempted this, and they believe that Josh is the only private pilot to have made this trip in a single engine airplane. During their flying career Josh and Wyn flew across 80 countries and territories of the world.

Perhaps the greatest legacy of the "Flying Haldemans" was their search for the Lost City of the Kalahari Desert in South Africa. Their first expedition to look for the Lost City was in 1953 in the family station wagon. On later trips they took the plane and would fly 200

Wyn and Josh admiring the names of destinations printed on the tail-wing of *Winnie*

[17] Haldeman Clinic Bulletin, July 5, 1952

18

feet off the ground in uncharted desert in order to look for evidence of a buried city. Scott shares the story that at times his dad would hire a local tracker and take him up in the plane while Wyn and the kids would have to spend the day with the car and supplies in camp, far

Campsite on the Kalahari, *Winnie* the plane in the background, Josh and Wyn in the tent opening.

from any living soul, let alone civilization, and with wild animals as constant neighbors. Josh would fly to a dry lake bed or pan where he could land the plane while Wyn and Scott would then have to drive to the pan with supplies for the camp. It was not uncommon to see hyenas or even leopards around the campfire at night, and on one occasion the family woke up in the morning to find a lion in their camp. Altogether they made 16 expeditions into the desert looking for the Lost City. Although it remains unfound, Josh continued to believe in its existence until the day he died.

Wyn supported her husband in his pursuits for lost civilizations

Josh and Wyn firing their pistols

and in his pursuits within the community. She supported him as he became the co-founder and president of the Aircraft Owners and Pilots Association (AOPA) in South Africa. She also took an active interest in the South African Pistol Association, which Josh organized soon after his arrival in Pretoria. While he served as its first chairman and won first place in the Pistol Championship contest twice, Wyn participated as well, taking first place in the women's national competition.

Wyn with the trophies from the Cape Town to Algiers Motor Rally on the station wagon

Josh and Wyn made an excellent team. Together they signed up to take part in what was considered the most grueling professional motor car rally in the world, the Cape Town to Algiers Motor Rally. This was a trip of more than 8,000 miles over some of the most unsuitable country for driving ever to be found. Joshua's mechanical abilities learned during his years of farming helped keep the car together throughout the race. By the end of the race, they had tied for first place after driving the entire course together in their family Ford station wagon.

Wyn remained devoted to her husband during their 30 years of marriage. She made sure her family had a stable, safe, nurturing environment in which they could grow and learn. The children were rarely punished because Wyn and Josh believed that, if left to their own resources, their children would inherently do the right thing. Thus the foundation of a successful, distinguished life had been laid for young Scott.

JOAN HALDEMAN IS THE STRENGTH

A discussion of those who have had the greatest influence on Scott would be incomplete without the mention of perhaps the most important person in his journey—his wife. Joan Haldeman (ne Surridge) made possible much of what Scott has accomplished. She was truly a partner in all of his achievements. Their life together started when they were teenagers. It has included frequent turns and twists that Joan could not have anticipated in the first years of their court-ship and marriage. She was willing to leave her family and friends in South Africa and travel around the world as Scott's career took on new directions. She elected to give up her own promising career and support Scott in his private practice, organize conferences that Scott felt were important, and put up with long and repeated periods when he was away from home at meetings while at the same time bringing up their two children with love and a determination to provide everything they needed.

Scott, a third-generation chiropractor in the Haldeman lineage, is the summation of a heritage that helped form his beliefs, attitudes, and personality. Like each of us, he started with his basic genetic composi-tion inherited from his progenitors, and

Joshua Norman Haldeman—
the Flying Haldeman

grew in personal stature from there. His life expanded to become a rare product of the multiplicative influences of home-life, parental example, school, and the culture in which he lived.

Chapter 2

CHILDHOOD DEVELOPMENT
AND ADVENTURES
Toddler to Teenager

Joshua and Wyn Haldeman started their marriage in a very small trailer in Saskatchewan, Canada. Initially they had to make do with very little money. When they lacked a cradle, for example, they improvised by hanging an apple box on the wall of their tiny trailer to act as a bed for baby Scott. Fortunately, Scott's stay in the apple box was brief, since Josh opened a chiropractic office in Regina that was eventually very successful. Not long thereafter the family moved into a large home in Regina that housed Wyn's dance studio along with her parents, Mom and Pop Fletcher, who wanted to be close to their ever-increasing number of grandchildren. In the next four years Scott's younger sister, Lynne, and then the twins, Maye and Kaye, were born. There are no tales of his "terrible twos" but a few photos of him around the age of two may be worth a thousand words.

Scott went to Kindergarten and Grade One in Regina. He recalls walking to school in the snow and especially using the slide from the second floor of the school during a fire drill. He spent a great deal of time in his mother's dance studio and participated in classes from a

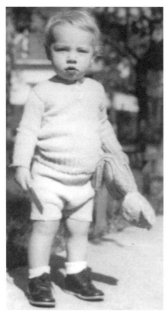

very young age. He even danced on stage between the ages of four and seven.

Josh and Wyn traveled a great deal, often for political and chiropractic reasons. Josh stated that he had flown over most of the states and provinces in the U.S. and Canada between 1947 and 1950. Many times the children were lucky enough to go with their parents if they traveled in Josh's single engine plane. Space was limited, but the kids were small and they learned to travel light.

When Josh decided to move the family to South Africa in 1950, Scott was seven. A trans-oceanic displacement from friends and family undoubtedly took its toll on Josh and Wyn but Scott recalls it as an adventure. They had to sell their house and decide what of all their possessions to take with them and what to leave behind—no easy task after living in a twenty-room home for seven years. Together they

Scott out for a walk with his sock doll circa 1945

packed up some furniture and all the equipment necessary to set up a chiropractic office. Josh also decided to take the airplane and the family Cadillac but insisted on disassembling and packing the airplane himself. One of Scott's few memories of those early years was helping his father dismantle his single engine Bellanca. They removed the wings in order to prepare *Winnie* to be shipped by boat to South Africa, and then put her back together once she arrived in Cape Town. Since his father did not trust anyone else to work on his airplane and always did his own repairs, Scott would usually be the

A handsome Scott circa 1945

Lynne and Scott circa 1948

one to hold the wrenches or other tools at the other end of the bolts as Josh worked. By the time Scott was nine years old, his father claimed he could fly the plane straight and level.

The move to South Africa was a brave step for the family, as Wyn and Josh did not know anyone there and had never even been to the country before their arrival in Cape Town in 1950. Nevertheless, they packed the four children in the back of the plane and began flying around the country looking for a proper place to settle. Josh did not like the ocean so decided against the coastal cities of Cape Town and Durban. Johannesburg was deemed too busy and dirty. The streets of Pretoria, however, were lined with Jacaranda trees in full bloom

Wyn, Josh, Scott, Maye and Kaye behind the seat, and Lynne in the window of *Winnie* circa 1950

25

that November. When Josh saw how beautiful Pretoria was from the air, he decided even before landing that this was where he wanted to settle.

For the first few months after their arrival in Pretoria, the family camped outside the city at The Fountains—a park with campsites set alongside a winding river. There all six members of the family lived in a small tent. It took some time for Mom and Dad Haldeman to find a house large enough to both live in and provide space for a practice. Scott recalls, "I have a number of memories of The Fountains, including exploring around the river banks for frogs and small snakes and, like a kid of seven, being scared and thrilled at the possibility of coming across a large snake or crocodile. There were no crocodiles."

When the family first landed in Pretoria, "Oupa" Parsons was the first person to greet them. (*Oupa* means *grandfather* in Afrikaans.) He was, among other things, a real estate agent, and he showed the family houses, including the one that Josh eventually bought. Oupa Parsons became one of Josh's first patients and a life-long friend. Despite knowing no one when they first arrived, the Haldemans' circle of friends and

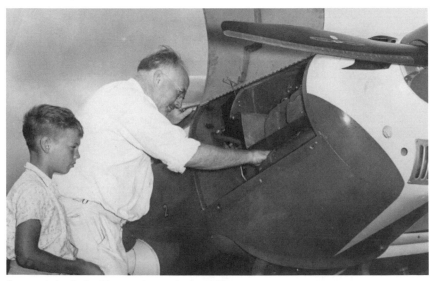

Scott assisting Josh with an engine repair circa 1950

family expanded quickly.

Parson's daughter, Thelma, became an adopted aunt. Aunt Shelly, as she was called, had no children of her own and, according to Scott, "took care of the kids when Mom and Dad were on their various adventures." Scott relates that he and Aunt Shelly would stay up late at night listening to stories on the radio and peeling and eating oranges. She also owned a secretarial school where all of the Haldeman children, as well as Joan Surridge—the future Mrs. Scott Haldeman—took both typing and shorthand lessons.

Scott in the right seat of *Winnie* ready for takeoff circa 1950

Aunt Shelly married Matt Brummer, a member of the Pretoria Pistol Club that Josh Haldeman started. Matt was a good friend of the family as well, and the children saw a lot of the Parsons through most of their early lives. They also got to know many of Aunt Shelly's family, including her sister and nieces.

THE PRIMARY SCHOOL YEARS: AGES 8 TO 13

Scott was enrolled at Rietondale Public Primary School within walking distance of their home. Scott thrived in school. He was active in swimming, general athletics, and cricket, and he was able to maintain his grades without too much effort. His leadership skills were recognized early as he was chosen by his principal and teacher to act as Head Prefect, the South African equivalent of the Student Body President.

During this period he accompanied his parents to the Pretoria Pistol Club every Saturday afternoon. This served him well when he had to carry a weapon on later expeditions into the Kalahari Desert looking for the Lost City.

Scott also joined a wrestling club that was run by one of his father's patients, a South African wrestling champion. He recalls that after two years of riding a bicycle at night for half an hour to get to wrestling practice—only to get roughed up—then riding back home again late, it became obvious to him that the club would not be his favorite activity.

Scott circa 1951

Scott shooting with Mom and Dad

Scott was enrolled in Sunday school at a conservative Calvanistic Dutch Reform church. This was due in part to the fact that one of his father's most loyal patients was a minister in the Dutch Reform Church and also so that he could learn to speak Afrikaans. Scott's mother remembers that early on he showed a remarkable attention to detail, as was illustrated in his scripture projects. She recalls that he would draw an abundance of stick figures illustrating the entire armies of the Israelites and Philistines. He learned much from his studies at the church, and eventually completed the very intense religious classes and examinations necessary to be confirmed as a member. During this period he was required to read the Bible from cover to cover but admits to merely skimming over those sections that endlessly list "the begats."

THE CLAPHAM YEARS

Scott, Joan, and Reg Engelbrecht all attended the Clapham High School in Pretoria. Reg was two years ahead of Scott and Joan, who were in the same class together. Reg was in Clapham 1955 to 1959. Reg and Scott would also become roommates when studying years later in Davenport, Iowa.

Recollections of Reg Engelbrecht

As a teenager in the mid 1950s (about 1955), I cycled approximately 15 km to school every morning—as did many of the students in most high schools of that time. My school was Clapham High School located in Queenswood, Pretoria. Each day we would pass an enormous home (address number 267 with the clinic at 259 Zoutpansberg Road). In the front garden was an impressive swimming pool. Just about every morning at 7:30 we noticed a grand, white-haired gentleman plunging into this pool. Although Pretoria is considered to be a sub-tropical zone, it can get exceptionally cold on winter mornings—so cold that one's fingers would virtually freeze on the bicycle handle grips, and the tears that seeped from one's eyes as we sped along would actually freeze into thin strips of ice along our cheeks. Now experiencing this almost unbearable cold, we found it difficult to comprehend why this fine gentleman would be plunging into his pool with such apparent vigor. Our comments to each other varied from, "he must be crazy," to some very comical expressions as only young lads could imagine. Little did I know that in time this man would play a decisive role in my future.

Clapham High School was a dual medium school—admitting both boys and girls—and was considered one of the finer institutes of academic education in Pretoria. The Headmaster of Clapham from 1949 to 1961 was Mr. Geen. In the early days of his term, the school took the pupils to the Capital Theatre in Pretoria to see the movie *Scott of the Antarctic.* Moved by the story, the pupils with Mr. Geen's approval, voted to name the school houses after Scott's exploration party. All pupils are assigned to one of these houses for intramural games and academic competition.

Joan Surridge, an exciting and talented girl, came to Clapham from the Robert Hicks Primary School in 1957. Joan was in Wilson House, excelled academically and was always in the top four of her class, competing with Scott for the top academic position. She excelled in languages to the point that Mr. Geen always thought she would be a great ambassador. Joan loved sports and was vice captain of our school's first field hockey team. In her final year (1961) at Clapham, she was appointed Head Prefect—or Head Girl—and graduated second place in her class.

Joan Surridge circa 1960

Now let me reflect for a moment upon a discussion I had with my good friend Arthur Purdy. We were considering our options for that day when we would matriculate (graduate) from high school. Arthur thought he'd become a chiropractor. I'd never heard of such a profession and was intrigued with the thought of a health profession that was virtually "bloodless." I wanted to know more, so Arthur arranged a meeting with a respected and highly qualified chiropractor. When we went to see him at his clinic at 259 Zoutpansberg Road, we made a surprising discovery; you guessed it—this was that "crazy" fine looking gentleman that plunged into his pool on the coldest of mornings—and every day of the year! This was none other than Dr. Joshua Haldeman. He was a second-generation chiropractor who graduated from the Palmer School of Chiropractic (PSC '26). Dr. Josh was a great adventurer, and we had heard many tales of his visits to the Kalahari Desert in search of a fabled Lost City with his wife Wyn and their son, Scott. Now it all came together—Scott was the fellow in Joan's class at school. He was the academic competition of whom she often spoke, and the fellow who danced so well at our parties!

Scott came to Clapham in 1957—the same year as Joan. He was placed in Shackelton House. Like most of us, he cycled to school along Zoutpansberg Road. He was lucky—it only took him 20 minutes to cycle the distance. This he did for the next four years. During his final year at school, his father acquired a 1948 World War II Willey's Jeep to use as a second vehicle in the Kalahari expeditions. Scott was allowed to drive the Jeep and delighted in picking up any stragglers along the way who might be late for school. Because of his position as Head Prefect he was the only student allowed to park a car on campus.

Discipline at Clapham High was very strict and at times corporal. Getting "caned" or "whacked" was a common punishment, and if a student was silly enough to report to his parents that he had gotten caned at school it was not uncommon for a student to be whacked again when you got home. Scott, like many students, was caned a few times in high school. His father, however, rarely punished Scott, and when he found out he had been punished at school felt that this should be considered a learning experience. He was only caned once by the principle, Mr. Geen, however. In Form 1 he and five friends were cycling down a street six abreast, obstructing traffic. When a car approached and honked, one of the boys let loose with some obscenities. The car stopped and when the driver got out of his car the kid who swore stopped and got off his bike. The driver asked for the names of the boys. The kid gave up all the names except his own, and all five were called into the principal's office and "whacked" as a disciplinary procedure.

Scott was an academic "whiz"—always one of the top four scholars of his class. He excelled in math and science but admits he was not that great with languages. There was strong competition between Scott and Joan. The latter often just very slightly ahead of the former; however, in Matric Scott made first place with Joan coming in second. Scott was deservedly honored with the Valedictorian award while Joan earned the position which, in the U.S., would be the Salutatorian.

Once a week at Clapham all boys came to school in their School Cadet uniform. Cadets were a paramilitary form of training that was compulsory for all high school boys. The training was mostly marching and parading just as in the armed forces. Officers had to go to a two week camp at the local military base. We enjoyed the two hours set aside for this every week. Scott naturally was soon promoted as a senior officer in the Cadets. I volunteered for the band and soon found myself as the Sergeant Bugler. Once every term, the entire Cadet platoon would go on an extended march, led by the band with drums and bugles, through the suburb of Queenswood where Clapham was located—much to the delight of local residents.

Scott's interests and activities were very diverse. He simply was too likeable a fellow. During his final year at school he was appointed Head Boy—and Joan as mentioned earlier, Head Girl. They were the two Head Prefects. The school staff appointed twelve prefects each year. These prefects were responsible for organizing scholastic activities and also had certain disciplinary responsibilities.

Scott was elected House Captain for Shackleton House in Form five. He was required to coordinate the intramural sports and academic competitions. The combination of house captain, Head Prefect, and rugby captain were important in his being elected Krause Scholar by the members of the faculty. This is the most distinguished award handed out by the school "in recognition of exceptional qualities in Leadership, Scholarship and Sportsmanship."[1]

---

[1] Personal Communication with Reg Engelbrecht, D.C., 2008.

Extracurricular Activities

He was very active in sports at high school. He played rugby throughout his high school days and captained the first team during his matriculation year. He was on the school's swimming team (swimming freestyle and breast stroke) for each of the five years, being coached by a South African Olympic coach who was a patient of Scott's father. Scott played cricket too—but was less serious about it than his rugby and swimming.

Scott was a real all-rounder. Always keen to assist and help wherever he could. Our workshop teacher often required assistance in the maintenance of outbuildings and fixtures on the school grounds. Scott was always ready and willing to assist. He involved his best friend, Gavin Nettleton, on Friday afternoons and even during some vacations to assist. They repaired gates, bicycle sheds (where pupils could park their bicycles), shelters at the tennis courts, and constructed a number of 5-level grand stand seating units for the sports fields. Under the supervision of the workshop teacher, they were taught both acetylene and arc welding. Scott loved these extra-curricular activities.

There was never a dull moment in Scott's life. He went for ballroom dance classes with Mrs. Joubert once a week throughout his high school career. Eventually he took extra classes from his instructor and trained for national examinations in ballroom dancing. He and his sister Lynne did quite a few shows, including the Rose Ball at the Pretoria City Hall, and the newspaper reported on his performances. He accomplished, with honors, the bronze and silver medal levels established by the South African Dance Teachers Association. Lynne went on to get her Ballroom Teachers Certificate. The next level—Gold—would have qualified Scott to teach ballroom dancing, but he matriculated and left Pretoria to study chiropractic at Palmer before he could complete this examination.

Stephen Zondagh was Scott's first music teacher. Scott later changed teachers and went to Mrs. Blignaut in Rietondale, close to his home. His teacher favored classical music, and thus for eight years Scott and his fellow students were taught to play classic pieces for national music examinations. Scott completed his Preliminary and Qualifying Theory exams up to Grade Eight, and his Intermediate Grade Seven Music Performance Exams through the University of South Africa (UNISA). This experience eventually gained him a great part time job at the Griggs Piano Company in Davenport, Iowa. Scott also chose to take harmonica lessons but only for a short period of time.

Scott's parents were very active in the South African shooting community, partly in preparation for their tours into the Kalahari to look for the Lost City. At one point Josh won the South African Pistol Championship and Wyn won the woman's championship. Every Saturday afternoon, Scott joined his parents to attend the Pretoria Pistol Club event and most mornings around 6:00 am did dry shooting (without ammunition) at home. He won a few minor junior awards that allowed him to carry a weapon for protection purposes on their Kalahari excursions.

THE HALDEMAN ADVENTURES

There are few children who could rival the adventures that Scott experienced during his school years. His family traveled extensively throughout southern Africa by private airplane or by road worthy vehicles such as a truck or station wagon. It was rare that the family stayed in a hotel. When evening came they simply pulled off the road, laid out a ground sheet, and slept in sleeping bags. Josh took the family to South West Africa (now Namibia), the Bechuanaland Protectorate (now Botswana), Swaziland, and Lesotho. They went hunting in Rhodesia (now Zimbabwe), and visited many of the game reserves in South Africa.

Josh particularly enjoyed going to Richards Bay or the St. Lucia Estuary at the coast. This was about a 3-hour flight. They would stay at a small motel or camp near the plane, and Scott would rent a boat and fish despite the presence of crocodiles and sharks. The other common flying weekend trip was to Victoria Falls where it was possible to walk from the airport to a camp—a series of very elementary cabins—and from the camp to the falls. At that time there was only one real hotel in the town but it was too posh and expensive.

Scott accompanied his parents on one major trip to central Africa, which included Uganda, Kenya, and Zanzibar. In his book, *The Flying Haldemans*, Josh relates the following about ten-year-old Scott:

> On approaching Moshi, we saw the white snow-capped peak of Kilimanjaro shining in the sun. It had been covered by a cloud on our previous trip. We were quite excited about seeing this magnificent spectacle, so we looked back to see if Scott was enjoying it. He was sound asleep. We prodded him awake and Wyn said, "Look, Scott, there is Kilimanjaro." He opened one eye and said, "Oh," and went back to sleep.
>
> Scott's chief interest on the trip seemed to be the comics he could buy at different places we landed. He could tell us which comics he had been able to get at all points on the route. He got the best bargains in Zanzibar and he learned his way around the maze of narrow, crooked streets quicker than we did. Within a couple of days, he was able to act as our guide. We did not think he was getting much out of the trip, but found later that he could remember most of it.[2]

Haldeman Family and *Winnie* circa 1958

[2] Haldeman, J.N. *"The Flying Haldemans."* Unpublished manuscript

Camp in the Kalahari

The most memorable traveling, however, was the continual searching for the Lost City of the Kalahari Desert. An Italian adventurer by the name of Gilarmi Farini spent time in the Kalahari and reported in his 1886 book that he had come across a Lost City during his travels. He reported this finding to the Royal Geographical Society in London. Josh, on reading a translation of this book, decided to begin searching for the Lost City. Altogether he conducted sixteen air and ground searches, most of which included the family. These expeditions were into remote areas without roads, water, and often uninhabited with the exception of a few nomads and San (bushmen) families. The searches were conducted during school vacations and took up to one month. Initially they traveled in a station wagon. Later Josh purchased an International two-wheel drive, one-ton truck, and finally they explored in the "Kalahari Kamper," their four-wheel drive, one and one-half ton truck. It was necessary for Josh, Wyn, and Scott to carry weapons as there were lions, leopards, and hyenas around the camp on many occasions.

Despite his skills with both pistol and rifle, Josh was not an avid hunter and would only allow hunting for the pot. He did not want to waste time hunting and would not permit trophy shooting. It was, however, necessary to hunt for meat every few days in the Kalahari as the alternative was canned sardines. Scott would ride on top of the truck with a .375 mm rifle and hope that an antelope could be flushed out of the brush by the truck. If lucky, the family would have fresh meat for the next few days. Scott and his sisters were required to learn the art of skinning and butchering springbuck, gemsbok, or the smaller duiker. Scott developed his "Indy 500 level" driving skills by chasing antelope on the large salt pans in the Kalahari, and he drove the second car, the Willey's Jeep, on the last expedition he participated in before leaving for the U.S. to study chiropractic.

The Willey's Jeep. Scott is on the ground doing engine repairs.

HEALTH CARE PHILOSOPHY

Josh established a very successful chiropractic practice and was active in the South African Chiropractic Association, serving as its president for many years. The children all received chiropractic adjustments from birth and on a regular basis throughout their school lives. Josh had a traditional chiropractic philosophical approach to health. He felt that the body had the innate ability to maintain a healthy state if treated properly. There was no smoking in the house and alcohol use was prohibited until the children reached the age of 21. Although Josh loved his coffee, Scott was not permitted to drink it while he was in school and still does not like the taste. Josh and Wyn were also careful about the food that was eaten. Cereals were fresh ground, only whole grain bread was allowed, and there were always large quantities of fruit available for snacks. As noted earlier, Josh also swam every day—summer and winter. His mantra was that "Haldemans did not get sick or upset," and he never got angry or shouted. His worst curse was "darn" when things did not go well.

Scott cannot recall ever visiting a medical physician or taking even an aspirin while being brought up. He did receive regular chiropractic adjustments whenever he did not feel well or if he was hurt while playing rugby.

From his earliest years Scott always anticipated going to chiropractic school and joining his father in practice. It was inevitable that upon graduation from high school he would leave to further his education at Palmer College in Davenport, Iowa—his father's Alma Mater.

Chapter 3

TRAINING AT THE
CHIROPRACTIC FOUNTAINHEAD

Davenport, Iowa

Scott Haldeman's most vivid memory of when he first arrived to study chiropractic is sitting on the sidewalk, in the snow, in front of a closed Quad Cities airport. It was midnight on New Year's Eve, December 31, 1961. He was 18 years old and just out of high school, 10,000 miles from home, and expecting to be picked up by his friend from high school, Reg Engelbrecht, who was a student at Palmer.

He had left Joan in Pretoria with a promise to return in three years and asked her to promise, in return, that she would give him at least one date when he got back. And with that, he boarded a plane and flew from Johannesburg, South Africa, to London where he spent a few days with Dr. Elizabeth Bennett, daughter of his father's associate, Dr. J. A. Blackbourn, and her husband Dr. Don Bennett. Dr. Blackbourn's family included 22 practicing chiropractors. Don and Elizabeth were very active in the chiropractic profession in England and in Europe. They were later to head the Anglo European Chiropractic College.

Scott continued on his eventful journey from London to Montreal where he spent Christmas with his grandparents, Harold (Pop) and

Edith (Mom) Fletcher and his Aunt Kay (Wyn's sister), her husband, Elmer Lach, and Cousin Ronnie. Kay had been one of Canada's leading models and Elmer was in the Montreal Canadian's hockey hall of fame. He took Scott to a Canadians' hockey game where they got to sit in the VIP box and take a tour of the locker room and meet the players. The second leg of his journey had been quite eventful, but he was ready to arrive at what would be his final destination for the next three years. That would prove more difficult than expected, however.

Though he left South Africa for England in a jet airliner, when Scott finally flew into Davenport, Iowa, it was on a small vintage DC 3 aircraft. Sitting outside the remote airport after arriving in the ancient plane, and being wholly unprepared for the mid-western winter cold, Scott couldn't be picked up fast enough. He had no heavy winter clothing to speak of, and it was snowing. Unfortunately, Reg had forgotten his friend's arrival and never made a showing at the airport. Scott could not have felt more alone. A limousine driver, making his last round at the airport, saw this forlorn young kid standing outside (by this time the airport had closed down, the lights were out and doors locked). He took pity and offered to give him a ride to wherever he needed to go, but the problem was that Scott didn't know where exactly that was. Reg had not sent him any contact information. The driver, who was a student at Palmer working part time, decided to drop him off at a New Year's Eve party at a fraternity house. The fraternity brothers took Scott in until they located Reg at about 4:00 am. An apologetic young Reg then took Scott to the South African House where he ended up living with a number of other students from his homeland for the next eighteen months.

The South African House was just three blocks from campus, so Scott could walk to school. The owner of the house was quite religious and allowed no alcohol on the premises. This was not a problem for the South Africans as the ANZAC House, where the Australian and New Zealand students lived, had no such restriction, and the South African students could join them for drinks anytime. Though perhaps not as lively, the saving grace of the South Africa House was that it was much cleaner and quieter than ANZAC House.

There were a number of South African students attending Palmer,

Scott standing on the porch at the house where he and Frans van Leeuwen rented an apartment after leaving South African House in Davenport. circa 1964.

many of whom had been referred by Scott's father. In the school's 1962 January issue of the *Beacon* (the Palmer College newspaper) there is a picture of seven new students from South Africa attending a reception at the home of President David D. Palmer. Here they were greeted by Mayor Ray O'Brien of Davenport. The caption indicated that 19 additional students from South Africa and Northern Rhodesia attended Palmer.

On 4-5 of February, the State Board of Education hosted an event for all foreign students going to school in Iowa. Palmer provided three busses for the 98 foreign students to travel to Des Moines for the event. The group represented the countries of Canada, South Africa, New Zealand, Australia, France, Belgium, Switzerland, India, Ireland, and England. Scott was part of this group and was interviewed by a WHO reporter and later aired on WOC-TV.

Davenport Mayor greets South African students. Photo taken from the *Beacon*, 1962. Scott is on the far right. Courtesy Palmer College of Chiropractic Library.

ACADEMICS

Scott, who had just graduated from high school, was one of *the* youngest, if not the youngest student in his class. At that time the requirement for admission to Palmer for foreign students was a high school certificate and a letter from the chiropractic society in the home country stating that the student would be able to practice as a chiropractor upon graduation. Chiropractors were not licensed, but also not prohibited from practicing in South Africa so this was not a problem. All was in place for Scott to earn his license.

Scott had entered chiropractic education in the early 1960s, when accreditation of chiropractic educational institutions was more political than academic. The national political bodies, the International Chiropractors Association (ICA) and the National Chiropractic Association (NCA), served as the agencies of accreditation. Those schools whose educational philosophy and educational curriculum aligned with a particular political association sought accreditation/recognition from that association. While talk of obtaining accreditation from the more formal regional accrediting agencies of higher education and the U.S. Department of Education was occurring in both the ICA and the NCA, it would be many years (1974) before such recognition would be achieved by any school. In the interim between the early 1960s and 1974, a unified professional accrediting body, the Council on Chiropractic Education (CCE), was established and eventually obtained recognition by the U.S. Department of Education. The

1961-62 Palmer College of Chiropractic Bulletin published in October, 1961, just a few months before Scott's arrival, touted the fact that Palmer was *accredited* by the International Chiropractors Association, *approved* by the Iowa State Department of Public Instruction and the Veterans Administration of the United States, and *affiliated* with the North American Association of Chiropractic Schools and Colleges.

The 1961 College Bulletin listed seven full professors, nine associate professors, eight assistant professors, and four instructors, giving a total of 28 faculty members for nearly 1,000 students enrolled. All save one were graduates of Palmer with a DC degree. Harry Andrews, associate professor of pathology and diagnosis, held a BS, MS, PhD, and MD and was the only non-DC faculty member. He was also the only instructor to have achieved the academic rank of PhD. Three other faculty members, Kenneth Cronk, Catherine Miller, and H. Ron Frogley were all listed as holding master's degrees. Three additional faculty members listed their bachelor's degrees. All professors (and only those designated as professor) listed their PhC degree as well. To achieve the PhC—philosopher of chiropractic—a DC degree with "superior scholastic achievement" and "evidence of such personal characteristics as may be considered prerequisites for the development of professional competence and leadership in the field of chiropractic," were required.[1] In order to obtain the PhC a candidate was required to complete a nine-month graduate course culminating in a research project and an original thesis.

At the time Scott entered Palmer, the school offered an annual curriculum of four quarters. Entrance into the program and exit out of the program could occur in any of the four quarters. In the 1961-62 catalog, formal graduations were scheduled at the end of the winter and summer quarters. Scott entered the winter quarter of 1962 on 12 January. Each academic year was nine months in duration or three quarters. The college offered courses during summer term and the program could be completed in three calendar years if the student attended the summer quarter in each of the three years. The total number of classroom hours for the three years Scott was at Palmer

[1] Chiropractic, Palmer College of Chiropractic Bulletin, 1961

43

was 4,485. The college used standard text books in the basic sciences including Gray's Anatomy, Guyton's Physiology, and Boyd's Textbook on Pathology.[2]

Scott had a number of well-respected and experienced instructors that included Galen Price in philosophy, Virgil Strang, who headed the anatomy dissection laboratory, and Clay Thompson and Don Kern, who taught technique. Don Kern eventually became president of Palmer College. Scott became friends with Clay Thompson and, years later, they would often speak at the same conventions. Scott claims he could give "toggle recoil" adjustment, taught to him by Dr. Clay Thompson, on a Thompson Drop table, with precision.[3] Clarence Gonstead and Henri Gillet, two of the best known developers of chiropractic adjustment technique systems, often visited the campus and gave demonstrations and courses on their techniques. Scott actually took time as a student to visit the Gonstead Clinic in Mt. Horeb, Wisconsin, for further instruction, and he also spent time with Dr. Gillet when he was in Belgium a few years later. Dr. Heath "Nip" Quigley, who had headed the Clearview Sanitarium Psychiatric Hospital established by BJ Palmer, presented some of the most interesting cases from the hospital. Dr. Quigley and Scott would cross paths again in 1973 when both authored chapters in the textbook *Mental Health and Chiropractic* edited by Herman Schwartz.

Ron Frogley and Kenneth Cronk, two of the few faculty members with master's degrees, became Scott's academic mentors. Dr. Cronk took a particular interest in the South African students and would often invite them over for dinner and intense discussion of clinical and theoretical problems in chiropractic. He even hosted a birthday party for Scott when he turned 21.

Scott had memorized one of the "Green Books"—Stephenson's book on Chiropractic Philosophy published by the Palmer College—in the courses given by Dr. Price. Dr. Frogley taught the courses

---

[2] Chiropractic, Palmer College of Chiropractic Bulletin, 1961
[3] A toggle recoil adjustment is one of the more challenging types of high velocity, low amplitude adjustments to master.

Scott celebrating his 21st birthday at the home of Dr. Cronk, June 1964.

in physiology in which Scott took an intense interest. It was Dr. Frogley who attempted to reconcile the traditional chiropractic philosophical and theoretical concepts with modern physiological theories. The primary theory explained that the effect of chiropractic care was that misaligned vertebrae would put pressure on the spinal nerves and thus interfere with the normal transmission of nerve impulses to the organs. The discussions with Dr. Frogley and Dr. Cronk on nerve compression were to become the inspiration for Scott's master's thesis when he returned to South Africa.

Scott arrived at Palmer College during a transitional period in the school's history. BJ Palmer, who had taught and inspired Scott's father, had died only a few months before Scott's arrival. All buildings on campus were still covered with BJ sayings. By the time he left three years later they had been painted over by Dave, BJ's son and succeeding president of Palmer College, who also took the "BJ" out of the clinic name.

At the time of Scott's enrollment, Palmer College was considered "The Fountainhead," and was proud of its heritage as the first chiropractic teaching institution. It also taught many of the principles established by DD Palmer and BJ Palmer, his son. In each year's college bulletin, a statement of *Chiropractic Philosophy* followed by an explanation of *How Our Organs Work* and *The Profession of Chiropractic* explained the principles that were taught in the college. A few of these principles can be seen in the following excerpts from the

1961 Palmer College Bulletin:

> Chiropractic Philosophy is an explanation of the fundamentals
> upon which the practice of chiropractic is based. In order to grasp
> these fundamental values, it is necessary to understand the ana-
> tomical structure of the body and to know the primary functions
> of body organs. Each organ within the body has some function in
> the maintenance of life and health of the entire organism, and it
> must be coordinated with the needs and demands of the moment.
> Body organs are arranged in systems so that they may carry out
> their mission. Thus, the body is an organization of these systems.
> The state of organization found among the body organs and
> systems is maintained through the nervous system, and indicates
> the presence of an intellectual guiding entity – an inborn or innate
> intelligence.[4]

Scott took an interest in the history of chiropractic and the theories on which it was based. In a 1962 publication, *Wivern* (the Palmer
school yearbook), Scott is credited with an essay titled, "Our Heritage."
In this essay he pays homage to the three generations of Palmers, DD
the Discoverer, BJ the Developer, and David D. the Dignifier. Scott
gives special tribute to BJ, considered by some as the most influential
as well as controversial of the three Palmers:

> What kind of man was this BJ Palmer who developed a science
> born into contempt and ridicule into a great healing art?

> He was a world famous author, traveler and businessman. He wrote
> many books, five of which were completed by the age of twenty-
> eight. The majority of his writings show his tremendous dedication
> to the profession that he had unfailingly served. One volume is a
> description of his travels throughout the United States and abroad
> in order to spread the reputation of chiropractic. He gave lectures
> in large cities and small towns to explain chiropractic and to defend
> it, sometimes even in the courtroom. He was a man with out-
> standing qualities and was gifted with a remarkable sense of keen
> observation and foresight. He owed his success in business to the

---

[4] 1961 Palmer College of Chiropractic Annual Catalog. Property of Palmer College of
Chiropractic, Davenport, IA.

ability of observation and foresight, an example being the fact that he originated the first radio station west of the Mississippi.

At the time of his death, he was the president of the largest and most well-known chiropractic college in the world as well as the principle owner of two radio-TV stations.

The remarkable abilities of Dr. BJ Palmer enabled him to improve and modernize the methods of analysis and adjustment without ever straying from the true concept of chiropractic. After trial and investigation, Dr. Palmer recognized the value of such instruments as the x-ray machine and the neurocalometer to chiropractic, and he introduced them into the profession even though he was condemned by fellow members of the profession who did not have the foresight to recognize the significance of such advancements. By investigation, experimentation, and research, Dr. BJ Palmer developed chiropractic into one of the greatest healing arts of our time.[5]

This tribute supports the premise that the education Scott received at Palmer ingrained in him respect and admiration for both DD and BJ Palmer.

Scott was the Valedictorian of his December 1964 graduating class. He was one of two students graduating to receive the award from the International Chiropractors Association Students' Advisory board, Palmer Chapter, "for meritorious service."

In the Palmer College News of October 1964, Scott is featured with eleven other students who were accepted into the Pi Tau Delta National Chiropractic Scholastic Society.[6]

His transcripts provide a robust example of the curricular offerings as well as demonstrating his strong academic qualities:

---

[5] Chiropractic, Wivern, 1962
[6] Palmer College News, 1964,Vol. IV, No. 10, pg. 4

TRANSCRIPT
PALMER COLLEGE OF CHIROPRACTIC, DAVENPORT, IA.

NAME HALDEMAN, Scott

PAGE 1

MATRICULATION NO. 23211

DATE OF ENROLLMENT	1-03-62
DATE OF GRADUATION	12-31-64
DEGREE RECEIVED	D.C.

COURSE NAME / DATE TERM COMPLETED	HOURS	GRADE	CREDIT	HONOR POINTS	COURSE NAME / DATE TERM COMPLETED	HOURS	GRADE	CREDIT	HONOR POINTS
PRIN & PRACT 11	65	4			ANATOMY & PHYSIOLOGY 13	65	4		
PHILOSOPHY 11	65	4			CHEMISTRY 130	65	4		
PHYSIOLOGY 11	65	4			TECHNIC 130	65	4		
CHEMISTRY 11	65	4			NEUROLOGY 131	65	4		
ANATOMY 11 1 & 2	65	4			ANATOMY 135	65	4		
1962 WINTER					1962 SPRING				
SYMPT & DIAG 120	65	4			TECHNIQUE 25A	65	4		
HYGIENE 120	65	3			SPINOGRAPH 25A	65	4		
ANATOMY 115 ORTHOPEDY	65	4			CHEMISTRY 250 ORGANIC	65	4		
ANATOMY 120 SPLANCH	65	4			TECHNIQUE 240	65	4		
PHILOSOPHY 120	65	4			PATHOLOGY 250 HEMATOLOGY	32.5	4		
					PATHOLOGY 250 PEDIATRICS	32.5	4		
					SYMPT DIAG 250 SPEC SENS	65	4		
1962 SUMMER					1962 FALL				
PATHOLOGY 240	65	4			BIOCHEMISTRY LECTURE 260	65	4		
NEUROLOGY 242	65	4			BACTERIOLOGY LECT 260	65	4		
TECHNIQUE 250	65	4			BIOCHEMISTRY LAB 260	65	3		
ANATOMY 240 EMBRYOLOGY	65	4			BACTERIOLOGY LAB 260	65	3		
SYMPT & DIAG 240 1ST AID	32.5	4			PATHOLOGY LAB 260	65	4		
SYMPT & DIAG 240 GENESIOL	32.5	3							
1963 WINTER					1963 SPRING				
NCM NCG 370	65	3			TECHNIC 380	65	4		
SPINOGRAPH 370	65	4			CLINIC NUMBER ONE	97	4		
PHYSIOLOGY 370 METABOLISM	65	3			PATHOLOGY 255	65	4		
TECHNIC 370	65	3			SYMPT & DIAG 390 PHYS DIGE	32.5	4		
PHILOSOPHY 370	65	3			SYMPT & DIAG 390 DIGESTIVE	32.5	4		
NEUROLOGY 373	65	4			PHYSIOLOGY 390 ENDOCRINOLOGY	65	4		
					PATHOLOGY 390	65	4		
1963 SUMMER					1963 FALL				

GRADING SYSTEM

4 A-EXCELLENT
3 B-ABOVE AVERAGE
2 C-AVERAGE
1 D-BELOW AVERAGE
10-WITHDRAWN

6 I-INCOMPLETE
7 -OVERCUT
8 -NO CREDIT
9 -PASSING
11 -WITHDRAWN / ADMINISTRATIVE

DEGREE GRANTED _____ DATE _____

STUDENT/ALUMNUS COPY

REGISTRAR _____ DATE _____

TRANSCRIPT

PALMER COLLEGE OF CHIROPRACTIC, DAVENPORT, IA.

NAME   HALDEMAN, Scott   PAGE   2

MATRICULATION NO.   23211

DATE OF ENROLLMENT
DATE OF GRADUATION
DEGREE RECEIVED

COURSE NAME / DATE TERM COMPLETED	HOURS	GRADE	CREDIT	HONOR POINTS
SPINOGRAPH LAB 390	130	4		
STUDENT CLINIC NUMBER TWO	97	3		
SYMPT & DIAG 385 1	32.5	4		
SYMPT & DIAG 385 2	32.5	4		
SYMPT & DIAG 380 GYN OBST	65	4		
PATHOLOGY 380	65	4		
	1964 WINTER			
PHILOSOPHY 412	60	3		
ETHICS & JURISPRUDENCE	60	3		
PATHOLOGY REVIEW 412	60	4		
SPINOGRAPH 412	60	3		
PUBLIC CLINICS	120	4		
	1964 SUMMER			

COURSE NAME / DATE TERM COMPLETED	HOURS	GRADE	CREDIT	HONOR POINTS
DISSECTION LAB 410	120	4		
PHYSICAL DIAGNOSIS 410	60	4		
CLINIC NUMBER THREE	120	4		
TECHNIC 410	60	4		
	1964 SPRING			
PATHOLOGY 411 ABNORMALI	60	3		
PSYCHIATRY 411	60	4		
X RAY LAB ASSISTANT	300	4		
FINAL CLINIC GRADE		4		
	1964 FALL			
TOTAL	4389			

GRADING SYSTEM

4 A-EXCELLENT
3 B-ABOVE AVERAGE
2 C-AVERAGE
1 D-BELOW AVERAGE
10-WITHDRAWN

6 I-INCOMPLETE
7 -OVERCUT
8 -NO CREDIT
9 -PASSING
11 -WITHDRAWN / ADMINISTRATIVE

D.C.   12-31-64
DEGREE GRANTED   DATE

STUDENT/ALUMNUS COPY

REGISTRAR   DATE

WORK AND FINANCES

Scott's father provided $150 a month for his son's expenses. Tuition was $50 a month; rent $25 a month; books $25 a month; and everything else including food, health care, and entertainment took up the remaining $50. All of the South African students considered themselves frugal. When any of them would pass a supermarket that had a sale on canned food, they would buy a large quantity to share. They kept a perpetual pot of stew on the stove and ingredients were added as they became available. So if beans were on sale for $0.10 a can they would buy 20 cans and the stew would be primarily beans. When corn was on sale the stew had an over abundance of corn. Palmer College had just closed their Clearview Sanitarium at the time of Scott's arrival, and one of the South African students was a night watchman at the Sanitarium. In the basement were boxes of leftover food, consisting primarily of tapioca pudding and Rice Krispies. With this supply of goodies readily available, Scott remembers eating tapioca pudding and Rice Krispies on a regular basis. There was an American student they befriended who received food stamps. Rather than being redeemable at the supermarket, these certificates allowed you to go to the farmer's market and purchase food that was in excess. Split peas and peanut butter were the most plentiful and thus became another mainstay of the South African house, compliments of their American friend.

Scott entertaining at the South African House in Davenport, circa 1962.

Surviving on "not quite enough" money necessitated finding gainful employment while attending school. The owner of the South African house stored a bicycle on the premises and allowed the students to use it. This provided mobility for Scott to his first job in Davenport: shoveling snow for $1.00 per hour in the evenings and on weekends. This seasonal work did not provide a steady, dependable income, so he also tried selling encyclopedias by going door-to-door. After a period of training he would be dropped off at a street corner in a small Iowa town and would begin knocking on doors with a memorized sales pitch. Scott soon found, however, that the less-than-profitable world of encyclopedia sales was not for him, so he gave it up.

One South African student, Isaac Venter, the most senior man in the South African house, was paid $1.50 per hour working as a personal gardener for the owner of the Griggs Piano Co. When this job became available Scott grabbed it. Every Saturday that summer he would ride the bicycle for an hour to do his gardening work.

Griggs Piano Co. also employed another occupant of the South African House, Frans Van Leeuwen, as a janitor. As Frans moved on to another job, Scott was promoted from the garden to the piano store as janitor. He worked after school and all day Saturday keeping the piano store clean. Scott, while cleaning the piano store after hours, would often take a break and practice his piano skills learned back home. This was probably against the company rules, but no one was there to tell him otherwise. One day in November the sales manager was in the store and heard Scott playing. He was so impressed with Scott's ability that he offered him a job as a piano salesman for the Christmas season. This job paid commission only but offered greater potential than sweeping floors. The manager asked Scott what he had to wear that would be becoming of a salesman. Scott replied that he had a high school blazer, one tie, and one pair of long pants. This was not good enough for the store manager, but Scott had no money to put toward a new wardrobe, so the store manager advanced Scott enough money to purchase the proper attire—a plaid jacket, winged-tipped shoes, and a pair of striped pants. Thus Scott was transformed into an Iowa salesman. At that time in the early 1960s, the civil rights movement and racial unrest were big items in the news. Many of sales personnel for Griggs didn't feel comfortable with black customers; however, working with those customers was a non-issue for Scott, having grown up around black people all his life. As a result, all the black potential customers were referred to Scott who claims to have made $400-$500 dollars each of his last two months of that year selling pianos.

With his newly earned income he bought a 1948 Ford. After the Christmas season when sales slowed, Griggs put their sales force on the road, traveling to the many adjacent small towns in the countryside. Griggs taught Scott to play a simple organ, and even sent him to the Wurlitzer Company to be trained on how pianos and organs were made.

Scott on tour at the Wurlitzer Piano company, circa 1963.

Scott, standing on the left, observing a new piano sound board while touring the Wurlitzer Piano Company, circa 1963.

After school Scott would load a piano and organ in the back of the store van and drive out to a small town. He would arrange beforehand to get a list from the local piano teacher of all his or her students. If a student bought an instrument, the instructor would also get a commission. Scott would knock on someone's door, get them to help carry the organ or piano into the house, teach their little Johnny how to play Jingle Bells, and then sell them the piano. Scott did this for about a year and a half after school when time permitted. With this added prosperity, he upgraded from a 1948 Ford to a 1955 Mercury—a car with a big engine that allowed him to travel around the country in style.

Scott's economic success did not go unnoticed. Some suspicious person, probably at school, reported his unusual financial gains to the U.S. Immigration and Naturalization Service (INS). Agents from the INS came on campus and pulled Scott out of class, fingerprinted him, and warned that as a foreign student he was not to work and earn an income or he would be deported. Well before Scott's experience with the INS, he and Frans Van Leeuwen had decided to leave the South African house and move into their own apartment for their last year and a half of school. The apartment was much nicer than the South Africa House, but it increased Scott's living expenses. With his source of revenue suddenly eliminated, the nice apartment now became a heavy financial burden.

Unfortunately, Scott had boasted of his financial success in his letters back home and his father had stopped making the $150.00 a month payment for his support. He probably figured Scott didn't need the extra help anymore. Not wanting to reveal his predicament to his folks, he lived on his savings as long as he could. When he returned to South Africa in December of 1964, he had only $25.00 in his pocket.

SPORTS AND SOCIAL LIFE

Scott, together with Barry King from New Zealand and Frans van Leeuwen, also from South Africa, organized a rugby team at Palmer. There had been an attempt to start a rugby team two years before but it didn't last. This new team was made up of South African, British, Australian, and New Zealand rugby players plus a few American football players. The Palmer team helped to organize the Midwest Rugby League, which continues to field teams today. Teams from the University of Michigan, Notre Dame, and other major Midwest schools joined the league. The teams would drive in their own cars to towns where the schools were located. When the opposing team would come to Davenport, the Palmer team would house their opponents and the same would happen when the Palmer team traveled. At first the only uniform was a Palmer sweatshirt and shorts along with their rugby boots, which they had shipped from home. In the last year, the club was able to purchase proper rugby jerseys. Tom Louw, who was on the

National team for Rhodesia and played in international competition, enrolled at Palmer in the middle of Scott's time there. Because of his experience, he was made a player-coach and the team began to act like a college sports team rather than a social club. After Scott left Palmer, the rugby team became national champions and one of the most successful teams in the country. Barry, Frans, and Scott were the first rugby players to get their school colors (letter) from Palmer. Unfortunately, in the final season before returning to South Africa, Scott was injured on the field with an acromio-clavicular shoulder separation that never fully recovered and prevented him from playing any further rugby. Despite the injury, his love for the sport never diminished.

Scott, center of the huddle, playing rugby, circa 1963-64.

Somehow Scott became the official cook for the rugby team. He would serve the team bowls of very soft, overcooked rice and whatever meat and vegetables they could afford. Like rugby players all over the world, the Palmer team took pride in the ability to hold their beer. Beer was also essential to adequately entertain and impress a visiting team. Unfortunately, Iowa was a dry state and many of the students were underage and couldn't buy any beer. The boys overcame this problem when one of the Palmer students got a job for the Hamm's Brewing Company. He always had a keg of beer to sell for $10 after 11 p.m. at the warehouse; the team just had to make sure that the kegs were brought back after the warehouse closed. No questions were ever asked.

Palmer College Rugby Team, circa 1964. Scott is second from the right, front row.

Scott also played on the cricket team at Palmer. Cricket was not exactly popular in the American Midwest in the 1960s, so the team was made up mostly of British students. They played intramural competition only, but were dubbed as "not that good." When they traveled they played mostly club level teams composed of Indian and Pakistani players who were excited to play teams from nationalities other than their own. The cricket games were more an excuse to travel and meet people than a true effort to develop a competitive team.

Scott cannot be attributed with beginning the Palmer Flying Club as some might expect, although he did become its president. The club was actually organized by a flight instructor. It owned one old, two-seater, 140 Cessna, tail-dragger. It would cost the students $3.50 an hour for the plane and gas and the same amount for the instructor. The students repaired the plane themselves and, when necessary, would fly with a licensed member of the club. Scott flew all around the Midwest, landing on runways in farmers' fields and camping next to the plane at night. He had to be careful with his expenses but was active for a year and a half in the flying club. He passed the written exam and estimates that he flew nearly 40 hours. After completing a few more hours in the air once he returned to South Africa, he received his pilot's license.

In addition to being active in rugby, cricket, and flying, Scott was very involved in school clubs. He was the vice president of the South African Club and the International Chiropractors Association (ICA) Student Club; his dad had been active in the ICA all his life and Scott maintained this association. When the National Chiropractic Association and ICA were joining to form the American Chiropractic Association, Scott became active with the ICA efforts. But when the ICA broke away after the merger, Scott stayed active with the newly formed ICA, and this is where he became good friends with Jerry McAndrews, a faculty member at Palmer. Jerry eventually became president of Palmer, and served in the administrative offices of the ICA and then the ACA.

Many future leaders of the profession graduated from Palmer College in the same era and have remained friends and supporters of some of the projects Scott has promoted. Lou Sportelli, currently president of the National Chiropractic Mutual Insurance Company (NCMIC) was a junior at the time Scott entered Palmer and later served as Chairman of the Board of Governors of the American Chiropractic Association and President of the World Federation of Chiropractic. Peter Martin graduated in September, prior to Scott's arrival, and went on to join the administration of the Los Angeles College of Chiropractic faculty and then acted as president of the Palmer campuses in California and Florida. Andries Kleynhans, a fellow South African who graduated with the December class of 1960, became a faculty member at National College of Chiropractic and then principal of the International College of Chiropractic at the Preston Institute of Technology in Melbourne, Australia. Michael Pedigo, also a Palmer contemporary went on to become president of both the ICA and ACA and was active in the Wilk's trial that changed the ethical rules of the

American Medical Association regarding chiropractic.

Before leaving South Africa, Scott left Joan with the understanding that their relationship would continue while he was at Palmer. Though Scott had not been a great letter writer before coming to Davenport, he was motivated to write Joan at least twice a week, and she wrote back to him as often. Scott kept with him a photo album prepared by his mother which included pictures of Joan and the family. He kept a photo of Joan next to his bed. Scott says he maintained certain rules when dating in Davenport. First, it was crucial that his date enjoy dancing at parties. Second, the date's mother had to be a good cook since the food at the South African house was very routine, not always very healthy, and sometimes barely edible. One of his best dates, he recalls, was with a Catholic girl whose parents fed him fish every Friday night. Though he did not convert, despite their best efforts, he enormously enjoyed the culinary treat of having fish so often. Third, he made sure that every girl he met at a party knew about Joan and recognized that any relationship with him was unlikely to go any further than social friends. Understandably, he never developed a serious relationship with a girl while at Palmer.

Scott did, however, make many lasting friendships. One year, after he had purchased the Mercury and was able to travel fairly extensively, he and friends drove to Boston and then to New York and down the Atlantic coast to Ft. Lauderdale, Florida, for spring break. A group also drove across the country to Colorado. The owner of the Griggs Piano Company had a cabin in Estes Park and he let the boys stay there. Colorado was as far west as Scott ventured in those days. They traveled to Chicago often, once to see *The Sound of Music* at the Schubert Theater and once to visit National College of Chiropractic. He had the opportunity of shaking hands with the school's president, Joseph Janse, at their new Lombard campus. He also paid a visit to the Canadian Memorial College of Chiropractic in Toronto, Canada. Scott was able to see and experience much on his travels around the country, but that did not keep him from missing home occasionally.

Because Scott's parents had four other children, they were not able to visit him while in America. Telephone calls were prohibitively

Scott (on the right) traveling the United States with friends from Palmer, circa 1963.

expensive, and the only time he spoke to anyone in South Africa during his three Palmer years was a single call he made to Joan. Thankfully, Scott's mother wrote almost every week and sent newspaper clippings as well as bulletins put out by his father's clinic. This allowed Scott to keep up with the family happenings, including their ongoing search for the Lost City of the Kalahari.

Just before Christmas in 1964, Scott returned to South Africa. He was reunited with his family and Joan after three years of separation. He and Joan were engaged in February of 1965 and married in November of that same year.

Scott claims he never had plans to stay in chiropractic education but he knew at graduation his level of knowledge and understanding was not enough to satisfy his desire to learn. When Scott arrived back in South Africa that December, he immediately enrolled at the University of Pretoria to obtain his bachelor's degree, knowing his pursuit to obtain further education was far from finished.

Chapter 4

CLINICAL PRACTICE, RESEARCH AND INTERDISCIPLINARY COOPERATION

Pretoria, South Africa (1965-1969)

Joshua Haldeman proudly published the following in his November 1964 Chiropractic Health Bulletin:

> Dr. Scott Haldeman is expected to arrive on December 22, to join the staff of the Haldeman Chiropractic Clinic, having completed thirty-six months of continuous training covering over 4,000 class hours at the Palmer College of Chiropractic.

Scott was met at the Johannesburg airport by Joan, his parents, and siblings. While Scott was away at Palmer, Joan attended the University of Pretoria to study physiotherapy. She had been elected to the student committee of the South African Society of Physiotherapy in her first year at school. She graduated in December 1964 and started working at the Pretoria General Hospital. With Scott's return the same month, the correspondence relationship between the two transitioned back to a more personal one. They became engaged to be married in February 1965. On the 27th of November, 1965, they married and honeymooned at the coast on the Indian Ocean. Upon their return they moved into a small house behind the clinic.

CHIROPRACTIC PRACTICE

Scott joined his father's well-established practice in a clinic next to the family home. An article published in an unidentified journal (circa 1956) tells the story of the Haldeman Clinic in Pretoria. The initial property was 5,000 sq. ft. on one acre of land and included the main clinic, a small native clinic, a private office and residence. Josh later purchased two adjacent homes so that he could expand the clinic but still live next door. The three-acre property on which the clinic, family home, and a guest house were located was just two and half miles from the center of the town of Pretoria. The clinic had three adjusting rooms and 14 dressing rooms. There was a main x-ray unit and a small extra x-ray unit in the native clinic. The extensive grounds supported 38 large shade trees, 50 fruit trees, a sunken rose garden, three fish ponds, many fountains, exotic gardens, and swimming pools for adults and children.

Haldeman Clinic, Pretoria, South Africa, circa 1966

The clinic mailed out a monthly health bulletin to more than 3,000 patients as well as to family and friends from around the world. A total of 222 bulletins and travelogues were published in the clinic. Scott and his sisters often had to copy, fold, and place the bulletins into envelopes to mail. These bulletins would present news and tips to maintain good health and the latest information on the family and their adventures traveling the world. Josh and Wyn also organized an annual "Family Tea Party." Patients, friends, and neighbors were invited to attend this highly anticipated event. Since it was held outside on the extensive grounds, the Haldemans often accommodated more than 2,000 guests. Scott's mother would cook for months in preparation for these events. The highlight was the "good posture contest" where the guest who could boast the straightest spine would be awarded a highly-coveted trophy. The winner had to impress the judges—usually friends of the family who were active in the entertainment or modeling industry—in order to win the prize.

The family clinic was thriving, and soon after arriving home, Scott was given the opportunity to demonstrate his fledgling ability to run a busy practice. His father announced that he would be taking a month's holiday and Scott would be responsible for maintaining the practice in his absence. In his clinical internship at Palmer, Scott had been responsible for the treatment of 25 individual patients. His father was averaging 100 patients a day when he left on holiday. In his first week of private practice, Scott was seeing more patients per day than he had seen in his entire clinical training period at Palmer. The loyalty of patients who had to pay for their treatment and their reports of symptom improvement following care was very rewarding.

A revealing example occurred in the clinic when a patient came in for chiropractic care before receiving back surgery. This particular patient was actually on the way to the hospital for surgery and was in severe incapacitating pain. He decided to stop at the clinic and have an adjustment before going on to the hospital. As a result of the care rendered by Scott, instead of being admitted for surgery, this patient's pain improved sufficiently that he asked to postpone the surgery. It was never rescheduled. The Haldemans became known as doctors who should be consulted before surgery. Although no one was advised against surgery, patients would, on occasion, ask their surgeons if they could try chiropractic care before surgery. This did not endear the Haldeman name to the local spine surgeons.

In the July 1965 Chiropractic Health Bulletin, Scott took occasion to respond to the many inquiries he was receiving about his Palmer experience:

> Palmer College offers the student one of the finest and most complete courses of chiropractic available. The course consists of a complete study of all the basic science subjects... The standard is such that it is possible for a student to pass the state government examinations that are written by medical doctors as a preliminary for obtaining a license to practice. The student receives very intensive training in the taking and analyzing of chiropractic x-rays as well as all the latest and most up to date adjusting techniques. There is also a complete course in first aid, physical diagnosis, psychology, etc. A fully equipped student clinic enables the senior student to intern and put his theory into practice under the faculty doctors' supervision.

> On the lighter side, a South African student has never experienced a social life to compare with that of an American university and especially Palmer College. The South Africans and other foreign students at Palmer had started a cricket team as well as a rugby team (South African rugby) which now has full recognition by the college, and in the case of rugby, there are scholarships available to top players. These teams tour all around the United States to such cities as Chicago, St. Louis and even to New York to play against teams from other big universities. A South African college student will find that it is an education just to live as an American college student for a few years. In case of financial difficulty, there are scholarships available and part time work can usually be found to support the budget.

Scott and his father would encourage many to seek after the same exemplary chiropractic education that they had received at Palmer.

BACHELOR'S DEGREE AT THE UNIVERSITY OF PRETORIA

Scott returned to Pretoria with a strong sense that he needed to continue his education. It was during this time that legislation and a national commission of inquiry was challenging chiropractic's very existence. One day Scott's father was lamenting the lack of recognition of chiropractic. He felt that if the profession was ever going to succeed in its battle for respect, someone in the profession needed to learn to explain the principles of chiropractic in scientific terms. This challenge confirmed in Scott's mind the necessity of gaining additional education.

He enrolled at the University of Pretoria within a month after his return to South Africa. There he earned a bachelor's degree with a double major in physics and physiology and a double minor in mathematics and biochemistry. He was able to do this because the physics, mathematics, and biochemistry faculties repeated lectures in the evenings from 6 to 10 p.m. The laboratory classes in physiology, biochemistry, and physics (three hours each class) could be completed three afternoons a week. Scott was then able to practice every morning and some afternoons as well as Saturday mornings from 7:00 a.m. to 1:00 p.m. While studying hard for his night classes he was also practicing 30 hours a week with his dad, helping with the renovations on the house he and Joan rented from his parents, and traveling throughout South Africa whenever possible with Joan. Finally, after three years of this hectic routine, he earned his bachelor's degree.

In the January 1968 Chiropractic Health Bulletin, Dr. Joshua Haldeman reported that:

> Dr. Scott Haldeman has completed his B.Sc. degree at the University of Pretoria, while at the same time putting in over thirty hours per week in the Haldeman Chiropractic Clinic during the past three years.

> Since graduating from the Palmer College of Chiropractic, Davenport, Iowa, USA, he has continued with full-time studies at the university. To major in both physics and physiology it was necessary to take an additional subject. The purpose was to prepare for research in the physiology of the nervous system. He passed his final with a distinction. He studied physics to do research into chiropractic instrumentation. He will be continuing his studies at the university and his practice at the clinic.

An interesting side note found in the September 1968 Bulletin explains that while his father was taking the month of December 1968 off for holiday, the hours of the clinic were to be restricted to morning hours (6:45 am to 12:00 pm) due to Scott's rigorous school schedule.

MASTER'S DEGREE AT THE UNIVERSITY OF PRETORIA

At the age of 25, Scott transitioned from a bachelor's to a master's degree program without a break. At the University of Pretoria, Scott wanted to conduct research into the basic principles of chiropractic and submitted a formal proposal to study nerve compression as the basis for his research before he was accepted into the program. There were no professors in the department of physiology experienced in this topic to mentor Scott in his graduate proposal. The head of the Department of Physiology, Professor Ben Mayer, asked the only neurophysiologist in the department, Dr. van Niekerk to be Scott's promoter. Scott, however, decided what experiments he wanted to conduct and ended up conducting them with limited formal supervision. He wanted to use the only electron microscope at the medical school, but there was no one in the department who knew how to use it or who could arrange time on its schedule for Scott. Undeterred by this snag, Scott decided to learn to run the electron microscope himself by assisting the technician in charge of the instrument, Mr. Hugo, during the day. In turn, Hugo would assist Scott in his own work in the evenings. Professor Mayer, as head of the department, gave a great deal of support to Scott. Although he was not officially his supervisor (Dr. Mayer was a cardiovascular physiologist), he offered guidance and allowed free use of all departmental facilities and equipment.

One opportunity particularly impressed Scott. Professor Mayer had traveled to the U.S. to be mentored for his doctorate degree by Arthur Guyton of *Guyton Physiology* fame. Guyton came to the University of Pretoria to visit his old friend and Scott was able to have a personal meeting with him for 2-3 hours. Professor Guyton provided further encouragement for Scott to continue his research and even suggested that he go abroad to complete a PhD.

Scott's final thesis for completion of his master's degree in physiology was titled, *Changes in the Structure and Function of the Sciatic Nerve Caused by Constriction*. He wrote, "The effect of constricting or compressing a peripheral nerve has been studied from as early as

1862 when Waller described the effects of compression on the radial, median and ulnar nerves in his own arm." After reviewing the literature Scott began to question the severe criticism of chiropractic by the major medical societies who had implied that a theory based on compression of spinal nerves was not scientifically valid. The idea that pressure on a nerve could interfere with normal conduction of nerve impulses had been the basis for chiropractic theory since it was first proposed by D. D. Palmer. In order to study nerve compression Scott performed experiments on the sciatic nerve of the South African frog. He compressed the nerve using a device that he designed himself and which allowed for the application of graduated compression forces on the nerve. He then measured the action potential below the compression when the nerve was stimulated above the compression. He found that compression did reduce the measured action potential in the nerve and that release of the compression allowed for the recovery of conduction within the nerve in a manner consistent with what he had been taught at Palmer.

It was in the mid-1960s that the concept of axoplasmic[1] flow was gaining acceptance. Scott decided to study the effect of compression on the anatomy of the nerve above the compression to see whether compression could impact axoplasmic flow. Using both light and electron microscopes, he noted marked changes in the diameter of the nerves above a compression. This was consistent with the concept that compression could block axoplasmic flow. He further noted that the swelling in the axon contained a much higher concentration of organelles than a normal axon. A third observation that the axon appeared to telescope into itself above the compression was consistent with the theory that axons were actually growing and not simply conducting electric impulses and fluids. This observation led Scott to be convinced that the basic theory of nerve interference inherent in chiropractic was not only worth further study but was considerably more complex and interesting than he had learned at Palmer. He completed the master's degree with honors and defended it in November 1969.

---

[1] The flow or fluids, chemicals and organelles from the cell body in the spinal cord along the nerve fibers.

MILITARY SERVICE

In the 1960s there was compulsory military service in South Africa for all men over the age of 18, though it was easy to get deferment in order to attend a university. In the second half of the 1960s, however, South Africa instituted a new law that established the *Commandos*, a service that was similar to the Army National Reserve in the U.S. In the Commandos service, recruits would be required to complete two training camps of one month each followed by 15 years of service for a couple of weeks each year and reserve status thereafter. Commando training was compulsory for all graduate level university students.

In 1968 Scott was called up for Commando basic training. He approached this experience with high expectations despite the interruption to his studies and practice. He had been an officer in school military cadets that had been compulsory and had attended a couple of interesting cadet officer training camps. His experience in the South African Commando camp, however, was a major disappointment. The first camp was in Kimberly in the Orange Free State in mid-winter. The camp was located at an old air force base in the Karoo, which is a desert and very cold during the winter. The camp construction was not complete, and 100 new recruits were housed in a large hangar with only canvas over the doors. Most of the recruits became ill with bronchitis, or severe diarrhea, and there was not one medical officer in the camp. The official rank of the recruits on completing the camp was "skutter" or rifleman, but in the entire month each recruit fired only five bullets with World War II Lee-Enfield caliber 303 rifles.

The second one-month camp was in Pretoria at the Voortrekker Hoogte camp. On this occasion Scott spent most of the time translating standing orders from Afrikaans to English and doing parade ground marching drills and training. He then had to patrol an ammunition storage area every evening. One of the requirements for his master's degree was proficiency in German, so Scott spent this time reading German novels. When he decided to study for his PhD in Canada, he again received deferment from his duties on the assumption that when he returned he would complete his follow-up duties in the reserve.

LESSONS IN INTERDISCIPLINARY COMMUNICATION

It was during this period that Scott became aware that communication between medicine, chiropractic, and physical therapy was not only possible but easy if one was discussing science and not politics. Interacting with Joan's colleagues in physical therapy occurred without any concern about professional boundaries or differences, and instead focused on interesting patients and ideas.

The professors in the physiology department were very keen to find out about chiropractic and showed no bias or concerns that Scott was practicing as a chiropractor. Professor Grotepas, the chairman of the biochemistry department, was particularly supportive. He lived just down the block from the clinic and he and his family became friends of the Haldemans. He agreed to lecture at the chiropractic educational meetings, and when Scott was in his second year of biochemistry he asked Scott to help mark first-year papers.

It was Professor Mayer, however, who would be considered Scott's primary scientific mentor during this period. He showed major support for Scott's decision to study nerve compression, despite knowing that the motivation was to research some of the principles on which chiropractic was based. Professor Mayer also encouraged him to write. He agreed to co-author two papers based on the findings from Scott's research. Ben Mayer then suggested that they be sent to the South African Medical Journal where they were accepted for publication in 1970. It is likely that the editors of the South African Medical Journal did know about the Haldemans' controversial position in the medical world, yet they were willing to publish what they considered acceptable scientific papers.

Scott's most interesting and perhaps influential interaction with a member of the medical profession came when he met Dr. Maurice Lombaard, the head of the Neurosurgery Department at the University of Pretoria. Like Professor Grotepas, Dr. Lombaard had been willing to lecture to the chiropractors despite admonitions of caution from the South African Medical Association. As the senior, and perhaps, the only neurosurgeon in Pretoria, he did not seem to feel that he had to comply with regulations regarding chiropractic. When Scott was in his master's program, Dr. Lombaard used to invite him to scrub-in during his surgeries. On one occasion, when operating on a patient with a fracture-dislocation of the spine, Dr. Lombaard grabbed hold of the two subluxed vertebra and pulled them into position. With a broad smile, he announced that he had just performed an adjustment and should consider himself a chiropractor. Scott welcomed the light-hearted banter, since the usual conversations around the operating table more often consisted of the other surgeons complaints about the Haldemans and their claim of being able help some patients avoid back surgery. Dr. Lombaard would simply smile at Scott, who was masked for the surgery, and did not say anything.

THE SOUTH AFRICAN CHIROPRACTORS ASSOCIATION

In 1940, the South African Health Practitioners Association was formed in the Transvaal Province of South Africa and included chiropractors, osteopaths, and naturopaths. In May of 1945 the South African Manipulative Practitioners Association was formed in the Natal Province where most of the chiropractors of South Africa practiced. This association also included osteopaths and naturopaths. In 1952 a small group of chiropractors, who were mostly Palmer graduates and felt that chiropractic should have its own society, resigned from the South African Manipulative Practitioners Association to form the South African Chiropractors Association (SACA). Dr. J.A. Blackbourn served as the first president of SACA and practiced in the Haldeman clinic as an associate of Dr. Joshua Haldeman. By 1958 the South African Manipulative Practitioners' Association reorganized into an association that focused more on chiropractic and renamed itself the Pan-African Chiropractic Association (PACA).

In 1958, the Confederation of Labor in South Africa proposed to sponsor a Private Member's Bill in Parliament for recognition of chiropractic. The Bill would require unanimity of the profession over the scope of practice. The South African Chiropractic Joint Legislative Committee was formed with equal representation from both associations, SACA and PACA. Dr. Joshua Haldeman was the secretary treasurer of the committee. In a letter sent to the South African Chiropractors' Association (SACA), Dr. Haldeman outlined his meeting with Minister Hertzog along with other members of the Joint Legislative Committee. Hertzog was supportive of chiropractic legislation and offered good advice to those attending. The Committee was successful in drafting legislation and presenting it before Parliament in 1961 and 1962. However, Minister of Health Hertzog, faced with medical opposition and political reality, decided to appoint the Monnig Commission of Inquiry to investigate chiropractic, which put a delay on any further legislation.

The charge of the Monnig Commission was:

"To inquire into, report upon and make recommendations in regard to the work performed by chiropractors with a view to determining –

(a) whether their work could be useful and an essential addition to ordinary medical services,

(b) whether on the other hand it could possibly involve any danger to the health of the public, and

(c) if the practice has a definite advantage, whether recognition of chiropractors as a professional group is justified and on what conditions, if any, such recognition should be granted."

The Monnig Commission issued a very unfavorable report on chiropractic. After direct petition from Josh Haldeman, the report was shelved pending an investigation on the efficacy of chiropractic by the Department of Health. Due to changes in government, the investigation was never completed. At the time the Monnig Commission was established, Scott was in Davenport, Iowa, attending Palmer College and he never participated in the discussions that took place between the chiropractors and the Commission.

It was the experience with the Monnig Commission that made Josh Haldeman realize that chiropractors would require greater educational qualifications if future legislation could be successful. When Scott returned to South Africa in late 1964, he was inevitably involved in efforts to rebut the Commission's report up until he left for Canada to pursue his PhD in 1970. In a February 9, 1968 notice to the members of the SACA from President Joshua Haldeman, an invitation was extended to participate in an educational program on February 18 of the same year at the Pretorius Clinic with Dr. Scott Haldeman speaking on the physiology of nerves. In an announcement for the Annual Conference the following November, Scott was recognized as the Public Relations Officer of the SACA. In the April 1969 notice of a General meeting of the SACA, Scott was listed as a member of the Executive Committee and Moderator for the Examining Committee.

It wasn't until 1971, when Scott was in Canada studying for his PhD that the majority of members of the two chiropractic associations united under the banner of the Chiropractic Association of South Africa (CASA). This unity was another attempt to obtain legislative recognition of chiropractic. The minister of health, Dr. De Wet, announced the introduction of a bill, the Chiropractic Amendment Act, which "...would prohibit persons from practicing for gain as chiropractors." A large public outcry resulted in the bill being amended to allow the Chiropractic Association of South Africa (CASA) to provide a list of practitioners and students who would be recognized by the government. A total of 127 practicing chiropractors and 38 South African students had their names on the list. Josh Haldeman and a number of other prior members of SACA, fearful that this would mark the end of chiropractic in South Africa became very concerned that CASA had agreed to this legislation. They refused to agree to the requirements of this legislation and, consequently, resigned from CASA to form the Association of Straight Chiropractors (ASC). The assumption of this bill was that once these chiropractors died or retired, chiropractic would no longer exist in South Africa unless the bill could be amended by some future legislation.

The letters exchanged between Scott and Dr. Christiaan Neethling of Pretoria, personal friend and professional colleague of the Haldemans, during the years of 1970 and 1971 provide a vivid chronicle of the time. Scott, having completed his master's degree from the University of Pretoria and working on his PhD at the University of British Columbia in neurophysiology, was an obvious asset to any future legislative effort. Prior to leaving for Canada, Scott's activities with the South African Chiropractors Association (SACA) were colored by the fact that he was the son of a very politically active chiropractor who had taken a controversial position. This caused some in the Chiropractic Association of South Africa (CASA) to question his loyalty and position on the issues. When the Chiropractic Act was passed requiring CASA to submit a list of practicing chiropractors and students currently in school who would be recognized to practice chiropractic, nine chiropractors, Scott and his Dad being among them, were excluded. Dr. Neethling wrote Scott on several occasions encouraging him to sign the "Undertaking" before the deadline of October 31, 1971, his latest request coming in August of 1971. The "Undertaking" included a code of ethics, rules, and regulations and required attendance at educational seminars sponsored by CASA. Every chiropractor who wanted to practice had to sign the list. The Haldemans refused to sign, and Scott also resigned from CASA. Despite the controversy, the Haldemans' tenacity was rewarded. Through direct petition to the government, Scott, Josh, and the rest of the excluded chiropractors were finally added to the official list without having to comply with the initial requirements set down by the Chiropractic Association of South Africa (CASA).

In the April 1971 newsletter to the Association of Straight Chiropractors (ASC), Dr. van Zyl, Secretary of the ASC, thanks ASC members for their opposition to the Chiropractic Act proposed by Minister of Health Dr. De Wet. This is followed by a lengthy response by Dr. Scott Haldeman regarding the attacks on chiropractic in the Monnig Commission report. Scott first introduces himself and establishes his credibility on the basis of being a graduated chiropractor, holding a master's degree from the University of Pretoria and in the final steps of obtaining his PhD in neurophysiology from the University of British Columbia. He disqualifies the members of the Monnig Commission on Chiropractic stating they have no basis of fact or knowledge to assert that chiropractic is unscientific or that chiropractors are insufficiently trained to practice since none of the members of the Commission had ever visited a chiropractic educational institution or were familiar with chiropractic research. He argues that a four year curriculum is more than adequate to train a chiropractor to be a safe practitioner. He flouts the Commission's statement that chiropractic is founded on unscientific principles based on a theory of nerve compression that has been "rejected entirely by physiology," when eighteen months ago he had received his master's degree with honors for study of this "rejected" theory of nerve compression at the University of Pretoria.

THE SOUTH AFRICAN CHIROPRACTIC RESEARCH FOUNDATION

The need for research was clear to Josh, Scott and other members of the South African Chiropractors Association. In a 1967 Annual Report to the South African Chiropractors' Association, there was an announcement regarding the formation of the South African Chiropractic Research Foundation. The foundation was to adhere to the principles laid down by SACA, and research was to be conducted in the following areas:

1. Physiological experiments into the phenomena of nerve interference and its effects

2. Research and correlation of facts and knowledge related to physiology, anatomy and pathology of the spine, nervous system, and the body in general

3. Research into the use of x-rays by chiropractors, including techniques, analytical procedures, radiocinematography, etc.

4. Research into the practice of chiropractic to include:

a. Clinical statistical formulation of results in chiropractic

b. Correlation and research on new and existing means of adjusting the spine to remove nerve interference

c. Research into existing as well as new and better means of analyzing and pinpointing nerve interference by means of instrumentation and physical examination principles

The announcement also mentioned the establishment of a laboratory with research on rabbits. Members of SACA would meet every month at either the Haldeman or the Pretorius clinics and discuss literature or demonstrate adjusting techniques. Dr. Bert Pretorius and his wife, Maddie, who was also a chiropractor, were very active in forming the foundation. Bert was secretary of the SACA at the time. At many of these meetings, medical physicians or scientists were invited to speak. As noted above, Professor Grotepas gave a lecture on biochemistry and Professor Lombaard on neurosurgery.

From the monthly meetings of SACA, the South African Chiropractic Research Foundation was established with a simple animal laboratory in the garage at the Haldeman clinic. Scott recalls,

> We bred rabbits on site. We were interested in the works by Gordienko and Carl Cleveland who had developed methods of misaligning vertebra in animals and had noted changes in the structure of certain organs. We operated on a number of rabbits and did a few experiments. A medical doctor, who was visiting from the Netherlands and was related to one of the members of SACA, agreed to do the surgery. Unfortunately we never completed the study because I left for Canada and it was discontinued.

Clinical practice allowed Scott the time to explore his curiosities about the function of the spine. Achievement of a master's degree equipped him with the scientific background necessary to set up controlled experiments that could be meaningful. But before his research work would be fully recognized by the scientific community, Scott felt an urgency to complete the next stage of his life. Scott stepped over the threshold of the unknown and he and Joan began the process of making a new life for themselves in Toronto.

Chapter 5

Further Chiropractic Education
CMCC and Toronto (1970)

Scott's thirst for knowledge was only partially satiated with the 1969 completion of his master's degree at the University of Pretoria. As he approached the conclusion of his program, he was undecided as to what the next step would be in his unfolding life adventure. He knew that clinical practice—while gratifying through the experience of helping people—lacked the opportunity for greater academic growth. South Africa was a developed western culture but was a long distance from the rest of the world. Scott loved South Africa but was willing to set his sights on horizons that carried him beyond the home of his upbringing.

At first Scott, through a series of letters, explored the possibility of post graduate chiropractic education or a faculty position at various chiropractic schools in North America, as none were available in South Africa. Responses from his inquiries were less favorable than he had hoped. For a college to obtain a faculty member who possessed both a doctor of chiropractic degree and a master's degree in neurophysiology would have been a gift to any institution, but the mid-sixties was a time of low enrollments and limited financial resources at all chiropractic colleges. None of the chiropractic colleges in the U.S. were positioned to make an offer.

Concurrently, Scott explored his option of pursuing a PhD degree in neurophysiology. There were no leading neurophysiologists in South Africa in the fields that Scott was interested in pursuing. He, therefore, did a search of the literature and applied to a number of universities around the world. He received positive responses from the University of Tokyo but had to speak Japanese, the University of Heidelberg in Germany (but foreign students and their spouses were not able to get work permits), and the University of British Columbia in Vancouver, Canada. Language, family ties, the ability to get a work permit, and the strength of the program and faculty at the University of British Columbia cemented his decision to return to the land of his birth. He received a small grant from the South African Medical Council, which he had to pay back when he did not return to South Africa. However, he was also offered a modest post-graduate stipend at the University of British Columbia that sealed his decision to study in Vancouver. Moving halfway around the world was no small undertaking for Scott and Joan. This meant leaving a very comfortable home, family, friends, job security, and a country to which they had become accustomed. Both assumed his pursuit of a PhD would be a three-year adventure and then they would return home to South Africa. Had Scott and Joan realized what life held in store for them, perhaps they may have reconsidered their decision.

The application to the British Columbia Chiropractic Association and the Provincial Licensing Body to obtain a license to practice chiropractic in British Columbia while studying for his PhD brought significant disappointment for Scott. John S. Burton—an old friend of Joshua Haldeman from his days in Canada who was a barrister in Vancouver and serving as the secretary & counsel to the British Columbia Chiropractic Association (BCCA)—wrote Scott (Oct. 9, 1968) advising him that the law in British Columbia required eight months attendance in each of four 12-month periods to qualify for licensure. Scott had completed his course work at Palmer in three uninterrupted calendar years; thus, he needed to take one more year (8 months of class time) to qualify. Scott wrote a letter back to Barrister Burton on 21 November 1968 seeking some special consideration. He felt the ruling was an insult to his chiropractic education at Palmer and probably related to philosophical differences as much as legal statutes. Barrister Burton wrote back on March 12, 1969 telling Scott that his request had been considered at the February board meeting. The Board denied Scott's request stating, "Even well known and eminently qualified doctors of chiropractic have had to take an extra year of schooling to qualify for the British Columbia Boards. The Board passed a resolution requiring you to take at least an eight month course in a chiropractic school to qualify. You can also take the National Board Exam and, if passed, be admitted as a member of the National Association." This response equated to an extension of time to complete his PhD, which meant another delay before he could return home to South Africa—indeed a disappointment at the time. It also meant moving twice—to Toronto and then to Vancouver—setting up two households, finding new employment for Joan twice, and getting familiar with another set of surroundings.

VISITING EUROPEAN CHIROPRACTIC CENTERS

When it became obvious that he would have to spend additional time at CMCC in order to be licensed to practice in British Columbia, Scott decided to make the most of this interim time by visiting as many chiropractic centers as possible and meeting leaders of chiropractic in Europe, Canada and the U.S.

On leaving South Africa, Joan and Scott traveled to England where they visited the Anglo European Chiropractic College. This was the first and only chiropractic teaching institution in Europe at the time. Scott was asked to present the research from his thesis and had the opportunity to interact with the faculty and administration including the Drs. Bennett whom he had visited before and Dr. Singarajah, a neurophysiologist, who was hired as Dean of AECC in the expectation that he would improve neurological theories in chiropractic at the college. At the time, he was responsible for running the college with Dr. J.G. Anderson. Scott and Joan were invited to have dinner with the Sinjarajahs and enjoyed some tremendously superb Indian traditional food. The future of chiropractic education and practice in Europe was discussed in detail.

From England, Scott and Joan traveled to Paris where they spent time with Dr. Anton Gross, one of France's better known and controversial chiropractors. Dr. Gross was a friend of Scott's father and had visited South Africa and stayed with the family. Practicing chiropractic in France at that time was illegal; nonetheless, Dr. Gross had managed to continue practicing for more than 40 years and had a unique practice-building technique that he bragged about. He told the story that whenever his practice was slipping, he would send an anonymous letter to the medical authorities complaining that he was practicing medicine without a license. These authorities would have no choice but to investigate and send the police to arrest him. He would then inform the newspapers, and when the police arrived he would give an interview on the benefits of chiropractic. He would also alert his patients that this was happening and they would pack the courtroom. The judge, who was also a patient of his, was obliged to issue a fine. Dr. Gross would then pass his hat amongst the people in the court room and pay his fine.

From Paris, Scott and Joan stopped in Brussels where Scott's sister, Lynne, was performing as a Spanish Flamenco dancer. They were invited to spend a day with Dr. Henri Gillet, who had developed a new method for examining and treating patients and had written extensively on his methods. The techniques developed by Dr. Gillet had been taught briefly at Palmer, and Scott was very interested in seeing the master work. Many of his concepts—in particular the idea that loss of movement in the spine rather than vertebral malposition was the lesion to which an adjustment should be applied—are still widely accepted today as important.

THE CANADIAN MEMORIAL CHIROPRACTIC COLLEGE (CMCC)

The earlier positive response from CMCC, coupled with the need to obtain additional training to qualify for licensure in British Columbia, culminated in the decision to move to Toronto and complete the requirements for chiropractic licensure prior to starting the PhD program at the University of British Columbia. Dr. Donald

Sutherland, who was the school's president, allowed Scott to complete all the courses he needed to sit for the Canadian Board at no cost, and in exchange, Scott would teach students and do research on the Synchro-Therme[1] Instrument being used at the college at that time.

Scott considers Don Sutherland one of the most supportive persons he interacted with at the college. He relates that one day Don took him to the college bookstore where he was instructed to pick all the books needed to teach and do research and charge them to Dr. Sutherland's account. Scott was never asked to repay Don. With his DC and his master's degree in hand, Scott was the most credentialed member of the CMCC faculty in the basic sciences and was asked to teach the neurophysiology courses.

Scott had fairly free reign in picking the courses he was to take during the six months he was at CMCC, and he met a number of faculty who would expand his thinking on both the theory and practice of chiropractic. Scott decided to take courses in areas and topics that had not been emphasized at Palmer. He was also required to take physiotherapy courses to complete British Columbia licensure requirements and then focused attention on the technique courses taught by Adrian Grice and Ronald Gitelman. Jean Moss, a student in Scott's physiology class, later became the president of CMCC. She remains a good friend of Scott's, as well as a positive force for CMCC and the chiropractic profession.

There were several additional faculty members with whom Scott worked closely and who expanded his thinking: Robert Johnston, Dave Drum, and Herb Vear stimulated Scott to think beyond his training at Palmer or in South Africa. Herb Vear was later enticed away from CMCC to become the president of the Western States Chiropractic College (WSCC) in Portland. The close relationship between Scott and Dr. Vear continued later when Scott was in Vancouver.

Being with a group of critical thinkers in a chiropractic educational environment was just the kind of stimulation Scott sought. He was impressed by their enthusiasm and they, in turn, were impressed with

[1] An instrument used to measure skin temperatures on each side of the spine.

Scott's critical scientific mind and willingness to question and challenge their thoughts and beliefs—especially in regards to the effects of spinal manipulation on the autonomic nervous system. Scott relates that Adrian Grice and Ron Gitelman became his close mentors and introduced him to the concept that there was no single theory for chiropractic. The theories being discussed at CMCC included the concept of Somatovisceral Reflexes and Spinal Fixation Theory. The former concepts had been proposed by Earl Homewood, a prior college president who had written a book on the topic. The latter came from the theories developed by Henri Gillet. Given the strong personalities involved and their articulate abilities, what an experience it must have been to have these discussions! And the debates did not end when Scott later left for Vancouver. Drs. Gitleman and Grice and others maintained strong ties with Scott and frequently sought his intellect in issues of critical import for the chiropractic profession. Scott, when he was on the committee established by the National Institutes of Health, proposed that Adrian and Ron represent the profession in the discussion of chiropractic technique. The intellectual stimulation Scott received at CMCC ensured his continued interest in chiropractic research.

One of Scott's first assignments at CMCC was to evaluate the scientific and clinical significance of the Synchro-Therme, an instrument used to measure para-spinal temperature change as it related to the adjustment, and examine its scientific and clinical significance. This not only provided Scott with an opportunity to exercise his newly gained analytical research skills but presented him with the opportunity to tutor his mentors in research methodology and procedures. The project resulted in two publications in the *Journal of the Canadian Chiropractic Association* (JCCA), which were among the first of Scott's many publications. He also published papers with David Drum, who was on the faculty and Karen Hammerich, a student at CMCC. This project also helped develop a research culture on the campus of CMCC. Don Sutherland's confidence and investment in Scott brought fruitful returns to his institution and the profession.

In June 1970, Scott completed his courses and studied for, then passed the Canadian Chiropractic National Board examination before leaving for Vancouver.

THE FORMATION OF THE COLLEGE OF CHIROPRACTIC SCIENCES

While at CMCC, Scott found a series of papers that had been photocopied and stored in a cabinet. Most of these had been collected by Adrian Grice, Ron Gittelman, and David Drum but had not been widely circulated. Scott, along with a number of other faculty members, formed a journal club to review these papers as well as a debate group to examine the scientific literature. He would bring students and faculty together on a regular basis to review and discuss recent publications in the scientific literature—a new experience on all chiropractic college campuses at that time. With background and training which Scott brought with him from his master's program at the University of Pretoria, he was well equipped to lead such discussions and develop research interests and abilities in both the students and the faculty. Scott was never selfish when it came to sharing his talents and his knowledge. He was a person on a mission that was gradually being refined—a mission to link the emotional heart of chiropractic (something gained from his father and at Palmer) with the critical thinking skills of a researcher.

Supported by an enthusiastic faculty, the CMCC journal club began to accumulate an increasing amount of literature. We must remember this was in 1970, when computer technology was in its infancy, electronic literature databases were more imagined than real, and electronic copy technology wouldn't introduce its color copy machine to the mass market for two more years. The campus library was extremely helpful in obtaining, sharing, and eventually cataloging the most extensive accumulation of relevant scientific literature in the chiropractic profession. This file of articles was put into an order that others could access and use. It became one of the most utilized resources within the library and continued to grow and develop after Scott left for Vancouver. Eventually CMCC made this collection of literature available to other chiropractic educational institutions, and it was referred to as the *Chiropractic Research Archive Collection* (CRAC). While a phenomenal achievement in its time, computer technology and electronic databases have superseded the original CRAC collection, but the original database concept at CMCC had Scott's fingerprints all over it.

The expansion and utilization of CRAC supported and encouraged the growth of the newly formed journal club. Students and faculty would gather on a regular basis—usually weekly—and review a recent scientific publication. Under Scott's tutelage they would learn to read an article critically and dissect it into meaningful components. They would learn to analyze the methods employed in the study under review and determine if the results obtained were indeed realistic, meaningful, and supported by the data. The students were taught to reach their own conclusions about the article and not to rely solely on the conclusions of the authors. These initial activities of the journal club eventually led to the organization of the College of Chiropractic Science (CCS). Scott was a charter fellow of the CCS, although its formal organization did not occur until after his departure for British Columbia.

Minutes of the inaugural meeting of the Fellowship of CCS held on the CMCC campus on 17 May 1975 indicates the following were certified (grandfathered) into the CCS on that date. Most of these original members were on the faculty of CMCC while Scott was on campus:

David A. Churchill	J.O. Edgar Houle
David C. Drum	Lyman C. Johnston
Glenn R. Engel	Robert J. Johnston
Ronald Gitelman	John J. Kos
Adrian S. Grice	Henri L. Marcoux
Scott Haldeman	Thomas D. Maxwell
Herbert J. Vear	

As evidence of Scott's commitment to academic quality, shortly after being notified of his "grandfathered" status into the CCS, he wrote Dr. Tom Maxwell, newly elected president of the CCS, with the following recommendations:

1. Being a fellow of the CCS is an incorrect use of the term—you are a fellow of an institution or association—recommended the designation of FCCC, Fellow of the College of Chiropractic Clinicians or FCCS, Fellow of the College of Chiropractic Scientists.

2. There is a concern of the amount of reliance on CMCC. It created too much extra work for the CMCC staff. To be a fellow is to be honored by one's peers based on an accepted demonstration of excellence. CMCC was capable of providing the residency training, internship programs, and research experience but the CCS needed to be separate and distinct from any educational or political body.

3. The CCS should set up its own Board of Examiners and not depend on CMCC to set the standard and/or conduct the examinations. All those who were grandfathered into the CCS should take the initial examination to demonstrate their own proficiency.

The CCS stimulated the development of an on-campus, intensified training program with an emphasis on clinical expertise, teaching ability, and research. The two-year "residency" program was designed to prepare participants to sit for an examination to qualify as a "Fellow" of the CCS. On the 16th of November 1976, the program was modified and strengthened by recommendations made by Dr. Vear, Chair of the CCS Examining Board. Essentially, the objective of the residency program was to prepare doctors of chiropractic to become the future leaders and teachers of the profession by training them to do research, improving their teaching skills, and sharpening their clinical abilities through involvement in multidisciplinary experiences. The program was established as a two-year, full-time training experience with exposure to multiple clinical and research areas. There was a written exam at the conclusion.

In retrospect, it is intriguing to note that several leading DC and PhD research scientists now running research departments in major universities in Canada are the products of this early effort, partially stimulated by Scott's presence and interaction with the faculty at CMCC in 1970. This has become but one portion of the legacy Scott was beginning to develop.

Over the years, there has been some passing debate over the safety of performing chiropractic adjustments, mostly spawned by chiropractic critics. Rarely one would hear of an instance where a patient suffered from an adverse event related to an adjustment. It wasn't until the early 1970s that sporadic articles began to appear in the medical literature where blame for such adverse events began to take on more of a focused concern. Faculty colleague Dr. Adrian Grice was working with Scott at CMCC when the first public case of a Canadian patient suffering a stroke attributed to a chiropractic manipulation occurred. In their deliberations about such an event, Adrian said Scott came up with a figure of a "one in a million" possibility of a stroke being caused by manipulation. Such remote possibilities were not considered clinically significant. Both Scott and Adrian were brought in to testify on this particular case. Adrian said the "one in a million" likelihood of occurrence was based on the reported cases in the literature compared to the number of estimated adjustments given over a period of time. Adrian's testimony was discounted as being biased. Scott's similar testimony was considered by the court but not accepted as evidence in that particular case. Chiropractic witnesses in court proceedings were not granted much credibility in the early 1970s, even if they held a master's degree. The testimony of a medical expert estimated a frequency range of 40,000 to 100,000. The judge awarded a "small sum" of around $160,000 for associated damages to the patient. This judgment was made in spite of the fact that the victim's girlfriend testified that he was involved in a fight and was knocked down, hit his head, and then started to complain about his sore neck resulting in the visit to the chiropractor. Little did anyone realize at the time that Scott would go on to head a world-recognized task force that demonstrated that the relationship between visits to a chiropractor and stroke-related symptoms was no different than the relationship between visits to a medical physician and similar stroke-related symptoms.

VISITING CHIROPRACTIC CENTERS IN THE U.S.

On leaving CMCC in the summer of 1970, Joan and Scott decided to explore Canada and the U.S. on their way to Vancouver in an old van they had converted into a camper. They first traveled to Ottawa and watched the July 1 Canada Day celebrations and then on to Washington, DC for the July 4th outdoor extravaganza. Their Independence Day festivities were less than pleasant, however. While watching a Bob Hope show on the Mall, they were tear-gassed when the police decided to disperse an adjacent anti-war demonstration. After this eventful beginning, they set off across the country to visit some major chiropractic centers.

They visited the Kentuckiana Children's Center in Louisville and Dr. Lorraine Golden, its founder. The center provided free educational and rehabilitation services, psychological and family counseling, audiologic and dental referrals, and special education to multi-handicapped children. Both Scott and Joan were impressed with the dedication of Dr. Golden and the staff and noted for the first time that chiropractic could successfully be integrated into a multidisciplinary program.

From there they traveled to Tallmadge, Ohio, where they visited the Associates Diagnostic and Research Center, which eventually became one of the first chiropractic radiologic referral and postgraduate education centers. Here they were given a tour of the facility by Dr. Joseph Howe. It was during this visit that Scott became familiar with the concept of sub-specialization within chiropractic clinical practice—the creation of areas of limited practice, similar to medicine, such as radiology.

Joan and Scott then drove to Davenport, Iowa to spend a few days at his Alma Mater, and from there to Chicago to visit the National College of Chiropractic. At Palmer they were able to spend time with friends and a number of faculty members who had taught Scott when he was there. At National, Dr. Joseph Janse, the college president, gave Scott and Joan a personal tour and discussed some of the concepts being taught there and his ideas for future research. These visits allowed Scott to more clearly recognize the strengths and weaknesses of the two major schools of thought within chiropractic.

Next was Denver, Colorado and a tour of the Spears Chiropractic Hospital and Free Clinic for Poor Children that had been founded by

Dr. Leo Spears. This was the largest chiropractic hospital ever built and had more than 600 beds providing only "natural healing" without drugs or surgery to its patients. As Scott and Joan were shown around by Don and Howard Spears, the nephews of Leo Spears, they saw firsthand how chiropractic care could be provided in a hospital setting.

The time spent in Europe visiting leading chiropractors, the education and research at CMCC, and the visits to a number of the most influential chiropractic centers in the U.S. all gave a much broader insight into chiropractic for Scott and prepared him for further education and a research direction that would continue in Vancouver.

Chapter 6

The Pursuit of the PhD
University of British Columbia
1970-1973

S cott had been accepted into the physiology PhD program at the
University of British Columbia (UBC) for September 1969, as
acknowledged in a letter dated May 16, 1968, from Dr. Hugh
McLennan, PhD and professor in the Department of Physiology:

> With regard to your qualifications for entry, I think that there
> would be no difficulty provided that you complete the MSc degree
> at the University of Pretoria. The courses which you have presently
> taken appear to be appropriate for the study of neurophysiology,
> although any advance training in any field of physiology which
> you can obtain before coming here will clearly be an advantage.

In this same letter, Scott is given information regarding the requirements of the program and what he should plan in terms of time:

> The formal minimum time required for the PhD degree, on com-
> pletion of a MSc, is two years; although in practice the majority of
> students will take six months to a year longer than this. The formal
> requirements for the degree are the presentation of an acceptable
> thesis, its defense before an examining panel, and the passage of a
> comprehensive examination in physiology. It is usual also for the

candidate to be required to take one or two formal courses, but this is entirely at the discretion of the candidate's committee, and may or may not be applicable in your case.

He was advised that he would receive $3,000 tax-free Canadian dollars each year he was in the program for financial support and that he needed to look into confirming his status as a Canadian citizen. Initially this stipend was from the Department of Physiology. In 1972 and 1973 the stipend was replaced by grants of $200 per month from the Medical Research Council of Canada.

Scott deferred entry into the PhD program until September 1970 in order to complete his master's degree and the requirements for licensure to practice as a chiropractor in British Columbia. He completed the required courses at CMCC, wrote the examination established by the Canadian National Chiropractic Board of Examiners, and he and Joan drove across North America with everything they owned in their van. On arriving in Vancouver they stayed briefly with his older half brother, Jerry, Jerry's wife, Maureen, and their family in Richmond before moving into a small apartment in the West End of Vancouver overlooking English Bay.

Acceptance into a PhD program in neurophysiology at a major accredited university would bring Scott unexpected prominence in the debate over the role of chiropractic. Having a chiropractor enrolled in a basic science PhD program was a rare situation. His master's thesis, *Changes in the Structure and Function of the Sciatic Nerve Caused by Constriction*, at the University of Pretoria was in keeping with chiropractic theory, and it was Scott's desire to continue this exploration at a more refined PhD level. His doctoral thesis, *Evidence in Favour of Glutamate as a Mediator of Synaptic Transmission*, fulfilled his desire.

Perhaps only a person who has experienced the rigors of a PhD program can fully grasp the weight of the work required. Unlike an undergraduate bachelor's degree program where attendance in class and performance on examinations is all that is required, graduate education expects the student to learn to think and reason, explore and create new ways of looking at the world, and document original ideas for scrutiny by one's peers. Besides attendance at classes, the doctoral candidate may teach undergraduate courses and grade subsequent examinations. There is laboratory work to be done, seminars to attend, research to pursue, qualifying exams to pass, and the eventual defense of one's original thesis/dissertation. It is a daunting experience evidenced by the large number of ABD (All But a Dissertation) "degrees" in existence.

Scott was required to take advanced courses in all the major fields of physiology and pass a written and/or oral examination at the end of each course. A number of these courses also required a short essay or thesis on the topic. Scott's choice of topics for these essays was suitable for publication as literature reviews in chiropractic journals. He was able to satisfy the requirement to read scientific literature in another language as he had studied German during his master's program.

His research under the supervision of Hugh McLennon started immediately upon his arrival at UBC. Hugh McLennon was one of the leading researchers in the study of neural transmitters in Canada and the world. He had been studying GABA[1] as an inhibitory transmitter and was convinced that Glutamate would be one of the most important excitatory transmitters in the sensory pathways through the brain. There was a challenge as there was no antagonist of glutamate receptors in the brain that could be used to confirm that sensory neurons had specific glutamate membrane receptors. Scott's initial research project was looking for antagonists of glutamate in the large abdominal stretch receptor organs in crayfish. This was followed by a study of the uptake of labeled glutamate using rat cerebral cortex preparations. The final part of the research, however, required very extensive surgical preparations using cats. He had to place multichannel microiontophoretic electrodes near single cells in the spinal cord and also a number of brain centers. The object was to squirt small quantities of chemicals into the vicinity of the cell that could poten-

---

[1] γ-**Aminobutyric acid** (GABA) is the chief inhibitory neurotransmitter in the mammalian central nervous system. It plays an important role in regulating neuronal excitability throughout the nervous system. In humans, GABA is also directly responsible for the regulation of muscle tone. Watanabe M, Maemura K, Kanbara K, Tamayama T, Hayasaki H (2002). "GABA and GABA receptors in the central nervous system and other organs". *Int. Rev. Cytol.* **213**: 1–47.

tially block glutamate while recording the electrical activity of single nerve cells in these neural structures.

The experiments were done twice a week and required one day to prepare for the experimental surgery to be performed on the second day. Surgery started at 7:00 a.m. and took 4 to 6 hours to complete. The computer had to be loaded with its program using a perforated paper feed. (This was the most advanced bioscience computer system available at the time.) This took almost a full hour. The electrodes would then be placed near a single nerve cell in the brain or spinal cord and record the effect of small amounts of chemicals on the brain. Since these preparations were difficult to stabilize, Scott and often Dr. McLennon would stay in the laboratory until 1:00 or 2:00 a.m.—until either the preparation failed or the researchers failed. The fifth day of the week was used to correlate the results and decide what to do next.

Consistent with Scott's past pattern, working on and obtaining a PhD was not the only activity on his calendar. He was a married man with financial obligations. Not that he and his wife were hopelessly in debt from student loans—they were not available then. Rather, they had been living on a student budget in Toronto—under less than favorable circumstances—and continued on a low budget in Vancouver (see Chapter 10). Joan was a staff physiotherapist for a short period of time at the Vancouver General Hospital. She then found a senior position in the physiotherapy department at the Vancouver Neurological Center, a facility for the treatment of children with neurological disorders. Scott began practicing three nights a week in the office of Dr. Bill Hartwick, a chiropractor in the town of Burnaby near Vancouver. Bill Hartwick was very kind to allow Scott to work in the evenings without charging any rent. This, however, required an hour's drive from home in both directions. Skills acquired at Palmer College and refined in the Haldeman Clinic in Pretoria would be enhanced in Vancouver. Scott and Joan became very good friends with Bill Hartwick and his family and would go sailing with them in the Gulf Islands occasionally on weekends.

Scott recalls that a number of professors from UBC, including faculty from the medical school, would come into the office and ask him if he could treat their back pain. There was a problem however. It was against medical ethics to associate with, refer patients to, or even accept patients from chiropractors despite the fact that the provincial health program paid for chiropractic care. These professors, therefore, appreciated that they could come in at night to see Scott. One professor in pharmacology insisted that the only way he could continue to play golf was to have periodic care. It did not hurt that he was also on Scott's research committee. Hugh McLennnon did not mind that Scott was practicing and doing other things as long as the research was progressing. He used to refer to Scott's extracurricular activities as "doing his thing."

By the time Scott was beginning the second year of his PhD program, he was heavily involved with the British Columbia Chiropractic Association (BCCA). In September 1971 the BCCA hosted their Annual Association Meeting in Vancouver, at which Scott was the main speaker on the program. The theme for the convention was "The Experimental Basis for the Philosophy of Chiropractic." Scott produced a monograph for the conference with the same title. It contained five chapters (87 pages), each of which was written and published by Scott in that same year. A review of the chapter titles gives evidence of Scott's continued close ties to chiropractic principles:

The Evolution of Neurology and the Concept of Chiropractic

A Light and Electron Microscopic Study of the Sciatic Nerve of the South African Frog

The Compression Subluxation

Interaction between the Somatic and Visceral Nervous Systems

Renal Function and the Nervous System

For the average PhD student, completing course work, attending labs and lectures, and preparing for exams—before one ever embarks on an original research project—is all-consuming. In addition to the demands of a PhD program, Scott published two papers from his master's thesis, four papers from his PhD thesis, wrote eight papers for chiropractic journals, and wrote one entire chapter for a book. He also spoke at a number of conferences and practiced three nights a week all while maintaining good standing in his doctoral program. Scott was asked to speak at the 26th and 27th Annual Convention of the Industrial First Aid Association in Vancouver in November 1971 and 1972. He subsequently wrote two articles, one with Bill Hartwick as co-author, based on his presentations. They were published in the *Industrial First Aid Attendant*. The first was titled, "Chiropractic in British Columbia and its Relationship to Industrial First Aid," and the second, "Interruption of Normal Peripheral Nerve Function."

However, it was not all work and no play. Scott and Joan skied at Whistler Mountain and other ski areas in northwestern Canada and the U.S. in the winter months; they sailed when possible in the summer, and drove 6,000 miles from Vancouver down to Mexico as far as Guadalajara and Mexico City. They developed strong friendships in Vancouver that continue today.

To carry a significant academic load in a PhD program, run a part-time practice in the evening, and provide for family necessities while still having fun, requires a work ethic uncommon in society. Scott did not succeed because he had a "silver spoon" handed to him. He, with Joan's support and assistance, succeeded through persistence and hard work. The words of Longfellow so aptly apply in this instance and throughout Scott's life:

> The heights by great men reached and kept
> Were not attained by sudden flight,
> But they, while their companions slept,
> Were toiling upward through the night.
> Henry Wadsworth Longfellow
> "*The Ladder of St. Augustine*"

A VARIETY OF CORRESPONDENCES

Concurrent with attending to his studies, his practice, and his home life, Scott gave unselfishly to an expanding network of people with whom he connected through letter writing (e-mail was not even a concept yet), telephone calls, and meetings at conventions.

Legislative Action in Quebec **Province**

Quebec Province, the last province in Canada to pass chiropractic legislation, received a delegation of chiropractors who made representations before the Quebec National Assembly in favour of the adoption of the Chiropractic Act on September 14, 1972. This representation led to the adoption of the Chiropractic Act of Quebec in 1973. Scott was a member of this delegation.[2]

G.W. McConnell, DC

Dr. G. W. McConnell, an officer in the British Columbia Chiropractic Association (BCCA), corresponded occasionally with Scott. In a November 1973 letter, during the transitional year between his PhD program and medical school, Dr. McConnell discussed Scott's upcoming presentation at the local Rotary Club and his participation on a local radio talk show. With a myriad of other things to attend to, this is an example of Scott's willingness to support the chiropractic profession.

Pierre Jacquet, DC

Scott maintained contact with his fellow chiropractic colleagues in Europe during the time he was in Vancouver. In January 1974 he received an invitation from Pierre Jacquet, DC, of Switzerland to speak at the annual convention of the European Chiropractic Union (ECU) to be held in Denmark. Scott willingly accepted and offered to speak on the topic of his PhD thesis, "Synaptic Transmission in the Sensory Nervous Pathway." He also offered to speak on his MSc thesis and a couple other topics including, 'The Neurophysiological Theories Which Support Chiropractic Principles," and "The Problem Oriented Record," a subject of personal interest to him.

The ECU offered free registration for the meeting, but because Scott was still living on a tight budget, he was not positioned to fund his own international travel. Consequently, the invitation had to be declined. Scott's opportunities for international travel would be realized just over the horizon.

---

[2] Personal communication with Ms. Tache-Peitte, legal advisor for the Quebec Chiropractic Association, 2009.

Ralph Chatwin, DC

In October of 1974 Scott began communication with Dr. Ralph Chatwin, friend and devotee to Dr. Ralph Gregory, originator of the National Upper Cervical Chiropractic Association (NUCCA). NUCCA valued their specialized way of analyzing and adjusting the cervical spine. However, they failed to understand and appreciate the rigors of research. Dr. Chatwin, with Scott's assistance, was able to help Dr. Gregory express the exactness of the science in the work done by NUCCA. Scott offered to meet with Dr. Gregory and help him learn more about research methods and how to conduct good research projects. Dr. Chatwin requested information from Scott on how to prepare research material for publication and recommendations on where to publish NUCCA data. Scott sent Chatwin an article on how to set up a clinical research project.

At this point, further correspondence between Scott and Dr. Chatwin turned away from how to properly conduct a research project toward a review of a booklet, *Introduction to Chiropractic*. This booklet was used to explain chiropractic procedures in offices where these specialized techniques for adjusting the upper cervical spine were practiced. The booklet provided an explanation of NUCCA procedures that could stand up to scientific examination, according to Dr. Gregory. All statements were accurate, based on NUCCA research. Dr. Chatwin emphasized the scientific strength of the booklet and asked for Scott's comments. Scott remarked on the professional quality of the booklet but pointed out a number of errors, insinuations, and conclusions which could be debated. He referred to the absence of any published research to support the claims made by their measurement methods and recommended against general distribution. The string of letters ended with Dr. Chatwin thanking Scott for his frank opinions and telling him that the door was now open for dialogue that would result in an acceptable booklet.

FOUNDATION FOR CHIROPRACTIC EDUCATION AND RESEARCH (FCER)

Scott made early contact with the Foundation for Chiropractic Education and Research (FCER). In a letter written to the "Chiropractic Research Foundation" while he was in Toronto (April 1970), Scott explains that he had been asked to render a personal opinion[3], "...on the prospects of research in chiropractic and the practical approach..."[4] He offered five perspectives:

1. Research Procedure: The recommendation was to collect all the articles published for or against chiropractic in all the chiropractic, medical, and basic science journals. This would set the foundation upon which further research could be planned.

2. Research Scope: Due to the smallness of the profession and the insufficient funds, he recommended limiting research at this stage to the major premise of chiropractic, "...until such a time that the major premise has been substantiated beyond doubt."[5]

3. Research Personnel: He recommended a team of researchers headed up by a DC who had also obtained a master's or PhD in a recognized field, preferably the basic sciences. The remainder of the team should be composed of DCs working on graduate degrees to serve as research assistants, appropriate technicians, and secretarial support staff.

4. Location: The recommendation was for all chiropractic research to be done in a chiropractic institution (i.e., a chiropractic college or institute). He suggested that if the research was done outside chiropractic institutions it would lessen the right for chiropractic to claim the prestige of the work done, and the results could simply become another medical discovery.

5. Prospects for Possible Research: After assembling what had been published, he stated that the chiropractic profession must

[3] The source of this request is unknown.
[4] Personal letter to the Chiropractic Research Foundation, sent to Clearwater, FL, dated 3 April 1970. Personal collection of Scott Haldeman.
[5] Ibid.

fill in the gaps and correlate the information that would lead to the substantiation of the chiropractic premise. From there he listed numerous areas of possible future research.

As Scott was finishing up his PhD in British Columbia, he maintained contact with FCER. In a July 1973 letter to Dr. John A. Fisher, president of FCER, speaking on behalf of the Committee on Research of the ACA Council on Neurology, Scott asked Dr. Fisher for guidelines and a course of action the Committee on Research should follow. He expressed hope and asked for assistance in bringing those in the profession who were teaching neurology, either in a college or on the lecture circuit, to standardize what was being taught. This was another suggestion that did not bring about any visible results at that time, but Scott's interactions with FCER continued as he pursued his MD degree.

It has been said that if wars didn't happen there would be fewer heroes. A war of sorts had been occurring between organized medicine and chiropractic. With the AMA Anti-quackery Committee in full-force during the 1960s and early 1970s, an environment of hostility often existed when the two professions crossed paths. Obtaining a PhD in the basic sciences placed Scott in a position where he held credibility in the eyes of organized medicine with his PhD and his MSc, but was suspect due to his chiropractic affiliations and degree. To make the transition from academics into medical school was the making of a hero, for it placed Scott at the forefront of this continually antagonistic relationship between the two professions, and allowed him to overcome a myriad of challenges with remarkable success.

Chapter 7

An MD Degree from the University of British Columbia

1973-1977

It didn't take long for Scott to recognize what advantages might be gained were he to also obtain his MD degree. With a medical school in close proximity to where he was completing his PhD, Scott encountered other medical researchers who expressed frustration due to the limitations associated with having only the PhD and not the MD degree. In keeping with plans to return to South Africa, Scott inquired about gaining acceptance to medical school at the University of Pretoria in South Africa. He relates the following:

> In 1972, when I was close to completing my PhD I decided to study medicine, as it was not possible for me to conduct interdisciplinary research given the medical ethics of the time that would not allow communication between chiropractors and medical physicians.
>
> I applied to the University of Pretoria where I had obtained my bachelor's and master's degrees. When doing my bachelor's degree I had not taken a first-year botany course that was a prerequisite to get into the second year of medicine (a medical degree was six years with defined courses in each year). This would mean that

I would have to spend an additional six years to get my medical degree. The University of Pretoria would not make any concession even though I already had four degrees in the health sciences. They also had a prohibition against working while in medical school.

Scott spoke with the dean of the medical school at the University of British Columbia (UBC) in March 1972 about starting in the first year medical class in September of the same year. As he still had one year remaining to complete his PhD and the medical school admission process was closed for that year, the dean denied Scott's request. With persistence, he inquired of others about the possibility of admission but no hope was found until he talked with the Dean of Admissions. Coincidently, this dean was very interested in South Africa and was an amateur archeologist and intrigued by stories on the Lost City of the Kalahari.

He took a liking to Scott, and they derived a plan that for the average student would have signaled failure from the beginning. For Scott it shouted "Challenge," and he fully embraced it. The first-year curriculum at UBC medical school included courses in biochemistry, physiology, anatomy, histology, and a class in how to become a doctor. The stipulation was that if Scott could "demonstrate proficiency at the level of the top 10% of the first-year medical class in each of the subject areas," he would be allowed entrance into medical school as a second-year student. This meant Scott had to complete and defend his final PhD thesis and all other course work related to that degree, and also demonstrate great proficiency in the first-year medical courses. This plan was officially recognized in a letter dated March 29, 1972 from D.C. Graham, MD, Associate Dean:

> The above named student [Scott] is currently registered in the Faculty of Graduate Studies (Physiology) at UBC. During the current year [1972] he is taking certain first-year medical school courses and his admission to the Faculty of Medicine, second-year class, with advanced standing in September 1973 has been approved by the Admissions Committee of the Faculty of Medicine.

With a bachelor's degree and a minor in biochemistry from the

University of Pretoria and having almost finished his PhD in neuro-physiology, he went to the medical school instructors in biochemistry and physiology and asked to take a "challenge exam" for their respective classes. He performed admirably in both exams with scores that placed him soundly in the top 10% of the students currently in their first-year medical classes.

Anatomy and histology were a different matter. The medical students had been assigned to their respective cadavers in the lab, six per cadaver, and there was no place for Scott to work with anyone. The anatomy professor, who knew that Scott had attended chiropractic college, asked if had ever dissected a cadaver. He was pleased that the course at Palmer College did include dissection (although most of the course was dissecting the spine and muscular system, whereas the medical dissection course encompassed the entire body). The demonstration cadaver was being dissected on one side by the anatomy graduate student for demonstration purposes. The professor stated that if Scott wished to get credit in anatomy he would have to work on the demonstration cadaver at a skill level of a graduate student. It was Scott's task to dissect the other side with no help from classmates, and then to be examined on the work he completed. Anyone who has ever dissected a cadaver knows how technical a task it is even with group effort. The extra effort necessary to dissect half a cadaver on his own confirmed that Scott had the experience and knowledge to pass the examinations in the top 10% of the class.

Scott's histology professor was not as accommodating as some of his other teachers. He insisted there was no place left in his classroom for Scott to sit. Scott pointed to a stool in the corner of the room away from the laboratory work benches. The professor then retorted that there were no more microscopes for Scott to use. "I'll purchase my own," Scott said, "and borrow the needed slides from my classmates." Once again, persistence prevailed. He stayed in the course and obtained one of the highest scores on the final exam. The last course requirement was Introduction to Clinical Practice. Scott approached one of the professors in family medicine who accepted him into the course without hesitation. Scott would be joining the second-year medical school class in the fall, and his acceptance was officially recognized in an April 30, 1973 letter from Dr. Graham, Associate Dean:

> I am pleased to advise you that the Admissions Committee of the Faculty of Medicine has approved your request for permission to register in the second-year class in Medicine in September 1973. This offer is contingent upon your successful completion of [current course work of] Anatomy 500, Anatomy 501 and Introduction to Clinical Practice.

Acceptance into the medical school at UBC, starting as a second-year student, meant that he could complete his medical degree in three years. He was also permitted to continue to work part-time provided he kept up his grades. Scott practiced as a chiropractor in the evenings throughout his PhD and throughout his medical education, initially three nights a week, but eventually it reduced to one night a week in his fourth year of medical school at an office that was much closer to home.

FINANCING MEDICAL SCHOOL

Joan had resigned from the Vancouver Neurological Center when she became pregnant. She went to work for the Canadian Arthritis and Rheumatism Society (CARS) Center in Vancouver and became their senior research therapist, publishing a paper on arthritis of the hands. She also led the team that set up one of the very first back schools in the world. This entailed the preparation of a slide presentation for patient education and a group exercise program. Scott became very friendly with the rheumatologists at CARS and was offered the Louis Lipsy Toohill Scholarship in 1973, 1974, and 1975. This scholarship gave a small stipend for the three summer months of each of these years but required that Scott be in the clinic, see rheumatology patients, and conduct research. The clinical experience he obtained at CARS was invaluable in his understanding of how to examine and treat musculoskeletal disorders. During this period he, Joan, and other members of the physical therapy department conducted a clinical cohort study on the back school program they had developed. They published the results in *Physiotherapy Canada*, "Low Back Pain: A Study of Fifty Patients on a Group Exercise Program."

As Scott found it increasingly difficult to travel to Burnaby to work in Dr. Hartwick's office, Dr. Clint Heuser made his closer office and equipment available for Scott to use, free of charge, in the evenings and on weekends. He also provided a small metal desk, a single chair, and a file cabinet in the furnace room at his office for Scott's specific use. In return, Scott kept Dr. Heuser up-to-date on research and would review difficult cases with him. Scott hired a young high school senior who could type to be his receptionist. It was from this makeshift office that he sent out his articles and correspondence. Scott, Joan, and his secretary used to smile when they received letters from young researchers or clinicians—sometimes from foreign countries—asking if they could spend time in his laboratory.

Scott was very fortunate when the British Columbia Chiropractic Association agreed to cover his professional association dues, malpractice insurance, and licensing fees. In addition they provided a $4,000CAN/yr stipend for three years to pay for secretarial help. In return, Scott kept the BCCA informed on the latest research, organized educational conferences, presented lectures on chiropractic at various medical facilities, spoke on T.V. and radio shows, and was available for interviews resulting in 6-8 newspaper articles each year.

Scott paid tribute to the ICA when he noted to Dr. Forrest that the $4,000USD/yr stipend from the BCCA had been supplemented with support from the Canadian Chiropractic Association, the American Chiropractic Association, and the International Chiropractic Association with the most consistent support coming from the ICA.

Scott worked out a relationship with the Canadian Chiropractic Association (CCA) to provide reports and articles to the profession in exchange for a small stipend. However, in a December 1974 letter from Robert Brisco, CCA Board member and a member of the Ontario House of Commons, Scott learned that at their recent CCA board meeting a decision was made to discontinue support for Scott because his efforts seemed more focused on issues outside of Canada.

Examples cited were the NINCDS[1] Conference in the U.S., a response to the Web Report in Australia that threatened licensure, and the Chiropractic Act passed in South Africa that prevented the licensing of any new DCs in the future. While Scott's actual expense for the NINCDS conference was only $300USD to cover his airfare to attend the meeting in Washington, DC, the CCA Board was not swayed and cut funding. Brisco, from his seat in the House of Commons, continued his fight for chiropractic research funding through the Canadian Medical Research Council. This source of funds would not become accessible to individual chiropractic researchers until many years later.

Scott supplemented his medical school costs through a variety of small cash merit awards from the university. These awards were for obtaining the highest grades in specific courses or by vote of the department members when there were no grades. They included:

11 July 1975, Northwest Association of Physical Med & Rehab: $50USD

11 July 1975, V.G.H. Dept. of Psychiatry Attending Prize: $250CAN

18 May 1976, The Dr. Peter H. Spohn Memorial Prize in Pediatrics: $150CAN

26 May 1976, A.M. Agnew Memorial Scholarship for Obstetrics: $200CAN

4 June 1976, British Columbia Anesthetists' Society Prize: $200CAN[2]

Income from practicing three nights a week, the scholarships and awards, a brief stipend from the CCA, and Joan's income began to provide some relief to their tight budget. By living frugally they were able to renovate their small home and even take a few trips. Before their eventual departure to California they also welcomed two sons

---

[1] NINCDS is the acronym for the National Institute for Neurological Disease and Stroke of the National Institute of Health in Washington, DC. They sponsored a conference on the Status of Spinal Manipulation in 1975. Scott was a presenter at the conference and helped to organize the program. More details are provided in a later chapter.

[2] From *Official Documents found in Scott's Papers (Box labeled 1991 Conf Material)*

into their home—Reeve (born Dec. 1974, during Scott's second year at medical school) and Keatly (born Mar. 1977, during Scott's last year at medical school).

EXPERIENCES IN MEDICAL SCHOOL

It was very interesting to be a chiropractor in a medical school in the 1970s. This resulted in a number of unique experiences.

One day Scott was invited into the office of a medical school faculty member, the chair of the Department of Rheumatology. He had an x-ray hanging on his view box and asked Scott how he would manage the case. It was a film showing significant spinal degenerative disease. Scott began to describe a typical medical approach—after all he was a medical student speaking to one of his medical professors. The professor stopped him and said, "I know how medicine would manage this case. I want to know how chiropractic would manage the case." The x-ray belonged to the doctor himself. Scott ended up treating his professor for his remaining time at the University of British Columbia. While not a common experience in the 1970s when the conflict between medicine and chiropractic was raging, having one of his professors consult with "Dr. Haldeman, the Chiropractor" was surely a boost to Scott's confidence.

On another occasion, he was rotating through the orthopedic department with fellow students when the professor of orthopedics came in to teach how to examine the spine. He turned to Scott and said that he heard he was a chiropractor. He then suggested that Scott teach his fellow students how to examine the spine and left the room.

One of the more amusing incidents occurred when the class was given a lecture on medical ethics by the registrar of the College of Physicians in British Columbia. The registrar told the class that it was unethical for a medical physician to accept patients from, refer patients to, or even to talk to a chiropractor on matters related to patient care. One of the students in Scott's class then asked, "What would happen if you were both a chiropractor and a medical doctor?" The registrar became very red in the face and said, "It would be unethical for you to talk to yourself."

The uniqueness and the potential for controversy tied to having a DC, MS, and PhD compounded when Scott added the MD to his list of credentials. Even while in medical school, Scott was already drawing attention from colleagues in medicine and chiropractic. For example, an article published in the *Canadian Medical Association Journal* reviewed his background, then quoted Scott on his decision to pursue a degree in medicine:

> I decided that what I wanted to do was clinical and experimental research to try to find out exactly what the back was all about and knock down some of the dogma that has come forward from chiropractic, medicine and osteopathy, if such a position could be found.

> To do this I would have to get within a major facility, which in Canada would be under the auspices of the medical profession. I realized that any clinical research I would do as a chiropractor would be suspect or shot down by medicine. So I decided what I needed was a medical degree.

When queried in the article about the "decades-old" antagonism between medicine and chiropractic, Scott advocated a formal integration of the two disciplines into one healthcare team with common training. He said the isolation experienced in each profession led to misperceptions and misunderstandings. The article concluded with Scott saying, "...if there is to be agreement on the role of chiropractic, more research would have to be done."[3]

The article evoked an unfavorable response from a local medical doctor which was published in the *Letter to the Editor* section of the following edition of the *Canadian Medical Association Journal* suggesting CMAJ run educational articles on phrenology or teacup reading.[4] Conversely, Dr. McConnell of the British Columbia Chiropractic Association (BCCA) sent Scott a congratulations on his article in a

[3] Canadian Medical Association Journal, Vol. 113, 454, Sept. 6, 1975
[4] Canadian Medical Association Journal Vol. 113, 1024, 1975

May letter and said, "There is no doubt that this article will serve to promote co-operation between medicine and chiropractic."[5]

In 1976 and 1977 the Vancouver General Hospital established a Back Pain Special Interest Group and asked Scott to be a member of this committee. Dr. Peter Kokan was the chairman of the committee. The goal was to organize a meeting each year where leading authorities from around the world were invited to speak. Scott was able to suggest that the group invite speakers he very badly wanted to hear, including Professor Alf Nachemson from Göteborg, Sweden, and Professor William Kirkaldy-Willis from Saskatoon, Canada. It was at these meetings where Scott learned that differences of opinion on how to manage patients with back pain were not only present in the chiropractic profession but also amongst leading authorities in orthopedic surgery.

In 1974, Scott was asked to join a committee formed by the United States National Institute of Neurological Diseases and Stroke. This committee was formed to establish a "Workshop on the Research Status of Spinal Manipulative Therapy." He was required to travel to Bethesda, Maryland, while he was a second and third-year medical student and attend committee meetings. Scott recalls the bizarre situation where he was a lowly medical student one day and then was sitting in a meeting with some of the greatest neurology scientists in the world discussing who should be invited to speak.

Scott's chiropractic background continued to be a difficult concept for many of his medical colleagues to reconcile. In 1975, the North American Academy of Manipulative Medicine held its convention in Vancouver. This meeting was open to medical students, but when Scott showed up he was initially denied entry to the meeting. Some of the members felt that Scott may take the material they presented and the techniques some of the members had developed and teach them to chiropractors. They then had a quick meeting of the executive committee and decided that Scott could attend after all. Ironically, after the meeting Scott was invited onto the council and eventually worked his way up to become its president in 1983.

[5] Letter to Scott Haldeman from Dr. G.W. McConnell, May 1975. Letter is in the Haldeman Collection.

INTERNATIONAL SOCIETY FOR POST GRADUATE CHIROPRACTIC EDUCATION AND SPINAL RESEARCH

Amidst Scott's many obligations, he never lost his vision for research related to the spine, initially from a chiropractic perspective but eventually from an international, interdisciplinary perspective. To review the evolution of his experience,

- He had started the South African Chiropractic Research Foundation by setting up a small animal research lab in his father's garage.

- His master's thesis was a study of nerve compression.

- In less than one year while on the campus of CMCC in Toronto, he was instrumental in the establishment of a journal club that eventually grew into the very first archive collection of chiropractic relevant scientific literature—*Chiropractic Research Archive Collection* (CRAC).

- This collection coupled with Scott's forward thinking was part of the stimulus for the creation of the College of Chiropractic Scientists (CCS) that continues to function to this day.

- His PhD program was but a refinement of chiropractic principles beyond what he had done at the master's level, and

- His intent for seeking a medical degree was to add legitimacy to the research work he yet hoped to do.

His vision may not have been completely established when he entered Palmer College, but every step of the way, line upon line, precept upon precept, the vision grew, and the focus sharpened—never dulled by criticism, setbacks, challenges, or disappointments.

One very fascinating example of Scott's vision was the development of an organization within chiropractic for the sole purpose of supporting and directing research. The actual initial proposal was printed in June 1977 at the time he was graduating from medical school. Where did he find the time and the energy to even conceive, let alone deliver on such an idea? Surely, he spent many hours and sleepless nights nurturing this idea and producing a plan.

The original proposal was for the establishment of an Institution for Chiropractic Research and Postgraduate Education. The institution was the fourth and final phase of development. The initial or first phase was to establish a society where those interested in research could meet and help develop a research consciousness among chiropractors. The proposed name for this society was the International Society for Post Graduate Education and Spinal Research. Phase two was the establishment of an apolitical foundation for the collection of funds for research. Phase three was the establishment of a research clinic in which comprehensive research programs could be instituted and eventually serve as the base for phase four, an Institution or Postgraduate Educational Center. Expansion of the plan to become "International" was not part of the original proposal but likely more of an oversight than a purposeful omission given Scott's international complexity.

In the initial proposal Scott identified two problems (A & B) and their resulting effects:

A. <u>Lack of recognized postgraduate education courses for chiropractors who wished to join the academic community, resulting in:</u>

> 1. Difficulties in the standardization of both undergraduate and postgraduate chiropractic education.

> 2. A shortage of high quality articles in chiropractic journals and chiropractic textbooks.

> 3. An ineffective dissemination of available scientific information to practitioners.

> 4. The existence of multiple factions within chiropractic without the forum or format for adequate discussion and decision making.

B. <u>Lack of Research, resulting in:</u>

> 1. An excessive amount of dogma still being taught as fact.

> 2. A proliferation of treatment techniques without any studies comparing their efficiency.

> 3. A lack of understanding of the principles behind spinal adjusting.

4. The existence of numerous diagnostic devices whose usefulness is unknown.

5. The lack of a definitive standard of practice which is held to by all practicing chiropractors.

The "Answer" to problems A & B:

Construct a large Chiropractic Research and Postgraduate Education Institution with the following goals:

1. To attract the finest chiropractic researchers, clinicians, and educators into an environment that would permit the greatest degree of freedom of inquiry.

2. To conduct clinical research into the efficiency of chiropractic and the testing of chiropractic therapeutic procedures and diagnostic instrumentation.

3. To conduct experimental research into the principles of research [chiropractic].

4. To train chiropractic educators to the highest level possible in order to upgrade the undergraduate programs of the chiropractic colleges.

5. To provide courses and internship programs from one week to one year in length for practicing chiropractors wishing to upgrade their clinical skills or academic knowledge.

6. To organize continuing education seminars of the highest possible standard to the field practitioners of chiropractic.

7. To publish textbooks of the highest possible standard for the profession.

8. To upgrade the standard of articles in chiropractic journals.

Scott estimated a start-up cost of $5 million dollars and an annual operating cost of $1 million dollars. The lack of appreciation for the value of research and the generalized distrust of new ideas or organizations among many practitioners of chiropractic were no easier obstacles to overcome than the $5 million projected start-up costs. Scott was undaunted.

A grassroots organization was the best way to lift this professional dirigible off the ground. Local chapters of five to twenty members would meet monthly for two hours to discuss and review specific chiropractic-related topics and research projects. Chapter members would interact and debate clinical chiropractic issues, report on clinical results, and conduct small clinical research projects. Some of these reports would be published in a major journal. A central chapter would serve as the collection and distribution center for the entire network of local chapters. New information would be quickly disseminated. Staff in the central chapter would assist the local chapters and their chairpersons in the performance of duties in literature searching and analysis, maintaining a library of texts and important articles, facilitating the organization of meetings, and so on. Staff at the central chapter would prepare tapes and supporting material for the monthly meetings of the local chapters. Noted authorities in various areas would be contracted to develop the audio tapes used in the monthly discussion sessions. Ultimately, the society of chapter members would organize an annual scientific research conference where the latest research findings could be presented by world-renown specialists.

Financing of this grand plan was also grassroots-oriented. Each chapter would pay an annual fee of $3,000. Depending on the number of members in each chapter, the individual assessment would vary. It was hoped that by the time the organization had grown to phase two, an established foundation with external funding would be adequate to carry the activities and workload of the central chapter.

In a modified proposal printed a year later in 1978, Scott states:

> The Society has already been presented to chiropractors in formal discussion throughout Canada, the United States, and Australia and by correspondence and personal communication to chiropractors in New Zealand, Japan, South Africa, and throughout Europe. The response has been most encouraging and in each of these countries, states, and provinces there are individuals currently working towards the goals of the Society.

The two major national chiropractic political organizations, the ACA and the ICA, and their respective research affiliated foundations, FCER and FACTS, took immediate umbrage to Scott's new proposal. He would be competing with them for precious funds, reputation, and the ability to direct the research enterprise. In a letter to Dr. Jack Donovan of Carroll, Iowa, in October 1977, Scott defends the role of the Society:

> The Society's primary goal is to establish a research consciousness within the profession, and to offer a service whereby information will be distributed to small groups of chiropractors who will thereby be kept up to date on the latest scientific material.[6]

The role described was not being fulfilled by either the FCER or FACTS. If the Society members were to engage in research projects, it was Scott's feeling that collaboration with the chiropractic colleges would be more productive than competing with them. Scott assured Dr. Donavan that members of the Society would be encouraged to lend support not only to their Society chapter but also to their alma maters and the foundations of their respective political affiliations. More on the growth and development of this plan will unfold when we explore the life of Scott as a neurology resident at UC Irvine in Southern California starting in July of 1977.

NEW AND CONTINUED RELATIONSHIPS AND OTHER SOURCES OF SUPPORT THROUGH CORRESPONDENCE

G. W. McConnell, DC, Chair BCCA Legislative Committee

Dr. McConnell sent his congratulations to Scott on his graduation from medical school in 1977. He was surprised Scott did best in gynecology and pediatrics. He further complemented Scott on his leadership and influence and believes his example motivated Doug Branvold, fellow Canadian chiropractor, to study physiology at the University of British Columbia.

---

[6] Letter to Jack Donovan, DC with FCER from Scott dated Oct, 1977. Letter is in the Haldeman Collection.

Doug Branvold, DC

An example of Scott's generosity is seen in his relationship with Doug Branvold, DC—one of many who Scott inspired and encouraged to pursue more education. In a December 1975 letter Doug expressed his excitement about attending the NINCDS conference and renewed his desire to go back to school and learn to do research. In the exchange of letters that followed over the next several months, Scott told Doug to decide, a) what he wanted to study, b) who he wanted to study under, and c) where he wanted to go to school. Doug, like so many doctors of chiropractic, lacked his bachelor's degree and would be required to obtain one prior to enrolling in a master's degree program. Using Scott as his model, Doug planned to practice part-time while going to school, and since he was a resident of British Columbia he wanted to attend UBC and work with Scott. By the time Doug could have completed his bachelor's degree, which never happened, Scott would have graduated from medical school and left for a residency training program. While Doug decided to pursue practice rather than a research career, he was instrumental in working with Scott in putting together two research conferences (1985, 1992) in Vancouver.

Doug Winter, DC

Scott managed to keep abreast of chiropractic happenings around the world through a self-generated network of friends and associates. In his early career, through a string of correspondence with Doug Winter in Australia starting in 1974, it can be seen how this network functioned.

Dr. Winter contacted Scott by letter in March 1974. He admired Scott's achievements and said he was near the completion of his own master's degree in psychology. He expressed sympathy for the recent loss of Scott's father explaining that his wife was from South Africa and she had a very high opinion of Joshua Haldeman.[7] He then turned to the purpose of his letter, a plea for help. The Australian

---

[7] Joshua Haldeman was killed in a plane crash in South Africa in 1973. The plane was piloted by his son-in-law who was also killed.

federal government was establishing an expert committee to inquire into chiropractic, osteopathy, and naturopathy focusing on their scientific validity. Dr. Winter asked Scott for relevant, recently published research that could be supportive of the chiropractic cause and wanted to know if Scott's work to date would be of value to the committee. If so, he said the Australian chiropractors would be willing to fly him down for a presentation.

Scott responded with an explanation of what he was doing in his PhD work and sent two articles already published. He pointed out that a fair amount of research in the medical and biological areas supported many aspects of chiropractic. He felt a reasonable argument could be made to support the practice of chiropractic as a valid therapy but, on the other hand, there were many areas where chiropractors claim success that needed investigation. He was available to travel if they thought it would be helpful.

Dr. Winters responded in July to see if Scott would be available to do a literature synthesis using the MEDLAR retrieval system, write a review of the literature of value, review and edit reports to be submitted, and assist in ways yet to be determined. He said they could probably pay $250 per week plus any translation or typing expenses. He also wanted to know if Scott would be available for an appointment on the committee.

Scott's July 23, 1974 reply was lengthy but valuable. He addressed the scientific validation of chiropractic by pointing out that one first had to decide exactly which aspect of the theory of chiropractic was to be validated since chiropractic theory had expanded considerably in the last decade. He emphasized the need and importance of clinical research pointing out that this type of research was not being done anywhere in the world. Scott then gave a detailed description of his involvements with the ACA, ICA, CCA, the U.S. federal government, the Colorado Project, and the Canadian Arthritis and Rheumatism Association. He did offer to travel to Australia but said it would need to be during the summer between semesters at school. He concluded by expressing the difficulty he was having meeting everyone's demand for research information with only minimal financial support to meet all the requests. He said he would need a minimum of $250 a month to help. He did not ask for the $250 per *week* that had been offered by Dr. Winter.

The Australian Chiropractic Association finally completed a brief to be submitted to the Committee on Inquiry and sent it to Scott for comment and review. It took Scott two months and over 45 hours of time to return an eight-page review and a three-page guide on how to write such documents. In Scott's cover letter for this report dated November 4, 1974, he addressed several specific points of concern:

> 1. The five points that Janse makes in his book cover only one of the theoretical concepts of modern day chiropractic thinking. If you maintain that this is the only basis of chiropractic you will find this point of view impossible to defend in the face of any fixed opposition by physiologists or knowledgeable scientist. There must be adequate description of nerve pressure, spinal pain syndromes, somatosympathetic reflexes, visceral functions, etc.

> 2. A section on medical mis-diagnosis would be completely out of place, would support bias and would most probably be incorrect since it is unlikely that any chiropractor in Australia has more than a superficial understanding of medical diagnosis and mis-diagnosis.

> 3. The explanation of chiropractic you have in your submission is not adequate and should be considered in greater detail.[8]

The suggestions made by Scott were implemented and the document was strengthened prior to submission.

Things were heating up in Australia, and interest in getting a chiropractic school started was gaining momentum. Two weeks after Scott's last letter to Dr. Winter, he responded to a phone call from Stanly Martin, DC, of Melbourne, regarding a chiropractic faculty in a university in Australia. His letter addressed five points:

> 1. The integration of chiropractic within a university

> 2. Entrance requirements necessary to prepare one for the course curriculum

> 3. Class size

4. Possible teaching faculty

5. People who might help them get established or offer advice[9]

The International College of Chiropractic (ICC) was founded in 1974 at the Preston Institute of Technology in Melbourne, Australia, as a result, in part, of Scott's nurturing.

The report of the Committee of Inquiry into Chiropractic, Osteopathy, Homeopathy and Naturopathy (The Web Report) was released in April 1977. It recommended that chiropractic and osteopathy not be recognized as an alternative health care system but did recommend that each state and territory in the Commonwealth of Australia enact legislation that would require them to be registered. This report on chiropractic and osteopathy was far from the desired goal of recognition and parity with medicine. Scott's impact regarding the growth and future recognition of the chiropractic profession would soon become more influential.

Lynton Giles, DC, PhD

Another example of Scott's international network was with Lynton Giles, DC, a fellow South African and graduate of CMCC (1970). Scott actually taught and helped Lynton on some projects while they were at CMCC together. Lynton, who was then practicing in Western Australia, asked Scott in correspondence beginning in 1975, about the potential for a chiropractic college in Vancouver, Canada. While Scott was interested in the possibility, their discussion was sidetracked when it was announced that Andries Kleynhans, faculty member at National College of Chiropractic, and fellow South African was going to Melbourne to head a chiropractic program at the Philip Institute of Technology. Lynton also revealed to Scott that the Australian government had denied a request to set up a chiropractic program at the West Australian Institute of Technology and at two other universities, but did provide postgraduate training facilities for physiotherapists and medical practitioners who practiced or desired

---

[8] Letter to Doug Winter from Scott Haldeman, 4 November 1974. Letter is in the Haldeman Collection.

to practice manipulation. The course required only one year of study. This awareness of governmental actions helped Scott keep his finger on the pulse of the profession around the world, and he would often use the knowledge of what was happening in one country to support the cause of another.

Scott asked Lynton about the Commission of Inquiry taking place in Australia, whereupon Lynton sent the summary copy of the New South Wales Committee of Inquiry's report on Chiropractic (Committee of Inquiry into Chiropractic, Osteopathy, Homeopathy and Naturopathy or The Webb Report). He drew Scott's attention to the report's reference on spine charts linking subluxations to various pathological conditions, a very unscientific approach to explaining chiropractic.

Lynton shared with Scott in a January 1976 letter his desire to perform blood and urine tests as part of his practice in Western Australia but expressed his disappointment in the unwillingness of the chiropractic registration board to render an opinion in favor or against such practices. The law in Western Australia spoke of chiropractic care being limited to the use of the "hands only" and said nothing of the privilege to perform any kind of diagnostic procedure including the use of x-rays. Scott supported Lynton's desire to perform lab tests by pointing out that the chiropractor practices as a primary contact physician and, therefore, is required to make a diagnosis based on the best information available. The use of a pin prick, venipuncture, and urinalysis do not pose a threat to the patient and offer valuable information that may lead to an early diagnosis of a medical or non-chiropractic condition. "Ideally," said Scott, "the DC should have direct access to the medical laboratories, but if not, they should be able to perform basic lab procedures."[10]

By late 1975, Lynton began to discuss his research interests with Scott, who took on the mentoring role again. Lynton wrote that his research in low back pain related to leg length inequality was progress-

---

[10] Letter to Lynton Giles from Scott Haldeman dated 11 Mar 1976. Letter in the Haldeman Collection.

ing and he had submitted a paper to the *Journal of the Canadian Chiropractic Association*. Scott sent Lynton publications not yet available in Australia on leg-length inequality and the report on the NINCDS Conference and expressed an interest in speaking in Australia after his graduation from medical school. Lynton had difficulty obtaining the needed 100 patients for a control group the study he had started and Scott advised him to use neck pain patients who had never experienced low back pain. Lynton's proposal submitted to NINCDS was denied, however.

He advised Lynton, who had planned a trip to the U.S., to visit him and Joan, the Suh Research Project at the University of Colorado in Boulder, and the cine-radiographic laboratory at National College of Chiropractic near Chicago. Scott recommended against a visit to NIH unless he had an appointment with someone.

Lynton expressed the probability that his International Society for Post Graduate Education and Spinal Research being successful in Australia was quite low.

The young chiropractor also drew upon Scott's credibility by asking him to write a letter to the University of Western Australia stating that the work he had done at CMCC would be at least equivalent to a bachelor's degree and should, therefore, qualify him to enter into a master's program. Lynton, with Scott's encouragement, completed his MS and his PhD and obtained a research post in a major Australian university. He became a successful researcher and published several papers in very prestigious journals on the structure of the zygapophysial (facet) joint.[11] Scott's encouragement was vital because through the process of obtaining his degrees, Lynton eventually became unable to continue practice due to irresolvable debilitating back pain. The two men have remained in contact over the years and to this day are good friends.

---

[11] A zygopophysial (facet) joint is the articular surface formed between to spinal vertebrae.

Henri Gillet, DC

A noted European chiropractor, Henri Gillet, communicated with Scott through very difficult to read, hand-written letters on the old blue "aerograms." He was very complementary to Scott for the progress he had made in his professional education and expressed his disappointment in the difficulty Scott appeared to be having in garnering support from American chiropractors for the research work he was doing. He even wrote a concerned letter on Scott's behalf to the ICA journal in 1977 encouraging better collaboration in developing a chiropractic science. Scott was grateful for the support rendered by Dr. Gillet and extended an invitation for him to embrace Scott's proposal to establish the International Society for the Advancement of Clinical Chiropractic and Spinal Research.[12] Scott told Dr. Gillet that he planned to form an Advisory Group of world renowned chiropractors for the Society and hoped he would consider being a member.

On one of their return trips from South Africa, Scott and Joan decided to spend a few days in Brussels and visit with Dr. Gillet. He invited them to be with him as he treated his patients. Scott explained that Gillet would bring all his patients into a room together and have them sit in a circle. Gillet would then proceed to treat each patient in this seated position while the others would observe. Once all in the room were adjusted, he would excuse them and bring in the next group. As the patients left they would hand Dr. Gillet some money in payment for his services, and he would put it in a box next to his seat. "At the end of the day he reached into this box for a little spending money and took us to dinner," Scott remembers.

David Drum, DC

Scott maintained communication with his colleague at CMCC, David Drum, DC, who congratulated Scott on finishing his PhD. Scott in turn asked David if he would be willing to assist him on a project in the UBC Physiology Department. It seems they had an interest in learning more about how chiropractors utilized diagnostic find-

---

[12] The variation in the name of this international organization is probably due to the fact that it had not yet been formally organized and due to its length would often be altered.

ings such as muscle strength; however, Scott's entrance into medical school prevented the project from ever starting. Both men expressed dismay with the lack of commitment in the U.S. and in Canada to provide funding for chiropractic research. Scott became especially discouraged over negative comments sent to him by other chiropractors about his willingness to work with medical doctors. Scott and David would speak at the 1975 BCCA Jubilee Convention program together.

In a September 1975 letter, David expressed concern over an upcoming CMCC research conference. He believed chiropractic was little more than a form of physical medicine with a specialization in manipulation. He felt what made chiropractic unique, especially in North America, was a mystical, philosophical, eclectic hodge-podge of techniques used in patient care. This, Drum felt, was what needed to be researched. This displayed the kind of mind-set Scott encountered while in Toronto.

Scott asked David to comment on his idea of establishing an international chiropractic research organization. He told David how well this concept had been accepted by others and was anxious to move his idea forward. A group of chiropractors in Seattle actually wanted to host a convention to get the organization started. Dave responded positively to Scott's notion and also informed Scott that his retainer from CMCC of $250 per month would be reinstated. David thereupon submitted his own application to join Scott's chiropractic research society. The convention in Seattle was a success, and Scott continued soliciting more memberships.

W.W. DeVore, DC

As Scott was advancing through medical school, significant innovations had been taking place in the health care delivery system in both the U.S. and Canada. Before Scott left South Africa in 1969, the Carter administration in the U.S. had introduced an early version of health care management by creating "Health Service Areas" (HSA) and creating local bodies to determine local health care needs and make recommendations regarding the distribution and utilization of health services. The Nixon administration, while Scott was in Vancouver, introduced HMO legislation modeled after the Kaiser Permanente program popular in the Northwest region of the U.S., just across the border from where Scott was going to school.

The mere fact that Scott was in medical school and held a PhD caused many chiropractors to consider him a worthy source for advice in many areas. For example, Scott corresponded with W.W. DeVore, DC, who was chair of the Committee on Research Studies for the chiropractic association in the State of Missouri. Dr. DeVore shared with Scott (1975) his involvement in the development of the local Health Service Area, the Comprehensive Health Service Hospital and his cooperative relationship with the local medical community regarding patient care. He was very complementary to Scott for the inter-professional relations he had pioneered, especially between the ICA and the ACA. He and Scott connected on the need for the national associations to sponsor an inter-professional conference on spine care. In fact, Dr. DeVore had already developed a proposal for the National Chiropractic Association in 1955 to form a Committee on Inter-Professional Relations. They had further discussion on expanding inter-professional relations to become inter-disciplinary relations.

Dr. DeVore constantly expressed his gratitude for the numerous articles Scott sent to him. Scott responded with the lament of how expensive it was becoming for him to copy and mail articles to the increasing number of requests he was receiving. He asked if the Committee on Research in Missouri was active and if it had any funding to offset his expenses. Dr. DeVore responded that what little money they had raised was being sent to the Colorado research project under the direction of Dr. Suh. He did offer some good news, saying that Missouri would be interested in hosting a research conference similar to the one in Vancouver. Scott took occasion to share with Dr. DeVore his organization of an International Society for the Advancement of Clinical Chiropractic and Spinal Research, his experience at the NINCDS conference, and material regarding the December 1976 Pneumoconiosis Conference in which he participated.

Robert P. Gagnon, DC

Many well-meaning chiropractors started contacting Scott for advice on how to conduct research in their own private offices. Robert P. Gagnon, DC, is one example. In July of 1976, the summer preceding Scott's final year in medical school, Dr. Gagnon complimented Scott on the great contributions he was making to the profession and asked, "How can I help?" Scott responded by telling him to keep good records and publish case reports, read the scientific literature, and financially support those doing research. Dr. Gagnon wanted to conduct a clinical trial in his office testing chiropractic management of certain visceral conditions with medical management serving as a control. He asked Scott for help on setting up the project but offered no funding to support the effort.

Regardless, Scott responded to Dr. Gagnon with the following list of things to consider:

1. Define patient population accurately.

2. Define chiropractic care accurately.

3. Define medical care accurately.

4. Consider the ethics of denying treatment to a control group.

5. Determine the current knowledge about the condition to be treated.

6. Draw up a plan of the research to be done with forms and follow-up procedures.

Dr. Gagnon said there was more to be done than he realized, but he was prepared to proceed. He asked for clarification on which conditions to consider, the correct make-up of the patient population, and how to obtain medical cooperation. Scott suggested using a musculoskeletal condition, searching the literature at UBC library, and using tests and flow charts to measure and track data. The absence of any future communication would suggest the ambitious project never took flight.

Throughout his career, Scott would take the time to respond to these kinds of requests, focusing on his mission of bringing scientific research more fully into the chiropractic profession. The Dr. Gagnons of the world probably had little comprehension of the enormity of their requests upon Scott, especially while he was still in school.

International Chiropractic Association (ICA) and the California Branch (ICAC)

Scott maintained his relationship with the International Chiropractic Association (ICA) from the time he was a student at Palmer College. When he began to anticipate his move to California at the completion of medical school, he established communication with the California branch of the ICA, the ICAC. Dr. Ross Forrest was his link at this time. Ross asked Scott to prepare a letter for him to pass around the ICAC board to see if anyone might have a need or an interest to assist Scott in getting set up in an evening practice. Scott stated the following in an August, 1976 letter:

> My wish is to be able to continue my identity as a chiropractor, to show that despite my medical training I still believe in the practice of chiropractic, to maintain my skills as a chiropractor, assist in promoting chiropractic, the teaching of chiropractors, and to increase my income.

Scott canceled an appearance at an ICAC seminar scheduled for March 1977 due to Joan's impending delivery of their second son but sent application material for his California chiropractic license. Scott spoke at several subsequent ICAC license-renewal seminars until his schedule precluded him from continuing.

Dale Forsythe, DC

In correspondence with Dale Forsythe, DC, from Rutland, British Columbia, Scott discussed ways of detailing patient history and clinical information and sent him a copy of a record system that he used. Dr. Forsythe asked his opinion about childhood vaccinations and Scott responded, "Vaccinations are a matter of conscience. I personally believe that most of the infant vaccinations such as P.D.T., polio, and measles are not particularly harmful and may save the child some discomfort. On the other hand, smallpox and T.B. vaccinations can be harmful and should only be given if necessary for travel, high risk, etc." In an attempt to provide funding for Scott's research Dr. Forsythe sent Scott a $50.00 check for the articles he had sent, along with registration material for an upcoming Parker Seminar. He suggested that if Scott would consider speaking at the seminar perhaps they would help support his research. Scott said he would be interested to know more of what they had to offer.

Dr. Forsythe sent Scott a list of questions in April 1977 about a variety of things:

1. Is spinal analysis and manipulation of the spine taught at medical schools, and if so, for how long? Is the same true for physiotherapists as well?

2. Define the difference between non-manipulative and manipulative adjusting.

3. What do you know of Dr. Murray Katz—he is very derogatory about chiropractic?

4. Can you send a copy of your research society proposal?

Scott responded:

1. Spinal manipulation is not taught at any medical school. A few may practice the art in a crude fashion. There are some weekend courses offered but not part of the medical school curriculum. Physiotherapists also do not have a course in their curriculum. There is an orthopedic physiotherapy group that is learning manipulation. This orthopedic physiotherapy group is quite well-trained in back evaluation and manipulation.

2. Non-manipulative refers to electro-therapy, exercise, etc. Physiotherapists do mobilization (within range of motion) and some do manipulation (a thrust at the limit of the range of motion).

3. I met Dr. Katz at a legislative meeting. He has a personal vendetta against chiropractic. You should contact Don Sutherland at CMCC for more information.

4. Copy of proposal enclosed.

Scott closed his letter indicating that he had accepted an invitation to speak at Parker in LA in July 1977.

Scott told Dr. Forsythe in a November 1977 letter that the proposal for an International Society for the Advancement of Clinical Chiropractic and Spinal Research originally presented in Seattle was gaining momentum with chapters in Australia, New Zealand, Europe, Canada, Washington, Oregon, California, Texas, Wisconsin, New York , and Florida. Four colleges and eight major organizations were also interested in starting a chapter.

Foundation for Chiropractic Education and Research (FCER)

In August of 1975, after considerable dialogue with FCER, Scott received notification of being the recipient of a "special research fellowship" in the amount of $3,000 to be paid in monthly payments of $500, beginning August 1, 1975.[13] This was the very first fellowship issued by FCER. The letter states that he was expected to provide at least two primary articles on research for the ACA journal for the time that he had remaining in medical school. In Scott's response of appreciation he also apologizes for the delay of his first article due to the heavy workload he was carrying for the profession in addition to keeping up with his medical studies. As an insight to what Scott was doing at the time, the following was excerpted from his letter:

> The delays [of his article for the ACA Journal] have come as a result of the additional workload which has been placed on me by the profession. These included organizing and presenting papers at the NINDS conference, serving on the NIH on-site inspection team of the Colorado Research project, preparing a paper for the University of California conference on spinal manipulation, preparing a report on a graduate school of chiropractic for Dr. Dallas, presenting lecture seminars for a number of chiropractic seminars, and a greatly increased correspondence load.

In March 1976, an apparent misunderstanding resulted in Scott inquiring of FCER as to why he had not received continued payments for his fellowship in February and March. Dr. Schierholz, Secretary-Treasurer of FCER, wrote Scott explaining that his fellowship

---

[13] Personal letter to Scott from Arthur M. Schierholz, DC, FCER Secretary-Treasurer, dated August 1, 1975. Letter is in the Haldeman personal collection.

of $3,000 had been fulfilled in January after six months of payments at $500 each. Scott responded to Dr. Schierholz in April 1976 with an apology for his mistake and expressed appreciation for the support thus far received but took the opportunity to express his needs if he were expected to continue to serve as a consultant on research, education, and inter-professional relations. It wasn't until December of 1976, eight months later, that Scott was awarded a second fellowship from FCER, this time for $6,000 to be paid at the same $500 per month rate through his Internship training. However, this fellowship came with some conditions:

> 1. That you will commit yourself for a period of one year to serve at an accredited CCE chiropractic college upon completion of your internship.

> 2. In the event a workable arrangement with an accredited CCE chiropractic college does not become a reality, then you are obligated to repay the Foundation—the amount of the fellowship within a period of two years with interest beginning when your internship is completed and you are employable.

> 3. In the event you decide to go into a residency program, the Foundation will consider a formal request from you for a fellowship while doing the residency, with the additional commitment to serve at an accredited CCE chiropractic college for each year you receive a fellowship or repay the Foundation.

> The Foundation may also during the period when you are receiving the fellowship call upon you for assistance and speaking appearances, subject of course to your schedule, as a part of your commitment.

Dr. Schierholz indicated at the end of the letter that this agreement has been a policy of the Foundation established "several years ago," yet Scott was the first such individual to ever receive a fellowship from the Foundation (followed by myself, Reed Phillips in 1977 as its second recipient.)

Not pleased with the conditions attached to the fellowship, Scott replied that he was unable to accept the conditions and objected to the inference that there would be no return on the money paid to him until after he completed his studies. He indicated a willingness to consider a position at a chiropractic college if "...the facilities and financing of research at that college are sufficient to allow me to do competitive research on the relationship between the spine and the nervous system."[14] He pointed out that he was already on the faculty at CMCC, making two trips a year to campus and supervising student research projects and he had inquired as to a similar relationship with the Los Angeles College of Chiropractic in anticipation of his arrival at UCI.

In justification for his external support, Scott gave quite a narrative of his activities in the name of chiropractic, all the while completing his medical training and internship. The enormity of his commitment is explained:

> My reason for inquiring as to the availability of funds was to help defray expenses and compensate partially for my time which is being used more and more as a consultant and representative of the chiropractic scientific community. I am being asked with increasing frequency to advise the leaders of the chiropractic associations regarding decisions on inter-professional relations, scientific conferences and committees and various research projects. Examples have included the NINDS conference, the on-site inspection of the University of Colorado Research Project, the University of California conference on Spinal Manipulation and just one month ago the Pennsylvania conference on pneumoconiosis. I have also just been asked by Dr. West to consult with a research group at the University of Utah next month. At most of these conferences I have been asked to present 1 or 2 written papers each of which take from 50-100 hours of research and require 10-20 hours of secretarial time. I am at present helping with the organization of conferences at the University of Michigan, the University of California at Irvine, and at the University of British Columbia which we planned for next year. I try to bring the chiropractic point of view across at each of these conferences on spinal manipulation and back pain and, where possible, I try to influence the conference organizers to invite chiropractic researchers to present their point of view.

[14]Personal letter to Dr. Schierholz dated 2 Jan. 1976. Letter is in the Haldeman Collection.

I also receive approximately 10 - 15 letters a week from chiropractors around the world requesting information regarding chiropractic research technique and on current medical and biological research. The answering of such mail and the required research to give accurate information is very time consuming and requires a reasonable secretarial and office expense budget which I do not have.

I also try to continue my research and publish 3-4 articles in various chiropractic and medical journals each year on topics related to chiropractic research and inter-professional relations...

In addition I have been trying to circulate to approximately 50 chiropractic leaders a regular mailing which includes photocopies with comments of articles from the medical or biological literature which I believe signal a trend in medical research and/or politics which chiropractic leaders should be aware of. I have been sending articles to the ACA which are currently being abstracted in the ACA journal.

All these functions require a great deal of time and encur [sic] ever increasing costs for secretarial, postage, photocopying and other expenses. I have tried to finance these tasks through personal savings and the intermittent very meager funds I have received from various chiropractic organizations around the world including the ACA and FCER. I find, however, that in the absence of any consistent or adequate financing I am unable to work at my maximum ability or at any ongoing project. The work done this year for the CCA Convention and the Pennsylvania Conference on Pneumoconiosis was carried out without remuneration and the lack of funds has made me stop sending important articles to the ACA and chiropractic leaders.[15]

Ultimately the FCER decided not to give the award to Scott.

How Scott was able to complete his education, sustain his home and family, maintain his practice, correspond with so many people over so many issues— without sufficient secretarial help or modern-day computers—and still have time to organize conferences, travel

---

[15] Personal letter to Dr. Schierholz dated 2 Jan. 1976. Letter is in the Haldeman Collection.

to speak, and even think about organizing an international research organization is a tribute to his intelligence, tenacity, energy, and love for what he was doing and where he was going. His time in Vancouver was one of professional acceleration and exhilaration. As this chapter of Scott's life was drawing to a close, greater doors of opportunity awaited him in Southern California.

Scott Haldeman circa 1977

Chapter 8

Medical Residency in Neurology
UC Irvine 1977-1980

THE TRANSITION—CANADA TO CALIFORNIA

When students graduate from medical school, their education and preparation for practice is not yet complete. There is a one-year internship to be completed in a hospital. Often this is a year of transition between medical school and a residency in an area of specialty. The internship is also a rite of passage to become accepted as a physician. It is during this internship year that young doctors are expected to spend an inordinate number of hours on duty at the hospital leaving no time for home, family, or personal pursuit.

Scott had applied to three South African universities for internship and residency positions but never received a response—(Joan shares more details in Chapter 10)—and so he accepted an internship for the 1976-77 year at the Vancouver General Hospital before pursuing his residency in neurology. This internship year required that he take call and stay in the hospital every other night and every other weekend. It is one of the most demanding and all-encompassing periods in any medical physician's training. During this year Scott was not able to carry on his chiropractic practice but did maintain his correspondence and provide literature searches.

Most medical students compete for acceptance into a residency program. Scott actually received invitations to three different residency programs. One invitation was from Professor William Kirkaldy-Willis, Chief of Orthopedic Surgery at the University of Saskatchewan in Saskatoon, Canada. Scott was already acquainted with Dr. Kirkaldy-Willis from the NINCDS Conference and the Back Pain Special Interest meetings at the University of British Columbia. Over the ensuing years they became close friends and co-authored a book titled, *An Atlas of Back Pain* in 2002. Scott turned down the invitation from Professor Kirkaldy-Willis even though it would have placed him back in the territory of his ancestral roots. He was not comfortable considering a surgical specialty and wanted instead to focus his research in neurological mechanisms of spinal disorders. He did not feel that a career in orthopedic surgery would provide the opportunities for this type of research. The second invitation Scott received was from Dr. Herbert Shaumberg, who asked Scott to consider a residency in neurology at the Department of Neurology, Albert Einstein College of Medicine in New York. Scott had met Dr. Shaumberg at the NINCDS conference on Spinal Manipulation while he was in medical school. While this prestigious position was very tempting, his third option better served both his personal and professional goals.

It was an invitation from the University of California, Irvine (UCI) that won Scott over. He was invited to participate in the development of a first ever attempt to perform a double-blind randomized clinical trial comparing rotational manipulation with soft-tissue massage in late 1976. Al Buerger, PhD, and Jerome Tobis, MD, the head of Physical Medicine and Rehabilitation (PM&R) at UCI where the project was being conducted, invited Joan and Scott to come to California for a visit. Scott was asked to speak at their grand rounds. He met with Stanley van den Noort, MD, the head of the Neurology Department who was also one of the decision makers for the 41st Trust[1] established when the old osteopathic school was taken over by UCI and

---

[1] The 41st Trust was established at the time the osteopathic profession merged with the medical profession in California (1962). It was established to support research on osteopathic manipulation. See Sibylle Reinsch, Michael Seffinger and Jerome Tobis, *The Merger: MDs and Dos in California*. Xlibris Corportation, 2009 www.Xlibris.com p. 11.

converted to a medical school. Van den Noort not only offered Scott a residency in neurology, he asked him to participate on the spinal manipulation project. Dr. Tobis also invited Scott to do a residency in Physical Medicine & Rehabilitation, but he decided that neurology would better serve his long term goals. Scott began working with Al Buerger as soon as he got to California in June 1977. Though Scott was not listed as an author for the clinical trial, he was actively involved—attending all meetings and spending time in the clinic where the trial was conducted.

Relocation brought its usual challenges, only this time Scott and Joan had company—Reeve (age 3) and Keatly (3 months)—along with all the typical accumulations of a young family started twelve years earlier. As before, moving across international borders resulted in some obstacles. First was the issue of immigration into the U.S. and obtaining a proper visa.

Persons seeking educational/employment positions in the U.S. were expected to meet a host of requirements to demonstrate that they were more qualified to take a position than any U.S. citizen. They also had to demonstrate moral character, have no criminal or police record, provide evidence of adequate financial backing to cover living costs, and have a specific invitation from a U.S. citizen or a U.S.-based organization.

In the fall of 1976, Scott had written to the Commissioner of the South African Police and the Commandant-General of the South African Defense Force to verify he had a good military service record with no police actions against him. Scott also started the process of liquidating assets he held in South Africa, closed an account he had maintained in Davenport since his Palmer days, and transferred all funds to Canada to establish his financial stability.

On February 19, 1977, Scott penned a response to a letter he had received from Arnold Starr, MD, Chief of Neurology at University of California Irvine, (Dr. van den Noort had been appointed Dean of the Medical School and Dr Starr had taken over as Chief of Neurology). In his letter, Scott detailed what actions he had taken and what problems he was having obtaining a proper visa to enter the U.S.:

...I have received additional copies [immigration form] from the U.S. Embassy. I have filled in most of the form and left blank that portion which you or the university would have to fill in. I have also completed the "Application for Physicians and Dentists" from the Veterans administration which you forwarded to me and send[t] them to the Veteran's Affairs Hospital.

I have received notice of having passed the "Flex" [a medical proficiency exam required of foreign medical graduates seeking a medical license in the US] examination with an 86.5% average and over 80% in every subject so I do not believe that there will be any problem with California licensing.

I have still not heard from the U.S. Consulate-general's office in Vancouver whether the "Flex" examination will be satisfactory for immigration purposes. Apparently the new immigration law is unclear and the Department of HEW has not as yet ruled on what examinations will be considered "equivalent" to the [medical] National Board Examinations. To cover all bases, however, I have sent in my application to write part I and part II of the National Boards at their next sitting...The filing of "Preference Status" form...by the University of California may be all that is necessary to satisfy the immigration department.

With a start date of July 1, 1977, for his residency at UCI, Scott wrote Dr. Starr on April 19th stating he was still unable to give an exact date of his arrival. In the letter he also notes that he has two U.S. Senators (Henry Jackson and Bill Day from the state of Washington) and one Congressman inquiring into the process. He also points out that he has taken part I of the American [medical] National Boards, is scheduled to take the English exam in May—coming from South Africa and living in Canada for six years apparently was not enough to convince the immigration office that he was proficient in English—and is taking part II of the Boards June 14-15. He was assured by the Vancouver consulate office that he would be eligible to cross the borders within three months of having passed the exam—that would have been September 15th, two months after his program had already started. The paperwork was approved within the month, however, and Scott was able to begin his residency on its scheduled start date of July 1. He was told that the rapid decision of the immigration department was due to intervention from either the senators or congressmen on his behalf.

California Chiropractic Licensure

Medical residents are paid subsistence salaries. With a family to support, Scott fully intended to obtain a California chiropractic license in addition to his California medical license required for his residency. He had practiced chiropractic in Vancouver and expected to generate additional income doing the same in California. His performance on the "Flex" and the Medical National Board Examination paved the way for obtaining his medical license. Obtaining his chiropractic license was his next challenge.

Not being a procrastinator, Scott had initiated the California licensure process with a March 1976 letter to Raymond Reid, secretary of the California Licensing Board, asking what examinations he needed to take to obtain a chiropractic license and the time and location of such exams. In May 1976, two months later, Scott received a response from Garrett Cuneo, executive director of the California Board of Examiners, with the requested information and the date of September 20-23 for the next exam.

Scott was unable to make the September dates due to his internship schedule. In October he wrote Mr. Cuneo listing his credentials and experience, including training in physical therapy, and expressed his hope that he would not need to take any additional exams. He suggested in this letter that he could practice chiropractic under his MD license but didn't think that would set the best image for the chiropractic profession. Mr. Cuneo responded back with a denial of Scott's request stating he lacked the required 120 hours of training in physical therapy. Eight months later, just before Scott arrived in California, Mr. Cuneo asked Scott to resubmit his documentation regarding his training in physical therapy for the Board of Examiners to conduct a "more thorough review." It wasn't until March 1978, another eight months, that the board waived the requirement of 120 hours in physical therapy but still requested Scott's transcripts from Palmer and CMCC. Scott complied by submitting his transcripts from Palmer and CMCC, his California examination application, and his results of the Chiropractic National Board examination, which he passed in September 1978.

Apparently Scott got too busy in his residency program to pursue his California chiropractic license any further. Mr. Cuneo sent Scott a notice of the next license examination scheduled for November 12-15, 1979, in Los Angeles reminding him that his application had been pending since October 1976. Scott wrote back shortly after the November exam stating that his hospital rotation schedule precluded him from taking the exams and that he hoped to take them next year. It wasn't until October of 1980 that Scott resubmitted his application for the November 1980 exam. He attended a State Board Exam prep course put on by Dean Cummings in late February 1980. Unfortunately, Scott's National Board test results were not sent to the California Board in time for Scott to take the exam in November so he had to request a postponement again until the next year.

In 1980, as Scott was completing his residency, it became necessary for him to obtain his own malpractice insurance as a practicing neurologist. He was advised against having a dual license because the malpractice carrier believed he could be held to two different standards of care and that would complicate any legal case he might be involved in. Also at this time, ethical standards of the American Medical Association prohibited any professional association between medical doctors and chiropractors. In the end, Scott's original goal to obtain a California chiropractic license was an unsuccessful saga.

National Board of Chiropractic Examiners (NBCE)

Part of obtaining a California license required successfully passing the Chiropractic National Boards. Scott took and passed these boards in September 1978 even though he eventually opted against getting a license. Given Scott's background, training, and experience, it was entirely appropriate that he should render an opinion about his experience with the NBCE in an effort to improve the standard and prestige of the exam. His comments were critical but on point:

1) The NBCE...is the organization which...reflects the educational status of the profession and the level which chiropractic has reached in establishing optimum standards of care...Its questions should reflect the very best the profession can offer...

2) Many of the questions in the various papers [exams] were a disgrace to the profession. They reflected the ignorance of the examining committees in the fields in which they were deemed to be experts.

3) If I were on the AMA Council on Quackery, I would...obtain a copy of this examination. I can think of no better way of documenting a low level of competency and a disgraceful level of ignorance in the chiropractic profession...

4) Poor results by examinees, if they exist, would I believe, reflect poor question selection rather than inadequate knowledge.

5) A great many of the questions, especially in the chiropractic sciences, had no correct answer or multiple correct answers. The exercise in many cases was to guess the bias of the examiner...

6) In one examination, 25% of the questions had answers which were dependent upon the knowledge of named orthopedic and neurological testing procedures...The emphasis on such named tests by the National Board...reflects neither contemporary chiropractic, medical or scientific knowledge and emphasis. My question is, what does it represent?

7) The chiropractic principles paper was an insult to the students... and the profession...in the majority of cases there were either no correct answers, the question did not make sense or there was bias on behalf of the examiner towards a specific school of thought or technique system.

8) There were multiple spelling, typographical and grammatical errors in the paper.

Scott was not alone in his opinions. Dr. Quigley, president of LACC, Dr. Reed, president of the California Licensing Board, and Dr. Howe, chair of the Department of Radiology, took the same exam and arrived at similar conclusions. Scott copied this letter to Drs. Quigley,

Reed, and Howe as well as representatives from FCER and CCE but otherwise asked that his letter not be made public at that time, for he did not wish to embarrass the current NBCE members. Scott passed all thirteen parts of the National Board Exam with an average score of 91.2%.[2]

EXPERIENCES AS A RESIDENT

The residency at UCI in neurology was for three years. In the first year, residents were primarily on the hospital ward service with rotations either at the UCI Medical Center or the Long Beach Veteran's Administration Medical Center. General ward rounds would start at 7:00 a.m. and Scott would rarely leave the hospital before 6:00 or 7:00 p.m. The first-year residents were also required to see patients in the neurology outpatient clinics at both centers and take first call for emergencies both on the ward and for the emergency room.

Unlike the internship at Vancouver General Hospital that required the residents to be on call every other day for approximately 100 hours per week, the residency at UCI required that the residents be on call every fourth night. The residents who lived within 10 minutes of the hospital could take call from home. If not, the resident had to stay at the hospital when on call. With this in mind, Scott and Joan found a home just barely within the 10 minute travel distance from the hospital. It was an old home but with a large lot. Joan was able to design a modern garden and supervise building onto the house so that it was very comfortable. The schools in the neighborhood were excellent, and they lived there until their sons were old enough to drive. The primary downside of taking call from home rather from the hospital was the added commuting time since Scott could anticipate from two to six emergency calls each night inevitably requiring that he get up and go to the hospital to see patients.

In the second year, residents were required to rotate through different departments or subspecialties in neurology. These included neurosurgery, psychiatry, neuropathology, pediatric neurology, neu-

---

[2] Transcripts of the September 1978 NBCE exams for Scott are in the Haldeman Collection.

Residents and faculty, Neurology Department, UC Irvine. Scott is third from the left in the front row. Circa 1978.

roradiology, and electrodiagnosis. At that time the neuropathology position at UCI had not been filled, so Scott was required to do his rotation at the University of Southern California under Dr. Richard L. Davis, a highly respected national authority in neuropathology. This required driving to Los Angeles each day and could take one to three hours depending on the traffic. It was, however, a very rewarding experience as the number of brain dissections for autopsy at USC Medical Center was one of the highest in the country. During this period Scott dissected the brain of a patient who had died from a hemangiopericytic meningioma. This is a very rare tumor that at that time had not been widely studied. Scott was asked to do a literature search and to write a case report on this type of tumor. Scott also had the opportunity to spend an elective month in the muscle disease laboratory at USC under Dr. Louis Chui, the leading neuromuscular disorders specialist in Southern California.

In his final year, Scott was appointed Chief Resident for the Neurology Service. This required that he help with the teaching of junior residents and arrange the on-call schedule. Since Scott was being asked to travel widely at this time, the ability to control the on-call schedule allowed him to arrange his time so that he could accept invitations to speak at conventions or participate in hearings. During the second year, he did not have to take call in some of the rotations, and his supervisors tended to allow him to attend meetings if it did not disrupt his duties. During his second and third years of residency, he gave presentations or testified at hearings in New Zealand, Australia, Canada, and across the U.S. He also continued to spend time at the Southern California Chiropractic Colleges addressing students on research principles.

CHIROPRACTIC RESEARCH ENDEAVORS AND RELATED SUPPORT

Scott's efforts to bring research into the chiropractic community did not slacken, nor did his financial needs to sustain his chiropractic research efforts become less burdensome. It had been Scott's pattern while in Vancouver to provide a "research consultant" role to various organizations in exchange for a modest fee. In this consulting role, he would remain conversant with the scientific literature relevant to chiropractic and share key articles with those who were providing support. He would participate in selected planning meetings for those organizations providing him support. He would submit to interviews with the media—newspapers, radio, and television—and write at least two papers for publication in these organizations' journals. Scott was also involved as an advisor when the Foundation for Canadian Chiropractic Research and Education was organized in Manitoba.

THE INTERNATIONAL SOCIETY FOR THE ADVANCEMENT OF CLINICAL CHIROPRACTIC AND SPINAL RESEARCH

During the first two years of his residency Scott continued to promote the society he had proposed while a medical student, overturning every rock he could. In June 1977, just prior to his relocation to California, he communicated with Dr. Louis Sportelli and Dr. Arnold Goldschmidt, attempting to get an audience with the New York Chiropractic Association (NYCA) and state associations from adjoining states. His request was taken before NYCA House of Delegates and it was determined that his idea was brilliant but impractical.

Scott responded back to Goldschmidt giving details of where this society was going, hoping that a better explanation would open the door for him to make a presentation in New York. He iterates the following:

> In my travels and presentation of many of these concepts, I have found that there is considerably more interest in this field than I had previously considered possible.
>
> Much to my surprise over the past four months since I initially presented this concept I have had so much response that I am unable to keep up with the correspondence, and it sometimes feels like my telephone will never stop ringing. There are already between twenty-five and thirty groups or chapters of the society being formed in Canada, the United States, England, Australia, Belgium and France, and I just haven't had time yet to send out information to most of the United States, Eastern Canada and places like South Africa and New Zealand. I have been asked to present this material and the proposal to chiropractors in Australia, to groups in California, Washington State, Texas, Florida, Toronto and Michigan. There has already been interest in the Canadian Memorial Chiropractic College, Western States, Cleveland, Los Angeles Chiropractic College, the Chiropractic College of Australia (international) and the Anglo-European Chiropractic College. Most of these colleges are hoping to form chapters both within the student bodies and within the faculty, in order to get access to information which is available in the scientific literature.[3]

After being denied audience in 1977, Scott continued to work with Dr. Goldschmidt attempting to get the proposal onto the NYCA convention program in 1978. Again, having Scott on the program was "postponed indefinitely." They kept pushing for a third time but Dr. Goldschmidt informed Scott in his September 25, 1978 letter regarding his appearance at the 1979 convention:

> It seems that there were several opinions why this program would be inadvisable. First, budgetary considerations. Second, the great

---

[3] Letter to Arnold Goldschmidt from Scott dated 11 Oct 1977. Letter is in the Haldeman Collection.

difficulty in attracting DCs to consider research as an important topic for the profession.[4]

His old friend, Earl Homewood, DC, offered Scott some personal advice in a letter sent on May 10th, 1978. After expressing his conviction that research was essential for survival in chiropractic, he acknowledged that support from the individual colleges for his Society was not likely to happen due to their limited resources. He also raised concern that Scott might get too bogged down trying to administrate the Society and when enthusiasm and support waned, he would be in charge of nothing but a paper organization. His recommendation was to continue to seek support and membership but hold the money in escrow until such time that he could go to FCER and ask them to help manage the society while Scott continued to lead it and do his research.[5]

In 1978, Scott testified at the New Zealand Commission of Inquiry into Chiropractic (see Chapter 15 for details) and met David Chapman-Smith, who was one of the attorneys representing the chiropractic profession. Following the publication of the report, Mr. Chapman-Smith continued to be interested in chiropractic and began talking about the establishment of a World Federation of Chiropractic (WFC). He discussed the proposal with Scott, who felt that such a society had strong potential to advance a research and scientific agenda within the chiropractic profession. After receiving the communications from Dr. Goldschmidt and the advice of Dr. Homewood and others, Scott put the idea of his society on hold and threw his support behind the WFC. He encouraged all of his contacts around the world to support the WFC and was asked to chair the research council of that federation and develop the academic program for the congresses. He continues to hold this position.

---

[4] Letter to Scott from Arnold Goldschmidt dated 25 Sept 1978. Letter is in the Haldeman Collection.
[5] Letter to Scott from A. Earl Homewood, DC, dated 10 May 1978. Letter is in the Haldeman Collection.

CANADIAN CHIROPRACTIC ASSOCIATION (CCA)

Correspondence with Dr. Maurice Bonvouloir, president of the Canadian Chiropractic Association, left Scott wondering about support for services provided. As early as 1974 the debate to continue Scott's support into the next fiscal year was on the agenda for the board of directors and came up annually. Bonvouloir suggested a stipend of $3,000 a year for Scott to write articles, copy research material, and answer letters on research for the CCA. The decision to continue funding apparently never passed. However, Scott continued to assist in many ways including assistance in lining up speakers for their national convention in Quebec in 1977. When Scott was invited to be a speaker at their 1978 convention, Dr. Bonvouloir could offer no assurance Scott would receive his requested $500 honorarium—only a promise to pay whatever they could afford.

In April of 1978, the Canadian government granted permission to form a corporation titled, The Chiropractic Foundation for Spinal Research/La Fondation Chiropratique pour la Recherche Vertebrae. The names attached to the original application: Ronald Collett, Terry Watkins, Edward Hawkins, John Bloomer, and Walter Savickey were all from Winnipeg, Manitoba. The purpose of the Foundation was:

> To promote and carry on or cause to be promoted or carried on research and scientific enquiries consisting of clinical, biome-chanical and kinesthetic studies relevant to the spine and other articulations, exclusive of infectious or malignant conditions; to help to secure for the chiropractic profession and for the people of Canada the benefits of research and scientific enquiries carried on elsewhere.

Scott served on the advisory board of this new foundation and was instrumental in getting it organized. He was hopeful that it would soon be in a position to host scientific conferences.

ASSOCIAZIONE ITALIANA CHIROPRACTICI

Scott received a plea from Thomas S. Louw, DC and chair of the Italian Chiropractic Association White Paper Committee, in September 1976. Louw explained the profession was under attack in Italy and needed Scott's help to put up a defense. Scott responded to Thomas Louw in Rome with a promise to help but knew they would be fighting an uphill battle. Scott asked for a $250 per month honorarium to provide their national association 6-8 articles a month (as he was still a student and had a family to support). Regardless, he offered to continue to render a service even if they could not come up with the financial support. The Italians were not able to find the resources, and after supplying a few articles, Scott did not hear from them again.

AMERICAN CHIROPRACTIC ASSOCIATION (ACA)

Henry West, DC, had moved from being president of the ACA in 1977 to the chair of the ACA Commission on Planning in 1978. In the Commission's April 26, 1978 report, Dr. West explains how the Planning Commission divided their planning efforts into political and educational areas. To his credit, Dr. West makes a profound statement in the document about how the future of the profession rests with a reasonable investigative documentation which may be called research. At the end he reinforces the ACA's position on research: "The prejudices and misinformation born out of 70 some years of relative isolationism must be removed through investigative research..."[6]

In this same planning document, Dr. West expresses great confidence in the recent formation of the Chiropractice Research Commission (CRC) placing it on equal footing with the NINCDS conference and the U.S. Office of Education's recognition of the Council on Chiropractic Education.[7]

Scott was not a member of the ACA at this time but he maintained a close relationship with Dr. Lou Sportelli as evidenced by his November 3, 1981 correspondence congratulating Lou on being elected to the Board of Governors of the ACA and expressing the hope that a relationship between himself and the ACA could be restored. Scott told Lou that he had some projects in mind that would be of value to the ACA and the profession.

[6] The American Chiropractic Association's Commission on Planning Report, 26 April 1978.
[7] The Chiropractic Research Commission (CRC) was formed under the direction of the Foundation for Chiropractic Education and Research in the mid 1970s.

FOUNDATION FOR CHIROPRACTIC EDUCATION AND RESEARCH (FCER)

The financial relationship between Scott and FCER was once again an issue in 1979 when then president of FCER, Dr. Van D. Mericas, wrote in August to inform Scott that the Board of Governors of the ACA would be dispensing his consulting fees through FCER and the fee would be $400 a month for fiscal year beginning in April 1979 and extending to March 1980. Mericas acknowledged that due to budgetary constraints, the amount was less than what Scott had been receiving, but he stated that it is "the best that can be done this year."[8] Scott was also expected to provide two original articles exclusively to FCER as part of the new arrangement.

In response, Scott expressed his opinion that his relationship should have been with FCER from the beginning. He also wondered how the transfer of responsibility from the ACA to FCER had taken place:

> It is, in my opinion, most unprofessional to simply inform a consultant of a change in status without some prior discussion of what this change in status entails, what the academic and political ramifications might be, and before asking his opinion on the matter. I consider this once again a reflection of the high-handed and inconsiderate (unintentional, I am sure) manner in which the FCER Board has handled everyone from whom it has requested assistance. It is primarily this attitude which has led to the current low esteem with which the FCER is now viewed by most of the chiropractic academic world.[9]

Scott agreed to the expectations but indicated the degree of commitment would be less than before. He complimented FCER as being a "...most important factor in stimulating chiropractic education and research," and expressed confidence in working with FCER's newly assigned research director myself, the author. Scott continued to review research proposals submitted to the foundation.

[8] Personal letter to Scott from Dr. Van Mericas, president of FCER, dated 14 Aug 1979. Letter is in the Haldeman Collection.
[9] Personal letter to Dr. Van Mericas from Scott, dated 21 Aug 1979. Letter is in the Haldeman Collection.

Chiropractic Research Commission

In 1977, FCER transitioned its focus from funding institutions (to assist in their efforts to obtain accreditation) to funding research more directly. At a meeting of representatives from FCER, ACA, CCE, and research directors of the various chiropractic colleges in Chicago on August 30-31, 1977, the Chiropractic Research Commission was formed with the following structure:

> The FCER shall develop a cooperative national program to focus energy and resources for the resolution of research problems facing the chiropractic profession. A Commission shall be composed of a chairperson appointed by FCER, a staff person appointed by FCER (non-voting), a member from each college who shall have the authority to act on behalf of the college, a member appointed by ACA and a member appointed by CCE.[10]

The first CRC meeting was held in Minneapolis in November 1977. Scott's involvement with the CRC began when he was invited to their second meeting in Houston in March 1978. It appears that Scott was brought to the meeting along with Paul Silverman, PhD, from the University of New Mexico, to serve as advisors to the CRC.

Mr. Woody Phend, recently hired executive director of FCER, relied on Scott quite heavily. Mr. Phend sent the agenda for the September 1978 meeting to him in August, seeking his feedback, prior to it being distributed to the members of the CRC. He sent a proposed "mini-grant" proposal to Scott prior to presenting it to the Board of Trustees of FCER at their October meeting. The mini-grant program grew out of the CRC with the intent of providing start up costs to chiropractic colleges as a first step to seeking larger grants. In October 1978, Secretary Califano opened the door for public input for the Department of Health, Education, and Welfare's new multi-year strategy. ACA came to FCER for a statement, and Mr. Phend asked Scott to prepare the statement—for which he never received credit.

In January 1979, Mr. Phend resigned from his employment with FCER and the activities of the CRC ground to a halt. It wasn't until

---

[10] American Chiropractic Association, *Action Digest*, January, 1978.

April 1980 when I, as the director of research for FCER, hosted a meeting of the Chiropractic Research Commission (CRC) in St. Louis that it came back into activity with representatives from each chiropractic college. Scott's involvement with the CRC remained on a consulting basis and his attendance at future meetings became less frequent as his involvements after his residency expanded significantly.

Low Back Pain RCT

In 1978-79, FCER organized the Low Back Pain Advisory Committee. This committee was tasked with the development of a proposal to submit a grant to National Institutes of Health to fund a major randomized controlled clinical trial on the chiropractic treatment of low back pain. Scott was appointed as the principle investigator. The estimated budget was $446,550 with FCER contributing $159,750 and the remainder coming from an NIH grant.

Committee members attending the first planning meeting in Pasadena, CA on November 18, 1978, included:

Scott Haldeman, DC, PhD, MD	Reed Phillips, DC, DACBR
Al Adams, DC	David Brunarski, DC
Hoyt Duke, DC	Ron Gitelman, DC
Paul Goodley, MD	Joseph Howe, DC, DACBR
Gerald Konsler, PhD	Woody Phend, PhD
Heath Quigley, DC	Leonard Savage, DC
Franklin Schoenholtz, DC	Deborah Streeter, MA
Col. E.W. Verner, DC	Alex Warner, PhD
James Winterstein, DC	

Not in attendance but acting as an advisor to the committee was Cheryl Montefusco, PhD.

In preparation for the November meeting, Col. Verner put together a manual that outlined the job descriptions for the major participants in the study, patient flow diagrams, and a floor plan for the Los Angeles College of Chiropractic (LACC) El Monte clinic where the project was to take place. Scott put together a four-page draft proposal with an estimated $24,500 in start-up costs.

The follow-up report to the Advisory Committee after the November meeting outlined a high profile medical orthopedist required as the principle investigator, someone with a track record of scientific publications. The trial was to include the randomization of 30 patients into either a manipulative treatment group or a non-manipulative treatment group. Assessment and outcome evaluation plans were outlined. Operational definitions were to be prepared by members of the Advisory Committee and submitted to Mr. Phend by December 14th in preparation for the next meeting scheduled for January 23rd and 25th in Miami. Transcripts of the November meeting were 53 pages in length.[11]

An unfortunate set of circumstances lead to the demise of the proposed Randomized Controlled Trial (RCT) before it was ever submitted to NIH. Though much of the paperwork was in place, when Mr. Phend resigned in September 1979, as mentioned earlier, the impetus for the RCT left with him.

In the aftermath of Phend's departure, FCER board member, Dr. Louis Sportelli, circulated a letter (February 13, 1979) to selected members of the Advisory Committee seeking support for Phend based on Phend's productivity, regardless of his qualifications. The letter contained 17 questions, and Scott was one of the recipients of the letter. Scott expressed disappointment about how this situation could affect current projects and future activities of the FCER. Phend received a copy of Scott's response and took objection to his mention that, "... he did not think the action taken by the FCER Board was political."[12] Phend pointed out to Scott that Drs. Keiffer of the FCER Board and Dr. Wolfe, president of Northwestern College of Chiropractic, were seeking his removal because he cut off the funding of "Project D" that was funneling money to Northwestern but not producing any viable research.[13]

---

[11] Minutes from the Advisory Committee Meeting for FCER Sponsored Low Back Pain Trial. Pasadena, CA 18 Nov. 1978. Minutes are in the Haldeman Collection.
[12] Letter to Woody Phend from Scott, dated 5 March 1979. Letter is in the Haldeman Collection.
[13] Letter to Scott Haldeman from Woody Phend, dated 23 March 1979. Letter is in the Haldeman Collection.

In March 1979 the Executive Committee of FCER made a decision to carry-on with the Low Back Pain Trial in partnership with LACC and its current president, Dr. Heath Quigley. As the research director of FCER, I prepared a proposal and presented it to the Advisory Committee, chaired by Scott, for approval in May. The committee met in July to discuss revisions and I was assigned to complete a second draft. Not long after this meeting, Dr. Quigley was dismissed from LACC, and LACC's commitment to the project fell to Dr. Tran. The school was in the process of relocating from Glendale to a new campus in Whittier and the attention to the project waned. Ultimately the proposal was submitted to NIH but was never funded. It was a gallant effort with a bright beginning. Unfortunately, it became clouded over by internal disputes and a glaring lack of organization which led to its final demise.

New York Academy of Sciences

In July 1979, Dr. Julian Dintenfass, trustee of the FCER, recommended an effort be undertaken to submit a proposal for a conference on Spinal Manipulative Therapy hosted by the New York Academy of Sciences, and a planning committee was organized with Dr. Dintenfass as chair. The members were:

> Van Mericas, DC, Pres. FCER
> Brian Cartier, Ex. Dir., FCER
> Scott Haldeman, DC. PhD, MD
> Don Harriman, DC
> William Hynan, DC
> George McClelland, DC
> Reed Phillips, DC, MSCM, Res. Dir. FCER

Scott responded with a letter in August to Dr. Dintenfass stating he was excited about the conference but knew nothing of the committee to which he had been appointed. Scott proceeded to challenge FCER's past lack of commitment to projects and did not want his name used except on the following conditions:

> 1. He would be allowed to review information on the committee and copies of all related correspondence.

2. He would also be given a copy of the rules and regulations of the New York Academy of Sciences (NYAS) that govern such conferences to review.

3. The FCER Board would sign a commitment to give complete support and full authority to the committee.

4. There would be a guaranteed account of $100K dedicated to this process.

5. A qualified editor would be hired by FCER to prepare and publish the proceedings.

6. The ACA would commit not to interfere with the academic freedom of the committee.

7. Dr. Dintenfass, as chair, would need to commit to dedicate ten hours a week to the project for two years.

At the first planning meeting held in March 1980, Scott admonished the committee "...if the chiropractors fail to get involved in the scientific world over the subject of spinal manipulation, then other people would do it for us."[14]

Scott used this opportunity to teach the FCER Planning Committee how to write a scientific proposal. The first step was to create a "Needs Statement" based on FCER's financial capacity and the expected related expenses. Scott proposed a Needs Statement that would include:

1. Trustee-approved $100K to support the committee chaired by Scott to write the proposal;

2. A trustee commitment to cover expenses related to the proposal and conference;

3. FCER staff available to help the committee;

4. Further funding to be applied for if justified;

5. The FCER executive director to be a responsible fiscal officer;

6. Revenue generated to be used to cover expenses.

7. $100K mark to be exclusive of Scott's personal expenses

[14] Letter to Reed Phillips, Director of Research for FCER from Scott dated 29 March 1980.

Scott was brought in as a consultant/committee member with the specific duties of drafting a proposal for a conference on Spinal Manipulative Therapy sponsored by the New York Academy of Sciences. If the proposal were accepted, Scott would act as chair of the conference and edit proceedings in preparation for their publication. For this, Scott proposed a monthly retainer of $1,500 with an additional monthly amount of $1,000 for proposal development related expenses (i.e., secretarial help, office space, phone, supplies, etc.).

FCER countered his offer—based on decisions made by Brian Cartier, the executive director who had replaced Woody Phend by this time, along with Dr. Van Mericas, president, and Frank McCarty, vice president—and offered Scott a $6,000 flat fee for four months of work to line up speakers and prepare the proposal, plus a telephone credit card and pre-approved travel. Once the proposal was accepted by the Academy, Scott would become chair and then FCER would pay $1,500 per month for the next 27 months until the conference had taken place and the proceedings were published. Disappointed in this offer as being considerably less than proposed, he nevertheless accepted it, believing the goal could still be met.

Scott was given the FCER password for access to the MEDLAR literature database and was granted $200 to hire Sherry McGee, a librarian at UC Irvine, to assist in his need to search the scientific literature.[15] Names of potential speakers started to emerge, Ken DeBoer and John Triano among them. Scott withdrew his request for a Statement of Financial Capacity of FCER on the basis that it wasn't needed for the proposal. It was probably a good thing since it appears FCER had to delay the second monthly payment to Scott due to cash flow problems.

By the end of June, a fourth draft of the New York Academy of Sciences proposal was circulated among the trustees of FCER. They were impressed. Feedback from the trustees was to be received by the end of August so the final draft could be prepared in time for submission

[15] Ms. McGee's services were extended beyond the initial proposal of two months as she was also assisting Scott in the preparation of the Haldeman Conference in Las Vegas that FCER was also supporting.

in November. To complete the proposal Scott requested the following from FCER:

1. Charter or Articles of Incorporation of FCER

2. Formal letter from the president of FCER committing to support the NYAS proposal

3. Formal letter from the executive director to accept fiscal responsibility

4. Formal letter of approval from Dr. Dintenfass, chair of FCER's Research Committee

5. Additional copies of the FCER brochure

In September 1980, Dr. Dintenfass sent a working draft of the proposal to Ellen Marks, conference director of the Academy, for a preliminary review. It received a favorable response from her. By the 15th of October, the planning committee of FCER unanimously approved the proposal.

The proposal was submitted to the New York Academy of Sciences on November 20, 1980. It was a request for the support of a conference on Spinal Manipulative Therapy, a five-year follow-up to the NINCDS Conferences. Scott emphasized the importance of holding this conference under the, "...guidelines and confines of a neutral organization with impeccable scientific reputation."[16] The conference dates were proposed for June 1982 along with a list of 38 participants and speakers. The FCER promised to support the conference in the amount of $100,000.

In spite of the excellent work of Scott and others from the Foundation, there was an unwillingness of many high profile individuals in the back pain world to commit to the conference, and the proposal was ultimately denied by the Academy—a disappointment to all.

Scott notified Dr. Dintenfass in April 1981 that the application had been denied. He suggested three alternatives: 1) shelve the project for five years and try again, 2) find another agency and resubmit, or 3)

---

[16] Haldeman, Scott., Conference Application to the New York Academy of Sciences on Spinal Manipulative Therapy, 1980, pg.7. Proposal is in the Haldeman Collection.

sponsor the conference through ACA. The project was permanently shelved by FCER.

CONGRESS OF CHIROPRACTIC STATE ASSOCIATIONS (COCSA)

An up-and-coming organization in the U.S. was the Congress of Chiropractic State Associations (COCSA). In a February 28, 1978 letter from Scott to Dr. Glen Hultgren, president of COCSA, he responded to a discussion they had the week previous in Denver regarding the problems of chiropractic research. Apparently the meeting in Denver was a COCSA planning meeting where they had decided to expend funds to establish a committee on research and education. Scott was serving on a COCSA committee tasked with preparing a report on research and education in the profession.

Scott recommended an intensive review of the, "...chiropractic literature, all literature which has been written inside and outside the profession on chiropractic, a tabulation of current post graduate programs and a projection for future requirements, a review of the role of other health professions and their encroachment on traditional chiropractic practice and recommendations on how this could be limited."[17] Scott then laid out what it would cost to do what he recommended and suggested that without that support they would end up with another report merely composed of the opinions of the members on the committee.

Scott then let loose with some personal frustration that probably had been growing within for some time:

> I am becoming increasingly concerned at the ease with which chiropractic leaders expect their academics to take off weekends, do extensive research, write long reports, pay their own research and secretarial costs, etc., without remuneration...The main reason for my tirade and concern was the dissatisfaction I discovered from John Triano at this meeting...This individual is extremely talented. He has an excellent brain, the willingness to do the necessary work

---

[17] Personal letter to Dr. Glen Hultgren from Scott dated February 28, 1978. Letter is in the Haldeman Collection.

and studies to become a top notch researcher and the opportunity to study and gain experience in a major university. Instead of gaining the support and encouragement of chiropractic leaders and academics, he is seriously considering leaving the academic field and going into practice...

Scott apologized at the end of his letter for the ranting but made a plea that the Congress would not take the report they were doing lightly and that some action may be taken.

INTERNATIONAL CHIROPRACTIC ASSOCIATION (ICA)

FACTS—FOUNDATION FOR THE ADVANCEMENT OF CHIROPRACTIC TENANTS AND SCIENCE

In the early days of his residency, Scott would lecture at license renewal programs sponsored by the International Chiropractic Association of California (ICAC). After a presentation in October 1977, Scott received a critique of his presentation from David Noles, DC. He advised Scott that he did not communicate well with his audience and presumed it was because Scott did not have much, if any, practice experience. He then complimented Scott on his efforts to organize an International Society dedicated to chiropractic research. He concluded by offering Scott a solution to the problems he faced by joining his practice in San Francisco. By doing so, Scott would get back in touch with patients and they would provide him a small office with a computer from which to manage his international research society.

It was a generous offer, and Scott thanked him for his thoughtfulness. However, Scott did point out to him that he had been in practice for the last twelve years as a chiropractor, ranging from seeing over 100 patients a day in Pretoria to a part-time evening practice in Vancouver. He further iterated that he continued to see patients in his residency training and that he fully intended to obtain his California chiropractic license and resume his clinical chiropractic practice in the near future.

In July 1977, Joe Mazzarelli, DC and president of the ICA, put out an appeal to all ICA members to contribute to the founding of FACTS.

In August 1979, another appeal for state societies and associations to support FACTS in the amount of $2000 by December 31, 1979, came from Dr. Mazzarelli. Scott's friend, Dr. Lou Sportelli, even encouraged his state association of Pennsylvania to join. Scott offered a criticism that both FACTS and FCER were too closely tied to national political organizations.

In the summer of 1978, Scott called upon the ICA to provide supportive documentation to the struggling chiropractors in South Africa. In 1981 Scott requested support from FACTS to travel to the International Society for the Study of the Lumbar Spine (ISSLS) meeting in Paris. He was chairing a "Symposium on Manipulation and Mobilization" and had a paper accepted, "The Electrodiagnostic Evaluation of Sacral Nerve Function." In May FACTS approved his request and issued a check for $1,344.00 for travel to the ISSLS meeting.

CALIFORNIA CHIROPRACTIC ASSOCIATION

Now that he was a resident of California, it was only natural for Scott to establish a relationship with the California Chiropractic Association (CCA). One of the first to interact with Scott was LeRoy Perry, DC, who invited Scott to speak at the upcoming 1979 CCA Convention: "Spinal Pain, Manipulative Therapy and Research – A Search for Answers." Scott proposed to describe the current confusion over spinal pain syndromes and the research that led to the confusion. He would also speak on the challenges facing spinal manipulation. The meeting was to be in beautiful Monterey, and Scott requested accommodations for two extra days so he could bring Joan and the kids (ages two and four). The CCA did not agree to pick up the costs for the two extra days so Scott came to the convention, gave his talk, and returned home to his family the same day. In the end, Scott received a $500 honorarium and a per diem reimbursement of $118.00—a modest extra expense for the association; however, they lost the opportunity to have Scott there to draw attendance and to interact with the other doctors for the rest of the convention. Fortunately for the CCA, Scott agreed to speak at their convention in San Diego again the following year, receiving the same honorarium.

Scott continued to interact with the CCA by accepting numerous invitations to speak at the local societies of the CCA such as the LA Metro Society, the LA Southwest Society, the Orange County Society, and the San Diego Society, usually in exchange for no more than a meal. Scott also accepted invitations to speak at graduations for the Los Angeles College of Chiropractic (LACC)[18], the Pasadena College of Chiropractic (PCC), and Cleveland College of Chiropractic (CCC-LA).

CHIROPRACTIC COLLEGES

Canadian Memorial Chiropractic College (CMCC)

The Canadian Memorial Chiropractic College (CMCC) was one of Scott's more regular supporters although consistency waivered. Scott never knew from year to year who would be supporting his research efforts or for how long. This dilemma of uncertainty was demonstrated in an October 1980 letter from his friend, Don Sutherland at CMCC, who had been giving Scott a $250 monthly stipend (plus $20 for secretarial help) since April, 1975.[19] In the letter, Sutherland apologized for CMCC's failure to uphold its commitment to provide Scott with his monthly retainer for April, May, June, and July. He included a check for $1000 to catch up. He then informed Scott that CMCC would no longer be able to continue the retainer due to budget restrictions.

Cleveland College of Chiropractic Los Angeles

In September 1978, Scott communicated with Dr. Carl Cleveland, president of the Cleveland Chiropractic College in Los Angeles,

---

[18] Dr. Haldeman was a speaker at the December, 1978 LACC Graduation and Congressman Corman of California was an honored guest. Personal communication with Dean Cummings, 8 Jan 1979. Letter in the Haldeman Files.

[19] Personal letter to Scott from Dr. Sutherland dated October 1980. Letter is in the Haldeman Collection.

[20] JP Bergeron, president of CCA, wrote to Scott on November 26, 1980 as Scott was in the last year of his residency, giving notice that the bursary arrangement that had been in place since 1976 had been "abrogated" but the new CCA president, Dr. Rick Elder, would be contacting him to work out a new and more clear arrangement about how Scott could help the CCA. Personal letter retained in the Haldeman Collection.

regarding a research consulting role for the college. His proposal was patterned after the CMCC model.[20] However, in this recommendation to Cleveland College, as well as similar requests to Los Angeles College of Chiropractic (LACC), National College of Chiropractic, and Logan College of Chiropractic, he asked for $6,000 per year rather than the $3,000 per year he was getting from CMCC. To his alma mater, Palmer College of Chiropractic, he proposed $12,000 per year support but also expanded his obligation there by being on campus more frequently and assisting with more than one research project per year.

In the proposal to each of the schools, he requested that he be made a full professor and that his consultant duties would consist of the following:

1. Listing Cleveland College (or other school) on his CV, and in return allowing that school to list him in their school catalog (this would help accreditation efforts with the Council on Chiropractic Education by improving the educational attainment of their faculty.)

2. Researching the medical, biological, and scientific literature and provide copies of 8-10 articles per month

3. Assisting the library in selection of books and journals

4. Giving a 2-3 hour evening lecture once a month on campus divided between the student body, grand rounds for clinical people, and focused discussion with faculty

5. Coordinating and supervising one research project in conjunction with a senior faculty member

6. Working to improve the image of the college

7. Assisting in the development of postgraduate courses

This proposal was not accepted by any of the colleges. Nevertheless, Scott continued to communicate with the local colleges and address the students on a voluntary basis whenever possible.

CORRESPONDENCE

Digest of Chiropractic Economics Correspondence

Part of Scott's life blood was his ability to publish primarily scientific papers and to share the message of the importance of research to all, especially his chiropractic colleagues. Scott made reference to his journal publications in his negotiations for his various consulting arrangements. A widely read chiropractic publication in the late 1970s, *The Digest of Chiropractic Economics* is an example of how this aspect of Scott's life was occupied.

Scott had submitted his article, "The Search For Research," to be published in the 1978 Jan/Feb issue of the *Digest*, but it was postponed to the Mar/Apr issue. In July 1978 he submitted an article on the formation of an International Society for the Advancement of Clinical Chiropractic and Spinal Research and an article on the upcoming Haldeman Research Conference in Anaheim. These were to be published in the Nov/Dec 1978 issue. In November Scott was informed that the *Digest* would publish his article on the upcoming Haldeman Conference first, and delayed his article on an International Society until the Jan/Feb 1979 issue. By this time Scott was experiencing frustration and feeling some regret. Apparently he continued to submit numerous articles to the *Digest* in an effort to reach the chiropractic profession but they were slow to respond and publish his work. In February 1979 the *Digest* told Scott that some of his articles were out of date and already widely circulated and, therefore, would not be published. They would, however, publish "The Clinical Basis for Discussion of Mechanisms of Manipulative Therapy," "Low Back Pain: A study of 50 Patients on a Group Exercise Program," and "A Comprehensive Approach to the Management of Spinal Disorders."

CORRESPONDENCE WITH INDIVIDUAL PRACTITIONERS

Lynton Giles DC, PhD

Lynton Giles, DC, and former student of Scott's while he was at CMCC, maintained communication with Scott even though he had settled in Australia. This link kept Scott informed about chiropractic happenings "down under" and kept Lynton tied to the research world.

In January 1978, Scott told Lynton that his work for the profession was overwhelming without secretarial support and he would be limiting his responses to the many inquiries he received. He thanked Lynton for a copy of the "Webb Report" on chiropractic in Australia and encouraged Lynton to join a chapter of the International Society Scott was organizing. Though Lynton had resigned from the Australian Association out of disgust for the low standards of education and patient care they supported as an organization, Scott encouraged him to work on improving the association from within.

Scott informed Lynton of the upcoming educational conference—the Anaheim conference that was the basis for the first book edited by Scott (See chapter 15)—supported by the ICA in February of 1979 and that multiple speakers were being invited. Lynton expressed a desire to attend. In August Lynton sent Scott $100 to be put towards his new book apologizing for not sending $200 but explaining his funds were limited because he was only practicing half days while working on his research at the university. Lynton did attend the Anaheim conference.

Scott acted as a valuable mentor to Lynton. In 1979 he reviewed Lynton's paper, "Low Back Pain Associated with Leg Length Inequality." Though complimentary of the paper, Scott was not afraid to critique the weaknesses that would surely keep it from getting published—this was an area of expertise for Scott which greatly benefited Lynton.

Eventually Lynton completed his master's and PhD degrees, in spite of some political opposition from the medical community, and went on to obtain a faculty position at a major university. He had several papers published in medical refereed journals and gained international respect for his work. Scott invited him to submit a paper for the research conference scheduled in Las Vegas but Lynton was diverted to South Africa to be with a sick brother. Their friendship has continued since these early exchanges.

G.W. McConnell, DC

G.W. McConnell, DC and chair of the British Columbia Chiropractic Association's (BCCA) Legislative Committee, included Scott on all general mailings to chiropractors in the province. Scott was someone they always wanted to introduce to various legal and legislative individuals. With his degrees, he was the mark of credibility for the chiropractors. Dr. McConnell was also very helpful to Scott in encouraging others to join the International Society on Chiropractic Post-Graduate Education and Spinal Research. He would pass out flyers and talk about the society with any gathering of chiropractors at every occasion. Scott learned in an October 1978 letter from Dr. McConnell that the BCCA waived his licensing dues as long as he was not in active practice in British Columbia and that the BCCA board had approved his upcoming research conference in Anaheim for six hours of license renewal credit.

Robert Anderson, PhD, DC, MD

Robert (Bob) Anderson was a PhD anthropologist from Mills College in Oakland, CA who took an interest in chiropractic initially for research purposes only but later for clinical skill development as well. Thus, unlike Scott, his clinical training came after his academic career was fully developed.

Bob first struck up communication with Scott in early 1979 while planning an extended trip to Europe. He asked Scott who he should see while in Europe and if Scott might even provide an introduction. All this was part of Bob's anthropological research work into the care of back pain. Scott sent Bob a program of the Federation of International Manual Medicine for names, and he suggested meeting Maigne in Paris, Stoddard in England, Lewit in Prague, and Kaltenborn in Norway.

Upon his return in July, Bob informed Scott that he met with Finn Christensen in Denmark, who remembered meeting Scott in South Africa when he was just 12 years old. Finn was the past president of the Danish Chiropractic Association and organizer of the short-lived Danish Chiropractic School. Bob also visited MDs and PTs who practiced manipulation in Denmark, Henry Gillet in Brussels, and Robert Maigne in Paris. He reported on his time in England at the Anglo-European College of Chiropractic (AECC.)

Scott was also helpful in critiquing some of Bob's research. In June of 1980, after some training at Pacific States Chiropractic College (PSCC) where he focused on adjusting of the upper cervical spine, Bob sent Scott a paper called, "Rotation at the Atlanto-Occipital Joint," which Scott reviewed and made several recommendations for improvement, stating it lacked statistical evaluation and the x-ray procedures were limited. Bob also sent Scott a National Upper Cervical Chiropractic Association Monograph titled, "Anthropometery and Spinal Biomechanics."

J. David Cassidy, DC, MS, PhD, DMed Sc

David Cassidy, CMCC graduate and a product of the College of Chiropractic Science program, spent time working with Dr. Kirkaldy-Willis in Saskatoon as part of his residency training. David eventually completed his PhD, Doctor of Medical Science, and held major research positions at the University of Saskatchewan, University of Alberta, and the University of Toronto. David served as scientific secretary of the Bone and Joint Decade Neck Pain Task Force that Scott chaired (see Chapter 15).

As Scott was in the leadership of the North American Academy of Manipulative Medicine (NAAMM), David wrote Scott in August 1978 asking for permission to attend their upcoming meeting to assist Dr. Kirkaldy-Willis who was presenting at the meeting. Scott informed David that NAAMM feared sanction from other medical groups and would not allow DCs to attend. He suggested David write Dr. Harold Swerdloof, who was president of NAAMM, and make a special request. Eventually, through the efforts of Scott and Dr. Kirkaldy-Willis, a few DCs were able to attend some of the NAAMM meetings, but only on a very limited basis.

In January 1979 David invited Scott to speak at the Western Canadian Chiropractic Convention to be held in Saskatoon and to also come to the hospital where David was working in the orthopedics department under Dr. Kirkaldy-Willis's supervision and speak to the residents. Scott would always extend his visits for the opportunity to meet and present beyond the actual conference he was attending. He especially enjoyed speaking to residents in both chiropractic and medicine.

In 1980 David applied for a grant for $26,000 from FCER to support his research and asked Scott to send a letter of support to the FCER board of trustees. Scott also wrote a letter of recommendation for David to become a member of the International Society for the Study of the Lumbar Spine (ISSLS). David did eventually become a member of ISSLS, thanks to Scott's influence and on his own personal merit.

Fred J. Gehl, DC – Florida Project

Scott had business opportunities to negotiate while in his residency as well. Dr. Fred Gehl, a chiropractor from Florida, approached Scott to join him in a venture in Naples on what was called the Remuda Ranch. Scott made it clear that he was in no position to invest financially, but Dr. Gehl was hoping to get Scott's name attached to the project to enhance credibility. Scott was invited to come see the property in the summer of 1978, but his obligations at the hospital prevented his ability to travel. There was no further information on this project, hence its probable demise, but the initial prospectus talked of the purchase of 4,143 acres of land east of Naples, Florida that included an existing resort and hotel. The unused portion of the land was to be used to build a multidisciplinary health center with a focus on wellness and nutrition. It was to provide a venue for chiropractors and medical doctors to work together as a team.

Jean-Paul Bergeron, DC, president of the Order of Chiropractic in Quebec

In October 1978 Jean-Paul informed Scott that the Quebec government had given a green light to form a committee to start a chiropractic program in a University in Quebec. He invited Scott to consider being nominated as the first dean of the program slated to begin in the fall of 1980, just after Scott would finish his residency program.

Scott appreciated the invitation but declined on the basis that he was too young to step away from his career in writing and research and go into administration.

Jean-Paul asked for more information on Scott's involvement with the New Zealand Inquiry on Chiropractic and Scott responded that he had been sending leading articles on the spine to the Canadian Chiropractic Association (CCA) every three weeks for many years and assumed they were being circulated. Scott said he would like to send material to the entire CCA Executive Committee but his support from the CCA had not changed in five years and due to inflation the stipend he was now receiving was worth about half of what it was when he started. Scott explained that the amount of material on the spine was growing quite fast and it was hard to keep up. If he didn't get some support, his report to the New Zealand Commission may be the last report he did for chiropractic. Scott had been conducting a course on spinal neurology for chiropractors as a means for supporting his work for chiropractic and offered to bring the course to Quebec if they could get 100 doctors to sign on for the program. The program never happened.

In September 1980 Jean-Paul reviewed Scott's financial dealings with the CCA, a $400 per month stipend since 1976[21] to assist him in the pursuit of his PhD and his MD degrees. Now the pursuit of degrees was over, Jean-Paul asked Scott what his needs would be in the future. Scott again explained the support from the CCA was never used to pay for his education but the money went towards his many and varied activities related to research and politics in chiropractic and hoped the CCA would continue to see the value of what he had done and continue their support. The CCA continued to provide some support for Scott though amounts fluctuated and consistency of payment varied.

---

[21] Amounts and length of time seem to vary depending on who is reporting on the situation.

ENDNOTE

The following is a lengthy document that shows Scott's continued commitment to chiropractic in South Africa (and chiropractic in general).

CRITIQUE AND DISCUSSION OF A SOUTH AFRICAN PROPOSAL TO THE GOVERNMENT

In addition to all that Scott was doing, he never lost touch with his ties in South Africa. He was asked to do a critique of a document the Chiropractic Association of South Africa (CASA) was planning to submit to the government in an attempt to overthrow a bill that had been passed limiting the licensing of DCs in South Africa. Scott's critique of the document has been added as an endnote to this chapter.[i]

---

[i] MEMORANDUM BY THE CHIROPRACTIC ASSOCIATION OF SOUTH AFRICA TO THE MINISTER OF HEALTH, GOVERNMENT OF SOUTH AFRICA

By Scott Haldeman, D.C., Ph.D., M.D.
May 15, 1978

I received the draft of the memorandum under discussion on May 2, 1978 and have read the manuscript in some depth. The following comments are personal opinions on the draft as it stands and on how I believe it can be improved.

In compiling a memorandum of this type the following points should be kept in mind at all times:

Point #1: The reason for submitting the memorandum. This must be clear in the mind of the individuals who compose the draft, it must be repeated often and it must be absolutely clear in the mind of the individual who reads the draft. It must be obvious from the first page to the last. Any material or argument which does not address the primary concern of the memorandum is superfluous.

Point #2: The individuals to whom the memorandum is being addressed. An argument must be presented in such a way that the individuals who read it are not antagonized. They must be able to associate with or become sympathetic to the positions taken in the memorandum. Any position or opinion the individuals who will read the memorandum might have by training or position must be respected. To include criticism of any group they belong to is to create a hostile audience.

Point #3: A memorandum of this type must be readable, it must flow from one topic to the other with smooth argument, it must be complete but not so lengthy as to make it an effort to review. It is possible to add any supportive material as addenda which can be read by those individuals who require further information.

General Comments on the First Draft

1) Reading through the draft, it is not too clear why it is being submitted. This should be the major point on the first page after identification of the body which is submitting the memorandum. The remainder of the memorandum should be an argument addressing this point and the last section should detail step by step what you wish the minister to do. As it now stands, the minister would have to guess at the nature of your request.

2) There are too many widely differing methods of writing. This makes it difficult to follow the arguments. There is a fair amount of repetition of the same points under differing headings. It does not read smoothly.

3) It is too long and verbose. There is too much flowery material which is difficult to follow and which does not add to the argument. I believe that a draft of this type should not exceed 50-60 pages. It can be accompanied by 200-300 pages of supporting information in the form of addenda if you so wish.

4) As a politician or bureaucrat I would be considering the licensure of South African chiropractors, not Dr. Janse, Dr. Illi, Dr. Haldeman, etc. I would want to know where South African chiropractors stand, what their opinion was of the evolution of chiropractic, the definition and scope of chiropractic, etc. I would want to see whether they were knowledgeable about the scientific and research aspect of chiropractic.

I believe that this draft does not demonstrate these points to the Minister of Health and his department. I believe that there should be much less material by foreign chiropractors and much more written by South African chiropractors using language and material which has meaning to South African politicians.

Specific Comments

1) Index: This is well thought out and contains most areas which should be covered. I believe that you should add a section on "Current Status of Chiropractic in South Africa" to include numbers of chiropractors, distribution of chiropractors, where they were educated, number with non-chiropractic degrees, etc. If I was a politician in South Africa, I would want to know this information.

2) Introduction: Write out C.A.S.A. in full. No indication of why you are presenting the draft.

Point I: is a very dangerous and unnecessary point. Why admit that others can manipulate on the first page.

Point II: Meaningless to non-chiropractor.

Point III: Good points but in wrong place in draft.

3) Evolution of Manipulation and Evolution of chiropractic

I believe that these two sections can be combined into a single very much shortened section. As it now stands these two sections take a great deal of time and effort to read and do not give much of a reason to open the chiropractic act.

Dr. Janse's history of chiropractic is well written and accurate but very verbose. The flowery language he uses is excellent for an essay or speech, but it is impossible to dig the facts out from under all the words. This is not a criticism of Dr. Janse. I believe that this section should be rewritten in point form by the same person who rewrites the draft. Dr. Janse's paper can be used as reference and included in full as an addendum.

Page 5 – NINCDS – should be written out in full.
Lancet – what issue? What year?
Page 6 – Dr. Tower, director of NINCDS –in full.

There is too much quoting of medical sources and not enough quoting of chiropractic sources. Having read the text I am still unsure how, step by step, chiropractic originated, evolved, and where it stands today. This is what I would want to know as a bureaucrat or politician.

Bibliography should be included as addendum, not supplied on demand.

The history of chiropractic written by Dr. Janse, in my opinion, has too much emotion and not enough facts. It contains unnecessary attacks on medicine which may antagonize the Minister of Health and his staff. His constant use of the word "we" suggests that he speaks for the entire profession. As a South African politician, I would be concerned that an American was allowed to use the first person in an official memorandum. The only valid "we" in the draft is from the Council of CASA which may speak for CASA members.

4) History of Chiropractic in South Africa

This part of the memorandum is the best written and most informative part of the entire draft.

There is one theme in this section I would deemphasize. That is either ignore the fact that there ever were two chiropractic groups, or, if you feel it is necessary to mention it, eliminate all mention of "ideological differences," "divided profession," etc. It serves no purpose to reiterate chiropractic weaknesses and it can give the minister an opening to attack old wounds. It is necessary to present a position which suggests that chiropractors have always been honorable, always respected each other and always acted in a professional manner.

5) I would follow this section with a heading titled "Current Status of Chiropractic in South Africa" with the points I mentioned at the beginning of this critique.

6) History of past legislation

This is somewhat repetitive of material presented under History of Chiropractic in South Africa. The two sections could be combined or maintained separated without the repetition.

7) Chiropractic Education Today

This section is essential. Again it is too difficult to select the facts from the emotional part of this section. There is too much introversion in this section which demonstrates chiropractic paranoia and makes one wonder if they can be trusted to act in a rational rather than emotional manner.

Example: Why say (page 47) "Deliberately exacting and, at time, painfully..." this is unnecessary and clouds the issue. This can be significantly shortened to include the essential facts that the Minister must know to make a decision.

8) Chiropractic Schools

This is much more relevant material. The accrediting procedure, requirements, curriculum, recognized colleges, continuing education, etc. is very important material. These points, however, only address the American methods of accreditation. I believe that comments should be made on the Canadian, Swiss, Scandinavian, and Australian rules regarding accreditation as well.

The first paragraph ignores those colleges which do not have C.C.E. accreditation. The figures are far more impressive and valid if the entire chiropractic student population is used.

9) Australian Assessment

I believe that the comments of Dr. Webb are very relevant. However, I would reverse the order in which Palmer and National are discussed. His comments on National College are far more complimentary than on Palmer. This should be the first section to be read under this heading. Many readers will skip the evaluation of Palmer having read about National.

10) Institutional Recognition

Excellent material to support your argument. I would mention the college names which were recognized under each section.

11) Research and Development

Another important area presented. You again have failed to present all the facts. In addition to FCER there is FACTS and the Canadian and Australian Research Foundations who are collecting funds for research. This would also be a place to mention the Colorado Project and the combined medical-chiropractic research programs at the Universities of Saskatchewan and Toronto.

12) Comparative Costs

Should be under a separate heading which tries to justify a role for the chiropractor in our society. It is an important part of the presentation and brings up an entirely separate argument in favour [sic] of chiropractic.

13) Repeat Social Studies

You should be able to do much more with the Utah Study. It presents an important argument in favour [sic] of chiropractic which you miss, i.e. patient satisfaction.

Where did page(s) 78-87 come from? This is material for addenda only. You may wish to break down the faculty as to numbers with PhD, MS, BS, etc. in the memorandum.

14) Definition and Scope of Practice.

As usual when chiropractors discuss this topic, it is long winded and meaningless. Having read these ten pages, I still don't have a clue what chiropractors in South Africa consider themselves to be or what they consider their scope of practice. This section alone is enough to disqualify the brief for serious consideration. You mention what the Swiss chiropractors, Janse, Mennel, Cyriax, etc. think of chiropractic or manipulation is but not what you think it is. The Minister will be licensing you, not Mennel or Janse. Tell him what your opinion is and do so scientifically. You may wish to justify positions you take by quoting sources but the position must be yours.

Page 92 contains mostly speculation which is probably false and again confirms that chiropractors deal in ideology and speculation rather than fact.

Page 96 – This is pure bull. The conference had nothing whatsoever to do with the changing of the title of NINDS to NINCDS.

15) Conditions Amenable to Chiropractic Care

Very important and well presented. It is unimportant if I or anyone else disagrees, at least you have presented your views for consideration.

16) The Chiropractic Subluxation

I would change this title to 'The Specific Effects of Manipulation on the Spine." Again there is too much verbiage. You are not writing an article on the various opinions of a subluxations but instead trying to present an argument in favour [sic] of relicensing chiropractic. This section should simply show that you know what you are doing when you give an adjustment.

Much of the argument you present is confusing and conflicting. You use repeated quotes of people who are unknown to most scientists and physicians without giving references. The graph on page 108 is meaningless to me. I do not know what the Minister will think of it.

17) Neuropathological Reflexes

This is poorly written and assumes considerably more than is known. It should be completely rewritten or scrapped. Who cares what Mennel "thinks." He has not demonstrated that he can influence somato-visceral reflexes. Forget about Speransky. He is not a well known or respected researcher outside of chiropractic. Quoting his opinion as gospel does no more than demonstrate that chiropractors read only those texts which agree with their original premise.

18) Hostility of Organized Medicine

Why end on a completely negative note and convince the Minister that you are unable to work with other health professions? A large number of bureaucrats who will be reading this memorandum are medical doctors or medically indoctrinated. Why antagonize and ridicule the people you are asking for help? This section should be scrapped with the exception of the last two pages.

Your best argument in the entire memorandum i.e. "the need for more health practitioners in South Africa" is poorly written and tacked on to the worst section of the memorandum, thus ensuring that it is ineffective.

Recommendation

1) A committee of not more than three individuals be drawn up to rewrite the memorandum from page 1 till the end with uniform language and with a constant theme.

2) The basic headings be kept as is with changes to fit the argument.

3) That the reason for the memorandum be clearly expressed in the introduction.

4) That a concluding section include specific recommendations to the Minister of Health.

5) That the memorandum not exceed 80 pages in length and may be as short as 50 pages.

6) That there be a large number of supporting references, texts, articles, etc. as addenda. These should be properly indexed to support arguments presented in the memorandum.

7) At all times remember who and to whom you are presenting the memorandum

SECTION II

BALANCING FAMILY, TRAVEL, CLINICAL PRACTICE, AND PROFESSIONAL LIFE

Chapter 9

Establishing a Neurology Identity
The VA Fellowship, Research, and Practice
1980–1984

THE TRANSITION BETWEEN RESIDENCY
AND PRACTICE

The completion of Scott's neurology residency program at UCI in June 1980 was a pivotal time in determining the future direction of his career. He was faced with several professional opportunities that demanded a decision. He had the option of looking for further adventures, accepting a full-time teaching position at a university, seeking a full-time research position, opening a private practice to make a good living, accepting a senior position at a chiropractic college, or starting an enterprise to advance education within the chiropractic profession.

Scott inquired about a position in the Faculty of Medicine at King Faisal University in Saudi Arabia in June 1979. In response, the university informed him that the school only opened its doors in 1975 and students were just beginning their clinical rounds. This meant that there would be only undergraduate teaching with no possibilities for research. While a tempting adventure, it was not a good option for his career.

He had been approached to consider the presidency of a chiropractic college and could have demanded the position of research director of the chiropractic college of his choice. Scott knew a chiropractic college setting would be unable to support the research he had been trained to do and probably would have been a "dead end" selection for his career.

Scott had received gracious offers from both the University of British Columbia and UC Irvine to fill a full-time faculty position in the neurology departments of these institutions. Vancouver was a consideration as they had great friends there and the school was very interested in getting him on their faculty. UCI eventually did become part of his future but not as a full time faculty member.

He also had the option to enter into full-time clinical practice. Kevin Connolly was chief resident when Scott was a first year resident at UCI and had subsequently set up practice in Fresno, California. His practice was growing very fast, and he wanted Scott to join him. Joan and Scott looked over the practice in October 1979 while Scott was there on a speaking assignment; however, there would have been no opportunity to participate in any meaningful research if he took that position.

In the last year of Scott's residency an opportunity arose that would allow him to further advance his education and qualifications, be productive in an area of research in which he had a major interest, and start considering private practice while remaining in Southern California. Bill Bradley, MD, the world's leading neurologist in the field of neuro-urology, had just accepted the position of chief of the neurology department at Long Beach Veterans Affairs Medical Center (VAMC). He had more than 200 scientific papers in this field of study when he moved to the Long Beach VA Medical Center. He had set up a laboratory there and needed a fellow who was interested in neuro-visceral disorders and had experience in neurophysiology. This was an opportunity Scott had prepared for before the opportunity even existed.

The VA Medical Center also had a large and productive electro-diagnosis and electroencephalography department, and Scott could obtain all the credits he needed to be eligible for the three electrodiagnostic boards if he became a fellow at the VA Medical Center for two years. Furthermore, he was able to start a practice in the evenings while doing the fellowship during the day. Scott could continue to travel and participate in the chiropractic and spine society activities and make a reasonable living, provided he and Joan were willing to work about sixteen hours a day. Joan, always a willing partner in his many adventures, now had two growing boys underfoot and a nice home to enjoy, so she agreed to stay put in Southern California.

THE FELLOWSHIP AT THE VA MEDICAL CENTER

Scott recalls one of the first times he met Dr. Bradley. He was doing patient rounds as the chief resident in neurology. On completion of rounds, Dr. Bradley asked how many patients had symptoms of bowel, bladder, or sexual dysfunction. The residents reported that some of the patients had urinary catheters and were constipated, but they had not asked them about any sexual function or considered these symptoms serious. On subsequent rounds it became evident that almost all the neurology patients complained of bowel, bladder, and/or sexual problems, but for the most part, these symptoms were not considered of major importance by the residents. When asked further, many of the patients stated that these symptoms were having a greater impact on their life than the classic neurological problems of paralysis, tremor, gait disturbances, or seizures.

Dr. Bradley and Scott began to discuss what research could be carried out to help these patients. Bradley was looking for a fellow who had experience as a neurophysiologist and who had an interest in neuro-urology. Scott had spent some time studying the literature on neurovisceral control mechanisms and was hoping to do research to determine whether spinal disorders could influence the function of the internal organs. There was a strong synergism between Scott's goals and the research interest and experience of Dr. Bill Bradley, who arranged a small fellowship grant of $2,000 a month for a full-time position. Scott accepted the offer in July 1980. The work that ensued over the next two years, Bradley and Haldeman working together, was very progressive and fruitful. (For a more technical explanation of the research, see endnote.)

Upon completion of the two years of full-time fellowship, Scott continued with a part-time (50%) position at the VA for an additional three years so that he could complete his research which resulted in sixteen scientific papers and established Scott as one of the authorities in the field. He was asked to lecture at major neurology meetings including the American Academy of Neurology, and to write chapters on the topic in a number of books about electrodiagnosis. In 1993 he was asked to serve as facilitator of a guidelines document for the Therapeutics and Technology Assessment Subcommittee of the Academy titled, "The Neurological Evaluation of Male Sexual Dysfunction."

CLINICAL PRACTICE

In 1981, while still completing his fellowship at the VA, Scott decided that it was time for him to begin earning an income that was more than subsistence. He also missed private practice, although he had been involved with patient care throughout his residency and fellowship. By chance he met Dr. Robboy, an orthopedic surgeon who had just opened an office in Lakewood, California, not far from the VA. Dr. Stanley Robboy's practice focused on the treatment and evaluation of injured workers, and he was looking for a part time neurologist to join him. This suited Scott's schedule, as he was committed at the VA. Scott decided to see patients between 5:00 p.m. and 10:00 p.m., three nights a week. Since he did not have any staff, Joan agreed to come into the office and take over the required patient, staff, and administrative duties. Upon completion of his fellowship, Scott continued to commute to the Lakewood office for about ten years on a part-time basis two afternoons a week in order to serve the referral sources and patients that he had committed to during this period.

When Scott decreased his commitment at the VA to part-time (50%) he decided to open an office doing general neurology in Santa Ana, close to his home and the UC Irvine Medical Center. He started by sharing an office with Dr. David Lombardi, a neurologist who had just opened a practice. Joan again took on the responsibility of setting up the office. It soon became evident that Scott's practice was outgrowing the limited space available, so he and Joan opened their own office in the same medical complex.

Neurology and Electrodiagnosis Boards and Qualifications

As a Fellow in a neurology program, Scott hoped to affiliate with the major neurological associations, to complete the requirements for the major neurology board examinations, and to establish his credentials as a scientist within the field of neurology.

By this stage in Scott's life he had already been named a Fellow of the College of Chiropractic Sciences FCCS (C) in Canada. Upon completion of his residency in neurology, he would also be qualified to become a board certified neurologist and a Fellow of the Royal College of Physicians of Canada. All he had to do was pass the American and Canadian National Neurology Board examinations. At age 37, his life was scheduled to the max.

In 1980-81, Scott had a full-time research job at the VA Hospital in Long Beach, he was publishing multiple articles, setting up a private practice, and editing the first edition of *The Principles and Practice of Chiropractic* textbook (Chapter 15). He had two very young children at home and was traveling and lecturing extensively. He needed to pass exams to qualify in the fields of neurology and electrodiagnosis. In a two-year period, Scott ended up taking eight medical board examinations for five different qualifications:

- FRCP(C): Fellow of the Royal College of Physicians (Canada), 1981 (Part I: written, Part II: oral)

- Diplomate: American Board of Psychiatry & Neurology, 1982 (Part I: written, Part II: oral)

- Diplomate: American Board of Electroencephalography and Neurophysiology, 1981 (oral and written at the same time)

- Diplomate: American Board of Clinical Neurophysiology, Inc. (previously the ABQEEG), 1983 (Part I: written, Part II: oral)

- Diplomate: American Board of Electrodiagnostic Medicine, 1982 (written and oral at the same sitting)

Scott passed all these examinations on the first sitting with the exception of the American Board of Qualification in Electroencephalography (ABQEEG) which he had to retake. He retook Part I in November 1982 in Phoenix. He received a letter in November 1982 informing him that he had failed two sections of Part II, Technical Discussion and Interpretation II. Scott recalls, "...being in the oral exam and contravening one of my rules on examinations, I got into an argument with one of the examiners. We were discussing synaptic theory and I felt that he was wrong. I had done my PhD on the topic and made the mistake of arguing with the examiner." Scott felt this indiscretion was partly responsible for the failure on one of the two sections of this board examination.[1]

Scott did pass Part II the next time around.[2] He recalled the ABQEEG as being the most advanced scientific examination on EEG given and admitted that he probably had not studied adequately the first time around. He was also studying for six other board examinations—the neurology boards and the Royal College of Physicians board exams—and considered those to be the most important use of his time.

PROFESSIONAL ASSOCIATION MEMBERSHIPS

With qualifying exams behind him, Scott now was eligible (actually invited in some cases) to become a member of various professional organizations associated with his field of neurology and electrodiagnosis. He has retained membership in some of these organizations, while allowing others to lapse as his life has taken on new and different dimensions.

The following is an alphabetically arranged list of organizations Scott joined or was a member of during his residency and/or his fellowship at the VAMC (1977 to 1984):

[1] Personal communication with Scott Haldeman, January 2009.
[1] Personal letters to Scott from Dr. Erwin dated 16 November 1982 and 22 February 1983. Letters are in the Haldeman Collection.

American Academy of Neurology

1977   Junior Member
1980   Member
1985   Fellow of the Academy

American Association of Electromyography and Electrodiagnostic Medicine

1982-   Member
2004   Emeritus Member

American Back Society

1984   Founding Fellow
1984   Chair, Committee of Manipulative Medicine
1984   Council of Advisors
2003   President

American Chiropractic Association

1976   Member
1978   ACA Consultant on Research

American Chiropractic Association – Council on Neurology

1972   Research Committee
1983   Member
1988   Board of Directors

American Medical Electroencephalographic Association

1982   Member

Association for the History of Chiropractic

1981   Member

Back Pain Monitor Newsletter

1984   Conference Advisory Board
1983-89 Editorial Advisory Board

British Columbia Chiropractic Association – Committee on Continuing Education

1975-76 Chair

Canadian Foundation for Spinal Research (CFSR)

1980-   Advisory Board

Canadian Memorial Chiropractic College

1978   Postgraduate Faculty

Chiropractic Research Commission (ACA)

1978   Consultant to the Commission

Chiropractic Research Consortium (CRC-FCER)

1980-

College of Chiropractic Sciences (Canada)
    1976-77 Advisor
    1988   Member/fellow
Foundation for the Advancement of Chiropractic Research (Toftness)
    1979-   Consultant
Foundation for Chiropractic Education and Research
    1979   Consultant
International Chiropractic Association
    1963   Student Advisory Board Member
    1971   Member
    1985   Inter-professional Relations Advisory Committee
    1983   Editorial Advisory Board
    1988   Membership Reinstated
International Society for the Study of the Lumbar Spine (ISSLS)
    1979   Member
    1984-   Scientific Program Committee
    1983-   Membership Committee/Chair
    1992   Western US Representative to Board
Journal of Manipulative and Physiological Therapeutics.
    1979   Editorial Board
Journal of the Australian Chiropractic Association
    1983   Editorial Board
Journal of the Canadian Chiropractic Association
    1985   Editorial Board
Kentuckiana Children's Center
    1980   National Advisory Board
Los Angeles College of Chiropractic
    1979   Postgraduate Faculty
Manual Medicine
    1984   Editorial Board
Mississippi Association of Chiropractors
    1980   Committee on Research
National Back Foundation
    1982   National Advisory Committee
National Board of Physical Therapy Examiners
    1981   Board Member
North American Academy of Manipulative Medicine (NAAMM)

1975   Member and councilor
1980   Newsletter editor
1981-82 President Elect
1983   President
1987   Society Coordination Committee
1990   Conservative Care Fellowship Committee

North American Spine Society
1984-86 Executive Council
1987   Vice-President and President-Elect
1988-89 President
1989   Parliamentarian

Orange County Medical Society
1982   Member

Orange County Neurological Society
1982-   Member
1988   President

Orange County Pain Society
1984-   Member

Royal College of Physicians and Surgeons of Canada
1982   Member/fellow

Saint Joseph Hospital
1982-   Medical Staff

Second Opinion Associates/Health Data Inc.
1983   Consultant

UC Irvine Coordinating Committee on the Manipulation Project
1978-79 Member

UC Irvine Medical Center
1979   Chief Resident – Dept Neurology
1985-   Medical Staff

UC Irvine, University Physicians and Surgeons
1977-   Medical Staff

Veterans Hospital Long Beach
1981-   Attending Physician, Neurology

Western Medical Center
1981-   Medical Staff

Western States Chiropractic College
1980   Postgraduate Faculty
1981   Honorary Doctorate Degree

More detailed discussion regarding membership activities is contained in Chapter 14.

THE HALDEMAN INTER-PROFESSIONAL CONFERENCES ON THE SPINE

In 1979 Scott organized a very successful conference in Anaheim, CA, hosted by the International Chiropractors Association. This was the first inter-disciplinary scientific conference organized by the chiropractic profession. It resulted in a textbook, *Modern Developments in the Principles and Practice of Chiropractic.* (See Chapter 15 for details).

A second major scientific conference was planned for October 3-5, 1980 at the Dunes Hotel in Las Vegas. The conference did net a weak but positive balance sheet and encouraged Joan and Scott to fund a third conference. The third conference was held in Los Angeles with institutional but not financial support from the Cleveland College of Chiropractic. The conference was not financially viable and a fourth conference already planned for St. Louis in 1982 was cancelled along with plans for any future conferences. (See Chapter 15 for a more detailed account.)

While efforts to establish a research society and sponsor research conferences in chiropractic were faltering, there were endless opportunities in medicine to teach, do research, become an administrator, or practice; therefore, Scott decided to pursue a career as a medical neurologist. This would allow him to experience the patient care that he loved so much, to create and develop the concept of a multidisciplinary approach in the world of spine care, and to retain the independence that would allow him to pursue his interests in research, lecturing, writing, and essentially mold the future direction of spine care for all the health professions.

ANCILLARY ACTIVITIES

The model of leading, guiding, and helping others interested in the paths that Scott took resulted in his continued efforts to encourage others to follow their dreams and pursue their opportunities.

Consulting for the American Chiropractic Association

While Scott never planned on becoming a media personality, his accomplishments made him a natural draw for interviewers. (Segments of Scott being interviewed on a variety of shows can be found on the DVD accompanying this book.)

As a district governor for the American Chiropractic Association, Dr. Louis Sportelli was often in front of a camera or behind a microphone speaking for the profession. In December of 1981, he, along with Stephen Barrett, MD, and Reuben Hoppenstein, MD, taped an interview for the David Susskind Show. Following the Susskind show, Lou and Scott exchanged a series of letters over the summer of 1982 dealing with such topics as malpractice as a result of a stroke, appearances on TV programs such as *60 Minutes,* the *ACA Journal's* need for abstracts, and false advertising by the Academy of Straight Chiropractic. No mention was made of Scott not belonging to the ACA until late 1982. Responding to Sportelli's inquiry as to why Scott did not belong, he wrote:

> Regarding ACA application, I was an associate member of ACA while in Canada for many years, and when I came to California I requested continuation of that status. This amounted to yearly dues of approximately $20.00. It gave me access to the journals and other information. I was told at that time that I was not eligible for any membership in the ACA. It is not, however, possible for me to afford the $320.00 annual membership. I am a member of just too many organizations to allow me to pay full dues in the ACA. I, therefore, do not know what class of membership I would be eligible for. It notes in the application for membership that I am registered or licensed to practice in this state. I cannot sign an application form which requires this since I am not licensed in California [as a chiropractor]. I am possibly being unjustified in my concern about membership in ACA and decided a while back it was probably my pride that was hurt when ACA rejected membership rather than a realistic expectation of membership. The ICA has kept me as a full member for the last ten years without dues, as have the Canadian and South African associations.[3]

[3] Letter from Scott to Dr. Sportelli dated 17 January 1983. Letter is in the Haldeman Collection.

Dr. Sportelli obtained a membership for Scott in the ACA in April of 1983.

Scott was invited by Dr. Sportelli, then chairman of the Board of Governors of the ACA, to participate in an ACA Think Tank in August 1989. Twenty-four participants met in Chicago and attempted to identify key areas where chiropractic should make improvements, create a mission statement, discuss standards of care, and work on solutions for marketing chiropractic services. This material was to assist the ACA in its long-range strategic planning.

Consulting for the Canadian Chiropractic Research Foundation (CRSF), Foundation for Chiropractic Education and Research (FCER) & The World Federation of Chiropractic (WFC)

For many years and to this day, Scott reviews research proposals and papers submitted to the Canadian Spinal Research Foundation, the Foundation for Chiropractic Education and Research, and the World Federation of Chiropractic. His reviews evaluate the scientific merit of each proposal or paper which assists these organizations in funding decisions and program presentations.

CORRESPONDENCE

Michael H. Turner, DC, Redwood City, CA

Michael's letter to Scott is an example of many he received from chiropractors wondering if they should pursue an MD degree. Because Scott took such pains to address Dr. Turner's request in his May 12, 1981 response, this is used as an example of many similar responses:

I will try to answer your questions briefly.

1) I do feel that it is productive for a chiropractor to obtain a medical degree. The combination opens many doors and greatly enlarges one's vision concerning patient care. The access to facilities and expertise that the medical degree permits is a very valuable privilege.

2) I know of no medical school which accepts chiropractic qualifi-

cations for credit. This may vary from institution to institution. You would have to approach each one individually to get an accurate answer.

3) Be careful of foreign medical schools. There is a strong move afoot at both the state and national levels to prevent licensure of physicians who have graduated from one of the Mexican or Island medical schools that have been established specifically to train U.S. students. You could find yourself in the position of spending 3-4 years in school and not having a recognized degree at the end.

4) My basic advice is that you have to make the choice on life's priorities. I have never regretted my extra education and have found the long hours and lost income to be minor payment for the rewards of higher education.[4]

CONCLUSION

Scott provided sage advice to young chiropractors debating to pursue an MD degree after completing their chiropractic training. Using his words, "...you have to make the choice on life's priorities." Scott also faced some very serious decisions regarding his future direction in life—teaching, research, clinical practice, neurology, or chiropractic. From an economic perspective, the direction was clear but from the sentiments of the heart, following that direction was not an easy choice.

[4] Letters to and from Michael Turner, DC, from May 1981 are found in the Haldeman Collection.

ENDNOTE
The first research question was whether there was any means of recording the integrity of the neural pathways to the pelvic organs and whether abnormalities in these pathways could be documented. The initial studies consisted of stimulating the pudendal nerves in normal male and female subjects and recording responses from the brain. Scott and Bill were the first volunteers, and it became evident that pudendal somatosensory evoked responses could be recorded from scalp electrodes. They also noted that they could record bulbocavernosis reflex responses from the pudendal nerve to the anal sphincter muscles. The combination of these tests allowed for the determination of whether an abnormality in the neural pathways to and from the pelvic organs was in the peripheral nerve or due to lesions higher up in the

(continued on next page)

spinal cord or brain. Their initial publications in the neurological literature were on normal individuals, and were greeted by some of the reviewers as "brave" studies.

Scott then began studying these evoked responses in patients with spinal cord injuries, patients with peripheral neuropathies, patients with multiple sclerosis, and patients with brain disorders such as stroke or Parkinson's disease. It became evident that these tests did have the ability to differentiate between different causes of neurogenic bowel, bladder, and/or sexual disorders.

The third area of study was to look at the impact of neural lesions on the function of the visceral organs. Bill Bradley demonstrated to Scott the importance of cystometry where water or air were infused into the bladder and the volume and contractions of the bladder could be measured. These contractions are under the control of the nervous system, and abnormalities in neural control would change the nature of these contractions. Scott then collaborated with Michael Glick, MD, a fellow in gastroenterology, to conduct similar studies that had not seriously been considered in the past on the distal colon. They also measured colon muscle wall potentials in patients with different diagnoses. Finally, Bill Bradley had received a contract to study the possibility of screening for nocturnal penile tumescence using a Rigiscan device in patients with symptoms of impotence that needed to be scientifically validated.

Chapter 10

The Inside Story
By *Joan Haldeman*

Scott's mother, Wyn Haldeman, was always balancing the needs of family life with the huge demands of the adventures she shared with his maverick father, Josh. Many times, before and after our marriage, I heard her say with either a sigh or a chuckle, as she constantly multi-tasked, "Well, I may wear out, but I sure as heck won't rust out!" Likewise there have been no "rust-stops" on my life's journey with Scott, and her words have often echoed in my mind.

SOUTH AFRICA

Scott and I were part of a close-knit circle of friends, which formed early in our first year at Clapham High School in Pretoria, South Africa. The group was in the same class throughout the five years of high school. We stayed on for sports and other after-school activities in the afternoons, and organized social events together on weekends and school holidays. He and I "went steady" the last two years of high school, and after graduation survived a LONG three-year separation from 1962-1964 when he went to Palmer Chiropractic College in Davenport, Iowa, and I studied at the University of Pretoria, Physiotherapy College. This period was a test of our relationship, which nobody except ourselves thought we would pass. South Africa and the USA seemed extremely far apart in those years before affordable telephone calls and airfares or e-mail was available. There wasn't even a direct international telephone connection, and placing a "trunk call" was costly and required coordination and patience. International calls to and from South Africa had to go through three telephone exchanges—Cape Town, London, and New York. One had to wait on the line for one exchange to connect with the other, and then for the connection to be made at the required number. All the while the meter was ticking at $30.00 for the first three minutes and $16.00 per minute after that. We were students on tight budgets. Scott called once in the three years—the most exciting, memorable phone call I've ever had! We wrote to each other twice a week, filling two blue air letters every week of the 156 weeks that he was away. He arrived home at the end of December 1964. We were engaged on February 19th, 1965, and married on November 27th of the same year.

I brought the conventional element to our marriage. My sister Joy, my brother Leslie, and I were raised in a home where family life was governed by rigid routines and conservative values. Any hint of non-conforming was met with instant disapproval and discipline, especially from my father, who had been raised the same way. It is

Josh & Wyn Haldeman, Robert DuPreez, Gavin Nettleton, Billy McIntosh, Don Williams, Scott & Joan Haldeman, Joy Surridge, Lynne Haldeman, Kaye Haldeman, Maye Haldeman, Charlotte& Mervyn Surridge   Front row: Lee Haldeman, Leslie Surridge

a little surprising that his father, Alfred James Surridge, became so conventional after his rebellious behavior at the age of 14, when he ran away from his home in England. Managing to pass himself off as a 16-year old, he joined the British Army and went to South Africa to fight in the Boer War. He stayed on in South Africa after the war and married my jolly, but equally conservative grandmother, Constance Doherty Keightley.

My maternal grandmother and mother, my role models for as long as I can remember, were strong ladies who dealt with adverse situations that arose in their lives with grace and courage. My maternal grandparents were born in South Africa, but my grandfather, Alfred Charles Moorcroft, came from a British family and my grandmother, Maria Charlotta de Wet, was Dutch. The Boers fought a guerilla war, and in order to cut off food and supplies to the soldiers, the British had imprisoned the Afrikaans women and children under horrific conditions in camps. My grandmother and her family were among those who suffered in one of the camps. After the Boer War, the hatred between the English and Afrikaans (Dutch) ran extremely deep, and my great grandmother Moorcroft objected to my grandparent's marriage, refusing to acknowledge my grandmother in any way for many years. She cut my grandfather out of the equal division between her children of her large sheep and dairy farm near Queenstown, Cape Province, giving him only a small farmhouse and relatively small section of the farm. My grandmother was ignored by the rest of the family, but she continued raising her family of four children, helping with the running of their farm, and coping with the hardship of living with no electricity, water or sewage utilities—here were none in the rural area round Queenstown at the time. Eventually my great-grandmother included her in family events, but was always cold and aloof. My grandmother was sustained by her strong Christian faith. She never uttered one word of self-pity or bitterness when talking about this time of her life, or during the long years that she insisted on caring for my grandfather as he succumbed to senile dementia when he reached his eighties.

My mother didn't have any easier a time with her English in-laws than her own mother had so many years before. My dad's father had difficulty coming to terms with the fact that his oldest son married a daughter of "the enemy" he had fought in his youth. At the age of 21, my mom faced not only the antagonism of her in-laws, but the absence of her husband. My parents, Mervyn Alfred Keightley Surridge and Maria Charlotte Moorcroft, were married on the 14th of October, 1939, and before the end of the year my father left with the South African Army to fight in the Second World War in North Africa with the allied regiments known as "The Desert Rats." Except for the times that he was on leave, he served away from home for four years.

Dad was wounded in Italy, just outside Florence in 1944, shortly before I was born. Pieces of shrapnel lodged in his buttocks and legs, one of them shattering his right ankle, which turned gangrenous in the field hospitals and led to the amputation of his leg below the knee. He was in military hospitals in Europe for months, being transferred back to South Africa at the end of 1944 when I was seven months old. It was an uphill climb for both of them for several years as he learned to accept and cope with his disability. He underwent multiple surgeries for many years and suffered severe chronic pain for the rest of his life. When the pain was acute, he would grow quiet, retreating into himself, never uttering a word of complaint. Before the war, he served in the South African Police Force. It's interesting that on horseback and motorcycles he patrolled the area in and around the Kalahari Desert where Scott's family had their adventures in later years. Unable to return to this line of work after the war, he took a job in the Bantu Education Department, where he had advanced to the senior administrative position before he retired. My mother, like so many other wives after the war, had the difficult task of nursing the emotional trauma and stress to recreate a family life with a husband who had returned wounded after long years of a brutal war. She was strong, patient and adapted where she had to, drawing strength from her faith like her own mother. She was largely responsible for the happy, carefree childhood that Joy, Leslie and I were privileged to have.

Scott and I started our first professional jobs in January of 1965. I was a staff physiotherapist at the university teaching hospital in

Pretoria (then called Hendrik Verwoerd Hospital), where I had done my internship. Scott joined his father, Josh, who had long dreamed of eventually handing his practice over to him. However, Scott had been unhappy with the scientific background supporting chiropractic theory that he had learned, and we discussed ways open to him to further his studies as soon as he came back from the States. We came up with a five year plan—we thought that a BS degree, followed by a MS would solve the problem, and this could be done at the University of Pretoria after work in the evenings.

I had a personal interest in finding an academically acceptable argument for the validity of chiropractic treatment. The antagonism towards chiropractors in the medical community was virulent. I had heard many verbal attacks of contempt against "those quacks"—attacks which became directed at me for my connection with them when I became engaged and married. The name Haldeman was well known to all in the medical field in Pretoria since Scott's father was extremely active in his efforts to obtain legislation to license chiropractors. On my first ward round after our marriage, one of the residents drew the attending professor's attention to my new surname, Haldeman, on my name tag. With a sneer he said, "Unbelievable, unbelievable," and turned away, always ignoring me except when the most direct dialogue related to patient care was required, from that moment until the end of my rotation.

At this time, chiropractors in South Africa were not licensed or regulated. Josh, who had been the main force behind obtaining licensure for chiropractors in Saskatchewan, Canada, had been fighting for licensure from the government in South Africa since he opened his practice in Pretoria in 1950. Again and again the stumbling block was that there were no chiropractors with advanced degrees in the basic sciences who could explain the principles of chiropractic in scientific terms. He strongly supported our plan of action and agreed to work in the clinic around the afternoon laboratory class times that Scott needed to attend. So in February of 1965, Scott started the first year of his second degree, neither of us suspecting for a moment that this decision had set us on a path that would lead us to live half-way around the world, or that he would be a full-time student for an additional 16 years.

The parameters of our day-time jobs, Scott's evening classes, which lasted from 5 to 10 p.m., Monday-Friday, and his study time which took up the most part of each weekend during the academic year, left me with a lot of time on my own. I decided that the only way to live with an absentee husband was to be as busy as he was in the evenings. I received three wonderful educational gifts from long-time friends of the family, and I enrolled in the courses they offered, one at a time. Thelma Parsons–Brummer (Aunt Shelley) who looked after the Haldeman children while their parents were away on their adventures for months at a time, had her own secretarial school, Liefs College, and made sure that all of the kids—including Scott—completed the course in shorthand and typing by the end of high school—"just in case." When I officially became a Haldeman, she offered me the opportunity as well. The priceless value of her gift became very evident to us when we could complete her sentence and say, "just in case the PC is invented." Ponie and Lee de Wet (South Africa's top model), friends who flew in their own small plane through Central and East Africa with my parents-in-law and Scott when he was about 11, had a large modeling school. Germaine, who was married to Pierre van Zyl who worked tirelessly with Josh in the South African Chiropractic Association, had a modeling and etiquette school. Each of them gave me a modeling course in their respective schools. The courses and the modeling shows were an entirely new milieu for me, and I really enjoyed the experience.

I resigned from the hospital at the end of 1966 when I was fortunate enough to obtain a position in the physiotherapy department at the Pretoria Cerebral Palsy School. In the three years that I worked there as a member of a highly specialized staff team comprised of physiotherapists, speech and occupational therapists, teachers, a psychologist, and an attending neurologist, I gained experience in the treatment of babies, young children, and teenagers with brain injuries. I also had more time after work since I was now working shorter school hours, and I registered for the evening classes at the University

Photo of us camping with tarp.

of Pretoria to do a BA majoring in English literature. When we left South Africa, my studies were interrupted and to-date they haven't made it back onto my priority list.

It was not all work and no play by any means. We lived close to both families and were in constant contact with them, sharing close family times and vacations. Our friends were either still at the university or starting new careers, getting engaged and married, and a few having their first babies, so we all needed to work around busy schedules. We took great effort to keep our friendships warm and active. Scott and I went on one long road trip every year during the academic breaks. Back then he didn't think that it was necessary to do much planning for a trip, and hotel reservations were completely out of the picture, so we sometimes stayed in very colorful hotels in South Africa, Southern and Northern Rhodesia. We always had a tarp in the car, and if we had to camp it was used to make a tent by placing it flat on the ground and then folding it up and over the open car door, which was then closed to secure the tarp.

Soon after beginning his studies for his master's degree, Scott came up against the first of the successive "closed doors" that would determine the detours from our planned pathway. He realized that he had been naïve to think that a master's degree would be sufficient to be able to do the research required to scientifically understand the theory of chiropractic principles. He needed to have a PhD to be able to conduct his own experiments at a university level. At the time there weren't any mentors in South Africa in his field of interest and he would have to go abroad to continue his studies. There were three leading experts in the world doing work on nerve injuries, and Scott applied to all three and was accepted to all three PhD programs. One was in Japan, but the thesis had to be written in Japanese. Another was in Germany, and it was tempting to be in Europe for a few years, but no work permits were being issued to foreigners. The third was in Canada, where I could get a reciprocal license. Physiotherapy jobs were easy to find, and Scott was given a grant of $250 per month. Scott would begin his PhD studies with Dr. Hugh McLennon at the University of British Columbia in Vancouver in September 1970. I accepted this course of events with great reluctance, as my own roots went deep in my world in South Africa. However, it was the correct professional decision, it was to be for a limited time, and we began making the arrangements to leave as soon as Scott finished his master's degree in mid-November 1969.

TORONTO

We would have to live frugally while we were abroad, and I thought that I should take a few household items to set up my new home. My father gave us the tin trunk that was issued to him when he joined the South African Army to go to war in 1939, and which held all his belongings until 1945 as the Allied troops fought their way through North Africa into Italy. We still have it in our garage, a very well traveled trunk indeed, that could tell some amazing stories if it were animated! Into this trunk I packed essentials—linens, crockery, cutlery, pots and pans, a batik, and embroidered wall hanging which I had made—to have a little piece of home with us. Our furniture and the rest of our belongings were safely stored in one of Scott's parents' garages to await our return. We were saying goodbyes for a long time, as we boarded the train from Pretoria to Cape Town with me sobbing and Scott trying to console me by telling me how much fun it was going to be.

My father's parents and one of his sisters, Edna Boschard, saw us off at the dock in Cape Town. We traveled from there to Southampton on a small Union Castle ship, *SA Oranje*, making her last voyage. The crew celebrated as much as the 300 passengers, most of them new university graduates or young professionals heading off to work or study abroad. We celebrated our 5th wedding anniversary on board, and it was 15 days of nothing but fun. We then rolled, cork-screwed, and plunged our way from Southampton to New York across the Atlantic in fierce December storms, flat on our backs on a covered deck of the French flagship, the *S.S. France*. The first day out, we befriended the people who were assigned at our table in the dining room. We spent the afternoon playing table tennis as the tilting of the deck gradually increased in amplitude. This was fun! It was hilarious at dinner trying to load your fork before your plate slid madly across the table. It was murder lifting your head off the pillow the next morning. We found that it was possible to feel human and even eat a little as long as one was lying flat, so we gathered on a covered section of the deck and took turns at dashing to get snacks and drinks. Five days later we wobbled down the gang plank with our two suitcases onto the dock in New York—in below zero weather—to wait for our tin trunk to be unloaded and for the antagonistic customs officer to approve the contents.

We took the train to Montreal to spend a few days and a warm and wonderful white Christmas with Scott's Aunt and Uncle, Kay and Elmer Lach, his cousin Ronnie, and his grandfather Harold Fletcher, before going on to Toronto. We arrived on December 24th in a blinding, blowing blizzard that had dropped 24 inches of new snow and shut the city down. Scott had lived in Iowa and was used to Northern winters, but I was on sensory overload! Nothing in my experience had prepared me for weather like this. I had never even seen snow. In Pretoria our seasons were reversed. Winter is short, and in June and July there is often frost on the ground in the morning, but by mid-morning it has gone and a heavy sweater is usually all that is required for warmth. We had our South African winter sweaters, pants, shoes, and coats. The trouble was that my thin leather-soled boots weren't waterproof, and our coats were light-weight. Every time we went outside, even if only from the house to the car, my feet were frozen within minutes because the snow that was on my shoes melted in the heat of the car or a building, and when going outside again, my boots were encased in ice as the wet leather froze. In addition to the agonizing pain of thawing extremities, the extreme change in temperature from in to outdoors caused me to be dizzy and off balance, and I staggered around on the streets of Montreal.

We needed to spend seven months in Toronto so Scott could complete the required courses at the Canadian Memorial Chiropractic College (CMCC) in order to obtain a license to practice part-time while he was doing his PhD. We arrived in Toronto confident that we had completed all arrangements to start our lives in Canada. While still in South Africa I had applied for and received my Canadian license to practice physiotherapy, and I had obtained a full-time position at Sunnybrook Hospital across the street from the college. All the countries in the old British Commonwealth had reciprocal licensure. We had gone to the Canadian Embassy in Pretoria and submitted all the paperwork that they said was required for immigration and work permits. We had also budgeted for a month to see us through until I received my first paycheck, but we had based our calculations on South African prices. At the train station in Toronto, we were looking for a hotel to stay in for a few days until we could get our work permits signed and have time to look for an apartment close to the college to rent, when we realized that we were in deep trouble. The cheapest hotel was about 10 feet from the railway tracks, had no lobby, water stains on the walls, unlit passageways, and a bare light bulb hanging down from the ceiling in the room. The first night that we were there we were awakened by a thundering of feet down the passage and someone screaming, "Help, help, police—my wallet." We pulled our suitcases close and clung to each other in the not quite clean bed. We didn't have to worry about the trunk because that was lost somewhere between New York and Toronto. It eventually made its way to the college.

The next day we set out with plans to get the bureaucratic paper-work done quickly in the morning and spend the afternoon looking for an apartment. Ah, ignorance was bliss for all of an hour or so! We sat in the last row of the waiting room all day behind people who had been smart enough to line up at dawn. Finally when called, we were devastated by the discovery that the Canadian Embassy had not filed our paperwork correctly and that our work permits were invalid. Scott appealed on the basis that he was born in Canada, and for three days we were shuffled back and forth between offices in departments which happened to be in two buildings and a few blocks apart. We spent hour upon hour in waiting rooms, and when our application was refused by the last officer that we could see, I spoke up in des-peration, asking how it was possible when Canada was so short of physiotherapists and that I had a job waiting for me. He had heard about the shortage, he called the hospital to confirm my employment, and stamped our permits with a flourish!

The nightmare was over, or so we thought! We set out immediately to rent a place to stay. We'd had enough time in the waiting rooms checking every advertisement for apartment rentals to realize that a residence near the college was financially impossible at that time, or any other time during our stay in Toronto. In fact, everything was impossible except the lowest rent in the paper. We eventually caught enough busses to get us to the address that was in the Italian sec-tion of Toronto to realize that the nightmare still had a long run. The only person in the family who spoke English was the five-year-old son of the owners, and we conducted all the business via his transla-tion. As can be seen from the photograph, the space was small with the cooking and living area divided from the sleeping area by a thin plywood partition extending halfway across the room. One can also see the curtains of the only window, a four by two-foot piece of glass at ceiling level that looked out upon the ground level of the driveway. What one cannot see are the two metal frame single beds which each had springs sagging down to within inches of the floor, and which were the only furniture in a bedroom defined by two walls papered in deep, deep red velvet-flocked wall paper. A bathroom was located in a separate corner of the basement at the other side of rows of clothes lines that were perpetually full, and strung across the length of the basement. We moved in with only our two suitcases of totally inappropriate clothing for the Toronto winter, and I began to feel the first symptoms of culture shock. The change in my surroundings from the comfortable little house and spacious sunny garden which I had created in Pretoria, to the always semi-dark, spartan basement corner, with its ceiling height view of hubcaps was extremely difficult to accept.

I reported for work at Sunnybrook Hospital only to find that a recent policy change required new physiotherapists to sign a one-year contract. Since Scott had a September deadline in Vancouver, I lost my job before I even started it! I found work in a private practice, but the nightmare raged on. Instead of being able to walk to college and work, Scott and I now had an hour-long bus ride in opposite directions. The apartment was a mile from the bus stop, and trudging to it in snow, wind, and ice was a daily torture. I had a double dose, since I worked from 9 to 12 p.m. and then 6 to 10 p.m., walking four miles a day still wearing the boots and coat I had arrived in. I put my bus ticket between my index and middle fingers before I left home, because my hands were so frozen by the time I reached the bus stop that I couldn't move my fingers, and I'd just hold up my hand and the bus driver would pull the ticket out from between my fingers.

House and garden in Pretoria 1965-1969

The expense of bus fare was a drain on our dwindling finances, such as they were, and we were forced to continue the diet of bread, cheese, and orange juice, which we had followed when we were uncertain of obtaining work permits. We chose this menu because it was relatively inexpensive, the items could be frozen out on

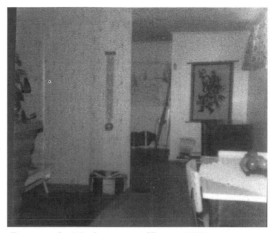

Basement furnished apartment, Toronto 1970

the hotel window sill, which served as our fridge, the bread would give us energy and bulk, the cheese was for the protein and calcium and tongue-in-cheek, the orange juice would prevent us from getting scurvy! We continued eating this fare for the month after my first paycheck as well because we had to buy winter boots, coats, gloves and hats.

We also badly wanted to replace the two soft, thin mattresses that lined the concave scoop of the bed springs, and one weekend I saw an advertisement in the paper for a warehouse blowout sale of mattresses for $5.00 at a location within two miles of our place. Of course they were slightly damaged and poor quality, but they were so much better than what we had—we purchased a double bed size. The salesman asked us to pull our car around to the back and was so flabbergasted when we told him that we didn't have a car that he announced it on the PA system and all the salesmen came to see how we would transport the mattress. We hadn't thought about that and had to make a speedy plan. I thought that we should be able to carry it—one on each end if it was rolled up—and asked the warehouse man to roll it and tie it with a rope. My idea didn't work. There was ice on the sidewalk and we kept dropping the mattress rather than be thrown down ourselves as we slid in different directions. We finally got it onto Scott's shoulders, but it kept sliding down his back every few feet, so finally we hooked the end of the fold over his forehead and he slithered the two miles home, with me paralyzed by laughter following him.

I was struggling with home sickness, culture shock, and the harshness of our lives. Scott left for college at 6:30 a.m. and returned after I had left for the evening shift that my job required. I arrived home after 11:00 p.m. The daily routine of freezing and thawing four times a day in get-

Scott, Toronto, January 1970

ting to and from work was extremely challenging. I was finding it harder and harder to cope with people not understanding my accent or laughing at my vocabulary. One day in February, after a particularly grueling walk to the bus stop in below zero degree temperatures, with the snow blowing horizontally and the bus being an hour late, with the prospect of three more trips that day still ahead of me, something inside me snapped when I asked an older patient to undress down to her petticoat and she burst out laughing, saying that she hadn't heard the word "petticoat" since her grandmother had died. On the way home at noon, I stopped and bought a paper. That afternoon I circled every used car with the lowest listings, around $200.00, and left the page open on the table with a note to Scott saying that when I got home that evening he had better have a car for me—and in the largest letters I could fit on the page, I ended with, "OR ELSE!" I went back to work, and when I got home around 11:00 p.m. he wasn't there. By midnight I was beside myself with panic, terrified that my "mission impossible" had driven him over the edge! Around 12:30 a.m. the door opened and he just stood there, pale as a ghost with the snow blowing in behind him, and said, "Do you want to see the worst car in the world?" And there she was, the 1956 Pontiac station wagon purchased from a used car dealer who was going to sell it the next day for scrap. If he could drive it out of the lot and never bring it back he could have it for the grand total of $70.00. On the way home it stalled on Lawrence Avenue, a busy main city street, in the midst of the continuing blizzard. He had to push it across the road to a gas station, where for $35.00 they installed a used alternator, which they happened to have. I proceeded to learn by trial and error how to drive on the right hand side of the road in ice and snow, doing a few spectacular slides across lanes and intersections in the process. The rear window didn't roll up any more, which was a very good thing because there were so many holes that had rusted through the floor and exhaust pipe that the fumes came up into the car and out the side of the mudguard and rear window, instead of out the exhaust pipe at the back. For some reason the right rear hub cap would pop off and fly across the road when I made a left hand turn. I would stop, retrieve it, and put it back on before proceeding, but that didn't last too long. At first it was a blow to my pride to drive this rusty old monster, and several patients teased me, but I soon got over that. She started with the first turn of the ignition key every morning, no matter how cold it was. She never needed a drop of oil and allowed for a dramatic improvement in the comfort and scope of our transportation and exploration of the city and surrounding countryside. When we left Toronto at the end of June 1970, I felt sad to sell her to the automobile demolition yard for $50.00.

Dr. Donald Sutherland, the president of the Canadian Memorial Chiropractic College, asked Scott to teach the neurophysiology classes because he had higher qualifications in neurophysiology than any of the faculty who were teaching the course. The extra income allowed Scott

Joan's Pontiac, Toronto, February 1970

Scott in our "kitchen," summer 1970

Joan, doing make-up, summer 1970

to purchase a secondhand van that was empty except for the driver's seat. We planned to drive it across the country to Vancouver and spent the summer turning it into a small camper. We paneled the sides and doors with wood, built a closet and a bed, which had storage space underneath, and carpeted the floor. I made curtains for the windows. There wasn't room to cook inside, so we bought a folding metal cabinet, a Coleman camping stove, and a set of pots so that we could set up our kitchen anywhere we liked. Our youngest son, Keatly, and his wife, Megan, still use the stove and pots on their own camping trips!

VANCOUVER

Everything we owned was in our camper, which was home for six blissful weeks as we traveled east to Vancouver and zigzagged across the border between Canada and the USA, free as birds. On the way, we visited the Associates Diagnostic and Research Center in Ohio, National College in Chicago, where Joe Janse offered Scott a teaching job, Palmer College in Davenport, and Spears Hospital in Colorado. We visited Mr. Griggs, Scott's boss from his student days, and he offered Scott the senior managerial position in his piano store!

We settled into life in Vancouver with a warm welcome from family: Scott's aunt and uncle, Gladdie and Ed Eberlein, her cousin, Daisie Hunter, and daughter and son-in-law, Maisie and Guy Johnson and their families, as well as Scott's half brother, Jerry, and his wife, Maureen. Jerry and Maureen welcomed us into their home to

Joan in Jerry's barn painting their furniture, August 1970

stay while we looked for a place to rent. We were overjoyed to find an apartment with a balcony overlooking English Bay only a short walk from Stanley Park. We did not want to invest in good furniture and planned to copy some of the simple Danish furniture designs and make our own. We decided that we would make the frames for the bed and the couches out of plywood and finish with a high-grade paint. I would sew the upholstery and cushions. I asked Jerry if we could use a corner of his barn to make our furniture, and I could not understand his look of discomfort and his hesitation to answer me. Finally he said, "I kinda like my barn." I kept pushing, saying that we needed only a small space and we would clean up and would not disturb the horses at all. His face lit up when he realized that I was not asking to use the barn wall to make the furniture! We used the couches and bed that we made in the corner of Jerry's barn all the years that we lived in Vancouver, and they came with us to California.

I worked for a short time at the Vancouver General Hospital, leaving to take the senior position in the Physiotherapy Department at the Vancouver Neurological Center, where I was again on a team treating babies and young children with neurological disorders. Scott started the PhD program in September of 1970 and saw patients three nights per week in Dr. Bill Hartwick's chiropractic office, which was an hour's drive from our apartment. Later, when Scott was doing his clinical rotations, the long drive became prohibitive and we were very fortunate and thankful when Dr. Clint Heuser gave him the use of his nearby office in the evening.

We fell in love with Vancouver and jumped into life there with both feet, wanting to experience all that the magnificent Canadian and USA Pacific Northwest had to offer before we went back to South Africa. During the first 18 months, with the relative flexibility that the PhD program gave us, we had time on the weekends for fun with family and friends. We forged bonds of friendship that will never be broken with Liz and Dave Wills, Carol and Mick Mahony, Ray and Judy Mahony, Brigid and Derek Gillis, Lis and Chris Grant, and Dot and Bill Zales—the core of our friends from the years in Canada. We skied, sailed, camped, hiked, walked the parks and beaches, partied and celebrated Christmas, Thanksgiving, birthdays, engagements, marriages and the births of first babies. We accomplished all of these activities by employing cost savings techniques. 1) We carpooled. 2) When over-night accommodation was needed we squeezed twenty people into a four-person cabin, never spending more than $4.00 per person per night. 3) We supplied our own food, sometimes cooking on our camp stove in the room or out on the parking lot, regardless of the weather. 4) We frequented two restaurants in a back alley in Chinatown—the Green Door and the Orange Door—where we could eat as much as we liked for $2.00. 5) Our parties were pot-luck and BYOB (bring your own booze).

Scott and Joan Skiing at Whistler, British Columbia 1972

We took long, magical road trips in the summer academic vacation time. In 1971 my parents came to visit. We needed to find a car suitable for four people for the trip because the seating in our van consisted of front seats only. The problem was solved by exchanging vehicles with a colleague of mine who needed a van to go on a tour of Alaska. Unfortunately my colleague was badly injured in an accident in Alaska and the van was totaled. We explored down the coastal highway, as far as San Diego, then inland to Las Vegas, and back to Vancouver via Yosemite, Crater Lake, and the Olympic Peninsula.

An old hatch back Volvo replaced the van and served us well the following summer when Scott and I drove down to Mexico, crossing the border at Tijuana, traveling 3000 miles as far south as Guadalajara and Mexico City. We returned via Chihuahua and El Paso and drove back to Vancouver via the Grand Canyon. The car was old enough not to attract thieves and had an enormous trunk, which held all our luggage safely out of sight. One of the most highly advertized features of this Volvo model was the steel trunk, which was supposed to be impossible to open without the designated trunk key. Our feeling of security lasted until Scott locked the key inside the trunk by accident one day. We eventually found our way to a locksmith. We had little hope of success, but we needed to try anyway because everything—including our wallets and passports—was locked in there. The locksmith was busy and called his son, who looked about eight years old, to do the job. He picked the lock in three seconds flat!

We anticipated one more year before our return to South Africa, and with this timeframe in mind, we purchased a new Mustang Mach II as an investment! At the time, one could sell Mustangs in South Africa for double the purchase price in Canada, and one needed to own it for a year in Canada to avoid import taxes. Scott had a chance to enjoy his one and only muscle car, and I never complained about the thrill of the G-forces and the deep roar of the hundreds of horses! However, as it turned out it never got to South Africa, and it was a very poor investment.

Soon after driving our car off the lot, Scott came up against the second "closed door" in his quest for scientific evidence and cooperation between the disciplines, and he began to think about enrolling in medical school. At the time there was no communication between clinicians and scientists. The rules of the Canadian College of Physicians and Surgeons made it unethical for medical doctors to cooperate with chiropractors. This was clearly brought into focus later when Scott was in his third year of medical school. The class had a lecture from the Registrar of the British Columbia College of Physicians and Surgeons on medical ethics who said, "Medical doctors shall not communicate with chiropractors on professional issues." In response, one of Scott's classmates raised his hand and asked, "What happens if you are both a chiropractor and a medical physician?" The registrar, red in the face, forcefully answered, "You shall not talk to yourself!"

At the beginning of 1972, Scott applied to the medical school at the University of Pretoria. He had all the requisite courses for the first and second years, except first year botany and second year anatomy subjects. They would not permit students to complete courses outside of the designated academic calendar and would not permit anyone to work while studying medicine. This would mean six years without Scott earning income. At the University of British Columbia, he was allowed to enroll in the first year medicine courses while he completed his PhD. If he finished in the top 10% of the first year class, he would be accepted into the second year. He enrolled in medical school in September of 1972, which meant that he was writing his PhD thesis and working three evenings a week while doing the first year medical courses. Of course this meant a delay in our return to South Africa, and we began to save for a visit home the following summer.

The PhD thesis needed to be typed at the end of the year. I had been taking a one-year course in weaving and spinning. I loved the craft and wanted a large loom of my own more than anything else. I stewed over the money that would be spent to have the thesis typed until I had a plan. Against all sane thought, I announced that I would do the job for a 38 inch Nilus Leclerc loom as my payment. Talk about blind faith! I had not touched a typewriter in the six years since I had completed the typing course at Lief's College, and I had not the faintest idea of what I was committing to. The pressure was on from the very beginning. For some reason, the thesis was not ready to be typed until four days before the deadline to submit it to the university panel of examiners. I had to work on a rented first generation electric typewriter. Only two corrections were allowed in the entire thesis, and there could be no cheating because the original had to be submitted. Tears of frustration soon entered the scene, as whole pages needed to be retyped—some more than once. I felt cursed. Why did the typographical errors almost always happen at the end of the page? Nothing to do but forge on—we were stuck with me. I sat on that dining room chair for four days, getting up only for bathroom breaks and four to five hours of sleep at night. Scott fetched and carried drinks and sandwiches and tons of chocolate; and miracle of miracles—I produced 167 perfectly typed pages with 10 tables and 20 pages of references, on time, and I had proofread them all! Yes, I still loved my loom when it arrived!

Our sense of accomplishment and happiness when Scott successfully defended his thesis was heady. We were ecstatic when we found out a few weeks later that I was pregnant, and I danced my way into the arrangements for our pending vacation to South Africa and for new accommodation—we would have to leave our apartment as no children were allowed in the building. Since we thought that we had another two years in Vancouver, we decided to use our small savings to invest in a house instead of renting. Once again we were looking at the lowest prices on the list and we were lucky to find an old 800 square foot fixer-upper in our price range. We ticked off the pros—the house was in Kerrisdale, one of the most desirable neighborhoods in Vancouver, even if it was on one of the most modest streets. Most importantly it had "good vibes," and an above ground unfinished basement which could be converted into a living space. The cons didn't seem to be great obstacles—rotten front steps, peeling paint, old plumbing and the drooping of one corner of the house, which caused it to lean sideways a bit—could all be corrected. I was excited to have a big creative project to work on, and with $3,000 down it was ours!

The dates for the close of escrow, Scott's year end examinations, and our departure for South Africa were all converging, causing a flurry of adrenalin-charged activity. We moved our boxes and furniture into the house the day after Scott finished his finals. At the same time our friends, Dot and Bill Zales, moved all of their possessions into our basement while they toured Alaska on their post PhD celebration before going back to Illinois. We left for our first visit home the next morning with great excitement and anticipation. They were wonderful weeks of reunion, fun, and quality time with both our families and dear friends.

While on vacation we had forgotten how rundown our new house was, but were quickly reminded when we were awakened the first night home by the hissing of water shooting out of a small hole which had appeared in one of the rusty water pipes in the basement. Everything was still in boxes, but I remembered seeing some wood toothpicks and I pushed one into the hole, securing it in place with a strip of cloth that I tore from the bottom of the tattered basement window curtain. This emergency plan to save the Zales' belongings sealed the leak so well that Scott left it in place until he had the time to install a new pipe about a year later! We eventually re-did every square inch of the house inside and out. The construction began with the conversion of part of the basement into a nursery, master bedroom, bathroom, and sauna.

The smoother path of the recent years suddenly changed to one of high peaks and rocky valleys. Our long awaited baby girl was stillborn on September 7th, and four months later Scott's father and our brother-in-law, Peter Ray, were killed in a small plane crash. Our lifelines were the support of friends, family, colleagues and patients. We are forever indebted and deeply grateful for the warmth and love that was extended to us in many different ways to give us comfort and hope. Our spirits soared when I was pregnant again in March. For a few years Scott was the only chiropractor in the world with a PhD in the basic sciences and had invitations to speak, testify at government commissions, and sit on professional and scientific committees, which started coming right after his defense in 1973. By 1974 he seemed to be gone most of the time. He was away the six weekends before Reeve, our first son, was born. He was in town the day I went into labor, but he nearly missed Reeve's birth even so. He was on the obstetrics rotation and fortunately for us, his patient delivered in time for us to share the most miraculous moment of our lives to-date as we held our healthy, perfect son, Reeve, on December 4th 1974.

In 1975 we ran up against the obstacles that permanently blocked our path back to South Africa. The South African government refused to renew Scott's passport on the grounds that he was a minor when he became a naturalized citizen, and he had been outside the country for five years. A re-instatement of his citizenship would be considered only if he returned to South Africa immediately and resided there for six months. At this point in our lives it was not a good option because he was in the middle of his clerkship year and it would have been too great a set-back to waste an academic year. We thought that we would go back at the end of the year and apply for his immigration based on my South African citizenship. However, his application to three South African universities for internship and residency positions went unanswered, and he accepted an internship at the Vancouver General Hospital. This turn of fate forced us to acknowledge and accept the fact that we would never go back to live in South Africa. It took a while, and I still have a deep ache, longing, and sense of loss that jumps out of its compartment from time to time, but part of me had already accepted Vancouver as my second home. We had lived very happy, full lives with close, treasured friends and Scott's extended family in Vancouver for six years. I had no doubts about raising our family there. Travel to and from South Africa was opening up. Our parents had been on several extended visits, and we anticipated going back regularly ourselves. I was content.

Then Scott received three invitations to complete exceptional residency programs. One was from Dr. Bill Kirkaldy-Willis in Saskatoon in orthopedic surgery, another from Dr. Herbert Shaumberg in New York in neurology. The third one was an offer he could not refuse, so Scott accepted the invitation from the University of California Irvine, where he could be on the manipulation research trial supervised by Dr. Tobias in the Physical Medicine Department while simultaneously completing a residency in neurology, a situation that was facilitated by Dr. Stanley van den Noordt, the head of the Neurology Department.

History does repeat itself! Here we were planning again to temporarily leave our home, this time for three years. Much of this period is a blur for both of us. At the time, medical interns were on duty five days a week, from 7 a.m. to 6 p.m. and were on call every other night and every other weekend, when they were required to sleep at the hospital residence. When Reeve was about two years old one of his favorite books was one with questions like, "Where do fish live? Where do birds live?" When it came to, "Where does daddy live?" he answered, "At the hospital," and could not be persuaded otherwise. Scott was earning a small salary as an intern, and I stopped working since I was pregnant again and my new job would be the organization and execution of the move to Southern California. We would have to sell our house to have the capital to settle in California. We were filled with elation when our family was complete with the birth of our second son, Keatly, on March 31st, 1977. Our house sold in April at a 250% profit! We had May to say our goodbyes and pack. At the beginning of June, I packed the necessities for our trip to California. The movers came for our furniture and belongings. We slept overnight on the floor in our empty nest. The next morning we closed the front door and were on our way to live in the USA.

CALIFORNIA

Once again Scott and I were heading to a new adventure in a van, but this time we had our two-and-a-half-year-old and three-month old sons with us. We had only two weeks before the residency program began, so we just headed straight down the interstate 5 freeway. One of the researchers on the manipulation trial had given Scott the name of a reasonable hotel to stay in while we looked for a home. "The Half Penny Inn, overlooking Tustin Meadows," he said. Doesn't that sound charming? We arrived at the "Inn," and before we got out of the van I knew that I would not be unpacking more than our overnight needs. This no-star motel was situated alongside the 5 freeway, on the corner of one of the busiest off ramps at Redhill Avenue, a main road. Tustin Meadows is a housing development, situated across the freeway!

We rented an apartment on a month-to-month basis. I wanted to purchase a home as soon as possible. Just before the July 4th weekend, there was a call from the USA customs office notifying us of the arrival of our belongings in the country. The items were in a warehouse and could not be released without the approved paperwork from customs, and one of us needed to go to the Official Port of Entry in San Pedro—approximately 50 to 60 miles away—with the required identification. Scott was already trapped in the hospital, so I tackled the job. Reeve and Keatly had to go with me because I didn't know a soul in California. I had an address and general directions, but no directional orientation or knowledge of the way cities run into each other in this area, or that one street can extend for miles and miles, through two or more cities. I had never merged onto a freeway with trucks speeding along at 70 miles per hour and threatening to drive right over me because I was driving too slowly. I didn't know how impossible it would be to get back on a freeway when you have taken the wrong exit. I had heard of gridlock, but never experienced it. I found out exactly what the idiom "the taste of fear" means. I arrived at the customs office around lunchtime, after two and a half hours on the road. The customs officer explained that a field officer would have to go to the storage warehouse to inspect the goods, but all of the personnel were out in the field and I should come back after the long weekend. I had two problems with this procedure: first, I had just gone through hell to get there and I wasn't going to leave without a fight, and second, I knew that if our furniture wasn't removed and delivered by 5:00 p.m. that day, it would have to stay in the warehouse over the 4th of July weekend at the rate of $450.00 per day, and I couldn't bear to waste our down payment on a house like that. I very politely asked him if he had any idea when a field officer might be back and he said one might come in later, but it was a slim chance and not worth the wait. I smiled sweetly, said that I would take the chance, sat down on the chair in his office, and let my kids be my weapons. Reeve and Keatly had been in the van all morning. I had stopped only briefly to breastfeed Keatly and give Reeve a sandwich and juice. Keatly was hungry and tired and began to scream. Reeve was full of pent-up energy and was running around like a maniac. I put myself into a stupor and sat there like a statue holding my writhing, apoplectic baby, doing absolutely nothing except staring into space. It wasn't very long before the customs official left the office to return with a stamped form. He had bent the rules, and I would have to take the form to the warehouse myself! Victory!

I didn't even unpack when the movers delivered our belongings. We "camped" in the apartment. My days were taken up with exploring all the wonderful parks, playgrounds, and beaches in the area with Reeve and Keatly while aggressively house hunting. Residents had to live within a ten minute drive of UCI Medical Center if they took call from home. Reeve would be starting Kindergarten before we left and a good school district was another main factor in the location. After many disappointing excursions, we drove into a driveway and were immediately embraced by the surrounding mature, tall eucalyptus trees in the front, and when we went round to the back yard

I was sold even before we had seen the house inside. The west side was completely filled by an enormous pepper tree, exactly like the one that I had played and dreamed under on my grandparent's farm in South Africa. The large lawn was surrounded by mature shrubs, which had grown into trees over the years, and there was a stand of white alders in front of the family room door. We were thrilled to have warm weather and outdoor space.

Soon after we arrived in California in June 1977, in addition to doing his residency, Scott made plans to pursue his interest in promoting research within the chiropractic profession and improving inter-professional relationships between all health care professionals involved in the treatment of the spine. He started the Journal Club. Interested local chiropractors and students met at our house one Saturday a month to discuss research topics and review papers. By 1978 he was organizing a national inter-professional conference with the support of the International Chiropractors Association. This conference in February 1979 was very successful and led to the publication of the first textbook that Scott edited. Because of the success of this conference, we thought that chiropractors would support other inter-professional scientific meetings. However, Scott was not able to obtain any further financial support, and we decided to finance a second meeting ourselves. In order to save money, I did most of the organization and all the leg work. The attendance was small, but we broke even and decided to finance and organize a third one in February 1981. Only 50 people attended, we lost all our savings and were forced to turn our attention from educational chiropractic conferences, to clinical practice.

In 1978 all physical therapists who had graduated outside of the state of California were required to do an internship of nine months duration, without pay, in an accredited facility, and to write the State Board Examinations to obtain a license to practice. I completed both and received my California physical therapy license, but I only worked part-time for a few months before I changed direction. I wanted to step away from the restriction of time and place that patient care demanded in order to have more time with the children. Scott was spending his time in clinical practice, teaching at the university, writing books and articles, research and traveling to conference meetings. A glance at appendix (B) at the end of this book will reveal the extent of his travels and underscore the fact that for all intents and purposes, I was a single parent.

While he was doing his fellowship, Scott was treating patients three evenings a week from 6 p.m. to 10 p.m. He joined Dr. Stanley Robboy, an orthopedic surgeon, in practice. The office was located in Lakewood, a city close to the Veteran's Administration Medical Center where he was doing his fellowship, but a 40-minute drive from our home. I was his only staff person, having to wear all the hats required and very quickly educate myself on the administrative needs of a medical office in the state of California.

After the third research conference failed and his fellowship was completed, Scott went to work part-time at the VA to complete his research, and we opened our own practice with another neurologist, Dr. David Lombardi. We needed two incomes, but I saw a way I could be employed that would allow me to spend almost as much time with my two boys as I would be able to if I was unemployed. I took on the job of administrating and building up Scott's practice. I attended courses in bookkeeping, payroll, and corporate tax requirements at a local junior college, studied medical billing procedures, and later when computers first crept into our world, I worked with a programmer to design software specific to our office.

We moved into an office on our own and built up a multidisciplinary clinic comprised of neurology, internal medicine, psychiatry, psychology, chiropractic, and physical therapy. I was extremely fortunate to have the circumstance where I was able to structure the practice in such a way that a full-time staff of 18 filled the needs of the office for the day-to-day requirements, while my administration and financial responsibilities allowed me flex time in the office. I have taken the bulk of my work home, completing it in the time allowed between our sons' activities all through their school years, continuing with this method to date.

This arrangement was perfect for our family. We took advantage of the myriad of opportunities that life in Southern California offered. While they were in primary school, both the boys played soccer and baseball and took judo and swimming lessons. Keatly was on the bowling team. They kept on with competitive swimming throughout their school years, and later in high school played water polo as well. Reeve got his varsity letter for water polo on his 16th birthday. For most of their school years, they took lessons in two musical instruments—Reeve in piano and flute and Keatly in piano and drums. They sang in the church choir. Reeve took drama lessons and performed in musicals and plays, going on tour to Northern California with the church group. Keatly and I made trips to the Lapidary Society shows in Pasadena to satisfy his passion for collecting semi-precious rocks and minerals, and to community colleges for pottery, art, and woodwork classes.

Scott stayed close to the boys by including them in his world in as many ways as he could. When they were babies and very young, they

Scott and Reeve in our home in Vancouver, December 1974

were at his side as he studied or wrote at home. When they were about six years old he began to take them to the office with him on a Saturday if there were no sports games. They have vivid memories of playing board games in the waiting room in the morning while he dictated his reports, eagerly anticipating the two-hour lunch break at a local pizza chain, Chuck E. Cheese pizza parlor, where they challenged their dad to every game in the arcade before returning for a few more hours at the office. He always took work with him to our mountain retreat, but got up at dawn to go trout fishing, tried to be at the cabin every Labor Day weekend to swim in the father-son swim races across the lake, and planned his day to include skiing at the local hill or driving an hour to one of the others in the area. We allowed no television or electronic entertainment of any kind, including radio. We talked, read, played games, and taught them to be independent, responsible, self–reliant, and inventive in their entertainment. To our joy, we succeeded in passing on to them a respect for and love of nature.

Scott's night off after 48 hours on duty, April 1977

Scott took Reeve and Keatly, together or separately, on conference trips in the USA and Canada. He always added an extra day or two to spend with them at the local attraction, often an entertainment or water park. While they were gone, I usually focused on two of my long-term projects and passions—the renovation of our house and the landscaping, planting, and maintenance of our garden, doing as much of the work as I could myself. After 16 years in the home where our sons grew up, we moved to our present home, which had the attraction of mountain, city, and ocean views and a property that had my creative juices flowing. In 2002 I was thrilled and honored to be asked by the Jack and Jill Guild to allow our home to be one of the four residences presented to the public in the annual fundraiser to benefit the outpatient clinic at Children's Hospital of Orange County. I was excited to have the garden included in the Tustin Garden Club Spring Garden Tour 2008. All proceeds from this fundraiser supported philanthropic projects including horticultural scholarships for college students, donations to local arboreta, and the main focus—children's gardens in 18 Tustin schools. I was elated when our youngest son and his fiancée, Megan, asked me if they could have their wedding in the garden in May 2008.

Aside from the trips with Scott alone, we included Reeve and Keatly

Scott and Keatly studying together in Santa Ana, 1978

at every opportunity when I joined Scott at meetings. As a result, by the time they graduated from high school they were well traveled throughout the USA, including Hawaii and Alaska, and nine other countries. They visited South Africa, Australia, and Canada several times and explored each country fairly extensively. Others on the list included, Swaziland, Brazil, England, Japan, Hong Kong, and Russia.

The main thrust of the vacations to South Africa with them was to visit their grandparents, uncles, aunts, and cousins on both sides of the family. We stayed with family and watched with great pleasure as they adapted to and enjoyed the South African family lifestyles and activities. Short trips with the South African families, to various local or regional sites gave Reeve and Keatly a taste of the aura and magnificence of Africa. The key word is "taste." We visited the Kruger National Park and some smaller game parks, which were more exciting in many ways, especially those where the hippos run past the huts at night, bellowing and shaking the ground. They loved the endless sandy beaches and surf at my parents' home on the coast. We haven't had the chance to do more than introduce them briefly to my homeland, and it is a top priority of ours to comprehensively explore Southern Africa with our sons and their families in the coming years.

The whole family eagerly anticipated return visits to Australia.

Scott and Joan Haldeman with their two boys Keatly and Reeve (l to r), 1989

On our first trip, Scott and I invested in a condominium that was rented out as part of the hotel rental pool on Hamilton Island on the Great Barrier Reef. We enjoyed three magical family holidays there, parasailing, snorkeling, boating to isolated islands, and fishing. We included road trips each time and have driven from Cairns through the rain forests to Cooktown, and down the coast from Brisbane to Sydney.

Since 1977 we have crossed the US-Canada border with Reeve and Keatly more often than any other, by car, in conjunction with a leisurely camping road trip along the coastal highway, or by plane. We have gone to British Columbia to celebrate Christmas time, weddings, and to enjoy skiing holidays with family and friends. In the latter part of the 90s, Scott's twin sisters and brother and their families immigrated to Canada one at a time. In 1999 Scott's mother and his sister, Lynne, decided to leave South Africa and move to Canmore, Alberta, to be closer to the rest of the family. Scott and I were delighted to

Great grandma Wyn, Raymond and Reeve, July, 2008

have our larger family with us on our last trip to Canmore. The purpose of the visit was to introduce our two daughters-in-law, Stephanie and Megan, and our then five-month-old grandson, Raymond, to grandma Wyn. Raymond is Wyn's first great grandchild with the Haldeman name.

When he was 11 years old, Keatly came with us to Japan and Hong Kong. While Scott was attending the ISSLS conference in Kyoto, Keatly and I went on all the "accompanying persons program" activities. He loved collecting the special calligraphy insignias from the monks at the temples as the Japanese students were doing. He enjoyed the cloisonné classes (I still wear the brooch that he made for me) and was a great sport when he was chosen to be the guest at a demonstration of a lengthy tea ceremony. Neither of us like tofu, and we had great fun finding ways to slip our portions unobtrusively into my purse at a lunch specially prepared for the group by the monks. In Hong Kong, the behavior of a waitress in a local dim sum restaurant was an unexpected illustration of the cultural difference between Chinese and American etiquette that has remained in the forefront of Keatly's memories of his experiences in that city. The restaurant was large and extremely busy. There were several waiters and waitresses wheeling large carts around between the tables and you took what you wanted from the cart as it went by. Our host had a particular dish that he wanted us to try, and he beckoned for a specific waitress to come over to our table. She made her way with some difficulty. Our host looked at the food, and not seeing what he wanted, turned aside and flicked his wrist at her to leave. She erupted into a tirade and shouted right into his face! Unperturbed he just kept on flicking his wrist until she eventually left with angry glances in his direction.

Reeve did not accompany us to Japan because he had gone to Moscow as a participant in a youth summit conference that was organized to promote interaction and communication between young people from western countries and those in the Soviet Union. The Soviet Union had been closed to the West for 50 years, and the people lived very different lives and had very different philosophies. However, the USSR had begun to open up, and there was a new and tangible interest that the Soviets had in things Western (like Pepsi, blue jeans, etc.). This made a huge impression on him, and he came back determined to learn more about the country and to participate in some way in the emerging Russian economy. Within six months of the trip, he had set up a sister school program with his high school and a school in the Russian village of Vologda. He asked us if he could have a Russian language tutor so he could have a leg-up when he went to college. We helped him find one, thinking that this passion would dim in time, but he ended up double-majoring in Russian studies and economics at Tufts University.

Over the last ten years, a top priority for Scott and I has been the inclusion of extended time to travel for pleasure in his work schedule. Scott uses his love of research to find unique places to stay, and to find special rates for them. We have enjoyed sojourns in palaces, monasteries and convents, castles, paradores, and pousadas, as well as hotels with spectacular views or historic interest. We love to visit the museums, art galleries, historic sites, beautiful gardens, parks, points of geological interest, and the stunning magnificence of nature, always enjoying the anticipation of a new addition to our collection of artifacts and artwork that we have built over the last 43 years. These are treasures which are displayed all over our home as constant reminders of the people and places that have enriched our lives beyond measure. Good walking shoes are a must on every trip!

Scott and I have made five road trips in Europe on our own, renting or leasing a car and driving ourselves. We have driven from Athens around the Peloponnese Peninsula, including Olympia and Delphi, and the islands Crete and Santorini. May and June 2004 found us and our son Keatly making our acquaintance with the Spanish and Portuguese cultures from Madrid via Cordoba, Seville, and Lisbon to Porto to attend the ISSLS meeting before driving on to Bordeaux, France for a Neck Pain Task Force meeting. In the spring of 2006, we spent a month driving through Southern and Northern Ireland, including the Ring of Kerry and the Skellig Islands. We celebrated my birthday at Glin Castle in the County of Limerick and a delayed 40th wedding anniversary at Ashford Castle, built in 1228 and situated on 300 acres of spectacular grounds with a variety of trees, shrubs, and rare plants. We flew from Dublin to Norway where we took a switch back train from Oslo to Flam to take a boat ride tour through the fjords before attending the annual ISSLS meeting in Bergen.

2007 was a great year for seeing the world! Scott needed to be in Vilamoura, Portugal, on the 15th of May for the World Federation of Chiropractic meeting and in Hong Kong for the ISSLS conference on June 9th. It was a marvelous opportunity to plan another road trip in the interim between the two dates. We flew from Los Angeles to Lisbon, where we picked up our car. From Lisbon, we drove to Vilamoura and on to Granada and Barcelona in Spain; Avignon, Cassis, and Eze in France; the Cinque Terre, Sienna, and Rome, Italy. We flew from Rome to Hong Kong, and from there back to Los Angeles, completing our first round the world flight! Later in September 2007, there was a Neck Pain Congress in Bern, Switzerland, which we reached by a long circuitous route. We drank in the stunning beauty of the Swiss Alps from Zurich to Innsbruck. Our brief drive through Slovenia and northern Croatia inspired the need for a second visit to these countries in the future. Romantic Venice came next, followed by two days in the Dolomites (Italian Alps) before driving to unforgettable Florence, city of art, antiquities, and history. From there we drove through the Alps via a multitude of the longest tunnels that we have ever encountered, to the Lake District in Italy to spend two days in a hotel—a former monks' retreat which hangs on the side of a cliff overlooking Lake Como—before making our way to Bern for the meeting.

One of the advantages of working in widespread venues is that we could often travel *to* friends. Over the past seven years, for the first time in twenty-nine years we have been wonderfully fortunate to be able to travel *with* friends, without any work inclusion, and have been on glorious group tours with dear friends who, like us, wish to see as much of the world as we can. To date we have shared experiences and memories in Turkey, Germany, Hungary, Poland, the Czech Republic, Austria, Egypt, Namibia, Botswana, Swaziland, Zimbabwe, and South Africa.

Neither Reeve nor Keatly have followed in their father's footsteps into the health care world. Reeve's interest in the business world was piqued by the budding awareness of capitalism that he saw while he was participating in the youth summit conference in Moscow in 1989. In his junior year at Tufts University, he completed a summer intensive-language program in Moscow and spent a full semester abroad as an exchange student in Moscow. After graduating in May 1996, he moved back to Moscow to work as an advertising executive for almost three years until he came back to the USA. He completed both his masters' degrees with a 4.0 GPA. He received a master's degree in business administration from the University of Arizona in 1999, and a master's degree in international management at the Thunderbird Institute in Phoenix in 2000. Since then he has followed a career in marketing & business management in the USA. Currently he holds the position of Sr. Channel Manager (retail), overseeing the marketing efforts and business strategy for Custom Building Products in retail channels, mainly The Home Depot, and to a lesser extent, Ace Hardware, True Value, and Do It Best.

Keatly showed a great interest in robotics in his school years. He and Scott joined a robotics club and built a small robot that could follow a line on the floor, and he attended a summer computer science course to learn to program more sophisticated tasks for his experiment. It was a natural progression of this interest for him to enroll in electrical engineering and computer sciences when he went to college at Duke University. He joined a group of students who were building a sports car, engine and all, from the ground up, to enter it in an inter-university race. He pursued another of his passions by forming what he calls a "totally kick-ass" rock band. He had a love of music from an early age. He asked to take drum lessons in addition to piano lessons, and from 4th grade to the end of middle school, he was the main drummer in the school band. He organized a group of his nine year-old friends into a band, which jammed in our garage from 5th grade right through their college years. The band re-united to compose for, and play at Keatly and Megan's wedding in May 2008! Keatly graduated from Duke University in 1999 with a BS in electrical engineering, cum laude, with a minor in religion. He was accepted into the post-graduate electrical engineering program at Stanford University, but deferred for a year to pursue a musical career with his band, Nine Hertz. After the first week of attendance in the electrical engineering program, Keatly realized that he was much more interested in music and quickly enrolled in the Music, Science and Technology program at Stanford. He earned his master's degree with honors in 2001. At first he followed the creative route, composing music for TV/film/advertising/videogames/websites. In time, he transitioned into the business side of music, specifically music publishing. He is currently CEO of a music publishing & licensing company, PigFACTORY, which he started with a colleague three years ago. The company owns and administers the royalties for musical copyrights and looks for opportunities to promote songs in TV/film/advertising/video games and with recording artists. It also represents other publishing companies and record labels for TV/film/advertising/video game synchronization. Megan, Keatly's wife, has joined the company to help with the early growing stages. She has a master's degree in public administration and is perfectly suited to adapt her skills to the company's needs. She is the copyright administrator for pigFACTORY, in addition to being the office administrator, HR, and accounting dept. This means that she makes sure all of their songs are registered with the various royalty societies around the world. She monitors the royalties as they come in and corresponds with the societies to make sure that they are getting paid properly. She also speaks with their partners worldwide to ensure that the company is collecting royalties properly in each country. She is in charge of all money flowing in and out of pigFACTORY.

Our warm and loving daughters-in-law have added a delightful, rich, new dimension to our lives. Megan (ne Johnstone), who was born and raised in New Zealand, has a fortuitous connection with Scott and I. Her father, Peter Beetge, who lived in New Zealand and now resides in America, is South African born and grew up in the same city, Pretoria, that we did. His childhood home was a few doors away from the Parsons, one of the daughters being Thelma—Scott's Aunt Shelley who looked after the Haldeman children and who gave us the typing course. Megan and Reeve, our oldest son, have the same birthday, although they are a year apart in age.

Reeve's wife, Stephanie, was raised in Los Angeles, CA, and attended UCLA where she obtained a BA degree in philosophy. She is passionate about helping people and animals. Most things in her life, including her career, will always be second to her children. She is busy with the most challenging, but also the most rewarding job that she has had—and she has interrupted her studies to obtain certification in special education to stay at home and raise their son, Raymond Scott Haldeman. His birth on February 25th, 2008, was the beginning of grandparenthood for us, a cycle which we embrace with unbridled joy, now made even greater with the birth of his sister Simone Mei Haldeman on October 12,2009. and Keatly and Megan's son in early November 2009.

Scott and I are standing at yet another pivotal milestone on our journey. He has told me that now he will leave the heavy doors that required years to push open, to the next generation of researchers. We need the time to concentrate on a plan to use our acquired academic knowledge and practical skills, and those of colleagues whom we have known or worked with, to introduce or improve the health care for spinal disorders in developing countries. We are blessed and

Keatly, Megan, Scott, Joan, Raymond, Stephanie, Reeve. June, 2008.

fortunate to have our family, Reeve, Stephanie, Raymond, Keatly, and Megan, living close to us. At this milestone our road stretches out wide and clear, as far as the eye can see, with innumerable avenues leading off from our highway for us to traverse with our family and treasured friends from the three countries that we have called home. Many lead back to familiar, loved faces and places. Many more are unexplored.

Chapter 11

Multidisciplinary Clinical Practice and Professional Leadership

Southern California 1985–2010

In 1984 Scott had just turned 40. He had completed five degrees, a residency in neurology, a fellowship in electrodiagnosis, passed all the examinations that existed for a specialist in adult neurology, and spent a period of time doing research. He had established his reputation as a neurologist in Southern California and was in demand to participate as a speaker at national and international scientific and professional meetings. His children were in school, and he and Joan had settled into their home in Orange County. It was now time for Scott and Joan to make a decision about where they would live, how they would make a living, and more than anything else, what was most important in their lives and careers.

It was at this point that Scott came to the conclusion that the most enjoyable aspect of his professional life was clinical practice and patient care. He had been seeing and treating patients with very few breaks since his senior year at Palmer College at age 21. He had tried full-time research, and although very stimulating, it alone was not as satisfying as he expected. He had been offered full-time academic positions in neurology faculties and at chiropractic colleges and decided that he did not want to live under the constraints that are typical in large institutions, nor did he wish to spend time in academic politics. He and Joan had tried to organize scientific educational courses for chiropractors and realized that the interest was simply not there. In the end, Scott decided that in his heart he was a clinical neurologist with a background in chiropractic and a specific interest in research into the mechanisms and treatment of spinal disorders and clinical neurophysiology. He set out to establish a career that would satisfy his yearnings.

Fortunately, the transition from his clinical residency training at UCI and his electrodiagnostic fellowship at the Long Beach Memorial Veteran's Hospital did not require a physical relocation of living accommodations. Joan and the boys were well ensconced in Southern California, and they realized their permanent home would not include South Africa. The weather was excellent, the schools were good, there were multiple universities and chiropractic colleges within driving distance, and Joan and Scott had developed an increasing circle of good friends.

Involvement has always been at a high intensity level for Scott, and transitioning into full-time practice was no different. He started seeing patients part-time in the evenings with Dr. Stanley Robboy, an orthopedic surgeon in Lakewood, while completing his fellowship. He then joined another neurologist in a medical center in Santa Ana briefly before opening his own office in the same center. Joan served as the office manager and kept the books. When Scott put out a general letter notifying others that he had opened practice, he listed his general neurological and electrodiagnostic qualifications and then noted:

> I have special interest and have published and lectured in the field of spinal pain. I am currently an active member (with paper presentations the past three years) in the International Society for the Study of the Lumbar Spine. I am currently President of the North American Academy of Manipulative Medicine and have had special association with the International, American and Canadian Chiropractic Associations at various times. I am currently on the editorial

board of the Journal of Manipulative and Physiologic Therapeutics, the ICA Review and the Journal of the Canadian Chiropractors Association.[1]

Scott already had hospital privileges at both the Long Beach Memorial VA Hospital and at the UCI Medical Center in Orange. His privileges stopped at the VA Hospital when he no longer held an appointment there. Scott also applied for and was given admitting privileges at St. Joseph's Hospital in Orange, Western Medical Center in Santa Ana, Anaheim Memorial Hospital in Anaheim, and Chapman Hospital in Orange. On occasion he acquired temporary privileges, for consultation purposes only, at other local hospitals when he was asked to consult on specific patients. Having hospital privileges also meant being available for emergency room consultations, taking evening and after hour calls, finding coverage when out of the area, serving on hospital committees, and maintaining a specified patient load. This became too much for a single doctor to fulfill. Over the years he resigned from Chapman and Anaheim Memorial hospitals. As his practice grew and became more focused on patients with spinal disorders, he had less time for emergency consultations and hospital inpatient care. He eventually allowed his privileges to lapse at St. Joseph's and Western Medical Center, but he continued to maintain his privileges at UCI Medical Center.

MULTIDISCIPLINARY CLINICAL PRACTICE

It is not surprising to find Scott spearheading a multidisciplinary practice. The practice expanded to include two neurologists, an internist, two psychiatrists, a full-time psychologist, as well as a physical therapist and two chiropractors. The practice opened an electrodiagnostic center which offered a full range of electrodiagnostic testing including EEG, EMG, nerve conduction, and evoked potential testing. As a result of his research at the VA in neuro-urology, there were multiple referrals of patients with bowel, bladder, and sexual disorders for testing to determine a neurological cause for these symptoms.

[1] Undated letter signed by Scott Haldeman. Letter is in the Haldeman Collection. From the material contained in the letter it could be assumed that this was a general letter going out to all professionals, MD and DC alike.

Scott wanted to maintain his chiropractic skills, and for many years continued to accept patients for treatment on referral from some of his orthopedic colleagues who were not comfortable referring patients directly to a chiropractor. At one point he was performing spinal manipulation or adjustments on up to 15 patients a day in addition to his neurology practice. At the end of the 1980s, Scott handed over patients requiring spinal manipulation to Drs. Joan Plevin or Mary Reilly who were the chiropractors practicing in the office. In 1986 MRI became a recognized diagnostic tool, but there were no MRI centers in Orange County, so Scott joined forces with a number of orthopedic surgeons to bring in a mobile MRI unit to Orange County. They then supported one of the first MRI centers in Orange County until it could become independent.

Mary Reilly-Tully, DC, who worked three years in the office in the late 1980s, shares the following:

> The clinical practice was focused on the care of work injured patients who were not receiving relief from their primary care provider. Typically, these patients had been treated at some industrial clinic with basic heat, ultrasound, and massage, the most common treatments back in the late 80s. The Workers Compensation Insurance adjuster had generally sent these patients to Scott for a second opinion regarding their back or neck problem.

> Scott had established a practice pioneering in applying a multidisciplinary approach to help rehabilitate injured workers and to return them to work. When I was there, in addition to Scott handling the duties of consulting neurologist and as the neuroelectro-diagnostician, there was another consulting neurologist, Alan Goldman, MD; an internist, Juan Mendez, MD; and Dennis Lindsay, PhD, a psychologist who performed psychological testing and instructed biofeedback for pain control.

> The department I worked in was headed by Joan Plevin, DC, RPT. We would instruct the patients in therapeutic exercise and self-care techniques. We would treat them with myofascial work, physiotherapy modalities if needed, and nearly every patient received chiropractic adjusting.

Scott and Joan Plevin were great mentors for me. So much of what I learned under their tutelage affects the way I continue to practice every day. Most particularly I learned that each patient was different and to apply whatever worked for that particular patient to control their pain and to get them moving. The more they were able to move, the more they would get pain relief, the ultimate goal being to return them to a productive life. Chiropractic was an invaluable tool in our armamentarium.

I also learned report writing from Scott. He would write thorough and understandable narratives. To this day, I hear from doctors and attorneys who appreciate the thoroughness of my reports. I learned this skill from Scott Haldeman.

The patients who were referred to him and who Scott referred to us had generally not received any therapeutic exercise instruction, any pain management instruction, and most often had not received any chiropractic care. Many had been told that they needed back surgery.

Frequently these patients had been on disability from work for months to years. The Workers Compensation system worked very slowly in those days. By the time they were referred to Dr. Haldeman, many of them had become overweight from inactivity, chronically depressed, and addicted to soap operas, and most of all, de-conditioned to work.

With the multidisciplinary approach to care that they received in this setting, most of the patients I saw were able to return to work, and very few of those that I came into contact with required surgery.

Scott is quite amazing in his ability to multitask. He was able to run a large office. He attended to his many patients. He attended to his research projects. He taught. He was frequently heading various organizations and moderating interdisciplinary symposia, and he appeared to be quite attentive to his family also.

One of Scott's special gifts was the ability to treat his patients with respect. Whenever I observed him, he was always gracious. He listened to a patient intently. He made them feel like he took their pain seriously. I am sure that this helped to give them the confidence that he would help them find a solution to their problems. There are many doctors who do not treat patients with common courtesy. These days it is quite difficult to find specialists who treat people as well as Scott treated patients who were referred to him.

Scott strikes me as a person oriented to service. He is focused on service to his family, service to his patients, service to his professions, both neurology and chiropractic and service to the greater good of humanity.

As good as he is with people, my impression was that Scott's true love was research—specifically research in chiropractic. While I was working in that setting, he tried to get me excited about research in chiropractic. I am sorry to say that I did not catch the research bug. I did help set up the structure of a study which utilized a neuroelectro-diagnostic method called magnetic evoked response to evaluate muscle spasm pre-and post-chiropractic manipulation. The ability to attend to minutiae which is required in research is not my gift. I am thankful to God that there is a Scott Haldeman who so enjoys research and is able to give the world his research in chiropractic.

His wife Joan was a partner in all of this. She was with him through his schooling. She had been a physical therapist, but she was not working in her profession when I knew her. She was raising their sons, running their household, a beautiful home in Santa Ana, and helping to manage the office. It would have been difficult for Scott to do all that he has done without her. They appeared to be a strong team.[2]

Scott brought in Alan Goldman, MD, as an associate neurologist in his practice. He practiced with Scott from May of 1989 to September of 2001. Dr. Goldman shared the following recollections of his experiences:

My first awareness of Dr. Scott Haldeman is a somewhat vague recollection of a very tall, very polite, very well-spoken, and very pleasant gentleman with a hard-to-place but somewhat British-in-origin accent who frequently attended the Orange County Neurological

---

[2] Personal reflection of the author.

Society monthly dinner meetings. As president of the Society, I was familiar with his name and almost all of the neurological practitioners in the county, but had never seen Scott in any of the hospitals or emergency rooms that I frequented at all hours of the day or night, nor had many of my other colleagues. I was somewhat surprised, then, when I received a call from him one day asking if I knew if any of the current senior neurological residents at the nearby university might be interested in joining him in practice. I took that opportunity to ask Scott about his practice and just what did he really do? It was during that call that I learned that Scott's practice involved the defense/insurance side of the Workers Compensation system along with a scattering of expert witness designations in the medical-legal worlds of personal injury and medical malpractice law suits. In addition, Scott let it slip out that he had no night calls, no hospital work, and no weekend patient responsibilities.

Twelve years earlier, when I had completed my neurological residency at UCLA, I had stayed on staff as a voluntary clinical assistant professor and had also joined my former chief resident in private practice. Over the ensuing years, we took in two other neurologists and built the largest clinical practice of adult neurology in the county. I was physically and emotionally exhausted and was looking for some type of "exit" strategy from the often overwhelming responsibilities of running the practice and taking care of patients. I, thus, told Scott that I would come over to have lunch with him. Scott's chance phone call, I believe, saved my sanity.

Without doubt, Scott Haldeman is the one of the most honest, interesting, charismatic, and down-right good guys that I have ever met. After our lunch that day, Scott and I shook hands on an agreement from which, over the next 15 1⁄2 years, we never wavered. Although I had had years of experience in the acute care of neurological cases, Scott spent the first six months of our association teaching me the Workers Compensation system and introducing me to insurance adjustors, nurse case managers, and attorneys. He unselfishly referred an enormous number of patients to me which then allowed me to build up a very successful practice. During those first six months together, Scott reviewed every case that I saw and, although I thought that I was "getting the knack" of writing the required, all-inclusive medical-legal reports, I was constantly

233

amazed at how Scott could pick apart my reports in a non-threatening, good-natured, always instructive manner which allowed me to more directly understand and comprehensively address the various issues in question. Never once did I see him lose his sense of enthusiasm in our tutorials, or his patience. He rightfully demanded, however, that all of my reports be letter-perfect and able to stand up to any reviewer's or court's scrutiny. I could never had asked for a more efficient, skillful, or dedicated mentor.

Over the years, Scott and I had lunch together two or three times monthly. Scott is a somewhat private person, but it was at those out-of-the-office get-togethers that I began to see his great sense of humor and to learn of his travels and experiences around the world. With time, we both realized the similarities in our thinking, not on just medical/neurological matters, but on the world in general. I greatly looked forward to our many casual conversations on politics, people, history, challenging medical cases, our families, and current events. Needless to say, we solved many world and social problems at those lunches!

Scott had always been very active in research, the politics of the various neurological and spine societies, and was frequently traveling to participate in and lecture at many such meetings. Upon his return to the office, I would always "grill" him on the discussions of those meetings, as he was, and remains today, a "mover and a shaker" in those societies and an absolute fountain of medical knowledge, especially about the spine. Scott's most recent role as president of the Administrative Committee of The Bone and Joint Decade 2000-2010 Task Force on Neck Pain and Its Associated Disorders for the journal, *Spine*, has produced a publication concerning neck dysfunctions that will be considered a "gold standard" for decades to come. Scott has an intellectual curiosity, honesty in research, and a great knowledge in the process of meaningful publication that has earned him the respect and admiration of his colleagues, both in the worlds of chiropractic and medicine. He also possesses great diplomatic skills in bringing together different opinions and being able to solve problems that, for many others, seem unsolvable.

Scott often described our role as physicians as being that of "problem solvers." We have also often discussed how our opinions, though always having to be accurate medically, may affect others financially or legally, and that to ignore those concerns is not being wholly appropriate to our patients or clients. With the many truly difficult cases that Scott and I both tackled, Scott taught me that, although there may not be a "best" solution for everyone, there most certainly was "a" solution that everyone could accept. I believe it was that sense of fairness in his approach to such problems and his decision-making abilities that has allowed Scott to enjoy the great success he has achieved.

Scott was well respected by our office staff. The smoothness of the functioning of the office was another tribute to the fairness with which he treated all of his patients and employees, no matter what was their station in life. Scott and his wife, Joan, went out of their way to ensure that office harmony existed and that "the ladies," as we called them, were shown our appreciation for the work that they performed. I greatly enjoyed and looked forward to going to work every day as the atmosphere in the office was congenial, and I knew that Scott and I would, even if for a few moments in our very busy days, discuss some great issue or ponder together some of the more challenging cases. It was also quite reassuring to know that a world expert was working in the examining room next to mine.

On a personal note, my wife and I have found Scott and Joan to be the most interesting people in our social circles. We have spent hours being entertained by them with stories of their upbringing in South Africa and their travels around the world. They are *involved* people who enjoy being a vital part of many, many activities. The Haldemans are also a very close family. Scott and Joan have raised two remarkable sons and are now greatly enjoying the expansion of their family with the grandchildren that their sons are bringing to them.

When I was first asked to relate humorous stories or unusual instances I have had in working with Scott, I realized that *every day* was a grand experience and that no one event could stand out more than any other. I feel privileged and honored to have worked with Scott and to still have him as a friend and medical colleague. Although I have mentioned that Scott is often a very quiet and private person, over the years, I have never met a more honest or compassionate person. I mentioned that Scott and I never had a "formal" written agreement of our association. Scott's word and his handshake were all that was needed. He is the only individual with which I have had such a business relationship yet I had never worried about him going back on his word. He is a man of strong character and a model of integrity.

I am currently the Medical Director of a medical device company and the Medical Chairperson for The State of Utah Labor Commission. I do not believe that I could hold either one of these positions had it not been for Scott's generosity, example, and mentoring many years ago. Scott is a member of my company's Scientific Advisory Board. I greatly value his medical input, experience, and easy, good-natured but business-directed interaction with the other members of the board. I still feel completely at ease, if necessary, in calling him to discuss some of my more challenging patient cases.

I consider it an honor and privilege to have worked with Scott and, to this day, greatly appreciate and value his friendship.[3]

Robin Mateski started working with Scott in 1983 at an office in Lakewood. In Robin's own words:

I was hired as a transcriptionist. I was told by the other transcriptionist that Dr. Haldeman had a different way of dictating, in that he would say "stop" rather than "period" at the end of a sentence. I was also told that there was a stash of Ding Dongs in the office kitchen that belonged to Dr. Haldeman, and so I respectfully left them alone.

His dictations could be really funny at times. I can imagine that dictating report after report and trying to remember so many different names while dictating must be difficult. On one report I typed for him, he said the phrase "the patient complains" or "she complains" many, many times in one paragraph, and then he started calling the patient "Mrs. Complains." (Of course, I changed it to her correct name.)

I worked later as his personal secretary. I then had to keep track

---

[3] Personal communication with Dr. Goldman, 2009.

of his expert witness cases, which consisted of volumes of medical records. I would do a preliminary review of the records, and then he would review them to prepare for a meeting or court appearance or to prepare a report. He would take the records home to review and bring them back to me when he was done. The pages would be upside down, backwards, and every which way, with post-it notes stuck all over them, and I'd have to put them back into order.

I also had to keep track of his association meetings and speaking engagements. At the beginning of every year he would say he was only going to do 10 meetings, but he would keep adding more and would usually end up attending 15 in a year, sometimes more. This didn't include court appearances, which he also did several times a year.

He had so many things going on and so many papers on his desk, and sometimes he would ask me what I did with a particular paper or document. I would look in files and on my desk and go nuts trying to find it; then I'd dig through the pile on his desk, and there it would be.

I left the job in 2001 but came back in 2007. By that time he had reduced his work schedule quite a bit and was only seeing patients twice a week, and only four patients a day. It's a much more laid back atmosphere now.

I've worked for a lot of doctors since 1979, and Dr. Haldeman is by far one of the nicest and easiest to work for. He and Joan are really great, and they have treated me and others at the office more like friends rather than employees. It has really been a pleasure to work for him all these years.[4]

FACULTY APPOINTMENT AT UCI DEPARTMENT OF NEUROLOGY

When Scott was completing his fellowship and then research at the VA Medical Center with Dr. Bill Bradley, he was given a faculty position in the Neurology Department at UCI. When he went part time at

[4] Personal communication with Robin Mateski, 2009.

the VA, he was appointed Assistant Clinical Professor. This continued from 1984 to 1990 when he was promoted to Associate Clinical Professor. In 1998 he was promoted to Clinical Professor and continues to hold this position. All his duties at UCI have been performed as a volunteer faculty member and have not been reimbursed. Scott feels that it is important for all physicians to perform some degree of pro-bono work. The opportunity to help the uninsured and indigent patients seeking care at the UCI county hospital, most of whom did not have the resources to consult with private neurologists, served his purpose. At the same time it allowed Scott to maintain an academic appointment and continue with his research.

In the first few years as an attending physician, he was asked to be attending neurologist on the neurology ward at UCI for one month of the year. This required that he be at the hospital at 7:00 a.m. for rounds with the residents, which would take about three hours. He would then return in the evening after his normal office hours to deal with problems. He would also be on call for the residents for that month. Since the wards were run by the first year residents, this would often require Scott to come in to deal with problems. The hospital rules were changed and clinical faculty was asked to take one month on the neurology consult service. This again would require Scott to do rounds every morning with the residents on the neurology consult service and also to be on call for that service on a monthly rotation. The residents were more senior, and this seldom required Scott to come into the hospital at night. A few years later the rules were again changed and the clinical faculty was asked to staff the clinics for one day a month. This was a much easier load as the patients were not acutely ill and there was no night call. Scott continues to attend at the UCI Neurology Clinic one day a month.

As part of his commitment to the neurology service, Scott would be responsible for presentations at the neurology grand rounds. On the wards and consult service this would require the presentation of an interesting case. Scott, however, was often asked to present the results of his research to the faculty for discussion during grand rounds.

Scott was considered the most productive clinical faculty in the department and received the Outstanding Achievement Award by Volunteer Faculty in the Department of Neurology, University of California, Irvine, in 1999 and again in 2003.

During the 1980s Scott was part of a national group of spine clinicians and researchers that had started a series of conferences called, Challenge of the Lumbar Spine. This was a very loose organization, and each year the chair for the next conference was chosen and his or her institution would sponsor the meeting. When it was Scott's turn he approached Dr. van den Noort, who was once again chair of the neurology department, asking whether the department would sponsor the meeting. When he agreed, a conference was scheduled in Long Beach. This conference, like others, was very successful and netted a profit that Dr. van den Noort placed into an account that Scott could use for future research.

After this Challenge of the Lumbar Spine conference, Dr. van den Noort asked Scott if he would organize a conference on spinal manipulation geared primarily to medical neurologists. Dr. van den Noort felt that neurologists should keep up to date with the current research and clinical use of this treatment approach. Scott organized two meetings with speakers such as John Mennell, MD, and Phillip Greenman, DO. The meetings were relatively well-attended and added further to the research fund.

FACULTY APPOINTMENT AT UCLA DEPARTMENT OF EPIDEMIOLOGY

In 2002 Scott received a faculty appointment at UCLA Department of Epidemiology. He was asked to serve as chairman of the research committee for a randomized clinical trial on manipulation for neck pain that had been funded by NIH. The principle investigators were Eric Hurwitz, DC, PhD, and Hal Morgenstern, PhD. The problem was that the neurology department had been objecting to a clinical trial of neck manipulation on the basis that it was a dangerous treatment. Scott made a formal appeal to the ethics committee noting that there were millions of neck manipulations being performed each year and it was unethical not to study the benefits and risks of this treatment approach, especially when the reported incidence of stroke following manipulation was considerably less than serious complications of other treatments for neck pain. The ethics committee gave its approval for the study. Dr. Morgenstern, who was serving as head of the department, then suggested that Scott be appointed adjunct professor in the Department of Epidemiology in the School of Public Health.

The appointment allowed Scott to offer an elective course for graduate students in the School of Public Health. His course consisted of one two-hour session each week for a full semester. The topic was, "Assessing the validity of complementary and alternative (CAM) healthcare procedures." He invited the students to pick a CAM therapy and do a simple literature review and presentation on the topic. This required him to leave practice in the early afternoon and drive to Los Angeles in traffic to arrive in time for his class to begin at 4 p.m. and then drive home again after 6 p.m. when the traffic was even worse. Scott provided this course for a number of years without compensation from the university. But Scott was a teacher at heart, and this gave him the opportunity to express himself in that role. He thoroughly enjoyed spending time with some of the brightest graduate students at UCLA.

His course description—to explore the validity of alternative and complementary healthcare procedures with special emphasis on disorders in the field of neurology—no doubt raised the eyebrows of some of the more traditional faculty at UCLA. He invited guest lecturers from the CAM community and engaged the class in discussion on what was presented.

FACULTY APPOINTMENT AT THE LOS ANGELES COLLEGE OF CHIROPRACTIC—WHITTIER, CA

Scott was offered an adjunct professorship at the Los Angeles College of Chiropractic (LACC) in 1985 and continues to maintain this appointment. In this position, Scott was often consulted (though infrequently compensated) on various research activities. One very interesting project was, "The Study of Spinal Related Injuries in Horse

Racing." Mr. Louis Eilken was a member of the board of regents at LACC and also closely tied to the horse racing industry across the country. Scott was brought in as a consultant to help draft the study and to line up co-investigators. An initial letter of inquiry was submitted to the Keck Foundation in Los Angeles in February 1987. The study proposed was divided into three phases:

Phase I – A feasibility study designed to gather and quantify the incidence and prevalence of spinal injuries in horse racing riders

Phase II – Using case control methodology, two groups (those with injuries and those without) to be followed for three seasons to determine change in health status and to study the biomechanical aspects of how injuries occur

Phase III – An intervention study to establish a model for prevention of spinal related disorders

This study was ambitious as it involved not only LACC but UCLA, the University of Michigan, the University of Delaware, and the University of Kentucky. The total budget requested for all three phases was $665,030. Even with Mr. Eilken's promising connections in the racing industry, the project was never funded.[5]

A more successful project for Scott at LACC was the Low Back Pain Clinical Trial funded by the Foundation for Chiropractic Education and Research (FCER) in 1988. This project was conducted in conjunction with the University of Vermont (UVT). Dr. Malcolm Pope, professor of Orthopedics and Rehabilitation in the School of Medicine at UVT, served as principle investigator. Scott served as a consultant and Reed Phillips was the on-campus coordinator.

The objective of the study was to treat low back pain patients from the LACC clinics with chiropractic care, transcutaneous muscle stimulation, immobilization with a corset, and soft tissue massage. Four objective measures were used to determine which ones responded the best. At the end of the one year trial, the research team determined that the patients receiving chiropractic care did far better than others. The difference was statistically significant, and the $150,000 study

[5] The Proposal and correspondence associated with this project are in the Haldeman Collection.

results were published in the *Journal of Manipulative and Physiological Therapeutics*. This was the first randomized controlled clinical trial to be successfully completed in a chiropractic college.

Scott would periodically come on campus once or twice a year to speak to students and to participate in various functions hosted by LACC. One of the more exciting continuing events was the Visiting Scholars Program where noted individuals would be invited to come on campus and present their research work. Annually, five or six of these noted professionals would be invited concurrently, and they would host workshops in the classroom as well as speak to the students and alumni as a whole. Scott would always draw a crowd and was very helpful in lining up other speakers. Periodically, Scott would also be invited to be the commencement speaker for one of the school's biannual graduations.

COUNCIL OF THE FACULTY OF NEUROLOGY UNITED KINGDOM

George Rix, DC and chair of the new Council of the Faculty of Neurology in the United Kingdom, invited Scott in an August 5, 1999, letter to consider being named the Honorary President of their new Council. Scott responded on August 16th stating it would be an honor to serve, but:

> I must, however, be sure that the college has no affiliation with or supports any of the positions taken by Dr. Fred Carrick and the ACA Council on Neurology in the United States. I find that the teachings and theories of this council and Dr. Carrick are in serious conflict with my own concepts of neurology and chiropractic.

Dr. Rix quickly responded to Scott (August 24) and assured him this new council was independent of all politics and especially Dr. Carrick and the ACA Council on Neurology. Two weeks later Scott thanked Dr. Rix for the clarification and further stated his position:

> My concern is not so much about North American politics as it is about the teachings of the American Chiropractic Neurology Board (ACNB). In my experience, the knowledge, theories, and teachings as well as the methods of practice by chiropractors with

Diplomate status with the ACNB has been, to say the least, strange and contrary to commonly accepted neurological principles. I have yet to meet a ACNB Diplomate with whom I, as a Board Certified neurologist and a Fellow of the Royal College of Physicians (Canada), could have an intelligent conversation on neurological science or clinical practice.[6]

Scott subsequently accepted the invitation to serve as their Honorary President.

MENTORSHIP—ALWAYS A TEACHER

Often accused of being a perpetual student, Scott was, in fact, more of a perpetual teacher. The list of people he touched and their stories verify that he lifted and trained those who sought his counsel.

After the NINCDS Conference (see Chapter 15) the director of Extramural Programs for the NINCDS, Dr. Murray Goldstein, interviewed numerous chiropractors, promising them that if they could get accepted into a legitimate graduate program to pursue a master's degree, the NINCDS would fund their tuition. I (the author) was fortunate to be one of those interviewed who gained entrance into a master's degree program in community medicine at the University of Utah School of Medicine after completing my studies at National College of Chiropractic. Prior to my pursuit of this opportunity, however, I sought Scott's counsel. I flew down on a weekend and spent an entire Saturday afternoon discussing graduate school, the importance of research, leaving full-time practice, paying the bills, and all the usual concerns of a new graduate student. All the time we sat on his back lawn in the warm California sunshine, Joan tended the two boys and kept us supplied with lemonade, never once giving any indication that she and the boys would also have enjoyed spending time with Scott on that particular Saturday. This time together helped turn my decision to pursue a research path. Scott and I interacted on many occasions after that.

Others were influenced to an even greater extent by Scott partially due to proximity. The Los Angeles College of Chiropractic, at which

---

[6] Letters with Dr. Rix are in the Haldeman Collection.

Scott held an adjunct professor status, was not far from his office and over the years he invited various chiropractic students to spend time with him. Several of these people, because of Scott's influence on their lives, became top-notch researchers.

Donald Moon, DC
Member of the National Upper Cervical
Chiropractic Association

Scott conducted a tremendous amount of correspondence with a wide variety of people. This April 25, 1988, letter to Dr. Donald Moon, a member of National Upper Cervical Chiropractic Association (NUCCA) in Fairborn, Ohio, is an example of Scott exerting his mentoring capability, always teaching, always lifting others to a higher scientific standard:

> As you mentioned in your letter (8 Apr), it is perception which is often more important than reality. I find it interesting that you perceived that I had some resentment and anger at NUCCA. In fact, having considered this for some time, I do not believe I have specific anger for NUCCA. It is simply for each of the technique systems which have dominated the profession. Again, the anger is not at the individuals involved or even at the group of technicians who practice. It is more at the fact that each of these groups has failed to present their material within the mainstream of chiropractic thought and practice for debate. Each of the groups tends to maintain their positions separate from their profession as a whole. The publications also rarely enter into the mainline chiropractic journals for generalized debate. I believe each one of these techniques has a great deal to offer the profession and it is their failure to be part of the mainstream of the profession which creates some resentment. If one is not part of the main debate in the profession, then any good that a particular technique has becomes hidden in misperceptions.

> I agree with you that much of chiropractic terminology is being buried and that this is very unfortunate. As far as I know, I am the only mainline speaker who still uses the word "adjustment" on a regular basis. The problem with many of these chiropractic terms

is that the chiropractors themselves do not agree on their meaning. This is a direct result of what was mentioned in the above paragraph, namely, that chiropractors do not debate with each other. This leads to the end result that chiropractic scientists have to use terms which are relatively well-defined in order to communicate with others what they mean. Thus, the definition of manipulation and mobilization is considerably better defined than the term adjustment and subluxation. There is no reason why we could not establish our own terminology. It would, however, require that the people in NUCCA, SOT, Gonstead, Cox and other technique systems become part of the mainstream academic chiropractic world, attend all the conferences, and come to some agreement as to what is meant by these terms. Since these groups have never gotten together and agreed to the meaning of these terms, the terms cannot be used in a generalized audience and thus are gradually getting lost. The insistence by each one of these groups that only their definition is valid has led to the concept of "true believer."

I am in agreement with you that the fault lies in many areas within chiropractic. The only way in which chiropractic can become part of the mainstream scientific community is for it to develop a terminology and scientific body of knowledge which is agreed upon by all chiropractors, not as being absolutely valid but at least as being representative of the chiropractic profession. This requires communication, attendance at meetings, the presentation of all research at forums within the chiropractic world, and participation at interprofessional meetings. Your attendance at the American Back Society is a beginning, but how much better it would have been if Dr. Gregory had been there.[7]

Jerrod Normanly, MD

Chiropractic acceptance by the medical community was improving, and in the late 1980s a few chiropractors were gaining access to hospitals. Jerrod Normanly, MD, was involved in the formation of a new hospital group in Gilroy, CA, and wrote Scott (July 7, 1988) to learn what he might recommend:

Your questions concerning the responsibilities of medical physi-

[7] Letter to Dr. Donald Moon from Scott, dated 25 Apr 1988. Letter is in the Haldeman Collection.

cians and chiropractors in a hospital setting are very relevant. There is tremendous debate currently on these exact questions. There is no easy answer, however. Each hospital has developed its own rules and regulations concerning the chiropractic admission privileges. Usually it is on a co-admission principle, where the chiropractor admits in conjunction with a medical physician. The responsibility of radiologists and clinical pathologists on sending information to a chiropractor has yet to be addressed formally in any setting, but is nonetheless becoming widespread.[8]

Sidney Rubinstein, DC, PhD

One of many students from Los Angeles College of Chiropractic who benefitted from Scott's desire to teach and mentor was Sidney Rubinstein. He shares the following:

> I first got to know Scott when I was a chiropractic student at Los Angeles College of Chiropractic (LACC). I was in my third term when a fellow classmate and good friend noticed there were two research positions available with a "Dr. Scott Haldeman." The truth is, I had only seen his name in passing from his first book on the Principles and Practice of Chiropractic, so I really didn't know who he was and was just looking to earn a bit of pocket money. Prior to starting chiropractic school, I was completing my masters in exercise physiology and was under a bit of stress to finish my thesis before starting at LACC. I was not looking for any additional major challenges other than attending classes and getting through school. What's more, I had no particular research ambitions and my experience with research prior to meeting Scott had been less than inspiring.
>
> At our first meeting Scott explained that he wanted to write up the cases he had acquired in his work as an independent medical examiner and submit them for publication. Over the years Scott had testified in several hundred cases of (purported) adverse complications following chiropractic care. These cases were filed away in boxes. No one had ever systematically inventoried the cases. He had proposed two major themes, cardiovascular complications (which

[8] Letter to Scott from Jerrod Normanly, Gilroy, CA, dated 7 Jul 1988. Letter is in the Haldeman Collection.

Scott had a definite preference for and needs no further explanation) and neuromusculoskeletal complications. Again, I wasn't sure if, given my load at school, I would finish the project and chose the neuromusculoskeletal topic. Ultimately, the work from this project resulted in three publications, one in *Spine*, while I was still a chiropractic student.

Gradually, Scott became an important mentor for me in my early years, a relationship that did not end upon graduation from LACC. He had instilled in me the need for research and had suggested, while still a student at LACC, that I should continue my education and work towards a PhD.

During our time together, I gained a certain wonderment and fascination for Scott. He was always fair and never spoke a bad word about a colleague, even though at times he would have not been chastised for doing so. He was a tireless worker, traveling in one year virtually every other weekend to one or another scientific meeting.

Scott should also be considered a pioneer. This might be obvious to many, but one particular aspect remains in my mind. Back in my days as a student in the early 90s, complications of chiropractic care was a taboo subject. Lawsuits were becoming commonplace, and most practitioners were afraid of them and rightly so. Most chiropractors wanted to sweep this issue under the carpet and pretend it didn't exist. The prevailing attitude was, if we ignored the issue it would just quietly disappear. Scott had the knowledge and the foresight to pursue the issue. Ultimately, complications for chiropractic care would become the theme for my PhD thesis.

Despite what some might think, Scott is a staunch supporter of chiropractic, spending many hundreds of hours talking to students and speaking at chiropractic meetings, often with little acknowledgement or recognition. Once when I was working on a systematic review on risk factors for cervical artery dissection, which included chiropractic care/cervical spinal manipulation and led to a less than favourable conclusion, he suggested a different approach to the analysis, which was more positive and most importantly, more correct. I believe Alan Breen, DC, PhD, best summarized how we in the research field feel about Scott. He embodies the title, "father of chiropractic research."

Over the years, I would consult with him regularly, and he always made time available for me, either to meet at his practice, at home, or chat on the telephone. He was always very patient. We would go on to write an additional three papers together, but most importantly, my time and contact with him over the years directly resulted in my pursuing a PhD in epidemiology on chiropractic-related subjects.[9]

Scott also had an impact on Sidney's wife, the former Tammy de Koekkoek, DC and faculty member at Los Angeles College of Chiropractic at the time Sidney was a student there. She shared this brief story:

I was a second trimester student at Logan College [of chiropractic] in 1980, and homecoming celebrations were held as only those mid-western schools know how to hold them! Scott was lecturing in the seminar program. My father, Laurens de Koekkoek, (a Cleveland College of Chiropractic graduate) had mentioned his name to me in the past, noting his South African background, and that he was "very clever." So while my classmates and other graduates lolled around the swimming pool, drinking, I attended the seminar in a darkened lecture room, listening to Scott for the first time. I don't remember the details of the talk, but I remember one message he was determined to bring over: collect data on patients in your own practice. However you do it, the profession must collect data. Without this, chiropractic would not advance. If I had to paraphrase this now, I would say, "publish or die." This message stayed with me and was my first encounter with a chiropractor who was also a scientist, who was saying to us that we had something to do for the profession that involved more than just treating the patients. I went on to develop more and more interest in the scientific world of chiropractic, influenced later by many others, and have accordingly participated in guidelines commissions and research projects. I have always followed and listened to Scott since then, whenever possible. I feel directly indebted to him for the vision that he created for me on that day in St. Louis.

---

[9] Personal Communication with Sidney Rubinstein, DC, PhD, 2009.

Later of course, I met Sidney, who at the time was already working for Scott on the collection of data from the cases of complications from chiropractic manipulation that Scott had reviewed for medical legal purposes. Sid got his scientific start with Scott, going on to continue this interest in research to the point that he has developed it today, as you well know.[10]

Simon Dagenais, DC, PhD

Another person rewarded by Scott's unselfish mentoring is Simon Dagenais, DC, PhD. His view of Scott's mentorship is quite revealing:

> I first met Scott after he gave a presentation to the students at LACC, but nothing came of it. About a year later, Paul Hooper, DC and faculty member, pulled me aside after class and told me a friend of his was looking for a research assistant. He knew I was interested in research and thought I should contact his friend. When he told me it was Scott Haldeman, I couldn't believe my luck. I called him right away and arranged to meet him at his office on a Saturday morning since that was his time set aside for research.
>
> As a 2nd year chiropractic student, it was pretty intimidating to be interviewed by Scott, but he quickly made me feel comfortable. He had been asked to give a presentation on cervicogenic headaches to a group of doctors at Kaiser Hospital in a few weeks and wanted help putting together some slides. I told him I'd love to help, so he welcomed me on board. We then went for lunch at a local Chinese restaurant in Santa Ana where the daily special was $3.99. Scott explained that one of the things he liked about his previous research assistant was that the two of them could always find something to eat for less than $5. After lunch he put me to work in his secretary's office, and that presentation became my first project with Scott. I obsessed about that project, looking up articles at the LACC library and trying to find the most relevant facts for his presentation. He didn't provide much direction, so I had to figure things out myself. I kept meeting with him for the next few Saturdays, and he was always happy with my progress, so he kept giving me more work. After the

---

[10] Personal Communication with Tammy de Koekkoek, 2009.

presentation, we were both still interested in the topic, so I kept digging for more articles and eventually he suggested that we write an article about that topic for a new journal that he was involved with.

We then fell into a routine of Saturdays at his office, starting with Scott's opening question of, "How's life treating you these days?" Our chats on Saturday grew longer as we got to know each other, always followed by a few hours of work, lunch, and then more work. Looking back at that initial project, I realize it taught me much of what I eventually came to know about Scott. By devoting Saturdays to research, he showed me the discipline that's been an important part of his success. It's not enough to simply say that research is important. Everyone pays lip service to that, but by devoting every Saturday to it without pay after having worked a very full week in practice, Scott was demonstrating his commitment. Scott has always told me that it's easy to succeed if you just work harder than anyone else, and those Saturdays were a good example. The project also illustrated Scott's willingness to give people a chance to show what they can do. He's been approached hundreds of times throughout his career by people interested in helping him with research. Rather than subject them to grueling interviews, he just puts them to work right away on a small project. Many were not willing to devote their Saturdays to research, so they never showed up. Those that did soon realized that once the initial chatting was out of the way, Scott put in a full day of work on Saturdays. To be helpful to him, they needed to put in a full day as well. Enthusiasm is great, but it doesn't accomplish much on its own.

Months later, Scott had a meeting on a Saturday with Jim Wooley, a chiropractor from Irvine who was interested in research on a special form of manipulation under anesthesia (MUA). Jim had talked about this with Scott years earlier and Scott's response had been something to the effect that clinical research is very expensive and that Jim should come back to him when he had half a million dollars to do the study he described. After that conversation, Jim successfully helped a patient suffering from debilitating chronic low back pain with MUA (Manipulation Under Anesthesia) treatment.

Jim tells the story of this disabled patient who recovered from a severely injured herniated lumbar disc and wanted to research the treatment protocol. I called Scott to see if he could help. Scott said he had two feet of research proposals on his desk. He said that to do the basic research on a treatment protocol would cost $500,000.

After talking to the healed patient and potential funder, Michael Marcus, a decision was made to fund the research. I called and informed Scott that the funds were available, and he said he would clear his desk. A meeting was arranged with Scott, Simon Dagenais, Chris Kemper, Frank Kohlbeck, and Eric Hurwitz. A decision was made to do a cohort patient study on Medicine Assisted Manipulation.

The funds were administered by Los Angeles College of Chiropractic (LACC), and I did my preceptorship in Jim's office while coordinating that study for Scott. That was another valuable lesson from Scott—if you can accomplish two tasks in a single effort, do it. He cautioned me that everyone eventually tries to do too much and gets in over their head once in a while, but he encouraged me to do everything I wanted to do and was always there to talk to people on my behalf if that would help out on a research project.

After our research team successfully completed this first study, Michael Marcus had us form a non-profit research foundation. We have been able to do high quality research on complementary and alternative medicine and organized the CAM Research Institute. Scott Haldeman was kind enough to offer his sterling name and reputation to these endeavors.

During the MUA study, I graduated from LACC and kept on working in Jim's clinic during the weekday while working with Scott on Saturdays. When the study ended and I started making plans to move back to Canada for graduate school, Scott started encouraging me to look at graduate programs available in Southern California. He was on faculty at UC Irvine and knew many people at UCLA, so perhaps there was a way to pursue a PhD locally instead. When Jim started talking about the possibility of Michael donating some additional funding to pursue research into prolotherapy for chronic LBP, I knew I wasn't moving back to Canada the following year. That led to the creation of CAM Research Institute, a nonprofit research organization in Irvine that Scott helped create with me, Jim, and Michael. With a strong letter of recommendation from Scott, I eventually enrolled in a PhD program at UC Irvine, where Scott was on my defense committee and my dissertation committee. He hit it off right away with the other committee members and put everyone at ease with my proposed research related to prolotherapy for chronic low back pain, a rather offbeat topic. He provided excellent feedback on my PhD whenever it was needed, and kept reminding me every now and then that he'd finished his PhD in only two and half years. That's a very short amount of time for a PhD, and Scott thought I could do likewise, so he encouraged me not to procrastinate.

During my PhD program, Scott was approached about doing a 3rd edition of the *Principles and Practice of Chiropractic* textbook. He was just starting to work on the 2000-2010 Bone and Joint Decade Task Force on Neck Pain and Associated Disorders, so he asked me if I could help him a bit with the book. He'd already done several textbooks, so this was him giving me an opportunity I wouldn't otherwise have on my own. It was by far the biggest project we'd done together and was quite daunting, with almost 60 chapters and 100 authors, but Scott was always very calm about it and kept encouraging me to work on it a little bit each week and eventually it would get done. It ended up being a much larger project than either of us anticipated at over 1200 pages, but Scott was right: line by line, paragraph by paragraph, chapter by chapter, section by section, it got done. The book took a few years to complete, during which time I also worked with Scott on the Neck Pain Task Force and with CAM Research Institute on prolotherapy research while doing my PhD at UC Irvine.

I realize now that was quite a lot to do at once, but through it all I had my Saturday meetings with Scott to talk about life, get some advice, ask for help, get some encouragement if I didn't think I could do it, or some deflation if my head got too big, always keeping an eye on the future so I wouldn't find myself without anything to do. Scott always says that you don't want to run out of things to do, because then life gets boring. I'm not sure he actually knows what it means for life to get boring, but he might be familiar with the concept from having heard others describe it to him. Scott is a fabulous mentor, and the more I achieve, the more natural he makes it feel and the more opportunities he presents for me to continue achieving. He views the role of a mentor as a lifelong position and stayed close to his own mentors until they passed on. It's simply not possible for me to imagine what my life would be now had it not been for that first lunch at a cheap Chinese restaurant in Santa Ana with Scott. Clearly he recognizes the benefits of mentoring and the best way to pay him back for everything he's done will be to continue the tradition by becoming a mentor when I'm in a position to do so. Done correctly, Scott's legacy of mentoring will carry on forever through others.[11]

Jim Wooley, DC

While not a direct mentor for Jim Wooley, DC, Scott met him through association with Simon Dagenais. Jim became well acquainted with the research enterprise. He shares his experiences:

> For the past 30 years, I have worked with Scott Haldeman in various areas. Our primary area was in management of patient care. I have referred many patients to Scott for neurological evaluation.
>
> Of the many cases that he evaluated, one case stands out. A middle aged woman was injured when a faulty Samsonite chair broke on the Queen Mary at a coin show in the mid-eighties. When the chair collapsed, the patient hit her head on the guard rail and injured her coccyx as she hit the ground. The resulting trauma caused the development of Reflex Sympathetic Dystrophy. Scott recognized the gravity of the condition, so the patient was sent to Frank Kozen, MD, at Scripts for confirmation of her diagnosis.
>
> After years of discovery and depositions, the case went to jury trial. Due in large part to Scott's testimony, the patient was awarded a $2.5 million judgment. At the time, this was the largest soft tissue injury award of its kind.[12]

CALIFORNIA MEDICAL ASSOCIATION COMMITTEE ON HEALTH

In 1984 the California Medical Association (CMA) organized its Committee on Health Care. Scott was officially appointed to the

[11] Personal Communication with Simon Dagenais, 2009.
[12] Personal Communication with Dr. Wooley, 2009.

committee by letter from Robert D. Burnett, MD and president of the CMA. C. John Tupper, MD and chair of the committee, contacted each committee member by letter in January, calling the first meeting for March 5, 1984. The letter clearly stated the focus of the committee was to study chiropractic. The California Chiropractic Board of Examiners had proposed legislative changes expanding the scope of practice for chiropractic. The Committee on Health Care was organized by the CMA for the specific purpose to plan an action against the proposed legislative changes.

Committee membership consisted of the following:

C. John Tupper, MD, Chair

Richard F. Corlin, MD	Scott Haldeman, MD
John C. McCall. MD	David Rubin, MD
David Scheetz, MD	John R. Strong, MD
Robert G. Taylor, MD	William B. Whiting, MD

Consultants:

Wallace I. Sampson, MD	William T. Jarvis, PhD

Staff:

Linda Ramsey–CMA

At the March 5th meeting, Scott was invited to make a presentation on chiropractic as an introduction to the profession for the committee. His presentation was followed by a discussion regarding the five chiropractic colleges in California with a concern noted that only one had any kind of accreditation status. In addition, the committee was in agreement that the 1922 Chiropractic Act governing the practice of chiropractic was unacceptable.

In preparation for the April 1984 committee meeting, Dr. Tupper asked members to submit suggestions of topics to be discussed. William Jarvis, a well known opponent to chiropractic, had already supplied the committee with material at his disposal from the National Coalition Against Health Care Fraud. Scott responded to Dr. Tupper's request with the following:

> I would like considerations of discussion into chiropractic to follow a fairly organized course. I would like to suggest that we first

of all discuss spinal manipulation separate from chiropractic from a clinical and research point of view, then consider chiropractic skills and training in these techniques and other related chiropractic procedures, followed by a discussion of chiropractic ethics, political structures and associations, and then perhaps concluding on what role chiropractic is likely to serve in the future and the relationship of physicians to chiropractors. This will allow for a final conclusion as to the relationship of the CMA to chiropractors.[13]

Minutes of the May 22, 1984 meeting show Scott's suggestions prevailed. The primary focus of discussion was on evaluating spinal manipulation and other methods of treatment employed by chiropractors. The committee concluded that spinal manipulative therapy must be considered of value for certain carefully selected patients if done by a capable practitioner.

One goal of the committee was to recognize those practices included in chiropractic which had value for patients and attempt to limit the legal definition of chiropractic to those areas. To do this, the committee asked to review textbooks used in chiropractic schools which were written by chiropractors, and Dr. Haldeman offered to provide some examples. The committee also agreed to discuss chiropractic with some knowledgeable chiropractors. The following recommendations were approved by the committee:

1. That the chairman invite a chiropractor to visit the committee as a guest at its next meeting.

2. That a site visit to a chiropractic college be arranged for members of the committee if possible. The site visit should be arranged when school is in session.

The committee added issues of referral patterns between physicians and chiropractors and professional liability problems related to chiropractic to the agenda for the next meeting. The committee reviewed a great deal of background information on chiropractic education and practice. The following recommendations were made for the next meeting:

[13] Minutes of the CMA Committee on Health Care, 22 May 1984. The Committee on Health Care file is in the Haldeman Collection.

1. That the committee receive the report of the governor of Wisconsin's Health Planning and Policy Task Force on chiropractic.

2. That the committee review current Medicare policy on chiropractic, including whether or not subluxations must be documented on x-ray.

3. That any available information on radiation risk resulting from chiropractic exposure be reviewed.

4. That the committee review information on operational procedures of the California Board of Chiropractic which has been compiled by the Santa Clara County Medical Society.

5. That the committee review any available statements from the offices of the Attorney General, District Attorney, or the Board of Medical Quality Assurance regarding prosecution of chiropractors for unprofessional conduct.

6. That the Committee review the Annual Report of the Board of Chiropractic Examiners.

The committee also reviewed the research report, *Chiropractic in California*, prepared by the Haynes Foundation in 1960. Although dated, the committee expressed interest in using it as the basis for a compilation of current information on chiropractic. Recommendation was made that the Haynes Foundation be approached to determine their interest in sponsoring a research effort to update the information in *Chiropractic in California*.[14]

At the October 22, 1984 meeting, Ron Lawrence, MD, James Gentry, DC, and Gerilyn Kaibel, DC, attended as invited guests of the committee. The committee reviewed several letters documenting instances of complaints filed with the Board of Chiropractic Examiners. The committee was interested in the methods of investigation and documentation used by the board and noted that in the instances studied, the Board of Chiropractic appeared to be less rigorous in its evaluations than the Board of Medical Quality Assurance.

The invited guests contributed information about the structure

---

[14] Minutes of the CMA Committee on Health Care, 22 May 1984. Minutes are in the Haldeman Collection.

and function of the Board of Chiropractic Examiners and explained how its members work to protect the public from unqualified licentiates. They also noted that complaints about chiropractors submitted by physicians were rare. Dr. Lawrence said that the board would accept medical testimony on issues of inappropriate practice. The board explained the difficulties regulating a profession defined by the 1922 Chiropractic Initiative Act that do not reflect modern day chiropractic practice.

At Dr. Tupper's request, each guest made a presentation covering their observations about chiropractic today. Dr. Gentry described the chiropractic training and licensure system, noting that far more chiropractors are emerging from training today than in the past; consequently, most practicing chiropractors are younger people. Dr. Gentry listed the following priorities for chiropractors today:

1. Better access to the professional referral system, including diagnostic services and consultative reports

2. Better inter-professional cooperation

3. More educational interchange with medicine such as exchange clerkships between chiropractors and physicians

4. Greater emphasis on research between chiropractors and physicians concerning changes in the health care system such as socialized medicine trends

In response to questions about journals most valuable to chiropractors, Dr. Kaibel and Dr. Haldeman cited the *Journal of Manipulative and Physiologic Therapeutics* as the best chiropractic journal. They noted that the *Journal of the American Chiropractic Association* and some Canadian journals also carry research articles written by chiropractors, as do some non-chiropractic journals such as *Spine* and the *Journal of Rehabilitation*.

In the ensuing discussion, the committee addressed concerns about variations in definition of the scope of chiropractic practice, variations in use of x-ray by chiropractors, and current theories of structural treatment for conditions such as joint dysfunction.

The committee then discussed details of its future visit to the Los

Angeles College of Chiropractic. Dr. Haldeman was able to obtain an invitation for the entire committee to visit and observe as often as desired. It was stipulated that the visits should not take place when examinations were being given. Members of the committee expressed a desire to interview the school's admissions officer, various faculty members, and students. They asked to see the examinations given and their associated scores as well as the school's libraries and laboratories. The visit to LACC occurred April 2, 1985.

The committee reviewed correspondence that they received back from the Haynes Foundation who stated that they no longer provided funds to entities not sponsored by Los Angeles County organizations. The committee recommended that the chairman and staff review the 1960 report, *Chiropractic in California*, and determine specifically what information was needed, how a revised study could be structured, and what possible sources for funding existed.[15]

The Committee on Health Care, after hearing testimony prepared by CMA legal counsel on regulations proposed by the California Board of Chiropractic Examiners designed to expand the scope of practice of chiropractors, proposed amendments to chiropractic regulations that had been hammered out in their May 15, 1986, meeting. They then passed the following resolution:

CMA Resolution 711-86

This resolution calls for support of a federal study to evaluate the vertebral subluxation diagnosis. The Committee supported the resolution but believed that implementation should appropriately be handled by the AMA. Doctor Haldeman noted that the NIH has spent over $2 million in grants to evaluate vertebral subluxation, but the agencies funded did not produce definitive results. The Veterans Administration is currently doing a similar study in response to a congressional mandate.

It was recommended that CMA ask AMA to consider sponsoring the actions requested by CMA Resolution 711-86.

[15] Minutes of the CMA Committee on Health Care, 22 October 1984. Minutes are in the Haldeman Collection.

The committee reviewed CMA's current position on chiropractic and the position paper recently developed by the National Council Against Health Fraud (NCAHF). The committee agreed that a more specific CMA position on this important subject would be desirable. The committee also noted that the National Council Against Health Fraud position had credibility primarily because its author was a disinterested consumer group rather than the medical profession. The committee considered various alternatives for a new position and agreed to explore possible language through correspondence before proposing a new position. To broaden the audience for the NCAHF position paper, the following recommendation was made:

> That the editor of the *Western Journal of Medicine* be asked to consider publication of the National Council Against Health Fraud Position Paper on Chiropractic.[16]

Linda Ramsey, staff support to the committee, sent a memo dated March 20, 1987, to members of the now past CMA Committee on Health Care:

> Although CMA's Committee on Health Care has been disbanded, we thought you would be pleased to see the attached ruling from the State Office of Administrative Law (OAL). This ruling officially rejects the regulations proposed in 1986 by the Board of Chiropractic Examiners which would have expanded the scope of chiropractic practice in California to such areas as prenatal care; drawing blood for diagnostic purposes; and soft tissue manipulation. [Scott had supported the need to draw blood.][17]

The actions taken by the Committee on Health Care in California seem harsh on chiropractic. One can only wonder what the outcome may have been without Scott sitting at the table. He was a voice they could not ignore because he was more credentialed than any of them. His participation on this committee probably did little to build his practice by obtaining referrals from his medical colleagues. His chiropractic colleagues probably never knew that all this was even happening.

[16] Minutes of the CMA Committee on Health Care, 22 October 1984. Minutes are in the Haldeman Collection.
[17] Letter from Linda Ramsey to past CMA Committee Members, 20 March 1987.

BACK PAIN FOUNDATION

With Scott's mentorship, Simon Dagenais went on to obtain his PhD and become a strong researcher in his own right. The friendship has continued, and in 2004 they brought their collective wisdom and experience together to form a national 501(c)(3) non-profit, tax-exempt, multidisciplinary foundation called the Back Pain Foundation.

Their vision for this foundation was to "...be devoted solely to conducting research and providing easy access to objective, reliable information to help those suffering from back pain [and] make informed decisions."[18] The following six concepts were the pillars of the foundation:

Concept 1 – Give patients one place to obtain information on back pain.

Concept 2 – Be an information clearing house with a focus on restoring function.

Concept 3 – Conduct research into the causes and treatment of back pain.

Concept 4 – Provide objective, non-commercial information representing multiple treatment disciplines.

Concept 5 – Be active in advocacy and public education.[19]

Jeff Skoll, co-founder of e-Bay, had been referred to Scott for consultation. Mr. Skoll had suffered from chronic low back pain that greatly reduced his activities for years. After discussion of his diagnosis and treatment options, he went on to get greater relief from prolotherapy than he had received from the multiple other treatments he had tried. Jeff Skoll became excited about the vision of the foundation that would provide information on spinal problems to the public and advance research in the topic. Mr. Skoll directed Scott to meet with Sally Osberg, director of the Skoll Foundation. Ms Osberg informed Scott that the Skoll Foundation would need a campaign feasibility

---

[18] Minutes of the Back Foundation, 2004.
[19] Ibid.

study before deciding to commit a significant gift to the project.

Simon and Christina Mac Isaac of the CAM Research Institute developed a request for proposal (RFP) and met with several companies regarding the feasibility study. The RFP was to be completed by April. Two questions were to be answered by the study:

1. Does this project have a reasonably high chance of success?

2. Can the project be self-supporting after the campaign is completed?

The study was to interview individuals of high net worth, foundations with a demonstrated interest in such research, and a limited number of corporate CEOs. Bob Sharp was to fly to Orange County to meet with Scott and Simon to hammer out more details of the study at the end of February 2004. On February 10, 2004, a meeting took place between Bob Sharp of The Robert B. Sharp Company of Colorado, Inc., Simon Dagenais, and Christina Mac Isaac to discuss a potential campaign for a national back pain foundation.

At a meeting held April 9, 2004, the Articles of Incorporation were approved by the board and Scott was named president of the foundation and Simon the secretary-treasurer. Additional board members were Judith Fuhr, Neil Kahanovitz, MD, and Elon Musk.

On May 28, 2004, the Skoll Foundation committed to a grant of $145,000 to support the Feasibility Study of the Back Pain Foundation proposal with the disbursement of the grant divided equally between June 4 and September 21, 2004.

In a subsequent business plan developed by Scott and Simon, the mission of the foundation evolved:

The Back Pain Foundation would be a nonprofit organization dedicated to public education, advocacy and fundraising for back pain care and research. Its main goals would be to:

1. Empower people to participate actively in controlling their back pain and to improve the quality of life of people suffering from back pain.

2. Bring together medical researchers and practitioners of all disciplines to study and publish non-biased research for the benefit of

people living with back pain.

3. Foster a community dedicated to learning more about effective ways to mange back pain.

4. Raise money for back pain research.[20]

A proposed list of potential board members included:

Jeff Skoll, chairman and founder of the Skoll Foundation

Sally Osberg, president and CEO of the Skoll Foundation

Elon Musk, founder and CEO of SpaceX [A relative of Scott's]

James Weinstein, editor-in-chief of *Spine*, head of back pain unit at Dartmouth

Louis Sportelli, president of National Chiropractic Mutual Insurance Corporation

John Frymoyer, editor of *The Adult Spine*

A celebrity spokesperson

The plan called for raising $10 million to provide working capital for the first five years, during which time substantial effort to raise another $50 million would be put into place.

A conference call on July 6, 2004, addressed several issues regarding funding, expenses, staffing, marketing and sustainability. There was also a review of a proposed brochure being developed to be used in fundraising efforts. A report from Robert B. Sharp on July 24th discussed the finalization of the brochure and the feasibility study. A cover letter from Scott explaining the feasibility study was developed for the study.

A 990-EZ tax form filed for the year of 2004 and extending to July 31, 2005, brought about the dissolution of the foundation. Expenses incurred were $21,192 for the feasibility study, $4,673 for miscellaneous expenses, $366 for registration fees and $1,712 for web site design. $41,610 was returned to the Skoll Foundation. There was no compensation to any of the participating officers or board members.

[20] Minutes of the Back Foundation, 2004.

The decision to dissolve the foundation was based on the outcome of the feasibility study that demonstrated the inability to achieve the funding levels set in the business plan and the failure to identify a high profile personality who would serve as spokesperson. Obviously all participants were very disappointed.

WORLD FEDERATION OF CHIROPRACTIC (WFC)

In the words of the secretary general of the World Federation of Chiropractic (WFC), David Chapman-Smith, Scott played an instrumental role in helping the WFC put on its First Congress in Toronto, Canada, May 1991:

> When the World Federation of Chiropractic (WFC) was formed in 1988, it established a research council with Scott as chairman. As such, he had prime responsibility for planning the program for the WFC's first International Congress, including the original research competition. Largely, through Scott's connections,
>
> a. The Congress was held in conjunction with the spring meeting of the American Back Society, at the Royal York Hotel in Toronto.
>
> b. Leading chiropractic speakers, including Dr. Haldeman, were joined by prominent international researchers such as Dr Akio Sato, the neurophysiologist from Japan, Dr. William Kirkaldy-Willis, orthopedic surgeon from Canada, Dr. Sam Wiesel, orthopedic surgeon from the USA, Dr. Bjorn Rydevik and Dr. Gunnar Andersson, orthopedic surgeons from Sweden.
>
> There was high anticipation as the first session was due to commence at 8:30 a.m. on a Thursday morning—and then all power to that wing of the hotel failed. Fifteen minutes had elapsed before proceedings could commence—but all went superbly following that. Tears of pride and joy came from members of the profession's first wave of North American researchers, such as Dr Adrian Grice and Dr Ronald Gitelman of Canada, who had waited throughout their careers for the time when the profession would mature to the point that it could present a research symposium of the most demanding standards.

A feature of the social program was the *Phantom of the Opera* attended by medical doctors and their partners attending the ABS meeting, and doctors of chiropractic and their partners attending the WFC Congress. It included a champagne reception with stars of the show afterwards. Chiropractors were delighted when a lead actor raised a toast to the chiropractic profession, saying there was no way this cast could survive without their chiropractic care. As Scott was addressing the gathering he was approached by the female lead, "Christine," who with her theatrical charms persuaded him to do something never heard before or since—to sing with her lines from the show. To everyone's surprise and pleasure, Scott responded with a clear, on-tune, strong, baritone voice that provoked a spontaneous applause of appreciation.

As chairman of the WFC Research Council, Scott was always available to support the international growth of chiropractic.

As the WFC was formed in 1988, he was the keynote speaker at the first major international meeting arranged by the Mexican College of Chiropractors, both at the academic program and at the lavish banquet attended by many leading medical specialists in Mexico City.

In the mid 1990s the Ministry of Health in Trinidad and Tobago was sympathetic to the recognition and regulation of chiropractic, but the government held back because of strident opposition from the Medical Council. Not knowing anyone there, Scott flew down for three days on behalf of the WFC, met with medical leaders, and solved the problem.

Having climbed all the mountains he needed to conquer in the medical world, Scott has very much come home to his roots in chiropractic. Many in the profession do not understand this fact because they only read about him from afar. I have witnessed many recent speeches where the audience is on its feet as he finishes speaking, well aware that it is in the presence of an extraordinary man.

One such occasion was the Canadian National Conference held in Vancouver in October 2006. Scott started with his upbringing in a chiropractic home—healthy natural foods, exercise, positive thought, adjustments as needed. He then provided all the technical information called for in the lecture. He finished by asking all present to dedicate themselves to a chiropractic lifestyle, one part of which was serving others.[21]

Scott continues to serve as the chair of the Research Council of the WFC. He advises Chapman-Smith on international research matters, assists with the organization of the biannual conference, oversees the selection of papers, posters and awards at the biennial meeting, and continues to be a voice of reason and credibility for the chiropractic profession internationally. Scott says the formation of the WFC with its research council was a big step toward his original idea of organizing an International Society for Chiropractic Education and Spinal Research. At the biennial congress of the WFC, members of the Research Council, the editor of *Journal of Manipulative and Physiological Therapeutics (JMPT)*, and an outside examiner formed a committee to judge the scientific papers for what has become probably the most prestigious scientific awards in the chiropractic profession. The first place award was named The Haldeman Award. Scott feels that this is one of the most important honors he has received by the chiropractic profession.

CONCLUSION

From the early days of his father's office in Pretoria, Scott enjoyed working with patients. Running his own multidisciplinary practice in Southern California was a capstone to his clinical capabilities. Having multiple faculty appointments, mentoring numerous individuals, publishing, and participating in a variety of committees fully occupied his time. But this variety of roles was a natural occurrence. Through his many years of schooling, he had been trained to take on the roles of clinician, mentor, writer, and leader in the field of spinal care. He transitioned enthusiastically from the one being trained to the one doing the training. And as his experience widened, so did his accomplishments.

---

[21] Personal communication via e-mail with David Chapman-Smith, 2008. A copy is in the Haldeman Collection.

Chapter 12

Trips and Speaking Engagements

EARLY TRAVELS

Scott's familiarity with travel started at a very young age. He made numerous trips with his parents as they scooted about Canada and the United States, first by car and later by plane. His personal travelogue begins when his family moved from Regina, Canada, to Pretoria, South Africa, halfway around the world. Scott was only six at the time.

While growing up, he traveled quite frequently with his parents, exploring Southern Africa in depth. His numerous trips to the Kalahari Desert and throughout the rest of Africa, flying as far as Kenya, Uganda, and Zanzibar, were only the first of many travels he would eventually make across the globe.

When Scott ventured off to Palmer College of Chiropractic at the age of 18 (1961), he crossed the Atlantic Ocean a second time. Students don't normally travel much, but when they come all the way from South Africa to America, it is logical that they should take advantage of every opportunity to see all they can on the assumption they may never get another chance. Scott made a point to drive around the United States whenever he had an opportunity. He traveled as far west as Colorado and east to New England and down to

Florida while at Palmer. He also traveled with the rugby and cricket teams and as a member of the flying club. His job at the piano shop allowed him to do some local travel. While he was becoming very familiar with a life of travel, he had not yet had much practice with speaking engagements, which would become such a prominent part of his later life. His only speaking engagements while at Palmer were for the Davenport Rotary Club where he spoke about South Africa on a couple of occasions and his valedictorian address.

Scott's return to South Africa via Montreal and London after graduating from Palmer (his third trip across the Atlantic) and his subsequent marriage to Joan did not curtail his yearning to be on the move. In fact, his mother advised Joan that, "...you should never clip the wings of a Haldeman. If you let them fly freely they will always come back home."[1] Wyn spoke with experience from her life with Josh Haldeman, and Joan recognized similar hereditary characteristics in Scott. She followed the advice and even took up traveling with him whenever possible (see Chapter 10 for more detail).

TRAVELING AND SPEAKING IN SOUTH AFRICA

When Joan and Scott were married, they decided to drive to the South Coast of South Africa for their honeymoon in the small coastal village of Ramsgate in the province of Natal. Over the next four years, they drove throughout Southern Africa, usually camping next to the car in the national parks or just pulling off the road at an interesting sight and putting down their sleeping bag. They traveled at various times down to Cape Town, to Swaziland, Basutoland (now Lesotho), and throughout southern and northern Rhodesia (now Zimbabwe and Zambia).

The year after Scott returned and he and Joan were married, they had a chance to hone their public speaking skills when they were asked by the principle of Clapham High School to speak at the graduation ceremony. The request was based on the fact that Joan and Scott had been head prefects when they were seniors at Clapham High

---

[1] Personal Communication with Joan Haldeman, September 2008.

and both had graduated from a university and were continuing their studies. The topic of their presentation was that working hard and supporting each other was the basis for their current and hopefully future success.

While pursuing his bachelor's and master's degrees, Scott began his professional speaking career—one that would take him across many oceans many times in the future. He first spoke in a professional capacity at the Annual Cape Chiropractic Congress in December 1967. His subject matter was the substance of his master's work, *Physiology of the Nerves.* Joan accompanied him on the dais, speaking about what was required to become a physiotherapist, a step she had already completed. The following February, he spoke to the South African Chiropractors Association (SACA) on the same subject. On a return trip home to Pretoria after three years in Canada, Scott was again invited to speak at the SACA convention in May 1973. Scott would return many more times to South Africa for family visits and professional meetings.

Scott began to formally record his speaking engagements in his Curriculum Vitae (CV) in 1985. What is contained in his CV is representative of his "invited" speaking engagements but does not include personal trips, trips to meetings where he was not invited to present, meetings where there were no formal presentations made (planning meetings), meetings where he was in charge but was not formally presenting, and meetings where he attended as a member of a particular association. The amount of time spent traveling and speaking was extensive, to say the least.[2]

TRAVELING AND SPEAKING IN CANADA

Scott and Joan traveled from South Africa to North America via London, Paris, and Montreal before spending eight months in Toronto in 1970. As noted in Chapter 5, they made their way from Toronto

---

[2] The pre-1985 travelogue in Appendix B was created from brochures of meetings, personal correspondence, travel vouchers, and payments for honoraria. The record is no doubt incomplete, although it is more inclusive than just the "invited" presentations noted in his CV. For more details on personal and family travel see Chapter 10.

to Vancouver by driving east to Ottawa and Montreal, then into the U.S. to New York and Washington, and across the U.S. to the major national parks in Colorado and Montana, crossing back into Canada at Calgary and over the Rockies to Vancouver.

While in Vancouver, Joan and Scott made multiple short trips skiing or hiking throughout British Columbia and Washington State. They also made two major road trips. The first was a seven-week trip down the Pacific coast to California and across the Mexican border to Tijuana. They then went south of the border to the other side of the gulf and down the coast via Hermosillo to Mazatlan. From there they traveled inland to Guadalajara and on to Mexico City. The trip was complete when they visited San Miguel de Allende and then drove back to the Vancouver via Chihuahua and El Paso. Altogether the trip was 4,000 miles of driving in Mexico. The second road trip was with Joan's parents who were visiting from South Africa. They again drove through the national parks in Washington State and Oregon to California to visit Disneyland and San Diego. They then drove to Las Vegas and back to Canada via Yosemite. Scott and Joan also saved up their money to go back to South Africa in 1973 to visit their family and friends.

While acquiring his PhD and MD degrees in Vancouver, Scott became more visible and sought after as a speaker. Over the course of the next six years he would speak numerous times to the British Columbia Chiropractic Association and the British Columbia Industrial First Aid Association. He was invited to attend several chiropractic and medical meetings as a keynote speaker.

Two standout events during this six year period were the NINCDS Conference where Scott was on the planning committee, and the Pneumoconiosis Conference where Scott was a speaker (see Chapter 15 for a detailed accounting of these two conferences). From September 1970 to June 1977, Scott went to and/or spoke at thirty-one venues (see Appendix B), the bulk of these events falling in 1976-77 when Scott was wrapping up his medical education. Anyone who has traveled considerably knows what a drain and distraction being on the road is to duties at school and on the home front. It must also be realized that as a relative unknown, Scott did not draw huge honorariums and was probably grateful when his travel expenses were covered. This was not a preferred way to build the family budget, but it was beginning to build his reputation.

SPEAKING WHILE IN HIS RESIDENCY IN SOUTHERN CALIFORNIA 1977-1980

Scott and Joan barely got their feet on the ground in Southern California before Scott was off on a speaking engagement with the Australian Chiropractic Association in Queensland, Australia. He had alerted Dr. Van de Noort of his travel obligations before joining the residency program and was granted permission to travel. He was not excused from keeping up with his necessary training and clinical obligations, however, and had to make up any commitments when he returned.

During his neurology residency at UCI from July 1977 to July 1980, the speaking opportunities mushroomed. Including his trip to Australia, he attended thirteen events in the last half of 1977 (an average of more than two per month after having just relocated his family), fifteen trips in 1978, sixteen trips in 1979, including a round-the-world trip with Joan and the kids, his own Haldeman Research Conference, and a special trip to present at the New Zealand Commission on Inquiry (see Chapter 15). Eight more trips filled up the first six-months of 1980. This equates to 54 trips in 36 months (see Appendix B).

If all his trips represented no more effort than getting on a plane and snoozing until he arrived at his destination, then spending time mostly around a swimming pool, the schedule would seem doable. But Scott rarely returned home sunburned. Some of his trips involved not only presenting at the conference, but in several instances, actually taking qualifying board exams at the same meeting. Other trips were in response to Scott's growing number of memberships in various organizations (see Chapter 14).

1980 TO THE PRESENT

Scott soon became a popular speaker in both medical and chiropractic venues. His knowledge, experience, and presentation abilities won the admiration of his audiences even when giving what some would consider a very dry topic. He was always on the cutting edge of information relevant to the interests of his audiences, and was able to place this information into a meaningful context. Scott's opportunities to speak and participate on a wide variety of committees soon exceeded his ability to meet expectations and requests.

Several times a trip to one location would actually entail multiple meetings associated within a single venue, such as planning and executive meetings along with general sessions in organizations like the American Back Society. Scott would also maximize his time by arranging speaking engagements with the local chiropractic association or college while in the area attending a medical meeting. Several of Scott's meetings were held in Southern California and may not be considered as travel, but getting around Southern California in traffic can be more stressful than a long airplane flight to some foreign country. And either way, they still took him either out of the office or away from home and usually required preparation for the presentation and often the compiling of notes. Scott never stopped crossing oceans. Beginning in 1980, he traveled overseas at least 59 times in the next 30 years.[3]

One of Scott's most noteworthy international experiences was working on a research project in China. He had been working very closely with Dr. Arnold Starr in the neurology department at UCI and his research associate Dr. Yu Zhu who was from China and very interested in electrodiagnosis. Scott wanted to study the impact of manipulation in patients with low back pain by recording brain cortical evoked responses on stimulation of paraspinal muscles before and after treatment. Dr. Zhu proposed that the study be carried out in

---

[3] A complete accounting of Scott's "invited" lectures can be found in his CV in Appendix C and a complete accounting of his total trips can be found in Appendix B. It should be noted that Scott's desire and opportunity to travel have continued beyond the completion of this biography in 2009.

Shanghai where he had connections with the hospital. There would be no difficulty finding large numbers of patients with back pain and the cost would be considerably less than in California. Scott was able to obtain a grant from the FCER to fund the project. During the clinical study, Scott spent two weeks in Shanghai walking to the hospital through the streets and parks from the hotel to the hospital and interacting with the clinicians and scientists involved in the study. Dr. Zhu then organized a speaking tour to the military medical institutes

Scott lecturing at the American Back Society Conference in Las Vegas June 2008

273

(three of the largest university medical schools in China) in Shanghai, Xian, and Beijing. At each university, Scott and Yu were wined and dined as VIPs by the staff physicians, who at that time were all in military uniform and looking for a reason to have a great dinner.

The following table is a summary of Scott's travels since 1980.

Year	# Trips/yr	# Overseas	Location
1980	20	2	London/Australia, New Zealand, South Africa
1981	22	2	Oslo/Paris
1982	21	2	St. Thomas/ London
1983	22	2	Cambridge/ Zurich
1984	27	0	
1985	30	5	Sydney/West Germany/Oslo/Vienna/South Africa
1986	16	0	
1987	17	3	Rome/Brisbane/London
1988	23	1	Switzerland
1989	15	3	Kyoto/Rio de Janeiro /Sao Paulo (Mexico City & Quebec are in NA)
1990	20	0	
1991	21	2	Heidelberg/Sydney
1992	21	1	Puerto Rico
1993	8	2	Shanghai/Xian/Beijing, Sun City South Africa
1994	6	0	
1995	11	2	Helsinki/Tokyo
1996	12	2	Trinidad/Geneva
1997	9	3	Sydney, Brisbane/Tokyo
1998	9	1	Moscow
1999	22	2	Auckland/Moscow
2000	16	1	Bournmouth
2001	15	3	Tel Aviv/Paris/Edinburgh, Turkey
2002	14	1	Spain and Portugal
2003	11	2	Fukuoka, Japan/Durban, South Africa
2004	14	2	Porto, Portugal/ Bordeaux, France
2005	17	2	Brazil and Argentina/Greece, Cyprus
2006	14	3	Ireland/Bergen, Norway/Jordan and Egypt

2007	17	4	Stockholm/Portugal, France, Italy/Hong Kong/Bern, Croatia
2008	17	3	Costa Rica/Southern Africa/Beijing
2009	6	3	Stockholm/Saint Petersburg/Belgium/Switzerland
Total	*493*	*59*	

Average Per year
      16   *1.9*

To anyone who has traveled extensively, the brutality of the experience is familiar. What is amazing is Scott's continued desire to see the world, albeit in a more relaxed schedule. Scott and Joan love the beautiful home and gardens they have created for themselves in Southern California, but they also love to see the rest of the world many times over.

PERSONAL TOURS AND ROAD TRIPS

Most of the travels noted above were to attend or speak at a convention or to meet with government or association officials. Some of these trips included visits to neighboring countries. In addition, however, Joan and Scott have enjoyed some exciting personal tours and road trips abroad. The list of places they have visited would be too extensive to present in detail; however, the extent of their travel experiences to visit interesting places and study the major historical, archeological, and geographical sites throughout the world would not be complete without describing a few of these trips.

Many of these travels were by road when Scott and Joan would rent or lease a car and travel for periods of two to four weeks. On trips to South Africa, they would take their sons Reeve and Keatly around the country from Pretoria through the major game reserves and down the Garden Route to Cape Town. On one occasion when asked to speak in Australia, Scott, Joan, Reeve, and Keatly drove from Brisbane via the Gold Coast down to Sydney. On another occasion Scott, Joan, and Keatly drove from Cairns through the rain forests up to Cooktown in Northern Australia and back to Cairns.

Most of the recent driving tours, however, were done after their sons had left home. For example, they spent four weeks driving all the way around Ireland, including Northern Ireland, visiting the Rings of Dingle and Kerry, and catching a boat to the Skellig Islands, staying in a couple of Irish castles and then going down the north coast of Ireland via Londonderry, the Devil's Causeway, and Belfast before returning to Dublin. On another occasion they drove around the Peloponnese Peninsula in Greece, and from Athens to Delphi, Olympia, Tripoli, Sparta, Nafplion, Corinth, and back to Athens. When Scott had to attend meetings in Porto and Bordeaux, they drove from Madrid through Spain via Cordoba and Seville to the Algarve of Portugal and then up to Lisbon to Porto, across northern Spain to Bordeaux, France, and back to Madrid. Whenever they could, they would stay in the Paradores or Pousadas, which are old castles and monasteries that have been converted to hotels. When required to speak at a conference in Bern, Switzerland, in 2007, Joan and Scott drove from Zurich via Lichtenstein to Innsbruck in Austria and then down through Slovenia and Croatia to Venice and back to Bern via the Dolomites, Florence, and the Italian Lake District. On another occasion they drove from Lisbon down to the Algarve to attend a conference, through Spain via Granada and Barcelona to southern France, staying in Avignon and Eze before traveling to Italy to walk the Cinque Terre and visit the historical sites and museums in Sienna and Rome.

Joan and Scott are also blessed to have a large number of friends who enjoy traveling together. They have participated in a number of organized group bus tours. One of these was through Turkey for 19 days, visiting the magnificent sights of Istanbul, Troy, Ephesus, Anatolia, Cappadocia, and Ankara. Another bus tour with friends was through Eastern Europe and included stops in Berlin, Prague, Warsaw, Krakow, Budapest, and Vienna. They have also joined friends in a tour of Egypt visiting all the major sights. Before this tour, Joan and Scott spent a week Jordan. They consider the sites in Jordan, especially the ancient city of Petra, the Roman city of Jarash, the crusader castle at Karak, and the Muslim Desert Castles, amongst the most interesting places to visit in the world. This visit complemented the history of the region that they studied during a visit to Israel a few years earlier. The Israel trip that Joan and Scott undertook was combined with an invited lecture in Tel Aviv immediately after the 9/11 disaster. There were virtually no tourists in the country, and Scott and Joan were almost alone when visiting the holy and historical sites.

Egypt , 2007. Abu Simbel
Left to right. Front Row. Joan Haldeman, Jackie Powell, Marilyn Cooper, Pat Wescombe, Joan Landers, and guide, A.T. Back Row. Bob Valentine, Scott Haldeman, Shel Glina, Kay Kurtz, Gary Wescombe, Sally Valentine, Barbara Urbanski, Ted Urbanski, Lyn Cooper, Don Powell, Tom Landers.

The highlight of recent travels with friends, however, took place in 2008. Scott and Joan had long promised a few friends that they would arrange a tour of their favorite places in Southern Africa. On completion of the Neck Pain Task Force, they finally had the time to organize the tour. To their surprise, 21 of their friends agreed to take off three to five weeks to join them in touring Southern Africa. The trip was unique in that Scott and Joan picked those sights they had visited many years before and a few that they had hoped to see but had not yet visited. Traveling with only close friends, mostly from Southern California, and showing them their favorite places was a very rewarding experience. On this trip they toured Namibia, including the sand dunes of Sussusvlei, the towns of Windhoek and Swakopmund, the seal colony of Walvis Bay, and the magnificent animals at the Etosha Pan and Caprivi Strip Game parks. They went on safari in the Okavango Delta of Botswana and continued on to a visit to the Victoria Falls in Zimbabwe. This was followed by two weeks through Swaziland and South Africa seeing Pretoria, Johannesburg, Kruger Park, Zululand, and Durban and finally down the Garden Route along the coast to Cape Town.

Victoria Falls, Zimbabwe, 2008
From left to right. Front Row. Ted Urbanski, Joan Landers, Alberto Varriale, Sally Valentine, Jackie Powell. From left to right. Second row. Linda Cops, Ann Nicholson, Barbara Urbanski, Graziella Varriale, Joan Haldeman, Pat Mathisen, Kathy Metzger. From left to right. Back Row. Todd Nicholson, Tom Landers, Bob Valentine, Greg Cops, Scott Haldeman, Jim Mathisen, Bill Metzger, Don Powell.

Joan Haldeman and Reed Phillips (the author) at Cape Point in
South Africa, October 2008

FUTURE TRAVELS

The requests to speak and the desire to travel have not stopped. In
2009 Scott will speak at meetings in Stockholm, Montreal, and Brussels as well as at a number of meetings in the U.S. In 2010 he already
has invitations to speak at conferences in Iran, London, and New
Zealand, and in 2011 he has penciled in meetings in Stockholm and
another project in Shanghai as well as the WFC Congress in Rio de
Janeiro. Scott and Joan are hoping to be able to attach a visit to Syria
and Lebanon to the Iranian meeting and a road trip around New Zealand after the conference in that country.

In June 2009, Scott and Joan planned a train and hiking tour of
Belgium, Switzerland, and the Dolomites in the Italian Alps with
their friends, Jackie and Don Powell. They were joined by Graziella
and Alberto Varriale, friends from Italy, in the Dolomites. They also
have plans for tours of India and another trip to South Africa in the

279

pipeline. Their wish list of countries and sights they are hoping to visit include Machu Pichu in Peru and the Galapagos Island, Southeast Asia, especially Angkor Wat in Cambodia, Bhutan and Tibet, the northern Africa countries of Libya, Tunisia, and Morocco, and the Patagonia area of Argentina and Chile. One of their dearest wishes is to include their sons, daughters-in-law, and grandchildren on these trips as often as possible.

It is likely that Scott will receive many more requests to speak at conferences in the future and that Joan and Scott will continue to find time to visit those parts of the world they have not already seen. Travel for them remains an adventure—they are always anxious to see new sights, experience new cultures, and broaden their appreciation for the great diversity in mankind. In the early years, Scott's travels were business-focused and augmented his research efforts and his income. More recent travels continue to have a business link but with a much greater emphasis on leisure time spent with Joan. The Haldeman fancy to travel, ingrained in Scott by his father, has never diminished.

SECTION III

PROFESSIONAL ACTIVITIES

Chapter 13

Research and Publications

I t seemed most appropriate to begin this chapter with one of
Scott's own sage remarks that is so characteristic of him *"It's easy
to succeed if you just work harder than anyone else."* This is a key
to Scott's success.

The adage "If it isn't published, it never happened" has relevance
to Scott's journey. In today's digital world where "publishing" now
extends beyond the written word into an electronic world, the ability to distribute the "word," even the "spoken word," was important
to Scott and his career, as evidenced by his many publications and
invitations to speak around the world (see Appendix C, Scott's Curriculum Vitae).

A chronological analysis of Scott's writings provides a window into
the changes that occurred within his life as he progressed through his
many academic attainments, professional experiences, and personal
challenges. His works range from very detailed scientific documentation, practical application of current information, and exhortations to
motivation for change and historical reflections. A detailed analysis of
the depth and breadth of what he has published is beyond the scope
of a single chapter. His CV lists nine books or theses, 188 published
articles and book chapters, and 70 abstracts accepted for proceedings
at various conferences.

SCIENTIFIC WRITINGS

Scott's scientific writings began with his master's thesis published in 1969 while he was completing his program at the University of Pretoria. The thesis, *Changes in the Structure and Function of Sciatic Nerve caused by Constriction*, was consistent with his desire to explore and explain the fundamentals of chiropractic as he had learned them from his father and while at Palmer College.

When settled in Toronto to meet requirements for chiropractic licensure in British Columbia, he published two articles as part of his research commitment to CMCC. "The First Impressions of the Synchro-Therme as a Skin Temperature Reading Instrument," and "Observations made under Test Conditions with the Synchro-Therme," were published in 1970 in the *Journal of the Canadian Chiropractic Association* (JCCA).

While working on and completing his PhD and its associated thesis (1970 – 1973), Scott published fourteen articles, most related to the work of his MSc and his PhD. Eight of these articles were published in chiropractic journals (at that time considered to be non-peer-reviewed publications). However, to his academic credit, he also published in prestigious peer-reviewed medical publications with articles in the *South African Medical Journal, Brain Research, Journal of Neurochemistry*, and others. He published his PhD thesis, *Evidence in Favor of Glutamate as a Mediator of Synaptic Transmission*, in January of 1973. This was a major achievement given that 1973 was a transition year between Scott's PhD program and medical school. Again, his PhD focused on broadening the scientific understanding of fundamental neurophysiological principles important in the understanding of sensory physiology and which could potentially increase the understanding mechanisms of spinal pain. In keeping with his commitment for the financial support he received, he also published four more scientific articles in 1973, two of them in chiropractic publications.

Attending medical school and completing an internship between 1974 and 1977 represented a major time commitment. During this period, Scott added fourteen additional publications to his CV—nine in chiropractic journals (three were opinion pieces), one in a physical therapy journal, and most importantly, two chapters in the *NINCDS Monograph #15, The Research Status of Spinal Manipulative Therapy* (see Chapter 15). Scott published two chapters in Buerger and Tobis's *Approaches to the Validation of Manipulative Therapy*. Scott's work with Drs. Buerger and Tobis at the University of California at Irvine (UCI) linked him to the work they were doing on manipulative therapy and provided the extra incentive that sealed his decision to do a residency in neurology at UCI.

In his concluding remarks in the chapter, "Why One Cause of Back Pain?" in *Approaches to the Validation of Manipulative Therapy*, Scott begins to exhibit an expansion of thought—that back pain potentially can have multiple origins as opposed to the idea of a "pinched nerve" so prevalent in chiropractic literature of the 1960s when he was a student a Palmer College:

> There are three alternative explanations for the current multiplic-
> ity of theories on the pathogenesis of back pain. Firstly, that all
> back pain comes from a single pathological process and that the
> other factors are unimportant. Secondly, that back pain can be
> caused by any of a number of pathological processes, and thirdly,
> that it is caused only when more than one factor is present at the
> same time. At least the physiological mechanisms exist which can
> explain each of these possibilities. It is likely that all three expla-
> nations have some degree of truth and that there is a complex
> interaction of etiological factors important in the genesis of back
> pain in a large population of patients. If this is true, any therapeu-
> tic procedure aimed at a single etiological factor in an unselected
> population of patients with low back pain could not be expected to
> help more than a small percentage of these patients.[1]

Time spent in his clinical residency program at UCI (1977-1980) was intense as exemplified by the fact that he could not write articles as often as he had before. Three publications in the chiropractic litera- ture, one article in a medical journal, and a chapter in each of three

---

[1] Haldeman, Scott. "Why One Cause of Back Pain?" Chp. 10 in Buerger and Tobis, *Approaches to the Validation of Manipulative Therapy*. Charles C. Thomas, Springfield, IL 1977.

books—*Neurobiologic Mechanisms in Manipulative Therapy* by Korr, *Low Back Pain* by Finneson, and a chapter in *Modern Developments in the Principles and Practice of Chiropractic*, a book he edited and published.

The importance of Scott publishing *Modern Developments in the Principles and Practice of Chiropractic* was no trivial matter, and the significance of this achievement should not be overlooked. No major publisher had ever agreed to publish a book on chiropractic written primarily by and for chiropractors. The book was designed to be a textbook that all chiropractic students would use, thus assuring its marketability. Scott passed his proposal by many publishers before Apple-Century-Croft accepted the offer. He also had to obtain a guarantee from the ICA to purchase a fixed number of copies. The probability of any future chiropractic authors ever obtaining a major publisher for their work rested heavily upon Scott's shoulders. He knew full well that if his efforts failed, the door of opportunity for others might well be closed. More information on this book can be found in Chapter 15.

In 1980, at the conclusion of his residency, he had a fellowship to pursue at Long Beach Memorial Hospital, a private practice to get started, and numerous board exams to prepare for and pass. Although this was a very busy time for Scott as a scholar, it was in his blood to write. This period was one of the most productive in his career and established his authority as a clinical scientist in the field of neurology. In the first five years after his residency (1981-1985), he completed twenty-seven citations: six chapters in books or conference proceedings, seventeen articles in mainline peer-reviewed medical journals, three articles in chiropractic journals (including an article on his grandmother as the first chiropractor to practice in Canada), and one chapter for a training course in neurology and evoked response testing. The majority of these publications were in the field of clinical neurology and neurodiagnostic testing. With Bill Bradley as his mentor, and with a number of collaborators at the Long Beach Memorial Veteran's Administration Medical Center, he was able to study the neurophysiology of the pelvic visceral organs important for bowel, bladder, and sexual function. These studies led to the development of clinical testing methods to study the innervations of these organs and diagnose how such disorders as peripheral neuropathy, spinal cord injury, multiple sclerosis, and Parkinson's disease impacted these functions. His hope was that the development of these tests, and greater understanding of the neural mechanisms controlling visceral function, would provide the tools to study the relationship of spinal disorders and visceral function.

A review of Chapter 12 and Appendix B regarding Scott's travel and speaking engagements will reveal that his published papers provided ample material for speaking presentations at meetings and conventions for his neurology colleagues as well as the chiropractic community. Armed with current scientific knowledge, Scott always provided a commanding performance—often mixed with provocation.

From 1985 to 2009, Scott's writing proliferated. However, consistent with his publication record, he also served on editorial review boards for several publications and as an external reviewer for several dissertations and promotions. His editorial review board and external review appointments included:

Alternative Therapies in Health and Medicine
    2001-2004   Editorial Board
Back Pain Monitor newsletter
    1984   Conference Advisory Board
    1983-1989   Editorial Advisory Board
Clinical Chiropractic (formerly British Journal of Chiropractic)
    2003   Editorial Board
International Review of Chiropractic
    1983-   Technical Paper Review Committee
Journal of the Australian Chiropractors' Association
    1983-   Editorial Board Member
Journal of the Canadian Chiropractic Association
    1985-   Editorial Board Member
Journal of Manipulative and Physiological Therapeutics
    1979-   Editorial Board Member

Journal of Manual Medicine
>1984-1992   Editorial Board Member

Journal of the Neuromusculoskeletal System
>1992-2003   Editor in Chief

Neuro-Orthopedics
>1986-1995   Editorial Board

North American Academy of Manipulative Medicine Newsletter
>1980-1982   Editor

Pacific Northwest Journal of Clinical Chiropractic
>1985   Editorial Board

Spine
>1988-   Editorial Board – Associate Editor

Spine Letter
>1994-1998   Editorial Board

The Back Letter
>1992-   Editorial Board

The Spine Journal
>2002-   Executive Board–Deputy Editor/Non-Operative Care

External Examiner on MS and PhD Theses and Dissertations

C. Myburgh	DPhil	Stellenbosch University–South Africa
P.S. Ebrall	PhD	RMIT University–Australia
Allan Terrett	MApplied Sc (Chiro)	Philip Institute of Technology–Australia
Niels Nilsson	PhD	Odense University–Denmark
Simon Dagenais	PhD	UC Irvine–California
Lynton Giles	PhD	U of Western Australia
Shaun Cashman	MSc	Maquarie University–Australia

External Examiner for Promotions
Rand Swenson   Associate Professor Dartmouth University

In February 1978, Scott was contacted by Roy Hildebrandt, DC, of National College of Chiropractic, to accept a position on the editorial board of a new journal to be produced by National College titled, *The Journal of Manipulative and Physiological Therapeutics (JMPT)*. Scott responded with a number of questions and comments:

1. He agreed with the need for a good journal supporting the scientific aspect of chiropractic but raised the issue as to why National College has not decided to support journals already existing in the profession.

2. He wondered how the JMPT would obtain adequate quality material for publication when other journals in chiropractic had failed to do so.

3. He questioned the wisdom of having the JMPT affiliated with a single chiropractic institution.

4. He asked who beyond the alumni of National College would subscribe.

5. He questioned the use of the term "physiological therapeutics" and what it represented.

6. He wanted a definition for the term, "conservative health care."

7. Based upon articles already published by National College of Chiropractic, he raised the issue of inconsistent editorial policy.

8. He wanted to know who else would be serving on the editorial board.[2]

Scott explained that if his questions could be answered he would consider the invitation to serve on the editorial board.

Dr. Hildebrandt apparently answered Scott's questions sufficiently in a letter dated March 1, 1978, and Scott accepted the invitation on April 12 to serve on the *JMPT* editorial board.

As accomplished as Scott was as a writer, not everyone agreed with what he had to say. The paper, "Controlled Clinical Trials of Manipulation: A Review and a Proposal" by Greenland, et. al [Scott was third

[2] Letter to Roy Hildebrandt, DC, from Scott Haldeman, DC, PhD, MD dated 22 February 1978.

author] submitted to the *Journal of Occupational Medicine* in 1979, was sent back for revision with eight points of concern. Dr. Greenland submitted a revised paper in February 1980 with an admission that it may not be possible to come to an agreement over "...the best methods for investigating effects and interpreting results" of manipulation. He suggested that if the reviewer could not agree, they should instead do a published exchange between the authors and the reviewer in the "letter to the editor" section. Scott sent a note to Dr. Greenland complimenting him on the revisions made.

The paper was published in the *Journal of Occupational Medicine*, Vol. 22, No. 10 in 1980. A vociferous letter to the editor was sent by a Dr. Pomerantz in December 1980 and forwarded on to Dr. Greenland for a response. Scott supplied Dr. Greenland with a response in his letter of February 17, 1981. He took Dr. Pomerantz to task:

> It appears evident that Dr. Pomerantz either failed to read the paper in detail or did not comprehend its content...Dr. Pomerantz suggests that manipulation is not described in terms of "applied physiology and anatomy" and that there is "no recognition of a scientific basis...by any of the great institutions of learning." He appears to be ignorant of or has forgotten that manipulation was part of the therapeutic armamentarium of both Hippocrates and Galen and that manipulation is currently being utilized and studied in such institutions as the University of Saskatchewan, University of California at Irvine, University of Paris to name a few. It is possible that Dr. Pomerantz does not consider these institutions to be "of higher learning."[3]

Not every writing attempt turned into a publication, especially in the early years when the conflict and lack of trust between chiropractors and the medical profession was a significant factor. In December of 1980, he submitted a proposal to Raven Press in response to their request to edit a book on *An Interdisciplinary Approach to Spinal Pain*. The production of such a book had been in discussion since October of 1981. Scott proposed thirty chapters authored by six MDs

---

[3] All letters between Dr. Greenland, Dr. Haldeman, Dr. Pomerantz and the *Journal of Occupational Medicine* are in the Haldeman Collection.

(including himself), two physical therapists (including his wife Joan), three PhDs, one person trained at the master's degree level, and three DCs with advanced degrees at the master's level. The final decision by Raven Press came in a letter dated July 2, 1981:

> It is obvious to our reviewers that you have devoted a great deal of time to developing the concept fully and structuring the book well. Each reviewer tended to have his or her own comments about alterations in the structure of the volume, none of which were critical. However, every MD who reviewed it for us commented on one particular aspect, which a leading orthopedic surgeon described as a "distinct chiropractic flavor" which, he added, "always forces (him) to ask about the hidden agenda of such a work."
>
> Coming as it did from one of our medical reviewers, this was a serious statement indeed, as I am certain you are well aware of the negative feelings about chiropractic held by the American medical establishment...It is for this reason that we are forced to conclude we cannot consider the book's continuing development and publication. We believe it would severely prejudice many of our readers about what they perceive to be the integrity of our list.[4]

As the relationship between chiropractic and medicine improved, Scott was approached by major publishing houses to write or edit books on spine care. In 1985, Williams and Wilkins, one of the largest medical publishers, asked Scott to consider editing a Spine Care Series, but he was not able to find the time and resources and had to decline the offer. He did accept W.B. Saunders offer to edit an edition of *Neurology Clinics* on low back pain that was published in 1999.

When the American Chiropractic Association (ACA) decided to create a new scientific journal in 1993 for their membership, the *Journal of the Neuromusculoskeletal System (JNMS)*, they called upon Scott to be the editor-in-chief and Rand Swensen, DC, PhD, MD, to be the editor. In his inaugural issue editorial, "The Justification for another Journal," Scott expressed skepticism similar to his initial response to join the editorial board of the *JMPT* one decade earlier:

---

[4] Letter from Margaret McLaughlin, Editor for Raven Press, to Scott Haldeman, dated 2 July 1981.

When first approached about the possibility of another journal I was very skeptical about the necessity, feasibility or viability of such a venture...There were also concerns about the availability of high quality material to fill another journal and the difficulties recent journals have had in maintaining subscription rates and thereby financial viability.

In meetings on the direction the journal should take...it was decided...primary contact clinicians, including chiropractors, osteopathic and medical family physicians, limited care independent practitioners such as physical therapists and psychologists and even many specialists are not being kept abreast of the latest scientific developments in a critical manner. A journal that attempts to satisfy this need and is directed at the practitioner in his office therefore has a chance of being successful.

A guaranteed readership and financial support is also necessary to assure the success of a new journal. The support of the American Chiropractic Association made the development of a new journal feasible...The decision was made to have an inter-professional editorial board and to attract comments and papers from authorities from all the professions and sciences with an interest in the field. This would allow the dissemination of ideas and research across professional boundaries.

The final decision makers on the success of any journal, however, are the readers...Time will tell whether the chiropractors and other professionals will accept and participate in the *Journal of Neuro-Muscular-Skeletal System (JNMS)*.[5]

These comments display Scott's ecumenical attitude toward practitioners of spine care in his ever-persistent attempt to keep them informed of the latest research in their discipline. Unfortunately, the *JNMS* survived only a few years and was dropped from production by the ACA due to financial reasons.

Spine, the first peer reviewed medical and scientific journal devoted solely to the spine, was first published in 1976 and became the official

---

[5] Haldeman, Scott. "The Justification for Another Journal." Editorial, JNMS, Vol. 1, No. 1, Spring, 1993.

journal of the International Society for the Study of the Lumbar Spine and then multiple national and international spine societies. Scott published his first paper in *Spine* in 1984 and has continued to submit articles to this journal over his career. As Scott's position in the ISSLS and the North American Spine Society advanced, he was invited to join the editorial board as an associate editor in 1988 and has been asked to review multiple papers for the journal each year since. On completion of the Bone and Joint Decade 2000-2010 Task Force on Neck Pain and Its Associated Disorders, it was important that the results of the task force be published in the most prestigious and rigorously peer reviewed journal in the field that had an international and interdisciplinary audience. *Spine* was the obvious choice. The results of the Task Force were published in this journal in February 2008 as a supplement. (For more detailed information see Chapter 15.)

In 2000, the North American Spine Society decided to publish a peer reviewed journal for its members and to expand the amount of published research on the spine. Scott supported the establishment of the new journal and was asked to be on the executive committee for the journal and to serve as Deputy Editor for Non-Operative Care. *The Spine Journal* published its first edition in January 2001. Scott, together with Simon Dagenais, contributed an article titled, "Cervicogenic Headaches, A Critical Review" in the first edition of the journal that remained one of the top 10 requested articles from the journal for a number of years. The January/February 2008 issue of *The Spine Journal* was dedicated to "Evidence-informed management of chronic low back pain without surgery." In this special issue, Scott and Simon Dagenais served as "issue editors" and were responsible for the assemblage of the entire issue—277 pages in length. It is in this issue that we find Scott's introductory article about the supermarket approach to the care of chronic low back pain. He also sets the stage for the twenty-six articles that followed:

> Patients with chronic low back pain (CLBP) are finding it increasingly difficult to make sense of the growing list of treatment approaches promoted as solutions to this widespread problem... This frustration is felt not only by patients, but by all interested stakeholders, including clinicians...All share a common goal and

293

wish to use limited healthcare resources to support those interventions most likely to result in clinically meaningful improvements... The current approach to the management of CLBP makes this goal virtually unobtainable.

With CLBP...treatment options appear virtually endless and increasing every year, have strong and vocal advocates, and often limited scientific evidence. Treatments that have never been subjected to methodologically sound randomized controlled trials are routinely promoted as cures to unsuspecting patients. Conversely, approaches that have demonstrated only minimal benefit in clinical trials continue to be recommended by proponents who allege that such studies were flawed and do not accurately represent current clinical practice.

Decades spent listening to presentations at scientific meetings, reading textbooks, discussing the problem with clinicians and patients, listening to advertisements on the television or radio, and browsing the internet, could lead one to conclude that the classical method of making healthcare decisions based on scientific evidence and expert consensus appears to have been replaced with a commercial and competitive model akin to shopping at a supermarket. This analogy is reinforced by visiting the commercial displays at spine meetings, where there is intense competition by pharmaceutical companies, surgical instrument makers, and devise manufacturers to convince stakeholders of the benefits of their products. Only rarely do such promotional materials accurately present the scientific evidence underpinning a particular approach, and rarer still are discussions of potential harms.[6]

In the concluding article of the special edition, Scott clearly puts the problem of caring for chronic low back pain in its place:

It is a generally accepted principle in most fields of health care that a treatment should not be offered to the public until there is sufficient evidence supporting its safety and effectiveness and a consensus by clinicians of different backgrounds as to its most appropriate indications and contraindications. It should be evident

[6] Haldeman, Scott, S. Dagenais. "A supermarket approach to the evidence-informed management of chronic low back pain." *The Spine Journal*, Vol. 8, No. 1, Jan/Feb 2008, pg. 1-7.

to most readers that this is not the norm when dealing with CLBP and additional research is required to achieve this long-term goal. In the interim, patients, clinicians, third-party payers, and policy makers have a responsibility to become thoroughly familiar with, critically appraise, compare, and openly discuss the best available evidence presented in this special focus issue. In this super market of over 200 available treatment options for CLBP, we are still in the era of caveat emptor (buyer beware). The enthusiastic support by providers of any treatment should be considered when reviewing available research evidence that supports its use.[7]

From a master's thesis in a university at the bottom of the world, to being responsible for the two most salient publications on the care of neck and back pain published in the two most internationally prestigious scientific journals, this scholar's journey has spanned the globe physically and has penetrated the innermost sanctuaries of every professional body claiming a stake in the back care arena. Without prejudice, but with merit, Scott has challenged every belief, explored every theory, and has been a member of or presided over every major spine care organization in existence. I suspect one of his greatest disappointments is that in spite of his efforts and others he has worked with, the supermarket approach to spine care, with upward spiraling costs and ever expanding treatment options has failed to reduce the prevalence of back pain and its associated maladies.

PROFESSIONAL WRITINGS

Professional writings differ from scientific writings in that while they may be scientific in nature, they are not reporting on specific scientific studies nor are they typically laden with the structure of scientific writing (i.e., methods, results and discussion sections). Granted, this is an arbitrary distinction with fuzzy boundaries, but is intended to offer insight into Scott's thinking on those occasions when he expands his writing to issues larger than a single project.

While Scott was attending medical school in Vancouver, he pub-

[7] Haldeman, Scott, S.Dagenais. "What have we learned about the evidence-informed management of chronic low back pain?" *The Spine Journal*, Vol. 8, No. 1, pag. 266-277.

295

lished several professional articles in keeping with his commitment to the support he was receiving from various chiropractic organizations. The following titles are indicative of his exhortations to his chiropractic colleagues. For complete references see Appendix C.

1974—Neurophysiological Concepts of Importance to Chiropractors

1974—Importance of Record Keeping in Evaluation of Chiropractic Results

1975—Why Chiropractic Needs a Post-Graduate School

1976—A Profession Deserves a Professional Conference

1976—The Neurophysiologic Mechanism of Pain

1976—The Importance of Research in the Principles and Practice of Chiropractic

1976—Chiropractic – A Dying Cult or a Growing Profession?

In an article titled "The Search for Research," published in 1978, we get an early view of his predilection towards the importance of research. Speaking to a group at his home in Santa Ana, Scott tells how important research is to the future of the chiropractic profession:

> By legitimate accountability...I mean acceptable, well-constructed, thoroughly documented scientific research—not theory, not clever empirical deductions, not exaggerated clinical claims—but sound, fundamental, old-fashioned, hard-core scientific research. And I certainly do not mean [research] for PR purposes, but to [do research to] underpin what chiropractors have been doing therapeutically for over eight decades and to validate or discard, if necessary, the abundance of divergent theories that the field has proliferated over the years to 'explain' why and how people get well under manipulative therapy.

> If we don't begin to move now into legitimate scientific research in a significant fashion...others will and, in fact, already have and with a great deal of enthusiasm to boot, and the future of spinal manipulation will belong to those whose training and scientific support will qualify them as the 'experts'—the ones accepted as those most

qualified to engage in this kind of therapy, and we won't even be in the ragamuffin status then.

I'm selling survival of the profession of chiropractic. I believe the profession is in grave danger, but not so the art of chiropractic. Others are moving into the spinal manipulative field at an increasing rate, so the art of chiropractic is going to survive, its benefits and its practice, but the profession may not do so.[8]

In an undated brief (presumably while Scott was a resident at UCI, 1977-1980), Scott made a presentation to the Department of Neurology at UCI titled, "What are the objectives of conservative treatments?"

Conservative treatment of patients with spinal pain is the most widely utilized yet most commonly maligned method of managing patients with this often debilitating disorder.

There are no widely accepted or agreed approaches to conservative care. Research trials, although not abundant, have been published on many conservative treatment methods. The tendency, however, by clinicians has been to criticize, condemn, quote out of context, or exaggerate the results of this research.

Patients with acute uncomplicated low back pain tend to recover spontaneously with or without treatment. The goals of conservative treatment, therefore, are to relieve symptoms while the patient recovers and to shorten the recovery period if possible.[9]

After completing his residency training at UCI and starting a clinical practice, Scott continued to publish professional articles focused on helping the chiropractic profession mature. Additional titles with dates are presented to give a flare of what he felt was important for chiropractors to know:

1981—Prospects for Research in a Faculty of Chiropractic

1982—How to Refer a Patient

[8] Godwin, Leonard, "The Search for Research." *The Digest of Chiropractic Economics.* Mar/Apr 1978, pg. 24.
[9] Haldeman, Scott. "What are the Objectives of Conservative Treatment." Unpublished manuscript, undated.

1983—Spinal Manipulative Therapy: A Status Report

1986—Spinal Manipulative Therapy in Sports Medicine

1988—How to Make DC/MD Relations Work After Antitrust

1992—The Evolution and Importance of Spinal and Chiropractic Research

1995—The Evolving Role of Chiropractic Within Mainstream Health Care

2000—Neurological Effects of the Adjustment

2001—The Evolution of Chiropractic–Science & Theory

2002—Chiropractic: A Profession at the Crossroads of Mainstream and Alternative Medicine

2002—Back to Basics: The State of Chiropractic Research[10]

Scott prepared an article for the *Journal of the American Chiropractic Association (JACA)* in 1985 titled, "Chiropractic in 1995: What will our Sons and Daughters Experience?" He begins with an historical backdrop:

> The chiropractic world has evolved phenomenally and can expect to continue to evolve. During my grandmother's era, it was unknown, unrecognized, without standards. My father spent his entire career fighting for legislative and social recognition. I have spent much of my career to date pushing for scientific research and professional recognition. Despite these advances, on reading chiropractic literature, there seem to be as many problems as there ever were. There is increased concern over health care costs and a growing malpractice litigation situation. There is encroachment on chiropractic practice by medical physicians and physical therapists. There continues to be inadequate research and it is increasingly difficult to define a standard of practice within chiropractic.
>
> The future, however, appears very bright for chiropractors and chiropractic. There is an accelerating acceptance of chiropractic into

---

[10] Titles taken from Scott's Curriculum Vitae.

the health care system. Chiropractors are knocking at the doors of hospitals, HMOs, the Veterans Administration and other systems which have traditionally excluded chiropractic care. Chiropractic colleges are demonstrating an increased commitment to research and higher standards of care and the CCE appears to have reached maturity in setting standards for chiropractic education.

I continue to believe that the most important factor that will impact the practice of chiropractic over the next ten years will be the evolution of chiropractic science...The role of manipulation, and specifically the chiropractic adjustment in the care of patients, will be defined...The various techniques or types of adjustment will be evaluated and compared. Many of the widely used and taught techniques can be expected to be discarded over the next ten years and new and better techniques developed in their place. I believe this will result in a better defined standard of care within chiropractic and a greater uniformity of practice between chiropractors.

Research will also cause a major revolution in chiropractic theory. Many widely held theoretical beliefs as to why the adjustment and manipulation works, can be expected to be disproved and discredited.

I believe chiropractors will gain access in increasing numbers to hospitals, HMOs and clinics. It is expected that they will be included within the Veterans Administration Health System and possibly within the Armed Forces. I believe that by 1995, very few chiropractors will practice totally independently...Chiropractors will have access, either directly or indirectly, to virtually any level of diagnostic testing or expertise. Chiropractic can be expected to be available to virtually all American citizens on a similar basis to other health care services...I believe by 1995 the growth and achievements of chiropractic will have exceeded all expectations of the founders and the developers of chiropractic over the preceding 100 years.[11]

Scott prepared an article on "Back Pain in the Next Decade." In this undated manuscript he outlined the many changes occurring in the world of back pain care and predicted revolutionary changes

11 Haldeman, Scott. "Chiropractic in 1995." Submitted to the *JACA* in 1995. Draft copy in the Haldeman files.

affecting all clinicians caring for the back pain patient. Some of the major predictions he made were:

1. The barriers between the various professions and between scientific disciplines would break down.

2. It is not always possible to link pathological changes seen on diagnostic imaging to pain symptomotology.

3. There is a close integration between social, psychological, and pathological factors in back pain.

4. Methods for understanding neurophysiologic changes, muscle strength, and biomechanical abnormalities would be improved.

5. There would be a growing emphasis on cost control and cost effectiveness.

6. Practice guidelines and practice parameters would be made and implemented.

7. There would be changes in preventive medicine and disability evaluation.[12]

Scott's 1988 article on improved relations between MDs and DCs, published after the Wilk's antitrust suit, brings to light his broad and inclusive approach to spinal care. His observations were:

Chiropractic has just entered another era in an exciting and evolutional history. Chiropractors and medical physicians are beginning to act friendly to each other. Chiropractors are finding medical physicians who are willing to speak at chiropractic meetings. They, in turn, are being invited, not only to attend, but to speak at medical meetings. Chiropractors are being invited into hospitals and onto public health and Olympic and other sorts of committees.

At the same time, chiropractic theory and practice is being looked at more critically. It is no longer being discarded as quackery, but instead chiropractors are being asked to justify each claim and theoretical statement. Chiropractors are being held to an increasing standard of education and practice. In addition, chiropractors are finding their uniqueness in terminology and theory under attack

---

[12] Haldeman, Scott. "Back Pain in the Next Decade." Undated and unpublished manuscript in the Haldeman files.

and their methods of practice being infringed on by other health care clinicians.

...many chiropractors perceive the improved DC/MD relations as a honeymoon with unlimited possibilities while others perceive it as a form of AIDS which has to be isolated and limited before it becomes terminal to the profession as a whole.

In reality, the improved relations between chiropractic and medicine were not foisted on the chiropractic profession by organized medicine. On the contrary, it was fought at every step by the major medical associations.

The primary question being asked is how can chiropractors make DC/MD relations work without losing their identity and weakening the profession. The answer is based on a few basic principles.[13]

Scott went on to list four guiding principles for the chiropractic profession to follow:

1. Chiropractic must function from a position of authority. This means that chiropractors must be more knowledgeable about what they do and remain more competent in delivering their service than any other health profession. In addition, chiropractic must develop highly educated, productive research authorities who can represent their positions at meetings and conferences and on government committees.

2. Chiropractors must maintain their identity. The concern that chiropractic could be swallowed up by the larger and more powerful medical community is real.

3. Chiropractors must develop a consensus of chiropractic opinion. One of the most destructive factors in developing better DC/MD relations is the inability of the chiropractic profession to present a consensus point of view.

4. There must be respect for the opinions of others. No relationship can work without mutual respect. Chiropractors must become edu-

---

[13] Haldeman, Scott. "How to Make DC/MD Relations Work After Antitrust." *International Review of Chiropractic*, Sep/Oct, 1988, pg 19-21.

cated as to the various theories and practice of medical physicians at the same [time] as they are educating medical physicians about chiropractic.[14]

True to his roots, Scott never attempted to supplant his philosophical foundation of chiropractic with science, but rather worked to find a balance between the two. In an article titled, "Philosophy and the future of chiropractic," also the keynote address at the ACA convention in Anchorage, Alaska in 1990, he shared the following:

> One of the most difficult aspects of chiropractic to understand is something chiropractors call their philosophy. The philosophy of chiropractic has been referred to by critics outside the profession as cultist on the assumption that it was somehow linked to a single individual. It has been called a religion or pseudo-religion because of the fervor and obvious belief system that certain chiropractors have built around it. It has been referred to as unscientific or anti-science, when certain chiropractors are perceived as adhering to so-called philosophical principles which are contrary to observed scientific observations.

> It is becoming increasingly clear, however, that in the same way that chiropractic is a fact of life in the health field, philosophy is a fact of life in the chiropractic field...Before chiropractors began serious research, it served as an explanation, albeit very simplistic, for how chiropractic treatment seemed to get patients better. It has frustrated attempts to unify the profession under a single political organization on at least two occasions, and it has separated chiropractic colleges and accrediting agencies to such an extent that communication between these groups has been stifled.

> The chiropractic philosophy has, at the same time, been the major factor that has distinguished chiropractic as a unique profession... the philosophy of chiropractic...if anything, is becoming more important.

> There are virtually no chiropractic-academic institutions with faculty qualified in the concepts of philosophy...There have been

---

[14] Haldeman, Scott. "How to make DC/MD relations work after antitrust." *International Review of Chiropractic*, Sep/Oct, 1988, pg 19-21.

no conferences dedicated to an evaluation or critical analysis of chiropractic philosophy. There are no journals where philosophical issues are presented...the majority of chiropractors believe their practice is guided by philosophic principles.

The one point that should be stressed is that there is no conflict between scientific observation and philosophy. Science is the basis of philosophy. Without science there can be no true philosophy. As science increases or changes a body of knowledge, philosophy must change and adapt to the new reality. It is not possible to be a philosopher without having an understanding of scientific knowledge...any philosopher of chiropractic who presents positions or beliefs contrary to scientific facts must be considered suspect.

The practice of chiropractic cannot advance without increased research. There needs to be an increased emphasis on research and promotion of scientific principles in order to advance chiropractic theory and expand our understanding of what happens when a chiropractor gives an adjustment.

It is however, the philosophy of chiropractic that will determine the future direction of chiropractic. Whereas scientific research is essential for a rational philosophy, it is the philosophy that will define the future of chiropractic research.[15]

Scott was interviewed by the *Journal of the American Chiropractic Association* along with other leading opinion makers in chiropractic regarding the future of chiropractic as we crossed the threshold into a new millennium. In response to a question regarding strengths and weaknesses of the profession he said:

...chiropractors are now widely considered the specialists in back pain, neck pain, and headaches, which medical physicians have failed to successfully treat. Chiropractors offer an alternative to medicine and surgery that is perceived as less traumatic and having fewer complications. Chiropractors are also recognized as being very caring and very interested in natural, healthy lifestyles. The wide variation between practitioners is a weakness that leads to confusion among patients. Chiropractors have a reputation for

[15] Haldeman, Scott. "Philosophy and the future of chiropractic." *JACA* July, 1990. Pg. 23-28.

believing they can treat anything. Patients don't know what's going to happen to them when they walk into a chiropractor's office...I don't think we can improve the weakness until we come to some form of unity of thought in the care offered to patients.

In response to the question about conflict within chiropractic:

The Dalai Lama stressed that the only way 'them vs. us' conflicts can be resolved is through open dialogue and an attempt to understand the positions of others. Chiropractors would see they have more in common than differences if they'd only spend time together and avoid strong emotional stances. The Dalai Lama also said if you aren't willing to compromise, you maintain a state of war, and your only option is to kill each other. If the profession doesn't wish to have dialogue, it will internally destroy itself.

Regarding those outside the profession affecting its future:

The elimination of barriers between chiropractic and other health care professions has opened new doors into group practices, hospital settings, and HMOs. But the corollary to that is that there is much greater scrutiny. It becomes increasingly important to monitor the practice, to describe the benefits and the risks, the cost of care and how they relate to other forms of care for the same population of patients.

When asked about the future of chiropractic education:

Those chiropractors who are unable to communicate with their patients and with the health care community find that their practices just shrink and disappear. Therefore, it has become increasingly important for chiropractors to be able to discuss their theory in scientific terms. This makes it even more important that college and postgraduate courses teach the basis for current theory and that doctors stay up to date with the latest research and methods of treatment.

On the future of chiropractic practice survival:

...more success for those doctors participating in group practices, which are often judged more positively that those in individual practices...the biggest growth will be in the practice integrated with other health professions and institutions...the isolated solo practitioner in an area with a high density of chiropractic care as the most difficult practice to maintain.

The ability of the profession working together:

Only the national associations such as ACA and ICA and the international societies such as WFC can develop sufficient resources to change the political and economic direction of the profession. I've always felt that the failure to join a major society is tantamount to giving a donation to those individuals or societies who believe chiropractic as a profession should be destroyed or limited.

On the importance of research:

Research has been the primary factor that has propelled chiropractic to its current level of acceptance. Without research, the chiropractic profession would stagnate the same as any other profession that just stopped progressing and stopped learning. If we don't understand the physiology and biomechanics of what chiropractic does, we cannot develop better methods of treatment.

The role of wellness:

Wellness is an excellent idea. It is gaining interest both in medicine as well as chiropractic. But whether it survives or not is going to depend upon whether we can show that a wellness practice truly has a benefit. That will require significant research. Without the research, it's just a sales pitch.[16]

In an article published in 2008 titled, "Looking forward to the future of chiropractic," Scott writes:

The future can be visualized if one looks at the changes in the opportunities practicing chiropractors are seeing and the increased role researchers with chiropractic training are assuming. These changes are significantly altering the perception of chiropractic as a profession and its position within the spinal care delivery community.

---

[16] Haldeman, Scott. "Chiropractic enters the third millenium." JACA, Dec, 1999, pg 11- 18.

Thirty years ago, it was possible to count the number of chiropractors with PhDs in the clinical and basic sciences on one finger... Today it is becoming increasingly impossible to keep up with the number of chiropractors who have completed advanced scientific and professional degrees. Best estimates suggest there are more than fifty chiropractors with PhDs and many more graduate students in PhD programs.

Less than twenty years ago, there were only a couple of faculty members at major universities who had any formal training in chiropractic. This is changing quite rapidly, especially in Canada. Research chairs or professorships have been established at seven universities in Canada and are being organized at three additional universities.

There was a time when chiropractors had no choice but to practice independently and were ostracized by other health care professionals. The successful integration of chiropractors into the VA and Dept. of Defense health systems has gone a long way toward developing a practice model in which chiropractors are part of the health care delivery system for patients with spinal disorders.

There remains one obstacle to the establishment of full integration and leadership of chiropractic within the health care community: participation. The numbers of practicing chiropractors who are members of the national societies, routinely read scientific journals and attend scientific conferences (especially in the United States) is relatively small. By not participating in the national dialogue on the future of the profession...many chiropractors are slowing down the process of developing cultural authority.

The full potential of the profession will become evident when essentially every chiropractor is a member of their state and national societies and thereby forces the leadership of those organizations to stay abreast of scientific and political change; when every chiropractor reads a number of scientific journals to maintain the highest level of knowledge and most up-to-date care of patients; and when the major chiropractic scientific meetings have thousands of chiropractors in attendance discussing and debating the latest development in their field.[17]

Scott succeeded in many ways, but as quoted at the beginning of this chapter, he worked hard. While gifted with numerous talents and abilities , his diligence and perseverance made an enormous difference. His example is one to be emulated.

[17] Haldeman, Scott. "Looking forward to the future of chiropractic." *Dynamic Chiropractic*, Aug. 12, 2008, pg 47, 49.

Chapter 14

Professional Organizations and Offices

Scott has always been an advocate of membership in multiple professional and scientific societies. He believes it is impossible to keep abreast of the latest research and clinical knowledge without regularly attending clinical and scientific meetings, regularly subscribing to and reading the published research, and then integrating this research into practice. Through most of his career, he has subscribed to or received, through membership in societies, up to 20 journals a month, spending 5-10 hours a week reading. Scott has also felt that the only manner in which one can influence the scientific, political, and clinical progress of one's profession(s) is to be active in the mainstream societies. He has felt that the approximately $5-10,000 spent each year in memberships and journal subscriptions was well worth the cost in ensuring that he was giving the best possible care to his patients. Membership in professional societies also allowed him to influence their policies and avoid the common complaint of clinicians that the associations were not doing enough for them. His feeling is that it is only through active participation in the professional associations that one can ensure they support the clinician, promote meaningful research, and influence government and other policy makers. Only through the associations can a clinician or scientist be sure that the highest possible care is being offered to the public and to individual patients.

Scott's participation in professional organizations can be separated into four fairly distinct groups that represent his different professional qualifications and interests. Often there was considerable overlap between the groups, and he was asked to be a liaison between them.

1. The chiropractic societies: This includes the South African Chiropractors Association (SACA), the Canadian Chiropractic Association (CCA), the International Chiropractic Association (ICA), the American Chiropractic Association (ACA), the Foundation for Chiropractic Research and Education (FCER), and the World Federation of Chiropractic (WFC).

2. The spine societies: This group includes the International Society for the Study of the Lumbar Spine (ISSLS), the North American Spine Society (NASS), the American Back Society (ABS), and the North American Academy of Manipulative Medicine (NAAMM), and to a lesser extent, its international affiliation (FIMM). He was also a member, though not heavily involved, in the North American Cervicogenic Headache Society (NACHS).

3. The medical societies: Scott maintained membership and was often active on committees or as a speaker in the Orange County Medical Association, the Orange County Neurological Society, the California Medical Association (CMA), the American Medical Association (AMA), the American Academy of Neurology (AAN), the American Academy of Electrodiagosis and Electromyography (AAEE) that changed its name to the American Academy of Electrodiagnostic Medicine (AAEM), and the American Medical EEG Society (AMES). He was occasionally asked to speak at meetings of other medical specialty societies including the American Academy of Orthopedic Surgery and the American Academy of Physical Medicine and Rehabilitation.

4. Government and university committees: These are listed in his CV (see Appendix C) and references to his participation and the impact he had on the different International, U.S. Federal, and California State agencies where he was asked to serve, can be found throughout this book.

For the purpose of this chapter only those societies where he had a major impact will be discussed.

THE NATIONAL CHIROPRACTIC ASSOCIATIONS

As previously documented, Scott was organizationally active beginning with his many positions as far back as Clapham High School (see Chapter 2). Application of his leadership abilities blossomed during his years at Palmer College of Chiropractic (see Chapter 3). Being a student at Palmer meant close affiliation with the International Chiropractic Association (ICA), and Scott became involved with full encouragement from his father, who was also an ardent advocate of the ICA. At Palmer he served as president of the student ICA and was given the ICA Student Achievement Award in his final year.

In South Africa he joined SACA and was very active organizing meetings and in forming the South African Chiropractic Research Foundation. He spoke at a number of conferences and actively assisted in the attempt to obtain licensure legislation for the chiropractic profession. This is presented in detail in Chapter 4.

When Scott traveled to Canada to further his educational ambitions, involvement with the Canadian Chiropractic Association (CCA) was a natural consequence. He also continued to maintain his relationship with the ICA as well. It wasn't until Scott was invited to participate on the planning committee of the NINCDS conference in 1974, and subsequently made a presentation at the conference, that he had any contact with the American Chiropractic Association (ACA). Following the NINCDS Conference held in Washington, DC in 1976, Scott rode home on the same plane as Henry West, DC, president of the ACA at the time. Dr. West later expressed his concern regarding Scott's strong attachment to the "straight"[1] form of practice of chiropractic found in the ICA.[2] This was no doubt a concern for the ACA and its future relationship with the young Palmer graduate. However, Scott was able to overcome these concerns and later joined the ACA and served on a number of committees of this organization.

Scott was asked to serve on the editorial boards of a number of fledgling journals of the national associations as they attempted to

---

[1] The terms "straight" and "mixer" were commonly used to depict chiropractors who utilized a very narrow scope of practice, or who utilized a very broad scope of practice, respectively.
[2] Personal communication with Dr. West, April 2009.

bring the latest research and information to their members. He joined the editorial board of the *Journal of Manipulative and Physiological Therapeutics* when it first began publishing in 1979, the *Journal of the Australian Chiropractic Association* in 1983, and the *Journal of the Canadian Chiropractic Association* in 1985. He remains a member of the editorial boards of these journals. In 1992 the American Chiropractic Association decided to publish a scientific journal for its members and asked Scott to serve as editor in chief of the Journal. Accepting the challenge, he helped develop and promote the *Journal of the Neuromusculoskeletal System* until 2003 when he handed the job to Bill Meeker, DC, MS.

As Scott progressed through his education, he provided service as a research consultant to each of these major chiropractic organizations. He never sought political power or any administrative office within these organizations—he didn't have the time. His commitment was always for the betterment of the chiropractic profession through the advancement of science and education.

His work for the chiropractic associations did not go unrecognized. He was voted the Chiropractor of the Year by SACA in 1998 for his work on establishing the South African Research Foundation. In 1990 he was voted Researcher of the Year by the ACA at a convention in Alaska. He has also been conferred an honorary Doctor of Science degree from the Western States Chiropractic College (1981) and a Doctor of Humanities Degree from the Southern California University of Health Sciences (2007). He has recently been asked to serve on the Board of Governors of the Canadian Memorial College and has been honored by Palmer College by an invitation to become a Fellow of the Palmer Academy.

THE WORLD FEDERATION OF CHIROPRACTIC

The World Federation of Chiropractic became the vehicle through which Scott could achieve his goal of advancing research and interprofessional interaction between chiropractic and the other health care professions. It was this organization that allowed him to work for higher standards in chiropractic as well as increased regulation, recognition, and licensure of chiropractic internationally. The WFC became Scott's vehicle to achieve many of the goals of his earlier proposal in the 1970s for an International Society for Post-Graduate Education and Spinal Research (see Chapter 7). Scott was part of the WFC from the beginning of this society, and it holds a special position in his history.

The official history of the organization of the World Federation of Chiropractic is found on the WFC web site (www.wfc.org). The following is a brief discussion of the evolution of this society and Scott's goals for the Association as one of its most influential members.[3]

In September 1987, at a World Chiropractic Summit convened by the European Chiropractors' Union in London, England, there was agreement that a Presidents' Committee be formed to inquire into and report upon the formation of a world federation representing national chiropractic associations. As a result, the World Federation of Chiropractic was established in Sydney, Australia October 2, 1988, at a World Chiropractic Congress organized by the Chiropractors' Association of Australia The first council meeting was held in Toronto, Canada, August 31-September 2, 1989, attended by delegates from seven world regions. Dr. Gary Auerbach (North America), Dr. Christoph Diem (Europe), and Dr. John Sweaney (Pacific), were elected as president, vice-president and secretary-treasurer respectively. A Secretariat was established in Toronto with Mr. David Chapman-Smith as secretary-general.

When early discussions were taking place about a "world" organization of chiropractic, Scott felt the International Chiropractic Association (because they claimed to be an internationally based organization) could, at least theoretically, take the lead internationally and incorporate the thinking of the entire worldwide profession. To Scott's disappointment, the ICA failed to seize the opportunity to become the world's leading chiropractic association and instead focused almost exclusively on promoting their concepts and scope of practice. The other national associations in South Africa, Canada, and

[3] The following discussion is a composite of information taken from the WFC web site combined with Scott's personal memories and those of David Chapman-Smith.

the U.S. were too involved in local affairs to spend time and money to influence chiropractic developments in other countries. It was clear, however, that the interests of chiropractic in individual countries could be influenced by the role chiropractic was assuming around the world and that the combined resources of all the chiropractic associations could influence the overall advancement of the profession.

Scott was aware of the formation of the WFC and felt that this movement had more potential than any prior attempt to form an international society. His concern, however, was that it would be a purely political body and focus only on the local concerns of the many membership associations. He was worried that the WFC may not recognize the importance of research in advancing understanding of chiropractic theory and practice. He felt that only through research and increased scientific understanding could chiropractic become recognized worldwide and WFC become a truly international society. Scott's friendship with David Chapman-Smith, beginning with their mutual involvement on the New Zealand Commission on Chiropractic, allowed him to strongly recommend an independent Research Council within the WFC. He also felt that the biennial convention should be organized as a scientific meeting rather than a political meeting. These goals were consistent with the deliberations of the WFC council, which then established the Research Council and asked Scott to be its chairman.

Over the next 20 years, the WFC grew rapidly in both membership and influence. The WFC's voting members are now national associations of chiropractors—representing 88 countries. The WFC was admitted into official relations with the World Health Organization as a non-governmental organization or NGO in January 1997, and has represented the chiropractic profession at WHO since that time. One product of that relationship is WHO's first policy document on chiropractic, *Guidelines on Basic Training and Safety in Chiropractic*, published in 2005 and now available in many languages. The WFC's "Chiropractors Against Tobacco" (CATT) campaign arose as part of the WFC's support for WHO's Tobacco Free Initiative. The birth and growth of the WFC was possible because of a strong spirit of volunteer effort by everyone involved. No one on the Executive and Research Councils ever received per diems, and many have never asked for full expenses for meetings; others have quietly contributed to specific projects without compensation.

When Scott was asked to form a research council, he approached some of the most prominent chiropractic researchers from around the world. The idea of having an international research forum for chiropractic was accepted with enthusiasm by everyone approached. The initial research council consisted of Scott Haldeman DC, MD, PhD as chairman; Philip Bolton, DC, PhD from Australia; J. David Cassidy, DC, PhD, Med Sc, from Canada; Niels Nilsson, DC, PhD, MD from Denmark; Alan Breen, DC, PhD from England; Jay Triano, DC, PhD; and Reed Phillips DC, PhD from the U.S.

The primary duty of the Research Council was to advance a research agenda within chiropractic and to organize a program for the WFC Biennial Congresses that would highlight the leading researchers in chiropractic from around the world and allow young and established scientists to meet and present the results of their research for discussion. The first congress was held in Toronto, Canada, on April 29-May 5, 1991. Scott was on the council of the American Back Society at the time and helped arrange co-sponsorship of the meeting. This ensured that the meeting was both scientific and inter-professional. Subsequent congresses were held in conjunction with the council meeting and the assembly of members in the following cities:

1993	London, United Kingdom, co-sponsored by the World Health Organization
1995	Washington, DC, as part of the Chiropractic Centennial celebrations
1997	Tokyo, Japan, co-sponsored by the World Health Organization
1999	Auckland, New Zealand
2001	Paris, France
2003	Orlando, Florida, USA
2005	Sydney, Australia
2007	Vilamoura, Portugal
2009	Montreal, Canada

The scientific symposium at the inaugural Congress of the WFC in Toronto featured speakers from around the world: Scott Haldeman, Akio Sato, MD, PhD from Japan—the world's foremost researcher on somato-automatic reflexes, and Bjorn Rydevik, MD, PhD from Sweden—the world's foremost researcher in spinal nerve root compression. The first clinical research trial comparing a chiropractic adjustment to medical mobilization techniques for neck pain and restriction of movement was presented. The chiropractic patients fared better in this trial.[4] Scott was the man who was able to get an Akio Sato or a Bjorn Rydevik to travel half way around the world to speak at a gathering of chiropractors. In each subsequent conference of the WFC, Scott was the force that brought other leading scientists and clinicians in the spine care world to the WFC podium. Scott's goals at WFC congresses were not only to foster original research but also allow leading researchers to meet. For this reason, at every congress there has been a Speaker's Dinner where scientists and clinicians could interact on a personal basis. For example, in Toronto in 1991, chiropractic researchers such as Dr. David Cassidy (Canada), and Dr. Alan Breen (UK), first met and spent an evening discussing common interests with leading medical researchers such as Dr. Akio Sato (Japan), Dr. Sam Wiesel (USA), and Drs. Gunnar Andersson and Bjorn Rydevik (Sweden). In Montreal in 2009, a new generation of chiropractic researchers was meeting medical leaders such as Dr. David Eisenberg of Harvard. The benefit of this exchange for the individuals involved and the profession are obvious.

Prior to each biennial scientific symposium, an invitation is extended to the profession in general to submit papers for presentation. Under Scott's guidance, submitted abstracts are reviewed by the Research Council and then weighted into platform presentations, poster presentations, and those in need of more refinement. Any final decisions are subject to Scott's oversight.

From the very beginning, Scott felt that there was a need to identify and acknowledge the top research papers submitted to the

---

[4] Dynamic Chiropractic, March 1, 1991, Vol. 09, Issue 05.

congress. He proposed that a number of high prestige cash awards be established, but at that time the WFC had no cash reserves. After communication with David Chapman-Smith, Scott and David each donated $5,000 to the WFC for these awards. They did so for the first three congresses but were very careful not to make this known outside of the WFC executive council. It was felt, at least for the first few meetings, that the awards should be WFC Awards rather than awards from specific individuals. At the fourth meeting, David persuaded the National Board of Chiropractic Examiners (NBCE) to sponsor the awards, and they did so for the next ten years. The size of these awards has progressively increased over the years. The NBCE continues to offer $10,000 for the best poster presentations. The National Chiropractic Mutual Insurance Company currently contributes $20,000 for the best full paper awards. These awards have become the most prestigious achievement that any researcher in the chiropractic field can achieve.

The WFC gives out three awards for the best research papers submitted at each congress by scientists who are primarily institution-based. It also gives out an award to the best paper submitted by a clinical practitioner as the first author and where the research was done in the clinical practice setting. These papers are published within the JMPT with recognition that they are award winning papers. The Research Council does the judging with Scott as final arbiter if needed. The poster presentations at the meeting are judged by a panel of researchers, and there is a place at the end of the program where the highest quality, most relevant research studies are presented in the plenary session of the congress. The top posters are then awarded a cash prize from the Foundation for Chiropractic Education and Research (FCER).

Behind the scenes, Scott also serves as an advisor to the Executive Council and the Secretariat of the WFC in matters related to science and research. One such example is the Neck Pain Task Force of the Bone and Joint Decade 2000-2010 discussed in Chapter 15. The Research Council, and specifically Scott's international reputation and influence, has helped the WFC rise above simply a membership organization focused on political issues, to a level capable of demanding respect from the international scientific community.

To honor Scott's efforts in support of the WFC, the executive council has attached Scott's name to the most outstanding research award—thus becoming the Scott Haldeman Research Award. In 1995 he received the Outstanding Service Award of the WFC, the highest award that has been established by this organization.

The impact and influence of the WFC in 2009 can best be illustrated by highlighting the 2009 Congress in Montreal and its participation in the 2008 WHO Congress on Traditional Medicine in Beijing.

At the Montreal Congress, there were more than 1100 registered attendees. The guest speakers were David Eisenburg MD, associate professor from Harvard medical school, and Jack Taunton MD, Chief Medical Officer for the Vancouver 2010 Winter Olympic Games and professor in the Department of Medicine at the University of British Columbia. Quite incidentally, Dr. Taunton was a classmate of Scott at UBC medical school. Eight chiropractors with PhD degrees, and who held faculty positions at major universities in Canada, were highlighted and asked to present their research. There were more than 130 original scientific abstracts submitted to the research council with approximately 100 accepted for either platform or poster presentation. The qualifications of the award winners demonstrated how far the WFC and chiropractic has evolved, adopting a truly inter-professional international identity. The award winners were from the U.S., Canada, and Brazil, and had strong scientific qualifications as well as diverse clinical disciplines with degrees in chiropractic, medicine, naturopathy, and psychology. It should be remembered that Scott was the only chiropractor with a PhD when he received his degree in 1973.

The first WHO Congress on Traditional medicine was held in Beijing in October 2008. One of the sections was on the manual methods of health care. The leaders of this conference at the WHO approached the WFC to organize this section of the conference. It was recognized that there was no other international society in this field that had the prestige, infrastructure, and capacity to bring together all the different disciplines throughout the world who offer health care by using their hands directly on the body. Scott was asked to be one of two keynote speakers at the meeting. The other was Professor Yan Jun-Tao who is director of the Shanghai Municipal Tuina Research Institute in Shanghai. The Congress was a great success and further congresses of this type are being considered by the WHO in which the WFC is expected to play a major role.

Scott Haldeman, Yan Jun-Tao, David Chapman-Smith (l-r). Scott and Yan Jun-Tao were the keynote speakers at the WHO Congress on Traditional Medicine, Beijing, China, October 2008

THE INTERNATIONAL SOCIETY FOR THE STUDY OF THE LUMBAR SPINE

The International Society for the Study of the Lumbar Spine (ISSLS) and its offspring, the North American Spine Society (NASS), served as the vehicle through which Scott could present his research and participate in the development of professional policy in spine care and research. ISSLS was the first interdisciplinary society that was devoted to spine research and has become the most prestigious forum for the presentation of research on the topic.

In his presidential address to the 30th Annual meeting of the International Society for the Study of the Lumbar Spine (ISSLS), Robert D. Fraser, MD, shares insights regarding the beginnings of ISSLS:

> ...the formation of ISSLS was the coming together at meetings of surgeons from different parts of the world in the late 1960s and early 1970s. Whereas North American surgeons established the Scoliosis Research Society (founded in 1966 as the Scoliosis Club) and the Cervical Spine Research Society (founded in 1973), the formation of ISSLS was both international and multidisciplinary from the very beginning.

> It was decided that the first meeting (of a proposed international spine society) would be held in Montreal with Farfan as chairman. Harry Farfan and Lee [Leon] Wiltse communicated regularly to organize the Montreal meeting. A variety of possible names for the society were considered before settling on Farfan's preferred title, namely, the International Society for the Study of the Lumbar Spine.

> Three specific guidelines were embraced when formulating the type of society to be established. The first was that members should be involved in some research aspect of the lumbar spine, rather than being totally consumed with clinical work. Second, individuals from the basic sciences, engineering, and various medical specialties should be encouraged to participate in the society as active members with full rights; there would be no associate members or second class citizens. Third, it was considered important that members demonstrate an ongoing and continued special interest in the lumbar spine.

> Of the 35 papers presented (in Montreal), nine were concerned with spinal mechanics and six were on basic science. Less than one third of the papers were related to surgical treatment. The presenters came from eight countries: Australia, Canada, Great Britain, Holland, New Zealand, South Africa, Sweden, and the United States. An international and multidisciplinary society for the study of the lumbar spine had been well and truly launched![5]

[5] Fraser, Robert. Presidential Address. *Spine*: Volume 29(10) 15 May 2004 pp 1059-1065.

Scott had his first taste of the intensity of discussion at the international level when he was invited to the 5th Annual Meeting of The International Society for the Study of the Lumbar Spine in San Francisco in 1978, while he was still a resident. Scott recalls vividly that he had previously met a number of the leaders of ISSLS, including Alf Nachemson and Bill Kirkaldy-Willis, at the UBC Back Pain Special Interest Group meetings and the NINCDS conference (see Chapter 15). In particular Scott recalls an incident where, at a party on a boat in the San Francisco Bay, he was approached by Dr. Bernard Finneson, one of the most prominent spine neurosurgeons in the country, and asked to write a chapter in his upcoming book on the spine. Scott had never before been asked to write a chapter in a major medical textbook and stayed awake all night hoping that Dr. Finneson would not have forgotten the invitation by the next morning (it had been a good party). This was the first of many chapters Scott was asked to write in multiple books on spinal disorders and their treatment.

Since San Francisco in 1978, Scott has attended most meetings of the ISSLS. In fact, the ISSLS meetings have been the primary audience for his research. He was asked to serve on the membership committee in 1980 and then was appointed to the executive committee in 1992. He has developed numerous close friendships with colleagues at these meetings that have continued over the years. Nevertheless, he began devoting the majority of his organizational time helping establish the North American Spine Society.

In 1976, the first journal dedicated to publishing research on the spine was launched by the same group of individuals who was incorporating the ISSLS. The journal, *Spine*, was published with Henry La Rocca as editor-in-chief, and soon became the official journal of ISSLS and many other spine societies. In 1988, Scott was asked to serve on the editorial board of the journal and has continued in that position, peer reviewing 10-20 articles each year for the journal. He has also published a number of his own original articles in the journal.

THE NORTH AMERICAN SPINE SOCIETY (NASS)

The birth of the North American Spine Society started partially due to the restrictive requirements for membership into ISSLS, along with the need to hold local meetings for spine clinicians in North America who were unable to attend ISSLS because of the requirements that members must be active in research on the spine. A brief historical review of the origin of NASS is taken from the *Burton Report*.[6]

In 1979, a letter from Kirkaldy-Willis, MD to Charles Burton, MD in Minneapolis documents an outline for a "North American Academy of Spine Surgeons." Kirkaldy-Willis recommended starting with a small group and expanding to include not only surgeons, but also non-operative care physicians and chiropractic doctors. In February 1982, Dr. Selby wrote to Drs. Kirkaldy-Willis and Burton discussing the "North American Spine Society" which is the first documented mention of the "NASS" name. During the 1984 American Academy of Orthopaedic Surgeons meeting in Atlanta, Georgia, Selby held a meeting in his hotel room, co-hosted by Dr. Vert Mooney. Present were Drs. Arthur White of San Francisco, Tony Dwyer from New Orleans, William Kirkaldy-Willis of Canada, John Frymoyer of Vermont, Mark Brown from Florida, Casey Lee of New Jersey, Henry LaRocca from New Orleans, **Scott Haldeman** from California, Charles Burton and Leon Wiltse. They proposed that the "North American Spine Association" be developed to include any orthopedist, neurologist, neurosurgeon, radiologist, rheumatologist, physiatrist, etc. who devoted at least 50% of their practice to the lumbar spine. Dr. Kirkaldy-Willis also strongly supported inviting PhD and spinal researchers into this group.

In July 1984, a group of 100 spine physicians met in Vail, Colorado. Dr. Leon Wiltse was elected as official President, Dr. Kirkaldy-Willis President-Elect and Dr. Robert Watkins as Secretary. (Scott was a speaker on this program and was active in the discussions on the new society). The goal of the organization was "to conduct and promote scientific research and education involving topics related to the entire spine including scoliosis and trauma, with a primary

[6] The Burton Report is found online at http://www.burtonreport.com/infspine/HistSpCareNASS.htm

emphasis on the lumbar spine. It is not the intention of the organization to supplant other spine-related organizations, but rather provide a forum for the development of the complete spinal clinician." Finally the group chose the name "North American Spine Society".

Later meetings at Laguna, CA fine tuned this merger. The group elected Dr. Kirkaldy-Willis as the new President, Dr. Richard Nasca as Secretary, and Dr. Elmer Nix as President-Elect. Dr. Vert Mooney was to succeed Nix under the "Alternating" mechanism. Dr. Wiltse then made a "cameo" appearance where he served as the President of the organization for about 20 minutes and then introduced the newly elected President of North American Spine Society, Dr. William Kirkaldy-Willis. Scott was asked to serve on the membership committee.

The first meeting after Laguna was at the Sagamore Hotel in Lake George, New York led by Dr. Kirkaldy-Willis. *That successful meeting spawned a rapidity of growth which has continued.* By 1987 the membership expanded to 362. The annual meeting in 1987 was presided over by Elmer Nix, MD who was instrumental in the formation of NASS. It was held in Banff, Alberta Canada. Beginning with Dr. Kirkaldy-Willis, the sequential presidents were: Dr. Elmer Nix in 1987; Dr. Vert Mooney in 1988; **Dr. Scott Haldeman** in 1989; Dr. David Selby in 1990; Dr. John Kostuik in 1991; Dr. Charles Ray in 1992; Dr. Arthur White in 1993 and Dr. Casey Lee in 1994.[7][**bold added**]

As noted in the foregoing history, Scott was associated with NASS from its inception. He was also the only non-surgeon to be invited to the initial meetings that led to the society. At all times, he strongly supported the proposals, usually put forward by Farfan and Kirkaldy-Willis, to expand the society beyond a surgical society. He was a founding member and served on the executive committee of the original North American Lumbar Spine Association (NALSA), which joined with the North American Spine Society (Association) to form NASS. He was elected president of NASS in 1988/1989. In addition he was

[7] Extracted from Schlegel, John D. *The History of NASS: The First Ten Years.* http://spine.org/Pages/AboutNass/History.aspx 1994.

appointed to the membership committee, the task force on chiropractic, the conservative care committee—now the non-operative care committee, and elected to the executive committee. He also served as parliamentarian in 1989, on the public relations committee in 1991, the long range planning committee in 1992, the membership committee since 1992, the practice guidelines committee in 1996, and the guidelines committee and advisory panel from 1997, the NASS News sub-committee/editorial board in 1997, the combined task forces of the North American Spine Society, American Society of Spine Radiology, and American Society of Neuroradiology—Nomenclature and Classification of Lumbar Disc Pathology in 2000, the task force on clinical guidelines work group—guideline consultant, 2002 – 2008, the recognition and awards committee 2003 – 2006, and as chairman 2007-2009. He was recently appointed to serve on the governance committee of the Society.

Scott also served as a member of the research fund management committee with Casey Lee as Chair. At the October 21, 1999 meeting, he, along with Dr. Whitecloud, reported on the Spine Research Foundation. Their goal was to raise $2 million over three years to establish an endowment fund for research.

Scott's rise to president of NASS in 1988 was primarily due to his relationship with Bill Kirkaldy-Willis. "K-W," as he is known, was very adamant that NASS include non-surgeons as members and on the executive committee. The first four presidents had all been surgeons, and K-W proposed that it was time for the society to elect a non-surgeon to the presidency. Scott was then nominated for the position of vice-president and then president. He presided over the meeting in Quebec City in 1989 where there were almost 500 attendees. His presidential address titled, "Failure of the Pathology Model to Predict Back Pain," was published in *Spine* and was widely quoted in subsequent literature.

By 1999 it was clear that NASS needed a journal of its own. There was a proposal by the then president elect, Dr. Neil Kahanovitz, to establish a new journal. In 2000, a committee was established and a contract made with Elsevier Press. The name of the new journal was to be *The Spine Journal (TSJ)*, and Tom Mayer was chosen as editor- in-chief. There were five deputy editors chosen with Scott taking the position of deputy editor for non-operative care, Howard An for basic science, Charles Branch for neurosurgery, David Fardon for special features, and Neil Kanhanovitz for orthopedic surgery. The deputy editors were responsible for encouraging scientists and clinicians to send their articles to TSJ and were required to read and edit all articles within their area of interest. Scott and Simon Dagenais, who was working with Scott, published a paper titled "Cervicogenic headaches: a critical review" in volume 1, number 1 of the journal that stayed in the top 10 papers requested from the journal for more than five years. Scott continued in the position of deputy editor until 2006 and remains on the editorial board.

At the 2005 convention, Scott was honored with the David Selby Award, "for individuals who have contributed greatly to the art and science of spinal disorder management through service to NASS."

When Scott served on the membership committee, he was an influential voice that opened the door for chiropractors to join NASS. Following are examples of Scott's continued effort to bring chiropractic into the mainstream of spinal care providers:

The Task Force on Chiropractic, with Scott as chair, faced the issue of whether chiropractors merited an invitation to join NASS. Early on, some chiropractors were admitted on the basis of their academic attainment. Reed Phillips was on the list of new member applications in November 1987 and received an "A" approval rating with two members asking for further discussion but recommending approval on the basis of his PhD.[8]

The Task Force on Chiropractic provided a master sheet of evaluation for proposed new members and in their October 1999 report to the Board made the following points:

1. There are more than 50,000 chiropractors in North America making it the largest non-medical group of practitioners of spine care.

---

[8] 11 Nov 1987 letter to NASS Membership Committee from Leia Walters, Comm Sec.

2. Chiropractors are becoming a source of referrals for NASS members.

3. An increasing number of NASS members are forming relationships with chiropractors. There is a need to do a questionnaire to determine the extent of these relationships.

4. Chiropractors have significant political skills and influence and are increasing their influence in HMOs, insurance companies and federal programs.

5. There are many ethical, political and social issues where NASS and chiropractic could agree on—patients' rights, managed care, terminology, coding, and technology. Using chiropractic influence could enhance the position of NASS.

6. There remains a concern regarding education and practice methods of certain chiropractors in the community. There is a particular concern about claims made for non-spinal conditions.

7. Additional concerns:

a. DCs without a master's or PhD have less formal education than NASS members.

b. Chiropractic practices are sometimes based on unscientific principles (eliminated in the final report).

c. Chiropractors appear to be responsible for excessive misleading and false advertising (also eliminated in the final report).

d. Allowing chiropractors to become full members of NASS could open the door for PTs, PAs, nurse practitioners and other allied health professionals.

e. NASS may lose prestige with other medical societies such as the AMA, AAOS, AANS, CNS, etc. if chiropractors are allowed to join.

Action Steps

The Task Force believed that there was a need for NASS to continue to explore options regarding their position on chiropractors. Failure to do so could weaken its influence as representing all aspects of spine care.[9]

The Task Force on Chiropractic made the following recommendations to the Board of NASS in 2000:

1. That the board authorize the continuation of the Task Force on Chiropractic for a further three years or until the task force feels it has completed its function.

2. That the board agree to send out a non-biased survey questionnaire to NASS members concerning chiropractic.

3. If the board desires a method to encourage greater participation by members of the chiropractic profession or other professions eligible for affiliate membership...it could consider creating a method through which the most committed chiropractors and other affiliate members may become full members. The following suggestions should be considered whereby an affiliate member can become an active voting member of NASS:

   A. Attendance at three out of any five meetings in a sequence

   B. Prior publication of three peer reviewed papers on the spine

   C. First or primary author of a scientific paper presented at a NASS meeting

4. If the board elects to establish a formal position concerning chiropractic, that the board authorize the Task Force to make informal contact with the major chiropractic organizations such as the American Chiropractic Association and the World Federation of Chiropractic to determine whether or not there is any interest on the part of these organizations to form a liaison with NASS.

5. That the board consider active recruitment of chiropractic affiliate members and publicize upcoming NASS meetings within chiropractic publications in the same manner as it does with other professions eligible for affiliate status such as physical therapists and nurses.[10]

[9] 23 Oct 1999 Task Force on Chiropractic meeting minutes.
[10] Fax Memo dated March 6, 2000 to Task Force members to review prior to submission to the Board.

Scott reviewed the survey results of the NASS membership regarding interactions with chiropractors and potential membership of chiropractors with the Task Force at the NASS meeting in October 2000. Only eight percent of the membership of NASS responded.

> The Task Force on Chiropractic reviewed the following results [survey] at the NASS 15th Annual Meeting. The general feeling was that NASS exists to provide education to all spine care providers, including chiropractors, and that it needs to cautiously open the doors to chiropractors and get them to attend our educational programs. The survey showed that most NASS members have some limited interaction with chiropractors in their communities, and members agree that they should be invited to our courses.[11]

As chair of the non-operative care committee, Scott moderated an open discussion at the 16th Annual meeting of NASS in 2001. The topic of the discussion was the role of the practitioner of manipulative therapy [primarily the chiropractor]. This symposium, along with a number of research papers presented at NASS by researchers with chiropractic qualifications, established that chiropractors should be considered as part of the spine care team.

AMERICAN BACK SOCIETY (ABS)

The small number of non-surgeons attending ISSLS and NASS and the lack of a significant forum for true interdisciplinary communication in these associations was a source of frustration for Scott. He found a forum for communication of ideas between different spine clinicians in the American Back Society. The following history and discussion has been modified from a communication from Aubrey Swartz, Executive Director of the ABS.[12]

The Society was founded in 1982 by Aubrey A. Swartz, MD, PharmD, in Oakland, California. Dr. Swartz, an orthopaedic surgeon, believed in a need for a society that would encompass a diverse multidisciplinary group of back care professionals. He was, like Scott, also concerned about the lack of communication among these disciplines,

[11] Report of Chiropractic Survey Results to NASS at their 15th Annual Meeting, 2000.
[12] Personal Communication with Dr. Aubrey Swartz, July 2009.

which appeared to be a significant impediment in patient care and in the further development and improvement in back care. Many patients were seeking back care from two, three, or more health care providers from different disciplines. The noticeable lack of communication among these back care professionals was frustrating for each provider, as well as for the patient. It became clear that this system was in disarray and was adverse to the best interests of the patient. Frequently, the health care professional was confused as to who would be the most appropriate person to whom the patient could be referred. There was often a lack of understanding of what the different disciplines had to offer. The patients were frequently seeking treatment from professionals without proper guidance. The Society was developed as a forum to bring together the various disciplines within the back care community so there could be a sharing of knowledge, methodology, and skills in order to create a better understanding among the professionals, with the goal of having a positive impact on patient care.

The first scientific meeting was held on July 27, 1984, at the Hyatt Regency Hotel in San Francisco, in which Augustus A. White, III, MD, professor of Orthopaedic Surgery at Harvard Medical School, was the course chairman and keynote speaker. The program was attended by a very prestigious group of spinal authorities, mostly in the field of medicine and specifically orthopedics, but also from other specialties. This meeting set a high standard and the tone for the direction and development of the Society.

The second meeting was held on October 4, 1985, at the St. Francis Hotel in San Francisco, in which the society was honored with new faculty members, including Scott Haldeman, DC, PhD, MD, and John Triano, DC. Chiropractors and physical therapists were encouraged to attend, thus establishing the interdisciplinary nature of the society. The faculty and attendance rapidly developed with subsequent meetings, and the society was establishing its message around the country and internationally. Inter-professional barriers were disappearing, and there was a spirit of increasing acceptance that permeated the ABS continuing education forums. The December 1986 meeting further confirmed this commitment and was co-sponsored by the Palmer College of Chiropractic West and St. Mary's Hospital, giving continuing education credits to chiropractors and medical physicians.

The first official board of directors was developed in 1985, at which time Rene Cailliet, MD, was the first president. The succession of presidents included W. H. Kirkaldy-Willis, MD, FRCS (C&E), Professor & Chairman, Department of Orthopaedic Surgery, University of Saskatoon; Edward H. Simmons, MD, FRCS (C), Professor & Chairman, Department of Orthopaedic Surgery, State University of New York, Buffalo New York; Philip Greenman, DO, Chairman, Department of Osteopathic Medicine, Michigan State University, East Lansing, Michigan; **Scott Haldeman, MD**, Clinical Professor of Neurology, University of California Irvine, Irvine, California, and James W. Simmons, MD, Clinical Associate Professor, Orthopaedic Surgery, University of Texas Health Science Center, San Antonio, Texas.

The ABS has progressively increased its speaker pool to include speakers from all disciplines that claim to manage patients with spinal pain. The Society has held more than 35 national and international meetings since its inception. There have been more than 70 newsletters published, 100+ books published by ABS committee chairmen, Board of Directors, and Council of Advisors members, in addition to ABS members at large. The ABS committees have been active in developing clinical research projects, and many of these studies have been published in scientific journals.

As noted above, Scott was asked to attend and speak at the second meeting of the ABS and has held offices in the society ever since. He was elected a Founding Fellow and appointed to the council of advisors in 1984 and then the board of directors in 1987. He was asked to chair the committee of manipulative medicine and served on other committees. He was elected president in 2003 and held this office until 2008, the longest period for any of the ABS presidents.

Aubrey A. Swartz, MD, PharmD, the founder and executive director of the American Back Society provided the following comments on Scott's involvement in the society:

Scott Haldeman has been very important to the growth and

development of the American Back Society. Scott has contributed his professional expertise as a lecturer, teacher, and as a positive influence in his participation as an active member of the Board of Directors over these past many years, since 1987, and as our past President of the American Back Society, a position which he held for five years.

Scott has made a major contribution to our educational programs over these past 27 years. His contributions have included his innovative ideas and his research-based scientific presentations on a wide variety of issues relating to spinal pain.

He has shared the benefit of his hard work as a doctor, an educator, and a scientist over these many years. His contributions have included the neurophysiologic mechanisms of pain and their relationship to change that occurs in the central nervous system during the transitional phase between acute and chronic pain. He brought an awareness to us over 15 years ago of the inefficient utilization of treatment and diagnostic testing and unsuccessful surgery, and these observations shortly thereafter became the basis for the changes in the health care system, giving rise to managed care and to the development of research-based guidelines by which spinal care and all of medical care is practiced today in the U.S.

Scott was one of the first to bring awareness to our educational programs regarding the concept of outcome research and cost-effective and managed care based upon such outcomes, which was also the basis by which the sweeping changes in the health care system were made.

Scott has taught us the significance of muscles as an important source of pain as it relates to the amplitude of cerebral-evoked responses to paraspinal muscle stimulation, which become depressed in patients with palpable paraspinal muscle spasms and low back pain, reducing activities. He further taught the concept of a strong correlation between improvement in pain and activity scores and normalization of palpable muscle spasms in cortical evoked potentials elicited from muscles. This was considered important work in the determination of the role that muscles play in the genesis of low back pain.

Over recent years, Scott has brought to our educational programs

331

the results of research studies in which there were observations made that science would be the prevailing criteria by which procedures would achieve acceptance in the medical and insurance communities. Scott emphasized the importance of continual study by health care providers, including continuing medical education, and recommended that health care providers critically analyze their own practices in the efforts to continue to improve the quality of health care that they provide.

He has lectured on the importance of practical common sense approaches to patient care and making sure that our continuing education is current high-quality research as it related to our practice and/or diagnostic testing and treatment. Scott has brought us the results of research demonstrating that 1-2% of patients with back pain will have a neurologic deficit and that 99% of the time the patient with back pain will not be found to have a destructive neurologic lesion. He stressed the importance of ruling out a compressive neurologic lesion which was essential. However, once that was ruled out, we would look elsewhere in the identification of perhaps a nociceptive lesion.

He has pointed out the importance of differentiating mechanical disturbances from a psychological component or a hyperalgesic process or a central nervous system pain process. Scott took a practical approach and pointed out that some patients will simply have unexplained back pain.

Scott has cautioned us with respect to the issue of red flags for spinal infection, spinal fractures, spinal tumors, metastatic tumors, osteoporosis, aneurysms, and other lesions that could result in spinal cord or nerve root compression. He has reminded us that we must always be careful to acknowledge the possible presence of these types of serious conditions.

Scott has recently lectured on the latest research in the natural history of low back pain, that many people continue to have ongoing back pain with recurrent episodes, and many people will improve no matter which treatment they receive. He explained the differences between claim-based recurrence rates, care-based recurrent rates, and disability-based recurrence rates and helped us to understand these concepts in order to consider risk factors in which we can develop values for the likelihood of recurrence. He has made us aware of the cost-effectiveness of various treatment approaches and to understand and appreciate the value of the new research-based guidelines taking into consideration the cost issues.

Scott's most recent research with the Bone and Joint Task Force on Neck Pain regarding whiplash-related disorders has made a substantial contribution not only to our educational programs, but to the health care community at large. His work in this area has resulted in a better understanding of these types of injuries, which would have the potential effect of improving the level of health care delivered for whiplash-associated disorder. Scott has also recently taught us the concept of patient empowerment and stressed the importance of including the patient in the decision-making process with respect to their care. Scott explained to us the importance of being sure that the patient clearly understands the problem and understands the options for treatment, including the pros and cons of such treatment.

Scott has always felt the need for educating the patient, which is one of the most important services we can offer, which would necessitate spending the appropriate amount of time with the patient and educating them carefully regarding their condition. He had advised us that all too often, patients who had received health care services from various practitioners did not actually understand their problem, as it had never been properly explained to them.

Scott Haldeman is a true scientist, scholar, and teacher, and most of all a true friend. His contributions to the American Back Society and to the entire field of spinal care have effected improvement in the quality of health care services, in addition to improved health care for our patients.

The American Back Society is grateful to Scott Haldeman for his unselfish devotion to the American Back Society educational programs over these 25 years.[13]

---

[13] Personal communication from Aubrey Swartz—a draft of the history of the American Back Society, July 2009.

The Society is currently directing its efforts to the development of an online journal, with plans in the near future for extending its continuing educational programs online through webinars, conferences, chat rooms, ABS Grand Rounds, special courses, and video conferences. The Society is currently developing continuing educational programs with the intent of improving inter-professional communication. The ultimate goal of the society is to improve the level of spinal care to the public at large. The welfare of the patient is the most important end result of the ABS continuing education programs.

In December 1998, the ABS presented to Scott a certificate in "Appreciation for Continued Unselfish, Outstanding and Dedicated Support of the American Back Society," he remains a member of the Board of Directors.

NORTH AMERICAN ACADEMY OF MANIPULATIVE MEDICINE (NAAMM)

The North American Academy of Manipulative Medicine (NAAMM) was established in the 1960s and may, in fact, be the first true medical spine society in North America. It was initially established by a number of very prominent medical physicians who had dedicated themselves to the study and practice of manipulation. John Mennell, MD, and Janet Travel, MD, were probably the most prominent early leaders in this society. John Mennell was the son of James Mennell, MD, an English physician and pioneer in manual medicine who published a textbook, *The Science and Art of Joint Manipulation*, in 1952. Scott found a copy of this book in his father's library in South Africa and was familiar with the name. John Mennell followed in his father's footsteps and published his own textbook on manipulation and practiced and taught these skills throughout his life. In later years John and Scott became good friends. One day after watching Scott working on a patient, John commented, "You have good hands." Scott considered this to be one of the greatest compliments he could have received.

Janet Travell had been the personal physician to President Kennedy, who had persistent back pain and who felt that Janet was the only person who could help him. Janet became famous for her concept of myofascial pain and the diagnosis and treatment of trigger points—concepts that she later published in a text. The third prominent member of NAAMM was John Bourdillion, MD, who practiced in Vancouver and also published a book titled, *Spinal Manipulation,* in1970. He assumed a senior position in the society.

When NAAMM was first organized, it was conceived to include medical doctors only. Osteopaths and chiropractors were refused membership and rights to attend meetings. Scott had the necessary credential to be a member and attend meetings, but at the first meeting he attended he was denied admission because of his DC degree. The governing board of NAAMM quickly reconsidered Scott's request for membership when they realized that, with his chiropractic and science background, he had a great deal to offer in the field.

On graduation from medical school, Scott joined NAAMM and was almost immediately elected to the executive council in 1976 while still an intern. He was the only member of NAAMM with a PhD in the basic sciences. In 1980 he accepted the position of editor for the academy newsletter. In 1981 he became president-elect, and in 1982 president of NAAMM. One of his first goals for the Academy when he joined the executive committee was to enlarge the membership to include clinicians from other disciplines who practiced manipulation. He was able to change the bylaws to include osteopathic physicians. Phillip Greenman, DO, joined the society and also advanced through the executive committee and governing board to become president. Chiropractors, however, never did gain privileges.[14]

As the Immediate Past President of NAAMM, Scott published an article in the April 1983 NAAMM Newsletter, criticizing the exclusionary stand of NAAMM toward non-medical providers:

---

[14] Reed Phillips, DC, MSCM and Director of Research of the Foundation for Chiropractic Education and Research (FCER) was invited to attend the 1982 meeting as a guest and participant of Dr. Kirkaldy-Willis, keynote speaker for the meeting. Special permission was granted for this one-time occurrence. Letter to Dr. Phillips from Dr. Greenman, Program Chr, 3 Aug 1982. Scott was President of NAAMM at the time.

Research and Knowledge Has No Boundaries

Spinal manipulation and its practitioners have, perhaps more than any other medical field, been criticized for not being active in research, ignoring the scientific method, and failure to develop a consensus of opinion and standard of practice. The retort from practitioners of manipulation is that this is primarily a manual skill which is very difficult to research, and that critics of manipulation so dominate the research funding agencies and scientific agencies, that access to resources for scientific research has been denied.

The accuracy of the criticism cannot be denied. The number of well conducted clinical and experimental trials before 1970 was minimal, and the proliferation of unsubstantiated theory and opinion among the different groups in manipulation has been profuse. This has led to a situation where practitioners of manipulation from different professions and schools of thought would isolate themselves and openly criticize, often without any greater basis for their own view, the practice and theories of other groups.

In the past ten years there has been a growing dialogue between practitioners of manipulation and the remainder of the healing arts. Manipulation is being increasingly included as a topic in conferences and courses on spinal pain and papers on manipulation are being accepted by most major medical and scientific journals. Medical practitioners of manipulation, osteopathic physicians, chiropractors and physical therapists are being accepted on the basis of quality of research they are presenting rather than their title. Thus, "Spine" has had four papers authored by chiropractors in the past year, and the International Society for the Study of the Lumbar Spine has admitted a number of practitioners of manipulation and a physical therapist to membership on the basis of their research.

Medical practitioners of manipulation must be careful to avoid the impression that they are not willing to participate in the search for a rational standard of care and consider themselves elitists or isolationists, and perceive research only to be of value if performed within their own organizations and institutions. Recently a large research trial performed by a basic scientist was rejected by FIMM simply because it was conducted in a chiropractic institution. It is also evident that research performed within the fields of physical therapy and osteopathy is not readily being accepted and integrated into associations which represent manipulative medicine. Of even greater concern is the practice of denying a voice to certain practitioners within medical manipulation simply because the officers of an association might disagree with certain of their ideas. Thus, the field of orthopaedic medicine appears to be developing with only minimal input to manipulative medicine.

The North American Academy of Manipulative Medicine has attempted to rise above this type of restrictive practice. The Academy is fortunate to have practitioners from many different schools of thought within its membership and counts as members virtually every authority in the field of manipulative medicine within North America. It also strives to include international members at every yearly conference, thus preventing national isolation of thought. Consideration must, however, be made for including research presentations by non-medically trained persons who have something to offer in the field

It is a privilege of any organization to restrict its membership according to qualifications. It is not acceptable, however, to restrict the knowledge of the members of an association. Knowledge, skill and ability in manipulation are not restricted to members of the North American Academy of Manipulative Medicine. Much of the research in this field is being conducted by others. In order to lead in the field of manipulation, members of the Academy must have access to information resulting from this research. The question must therefore be raised whether or not research or technique presentations at our conferences should be open to non-members when such information is relevant to the practice of manipulation. In striving for excellence are we going to open our minds to all ideas, research and skills available in our field by openly inviting papers by non-members, or are we going to deny our members this research and the skills and knowledge that goes along with it because we have a restricted membership? This question is becoming increasingly more important to NAAMM as orthopaedic surgeons, basic scientists, sociologists, chiropractors and physical therapists become increasingly active in researching spinal manipulation. Research and knowledge have no boundaries. Do we?[15]

337

The NAAMM sought international recognition and relation-ships in the early 1980s. There were preliminary discussions between NAAMM and the British Association of Manipulative Medicine in 1982, with a proposal to hold a joint meeting in Bermuda in 1983, but they never advanced any further.

While serving as the Immediate Past President of NAAMM, Scott submitted a research paper to Federation Internationale for Manual Medicine (FIMM) in 1983. The paper, "A Prospective Study of 2000 Patients Seeking Manipulative Therapy at a College Teaching Clinic," was denied acceptance by the scientific advisory committee of FIMM. While the committee recognized Scott as a highly qualified scientist and that many in FIMM received their manipulative training from chiropractors, they justified their denial accordingly:

> Despite the scientific qualification of the authors and the paper the medical-political situation between medical doctors and DC does not allow the acceptance of this paper at a Congress of FIMM in a country of Europe. We understand the unanimous decision of your Council but we cannot follow it. This decision has no rela-tionship with Dr. Haldeman.[16]

Dr. Greenman shared this rejection from FIMM with the Board of Councilors of NAAMM requesting how they would like to respond.[17] Despite the protests from NAAMM the decision of FIMM was not reversed.

Scott never did present any papers at FIMM or attend any official meetings of that society that subsequently became almost irrelevant in future discussions on manipulation. In 1997 it reorganized its sci-entific committee and in 2004 established the FIMM International Academy of Manual/musculoskeletal Medicine to advance educa-tional standards and research into the manual arts. FIMM claims membership in 29 countries but continues to restrict membership and attendance at meetings to medical physicians and U.S.-trained

---

[15] Haldeman, Scott. "Editorial," *North American Academy of Manipulative Medicine Newsletter.*" April, 1983.
[16] Exchange of two letters between Dr. Philip Greenman of NAAMM and Dr. Hubert Baumgartner of FIMM dated 22 March, 7 April 1983.
[17] Letter to the NAAMM Board of Councilors dated 4 May 1983.

osteopathic physicians. The statements made above in the article by Scott that a society that restricts the knowledge of its members and the distribution of their knowledge to others is limiting their impact and understanding of their topic and not doing any favor to their members, patients, or society in general could equally be applied to FIMM. This differs markedly from the policies of the WFC that has member associations (not members) in 89 countries and opens its conferences to speakers from medicine, physical therapy, osteopathy, and even naturopathy and naprapathy when there is something new and important that the attendees can learn.

The one true attempt to bridge the chasm between different professions and schools of thought in spinal manipulation took place in 1984 in a monastery in Switzerland. This meeting was organized by Jiri Dvorak, one of the leaders of the Swiss association of physicians who practiced spinal manipulation and who had become good friends with Scott. At this meeting, 31 clinicians with reputations of leading the field of manual therapy were invited. They represented Eastern European manual medicine schools of thought (e.g., Valdimir Janda and Karel Lewit), European manual medicine schools of thought (e.g., Hans-Dieter Wolff and Jiri Dvorak), U.S. Osteopathic schools of thought (e.g., Phillip Greenman and Robert Kappler), and chiropractic (e.g., Scott Haldeman). This meeting resulted in a book titled, *Manual Medicine 1984*. At the meeting each of the attendees were asked to demonstrate their manual diagnostic and treatment procedures for a number of spinal disorders. It was the one and only formal attempt to bring the different schools of thought within spinal manipulation together in one setting.

The Dissolution of NAAMM

After his presidency and the meeting in Switzerland, Scott continued to be active in NAAMM and served as the resident vice-president on the executive until 1988. NAAMM, however, never did expand its horizons or show interest in learning about the advancements in the science of spine care and the wider world of manipulation. At the time Scott had assumed the position of president of NASS and reduced his commitment to NAAMM. The membership and attendance at meetings of NAAMM slowly diminished and the academy slowly became irrelevant and out of touch with the developments in the general spine care community.

In a terse letter to the Council members of NAAMM, 2nd Vice-President Robert C. Ward expresses the following:

> NAAMM is, in my opinion, at a crisis stage and needs to redefine itself or risk dissolution.

Lack of Involvement

> Communication has been marginal at best. I have come to the conclusion that NAAMM is a group of independent "lone rangers." We need to actively seek ways to work together for the benefit of the organization, or soon there won't be an organization...

Committee Activity

> Committee activity is for the most part non-existent. Chair people, for what I assume are very good personal reasons, have deferred all activity. Literally, nothing has happened. We still have a discussion regarding by-laws in Quebec City. I assume that the name change will go through without major disagreement, but lacking any feedback there is no identifiable way to know.

> Using the new name informally this past year has been very useful, I might add, Minimum ambiguity. Thanks goes to those who initiated the change.

Officers and Councilors

> Officers and councilors are not making themselves available. A number of us have chosen not to attend the Quebec meeting. This also happened in Las Vegas. An organization cannot survive for long, given this kind of participation by its leadership. I think we had better discuss some strategies for dealing with these concerns, what do you think? Why is this happening? Too expensive? Is there something the administrative offices might help with?

Nominating Committee and New Council Members

> The nominating committee is slated to be the three most recent past-presidents under the new Constitution. Is this what we want

and need, or do we need some other system? Identifying candidates who will responsibly assume their duties needs to be a priority. Right now, we are in major trouble in this area. What do you suggest?

Cross Purposes

For the last several years we have dealt with membership issues, particularly in relationship to organizational stability and revenue generation for future activities. The need for a larger, and therefore, greater dues paying membership, has been discussed many times.

Our international affiliation with FIMM has been a valued relationship. It is my distinct impression that FIMM, and by extension, NAAMM, is primarily interested in manual medicine, encouraging its applications, clinical utility and quality research.

It seems to me that for this organization to remain coherent and clear in its goals, the primacy of this commitment to manual medicine should continue. I worry that the insinuation of other agendas will dilute both program content and participation. Specifically, I am concerned that our associate members, about 15 percent of dues paying members, will be unwittingly disenfranchised.[18]

During this period, the program at NAAMM meetings had changed from an emphasis on manual treatment approaches to focus more on other forms of treatment for musculoskeletal disorders and particularly the injection therapies. There was no consideration for the inclusion of original research or the ideas of other spine care professions. NAAMM changed its name to The American Academy of Orthopedic Medicine (AAOM). Scott felt that this change essentially made the society irrelevant in the discussion in both the spine research and the manual therapy world and resigned from the AAOM. NASS and WFC, through their emphasis on research and interdisciplinary care, had assumed the leadership in these fields.

THE AMERICAN ACADEMY OF NEUROLOGY (AAN)

As a resident, Scott was asked to present papers at The Orange County Neurological Society (OCNS) and would attend the educa-

---

[18] Letter from Robert C. Ward 2nd VP to NAAMM Council members dated 27 July, 1988.

tional meetings each month. There was usually a free dinner at a fine restaurant often paid for by one of the pharmaceutical companies. On completing his qualifications as a neurologist, he joined the society and continued to attend the meetings whenever he was in town. He was, on occasion, invited to be the speaker and discussed his research work in electrodiagnosis from the VA, his participation in the AHCPR proceedings and their impact, and on occasion he discussed chiropractic. In 1988 he was elected president of the OCNS.

During his residency and fellowship at the VA, Scott also joined the American Academy of Neurology (AAN) as a junior member and immediately became an active member when he was qualified. The AAN was established in 1948 and is the largest and most influential society of neurologists in the world. Despite its designation as an "American" academy, it has an international membership of over 20,000 neurologists and neuroscientists. Its history and scope of influence can be obtained from its website, www.ANN.com.

Scott's initial involvement in AAN affairs, apart from attending meetings to keep abreast of the advances in the field of neurology, occurred while he was actively doing research at the VA in the field of neuro-urology. When he joined Bill Bradley, there were virtually no papers or educational courses in the field at the Academy, and most publications on the topic were in the urology journals. Scott began to submit his research papers to neurology journals including *Neurology*, the official journal of the AAN, and *Archives of Neurology*, published by the AMA. He also began presenting this work at a number of neurology meetings. Initially they were presented at the Annual Conferences on Evoked Potential and Advances in Electroencephalography, sponsored by UCI Department of Neurology, Irvine that had become one of the most important continuing education courses on the topic in the field of neurology. His presentations were on topics such as, "Pudendal evoked Responses—Techniques and Applications," and, "Bladder and Genital SEPs." The latter paper was at the thirteenth conference on the topic put on by UCI. He was then asked to be a faculty member in the course on "Evoked Response Testing in Neurology," at the 1983 annual meeting of the AAN in San Diego and at a number of meetings by the major electrodiagnosis societies. As noted before, Scott co-authored sixteen papers from his research at the VA.

In 1993 Scott was asked to be the facilitator of a position paper by the AAN on "Assessment: The Neurological Evaluation of Male Sexual Dysfunction." He was required to establish a committee of experts, review the scientific literature, and present the results from this committee to the therapeutics and technology assessment sub-committee of the AAN. This was published in *Neurology* in 1995 and set forth the current scientific understanding and practice parameters in that field.

In 1989 the North American Spine Society decided to establish official relations with the major specialty societies and Scott was appointed as liaison with the AAN—a position he held from 1989-1995. This required that he report to the AAN on programs and initiatives instituted by NASS and obtain feedback for NASS from AAN.

In 1990 Scott decided to do a search of the neurology literature to determine the interest in spinal pain. He searched the official AAN journal, *Neurology*, and found that in the prior five years there had not been a single article on back or neck pain. There had been papers on radiculopathy, but no papers specifically on the mechanism, diagnosis, or treatment of spinal pain. When the AHCPR published its guidelines on the management of acute low back pain, Scott submitted a proposal for a course on low back to inform neurologists about current standards. His proposal was accepted, and he was appointed course director at the AAN meetings in 1993, 1994, and 1995. The title of the course was, "Recent changes in the treatment of back pain."

One of the most interesting courses in which Scott was to participate was at the 54th annual meeting of the AAN in 2003 in Denver. The course was proposed by Dr. Norris from Toronto, who had been outspoken about the dangers of chiropractic neck manipulation and the possibility of vertebral artery dissection and stroke. The title of the course was, "Carotid and Vertebral Dissection." Surprisingly, he asked Scott to be a speaker at this course and gave him the topic, "Neck Manipulation and Stroke." This allowed Scott to present some of his own research as well as other recent publications on the topic. The discussion after the presentation was as lively as one could expect.

Scott was elected Fellow of the American Academy of Neurology. This is an honor bestowed on only a small percentage of academy members and is considered an earned fellowship. The nomination for this position came from Dr. van den Noort, his clinical mentor and head of the department of neurology at UCI. From the AAN website[19] the following are the criteria to become a fellow:

Fellows may be elected only from among physicians:

1) Who have been certified in neurology, or neurology with Special Qualification in Child Neurology, by the American Board of Psychiatry and Neurology, the Royal College of Physicians and Surgeons of Canada, or the Professional Corporation of Physicians of Quebec; and,

2) Whose chief interest is directed toward practice, teaching or research in the neurosciences;

3) Who have been Active members of the Academy for no less than seven (7) years;

4) Who have attended no less than five (5) AAN annual or regional meetings after becoming an Active member; and

5) Who have demonstrated special achievement in the neurosciences. This requirement may be satisfied by providing documentation of any of the following:

a. Academic accomplishment. This is defined as holding a teaching appointment or evidence of contribution to the medical literature. In the latter case, both the publication of papers and presentations at national meetings will be considered. Although this will usually require more than two papers or presentations, the Membership Committee reserves the right to determine whether or not the criterion is satisfied on a case-by-case basis.

b. Service as a member of an Academy committee.

[19] http://www.aan.com/go/membership/join

c. Service as an officer in a state, regional, national or international neurological society. Consistent, documented community service in the area of clinical neurology. For example, dedication of time and effort to public education, indigent care, etc. The Membership Committee reserves the right to review evidence of community service on a case-by-case basis.

d. Other unusual accomplishments, as determined in the discretion of the Board of Directors of the Academy upon recommendation by the Membership Committee.

6) Whose overall professional reputation and standing, as determined by the Board of Directors of the Academy, qualifies such physician for this highest category of Academy membership.

THE MEDICAL SOCIETIES

Scott did not limit his activities to the spine and neurology societies. On completion of his residency and the decision to go into clinical practice, Scott joined a number of the medical societies and a number of specialty societies. Some of these were simply to be kept up-to-date with the latest scientific and political issues. Others related to his interest in electrodiagnosis.

In 1982 he joined the Orange County Medical Association (OCMA) and the American Medical Association (AMA), and in 1984, the California Medical Association (CMA). To state that he played a major or even minor role in these societies would be an exaggeration, but he was available when asked to sit on committees or to help on specific projects.

For example, he was asked to sit on the Committee on Health Care of the CMA for the period 1984-1986 although not much was decided in this committee during this period. He was asked to speak at the 118th Annual Session and Western Scientific Assembly, "Conservative Treatment: Objectives, Choices, Results," sponsored by California Medical Association, Anaheim, California in 1988. He was invited back to speak to the same group in March 1992 on "The Role of Chiropractic Manipulation" and "The Role of Electrical Studies in Evaluation of Surgical Candidates."

345

When the AMA decided to revise the *Guides to the Evaluation of Permanent Impairment*, fifth edition, published in 2000, he agreed to be a reviewer of the proposed guides before publication. He was asked to be the editor for the neurology section of the sixth edition that was published in 2008, but his commitment to the Neck Pain Task Force was overwhelming at the time and he settled to be a reviewer once again.

Scott also joined the American Medical EEG Society and the American Association of Electrodiagnosis and Electromyography (currently The American Academy of Neuromuscular and Electrodiagnostic Medicine) and attended many of their meetings and courses to maintain his skills and knowledge in the field. Although he was not active in these organizations, he was asked to speak at conferences sponsored by the major electrodiagnosis societies. For example, he was invited onto the faculty of the 9th Annual Conference on Evoked Potentials, sponsored by the American Society for Clinical Evoked Potentials in San Francisco. His topics were, "Evaluation of Bowel, Bladder, and Sexual Disturbances by Electrophysiologic Methods;" "Evoked Responses in Clinical Neuro-Urology;" "Pudendal Nerve Evoked Spinal, Cortical, and Bulbocavernosus Reflex Responses: Methods and Applications;" and, "The Neurovisceral and Electrodiagnosis Evaluation of Patients with Thoracic Spinal Cord Injury."

Scott has been asked to participate in meetings or serve on committees of a number of other societies. He was asked to sit on the guidelines committee for pain of the American College of Occupational and Environmental Medicine (ACOEM) in 2008 that was responsible for developing new guidelines on this very controversial topic. He served as a panelist for the Orthopedic Research Society Occupational Medical Science Study Group of the American Academy of Orthopedic Surgery (AAOS), and was a workshop participant in the discussion of "New Horizons in Low Back Pain" in 1995. He was also invited as a speaker at the 58th Annual Meeting of the American Academy of Orthopedic Surgeons on "Indications and Results of Manipulative Treatment for Low Back Pain," the 7th Annual AOA International Symposium: " Frontiers in Low Back Pain," sponsored by American Orthopedic Association in Chicago, speaking on both "Electrodiagnosis of Spinal Neurologic Lesions" and "Spinal Manipulative Treatment." He spoke at the Scientific Program of the 68th Annual Meeting of the AAOS, where there was a Symposium on "Complementary and Alternative Medicine (CAM) and the Orthopedic Surgeon."

GOVERNMENT COMMITTEES AND AGENCIES

Scott's participation on the National Institute of Neurological and Communicable Diseases and Stroke Committee to establish a "Workshop on the Research Status of Spinal Manipulative Therapy" in 1975, and the U.S. Department of Health and Human Services, Agency for Health Care Policy and Research panel on "Clinical Practice Guidelines on Acute Low Back Problems in Adults" in 1994, are discussed in detail in Chapter 15. He was also asked to be a peer reviewer for the consensus development program at Duke University on an AHCPR grant on the topic, "Headache Evidence Report Project," in 1997. These, however, were not the only government committees on which he was asked to sit.

He was repeatedly approached to participate on committees established by the California Worker's Compensation System. In 1986 he was asked by then medical director of the Department of Worker's Compensation, Dr. William Clark, to be a member of the Low Back Disability Schedule Committee of the State of California Division of Industrial Accidents. The goal of this committee was to develop a more equitable method of determining disability. With Scott's help they carried out a study to determine the reliability of the current system and a new system which they had developed. The results of this study were published in *Spine* in 1988 and titled, "Back Impairment and Disability Determination: Another Attempt at Objective Reliable Rating".

In 1992 he served as a member of the Spine Specialist Panel for the State of California, Commission on Peace Officer Standards and Training, which was hoping to reduce spine injuries amongst police officers. And in 1998 he was asked by the State of California, Division of Industrial Accidents, Medical Bureau, to sit on a Committee on Chiropractic Standards.

In 2007 he was asked to be a member of the Medical Evidence Evaluation Advisory Committee of the State of California Department of Industrial Relations, Division of Workers' Compensation. The state legislature had passed legislation that required the division to develop treatment guidelines that were evidence based and nationally recognized. Scott's involvement with the Chiropractic, ACOEM, AHCPR, and Neck Pain Task Force Guideline processes resulted in close consultation with this committee and the policy makers at the Division.

When the U.S. legislature mandated that the U.S. Department of Defense set up a Chiropractic Demonstration Project to determine whether it was feasible for chiropractic services to be offered to enlisted military personnel in 1995, the contract to facilitate this process was given to the consulting firm of Birch & Davis in Washington, DC. Scott had been asked to testify before a Congressional Committee when this project was being considered. When it was approved, Scott was asked by Birch & Davis to be a consultant on this project and serve as a liaison, and to some extent, interpreter between the medical specialist panel established by the Department of Defense and a panel made of up chiropractic researchers and association representatives. The result of this project is that chiropractic services are now established in a number of military hospitals, and the positive response to the inclusion of these services has led to the expansion of this program to multiple military hospitals.

When the National Center for Complementary and Alternative Medicine (CAM) was established, it was inevitable that Scott would be asked to participate. He has served as a peer reviewer on a number of grants. In 2002 he served on the Expert Review Panel to Assess Centers Programs. This panel reviewed grant applications to establish research centers for CAM treatment procedures. Center grants have been given to a number of institutions including Harvard Medical School and the Palmer College of Chiropractic. It has been instrumental in establishing the importance of research on CAM treatment approaches and chiropractic. In 2003 he was a Chiropractic Demonstration Project peer grant reviewer for the U.S. Department of

Health and Human Services, Public Health Service, Health Resources and Services Administration, Bureau of Health Professions. He also served as discussant for the National Advisory Council of National Center for Complementary and Alternative Medicine in 2008.

CONCLUSION

The patterns of involvement described in this chapter are consistent with Scott's nature to be actively involved in his work and his professions. His presence was felt by his physical stature, intellectual capability, willingness to serve, and his vision derived from his diverse background and training. Each society or organization in which Scott participated benefited, as did Scott. Each society and organization influenced the world of spinal care, and Scott influenced each society. His influence on the spinal care world is a tribute to his abilities and hard work. While his involvement was extensive, the succeeding chapter provides a more in-depth description of some of the more significant activities of Scott's life and his impact on the fields related to spinal care and spine research.

Chapter 15

Landmark Events in the Maturation of Scott Haldeman and Spinal Health Care

The construction of a life as complex as Scott Haldeman's is no easy task. This chapter has attempted to set apart events that could be labeled as "landmark" events in both his life and in the professions in which he was associated.

The selection of the events included in this chapter was not the result of any rigorous scientific process, so opinions may vary regarding which ones should or should not have been included.

The events have been placed in a chronological order with no intention that one is more important than another. It can be easily speculated, however, that the report of the Neck Pain Task Force will likely have more far-reaching effects than anything else to date. But Scott is not through creating "landmark" events in his life, and the possibility of other seminal events looms on the horizon.

To assist, the sections in Chapter 15 are as follows:

1975 National Institute of Neurological, Communicative Disorders & Stroke (NINCDS)
1976 Conference on Coal Miner's Disease (Black Lung Disease)
1979 New Zealand Commission of Inquiry on Chiropractic
1979 Haldeman Research Conferences/Books

> *1981 Wilk vs. AMA Trial*
> *1992 Mercy Conference*
> *1992 RAND and Appropriateness of Spinal Manipulation*
> *1994 AHCPR Guidelines*
> *2002 Expert Witness – Quebec*
> *2000-2010 Bone & Joint Decade/Neck Pain Task Force*

NATIONAL INSTITUTE OF NEUROLOGICAL AND COMMUNICATIVE DISORDERS AND STROKE (NINCDS)

It was the middle of 1974 and Scott had just finished his second year of medical school at the University of British Columbia (UBC). He and Joan had settled in their little home, which required a great deal of work to make it livable. Joan was pregnant, and Scott had obtained a scholarship to work in the Canadian Arthritis and Rheumatology Center where Joan was the research therapist. But by the time summer rolled around, Scott already knew he was getting involved in one of the most significant events of his career.

It all started when Senator Warren G. Magnuson (D-Washington State) initiated the Senate Report on the Fiscal Year 1974 Appropriation for the National Institute of Neurological and Communicative Disorders and Stroke (NINCDS) of the National Institutes of Health (NIH). The Senate Appropriations Labor-HEW Subcommittee specified that, "...this would be an opportune time for an 'independent unbiased' study of the fundamentals of the chiropractic profession. Such studies should be high among the priorities of the NINCDS..."[1] To fulfill their congressional mandate, NINCDS convened the Workshop on the Research Status of Spinal Manipulative Therapy at NIH on February 2-4, 1975.

Sometime in late April or early May 1974, Scott received a call from the secretary of the acting director of NINCDS, Donald B. Tower, MD, to see if he would be willing to participate on a committee established to plan for the Workshop. A letter of confirmation from Dr. Tower dated May 8, 1974, also indicated that Murray Goldstein, DO, associ-

---

[1] Goldstein, Murray, Editor, "The Research Status of Spinal Manipulative Therapy." DHEW Publication No. (NIH) 76-998, 1975, pg. 3.

ate director for Extramural Programs for NINCDS, would replace Dr. Howard Jenerick—a change that probably improved the objectivity of the conference, given Dr. Goldstein's background as an Osteopath—a distant cousin to chiropractic in the health care field.

A memorandum dated May 7, 1974, demonstrated that Dr. Goldstein was a man of action. From his comments, it would appear the recent inclusion of chiropractic services under Medicare stimulated the action by the Senate subcommittee referred to previously. He pointed out that NINCDS had already put out a notice[2] of available grant money, "...relevant to chiropracty..." that nearly two-dozen potential applicants had already made contact with NINCDS. He said the NINCDS was planning a scientific workshop for presentation and discussion of research on chiropractic and related areas and thus the formation of a planning committee was necessary. Members of this committee included:

Murray Goldstein, DO, MPH (Chairman)
Director, Extramural Programs
National Institute of Neurological and Communicative Dis
orders and Stroke, NIH
Bethesda, Maryland

Philip E. Greenman, DO
Professor and Chairman, Department of Biomechanics
College of Osteopathic Medicine
Michigan State University
East Lansing, Michigan

Scott Haldeman, DC [PhD not listed in the memorandum]
Vancouver, British Columbia, Canada

Horace W. Magoun, PhD
Professor Emeritus, UCLA[3]
National Research Council

---

[2] NIH Guide for Grants and Contracts, Vol. 3, No. 4, March 13, 1974, pg. 3 The announcement stated, "...grant-supported chiropractic research...includes research on areas such as spinal biomechanics, the anatomy, physiology and pathophysiology of the subluxation lesion, and controlled clinical trials of chiropractic diagnosis and therapy."
[3] While not noted as an original member of the planning committee, he was so noted on the actual program.

National Academy of Sciences
Washington, D.C.

James H. McElhaney, PhD
Professor of Biomechanics
Department of Biomedical Engineering
Duke University, School of Engineering
Durham, North Carolina

Donald B. Tower, MD, PhD
Acting Director, NINCDS
NIH, Bethesda, Maryland

Henry G. West, Jr., DC
Pocatello, Idaho

Andrew B. Wymore, DC
Osawatomie, Kansas

What an honor and a responsibility for the young 31-year-old chiropractor holding an academic doctorate and just finishing his second year of medical school. To be matched up with two very high officials at NINCDS both with clinical and academic degrees, a member of the National Research Council at the National Academy of Sciences, two professors of biomechanics/bioengineering from two very prestigious universities, and two seasoned political veterans of the chiropractic profession must have been a position that induced some sleepless nights.

The Goldstein memo asked the Planning Committee to make recommendations about the:

(a) Content of the Workshop
(b) Potential Participants
(c) Workshop Format
(d) Workshop Arrangements
(e) Editing and Publication

Accompanying the memo was a <u>Statement by the American Chiropractic Association (ACA)</u> submitted to the Public Health Service on October 1968, updated April 1, 1974. It was apparently supplied to Dr. Goldstein to give him an up-to-date synopsis of the chiropractic profession. Under Section IV, B is a comment about research. At that time, 40% of the dues of the ACA were directed to the Foundation for Chiropractic Education and Research (FCER) and 12% of that money went directly to the support of chiropractic research. A brief synopsis of their eight current research projects was noted.

In this May 1974 Goldstein memo, a face-to-face meeting for the Planning Committee was set for June 17, 1974, at the NIH.

At the June 17 meeting, Dr. Goldstein provided the Planning Committee an outline for the proposed conference with suggested speakers. It was only a preliminary outline for the committee to review but gave evidence of the sparse knowledge and understanding about chiropractic extant in the minds of the leaders at NINCDS. The outline was as follows:

1) History of Chiropractic
> Joseph Janse, DC, President of National-Lincoln College of Chiropractic
> Julius Dientenfass, DC, author

2) Basic Research relevant to Chiropractic
> *Biomechanics*
> C.H. Suh, PhD, engineering professor, University of Colorado
> R.M. Oliver, PhD, University of Colorado
> L.D. Ball, PhD, University of Colorado
> Joe Howe, DC, National College of Chiropractic, Chicago
> *Neurophysiology*
> S.K. Sharpless, PhD, University of Colorado
> R.J. McGregor, PhD, University of Colorado
> Scott Haldeman, PhD, Vancouver, BC [Did not list his DC degree.]
> *Neurochemistry*
> M.W. Luttges, PhD, University of Colorado

3) Clinical Research relevant to Chiropractic.
> John Allenburg, DC, Clinic Director, Northwestern College of Chiropractic, Minnesota

J.G. Anderson, DC, Dept. Neurology, Los Angeles College of Chiropractic, California

A.M. Kleynhans, DC, Director of Research, National College of Chiropractic, Illinois

J.W. Muilenberg, DC, DACBR, Texas College of Chiropractic, Texas

Clinical Research in Technique
Fred W. Illi, DC, Geneva, Switzerland
George Goodheart, DC, Detroit, Michigan
Henrie Gillet, DC, Brussels, Belgium
C.S. Gonstead, DC, Mt. Horeb, Wisconsin
Major DeJarnette, DC, Nebraska City, Nebraska

The chiropractors included in this list were prominent people in the profession, but aside from Scott, they all lacked research training or capability. The bulk of the other suggested participants were all associated with the University of Colorado chiropractic research program. The field of qualified chiropractors trained to do research or the number of people trained in research who were studying chiropractic was sparse.

Furthermore, Goldstein outlined in the memo for the June 17 meeting what he called "objectives" for the Workshop:

1) This is an opportune time for an "independent, unbiased" study of the fundamentals of the chiropractic profession.

2) There is a great need for engineers and biomedical scientists doing research in chiropractic to work together.

3) It is a time to use a portion of the Congressional increase to create bioengineering centers to create new and improved instruments and devices for the detection, diagnosis, and treatment of disease and study the fundamentals of chiropractic in cooperation with NINCDS.

The Planning Committee agreed at their June 17 meeting to plan a preliminary informal meeting for the fall, designed to bring together qualified interested parties to help define the problems and lay out the plan for the more formal workshop. The Committee made plans to meet again on August 1. Dr. Goldstein asked for feedback on this meeting within the month.[4]

Being fully capable of accessing the scientific literature, Scott did some thorough investigation about who was publishing in the areas discussed by the committee. He also expanded his network of connections within chiropractic to garner a greater list of potential chiropractic participants, including some of his former faculty members at Palmer. In response to Goldstein's request for feedback, Scott sent a letter to Dr. Goldstein dated July 9th with his suggestion of a fully outlined program divided by days, subject matter, and with a list of speakers for each subject for the committee to consider. In the program proposed by Scott, he subtly transitioned the focus of the workshop from "chiropractic" to "spinal manipulative therapy," which broadened the range of potential speakers and topics, yet retained an indirect focus on chiropractic. To Scott's credit, the final workshop was divided into six chapters almost exactly as he outlined in this letter:

Chapter I Introduction, Summary, and Analysis [proposed by Scott but not as a chapter]

Chapter II [Historical Review of the] Evolution and Development of the Concepts of Manipulative Therapy

Chapter III What Do the "Basic Sciences" Tell Us About Manipulative Therapy (Anatomical and Biomechanical Studies)

Chapter IV What Do the "Basic Sciences" Tell Us About Manipulative Therapy (Neuroscience Studies)

Chapter V What Do the "Clinical Sciences" Tell Us About Manipulative Therapy (Subluxation: Pathophysiology and Diagnosis) [Scott's version was Pathophysiological Studies and Structural Studies, Clinical Effectiveness of Manipulation]

Chapter VI What Do the "Clinical Sciences" Tell Us About Manipulative Therapy (Therapeutic Studies) [They moved Scott's proposed Clinical Effectiveness into its own chapter.][5]

Further to Scott's credit, 20 of the 40 names Scott recommended as

[4] Ibid.
[5] Ibid. pg.

participants ended up forming 30% of the 58 final workshop faculty. Early positive, aggressive action set the course for this landmark event in chiropractic and in Scott's life.

At the July 29th Planning Committee meeting a detailed proposal for the Workshop was laid out following Scott's recommendations. With input from other committee members, they had created a list of 103 potential participants. The final workshop ended up with the following:

> ...58 scientist and clinicians of national and international stature, including 16 Doctors of Chiropractic (DC), 24 Doctors of Medicine (MD), 7 Doctors of Osteopathic Medicine (DO), and 11 basic scientists (usually PhD); seven of the aforementioned clinical participants were holders of both the PhD and a clinical degree. Participants came from the United States and eight foreign countries.[6]

The August 7th edition of the *New York Times* railed against the NINCDS plans to host a conference by first referencing several negative government reports on chiropractic, commenting on the "cult" nature of chiropractic due to its lack of scientific validation, identifying a 1970 Department of Health, Education and Welfare task force on Medicaid that recommended a legislative amendment denying federal payments to chiropractors, and closing with a quote from the American College of Surgeons saying it was "unfortunate" that the NIH study did not precede the inclusion of chiropractic services under Medicare.[7] Given the political climate of the time when the AMA Committee on Quackery was in full force, Scott's involvement with this conference highlighted a medical prejudice more emotional than anything he had ever experienced in South Africa.

In an official invitation from Murray Goldstein to be a participant in the Workshop, Scott was asked to present a 20-minute discussion on three papers presented by other scientists in the area of the neurosciences. He was also asked to present a 20-minute paper on

---

[6] Goldstein, Murray. "The Research Status of Spinal Manipulative Therapy. DHEW Publication, NINCDS Monograph No. 15, 1975, pg. 3.
[7] *New York Times*, Wednesday, August 7th.

"Pathophysiologic Evidence for the Chiropractic Subluxation." He was instructed to provide a history of the "...research status of this area, presenting data on what is known, what is not known and what is controversial."[8] Given the paucity of research regarding the "subluxation," Scott was presented with a formidable challenge unless he was to focus his presentation on the "controversial" nature of the subluxation.

Scott accepted the official invitation from Goldstein in a September 9th letter, but he altered the title of his presentation from "...*Chiropractic Subluxation*" to "...*Spinal Subluxation*." He stated in the letter that this more correctly portrayed the entity "*subluxation*" since it was not exclusively a chiropractic concept. This change opened the door to a much wider base of research than had it been limited to simply a chiropractic focus.[9] Scott also provided Dr. Goldstein with a short list of chiropractors and scientists who should be invited to attend the Workshop as observers.

By mid-September, the program had been finalized, the date and location set, and instructions to the participants mailed. The time for organizing the meeting was past, and Scott was focused on preparing his presentations. Now that the public was aware of the Workshop, Dr. Goldstein began to receive communication of various sorts from both chiropractic and medicine, some proclaiming the wisdom of such an undertaking and others condemning the Workshop.

Scott soon realized that participation in a scientific meeting would be a new experience for some of the chiropractic participants. In October, letters to Doctors West, Wymore, Janse, Jeness, Howe, Drum, and Gitelman, Scott proposed to the selected chiropractic participants:

> ...a meeting where we could discuss the format and content of
> the various papers and assist those participants who are perhaps
> unfamiliar with what can be expected at a scientific conference.
> Similarly recent discussions with members of the executive of the

---

[8] Personal letter from Dr. Murray Goldstein, 30 August 1974. Letter is in the Scott Haldeman files.
[9] Personal letter to Dr. Goldstein from Dr. Haldeman, 9 Sept 1974. Letter is in the Haldeman files.

> I.C.A., A.C.A., and C.C.A. has further given priority of such a meeting to ensure that no one paper is totally out of context with other chiropractic papers and that some form of consensus on the principles and terminology be reached before the papers are read at the conference.[10]

The meeting was set for October 26-27 at the Canadian Memorial Chiropractic College.

The meeting succeeded in proctoring and preparing each of the chiropractic presenters. Dr. Joseph Howe wrote to the other chiropractic participants at the end of December, expressing both his appreciation and his anger over the many revisions of his presentation that had been promulgated and rejected since the meeting at the end of October.[11] No doubt each of the participants were under duress given they had been chosen to represent their profession before the world and before a body of scientists—something new for chiropractors.

Indeed, the entire chiropractic profession was anxious about the potential outcome of the workshop as exemplified by a memo to then ACA president William Bromley, DC, from Mortimer Levine, DC, New York state ACA delegate:

> Since Congress appropriated two million dollars for <u>chiropractic research</u>, it seems to me that our profession should have had at least equal say as to the parameters, participants and expense monies for the conference...
>
> Looking over the list of participants, we see the names of Dr. Thomas Ballantine, an avowed enemy of chiropractic, Drs. Cyriax and Mennell, leading medical proponents of manipulation, who are on record as stating that manipulative therapy should be preempted from irregulars like chiropractors.
>
> Remember that <u>we</u> are the authorities in anatomical geometry and neuro-mechanics. <u>We</u> are the experts in palpation and the adjustment of the human organism. Therefore, the following suggestions are in order.

---

[10] Personal letter from Scott Haldeman to each of the chiropractic participants dated 2 Oct. 1974.
[11] Personnel letter to the chiropractic presenters at the Workshop, 31 Dec. 1974. Letter is in the Scott Haldeman Collection.

1. Overwhelm the conference with our erudition. Expound on our advanced scientific concepts of postural mechanics and spinal analysis...

2. The theme of our presentation should not focus on manipulation as a therapeutic modality, but rather the reasons why we apply our adjustive techniques.

3. Finally and most important, inform the conference that the reversal of the tides of sickness that have engulfed us demands the restructuring of our health care system.[12]

This kind of input, regardless of its source, did little to deter or alter the focus and purpose of the proposed Workshop—to do an objective evaluation of spinal manipulative therapy.

The Workshop was an astounding success for all who acknowledge spinal manipulative therapy in the sense that it brought this ancient art into the limelight, engaged knowledgeable clinicians and scientists in dialogue over the subject matter, and set a course for future research. What the Workshop did not do, nor did it ever intend to do, was validate the practice of spinal manipulative therapy. Actually, the closing remarks in Dr. Goldstein's conclusion in the resulting monograph were quite telling:

> The NINCDS[13] Workshop on the Research Aspects of Spinal Manipulative Therapy and staff review and analysis of available data clearly indicate that *specific conclusions cannot be derived from the scientific literature for or against either the efficacy of spinal manipulative therapy or the pathophysiologic foundations from which it is derived.* The efficacy of spinal manipulative therapy is based on a body of clinical experience in the "hands" of specialized clinicians.[14]

[12] 2 Jan. 1975 memo to Dr. Bromley, president, ACA from Mortimer Levine, DC, Memo is in the Scott Haldeman Collection.
[13] It should be noted that the National Institute for Neurological Disease and Stroke (NINDS) underwent a name change in 1975 to the National Institute for Neurological and Communicative Disorders and Stroke (NINCDS) during the planning of and prior to the Workshop on Spinal Manipulative Therapy. Thus, the variation in the use of the two acronyms.
[14] Goldstein, Murray. "The Research Status of Spinal Manipulative Therapy. DHEW Publication, NINCDS Monograph No. 15, 1975, pg. 7.

A retrospective evaluation of the Workshop would label it as a major turning point in the science of spinal manipulative therapy. No more could it be labeled "cultish" or "quackery" due to the lack of scientific investigation, for from this point forward, the momentum of change shifted. NINCDS encouraged research into this area, and some major universities actually pursued related research areas. Chiropractic and chiropractors were encouraged, and a ground swell of young practitioners decided to follow Scott's example of pursuing graduate research education. Thirty years later, the use of spinal manipulative therapy for the relief of back and neck pain was more extensively researched and reported on than any other non-surgical treatment for back pain. And not surprisingly, the name of Scott Haldeman is found throughout those research publications.

CONFERENCE ON COAL MINER'S DISEASE— BLACK LUNG DISEASE

In the 1970s, chiropractic was suffering the effects of the American Medical Association's attack on "quackery." The profession desperately needed something that would heighten its credibility in the eyes of the public. The 1975 conference on "Spinal Manipulative Therapy (SMT)" sponsored by the National Institute of Neurological and Communicative Disorders and Stroke (NINCDS) brought a public and scientific focus to SMT and indirectly to chiropractic. But the results of the conference—that there is no valid evidence to support or refute the effectiveness of SMT—left everyone in a state of confusion. What do we do now?

Circumstances enumerated below would create an unusual opportunity for chiropractic to step into the public spotlight in late 1976. Black lung disease[15] was a hotly debated issue in coal mining country like Pennsylvania. According to Dr. Donald Rasmussen, who regularly treated coal miners, "[Black lung disease] is one of the most widely suffered occupational maladies in the U.S., no cure has been found for the disease that kills 4,000 U.S. miners every year. An estimated 70 percent of underground coal miners will be afflicted with some form of black lung during their lives."[16] No cure has yet been found for black lung disease, nor is there a satisfactory explanation as to why one miner would contract the disease and a fellow-worker would not.

The Federal Coal Mine Health and Safety Act of 1969 had created a black lung disability benefits program to compensate coal miners who had been disabled by on-the-job dust exposure.[17] In 1981 it would pay out $824 million in black lung benefits to miners, widows, and dependents—anyone who had worked in a mine for 10 years was "presumed" a black lung victim and received up to $559 per month—a third of which came from a tax on mining firms, which in turn had a negative effect on state revenues. As such, the state needed to take some action.

Milton J. Shapp, governor of the state of Pennsylvania, had been successfully relieved of back problems under chiropractic care, and his lt. governor, Ernest Kline, was also a chiropractic advocate. Lou Sportelli, DC and past president of the Pennsylvania Chiropractic Society, was a good friend of Governor Shapp (though not his personal chiropractor). Dr. Sportelli was closely connected to the American Chiropractic Association and its current president, Dr. Henry West—and

[15] Gale Encyclopedia of Medicine, Published December, 2002 by the Gale Group The Essay Author is Carol A. Turkington. Article last updated on 08-14-2006, http://www.healthatoz. com/healthatoz/Atoz/common/standard/transform.jsp?requestURI=/healthatoz/Atoz/ ency/black_lung_disease.jsp Black lung disease is the common name for coal workers' pneumoconiosis (CWP) or anthracosis, a lung disease of older workers in the coal industry, caused by inhalation, over many years, of small amounts of coal dust. The risk of having black lung disease is directly related to the amount of dust inhaled over the years; the disease typically affects workers over age 50. Its common name comes from the fact that the inhalation of heavy deposits of coal dust makes miners lungs look black instead of a healthy pink. The particles of fine coal dust, which a miner breathes when he is in the mines, cannot be destroyed within the lungs or removed by natural processes. Eventually, this build-up causes thickening and scarring, making the lungs less efficient in supplying oxygen to the blood.
There is no treatment or cure for this condition, although it is possible to treat complications such as lung infections and cor pulmonale. Further exposure to coal dust must be stopped. Those patients who develop black lung disease at an early age, or who have progressive massive fibrosis, have a higher risk of premature death.
[16] Weiss, Michael. "Dr. Donald Rasmussen, life-long campaigner against black lung disease, says the new budget gives miners the shaft." *People Magazine.* May 11, 1981, Vol. 15, No. 18.
[17] Gale Encyclopedia of Medicine, Published December, 2002 by the Gale Group The Essay Author is Carol A. Turkington. Article last updated on 08-14-2006, http://www.healthatoz. com/healthatoz/Atoz/common/standard/transform.jsp?requestURI=/healthatoz/Atoz/ency/ black_lung_disease.jsp

was also impressed with a budding young chiropractor who, with a PhD in hand, was working his way through medical school in British Columbia—Scott Haldeman.

The governor, with the encouragement of Dr. Sportelli, called a conference, "Experimental Approaches to the Investigation of Chiropractic Management in Pneumoconiosis," for December 1-2, 1976. The purpose of the conference, according to Sportelli was to, "...see where and how chiropractic might fit in with black lung—in the prevention or treatment aspect of the research on the disease."[18] Though not on the same magnitude as the NINCDS conference held the year before, the model of bringing scientists and clinicians to the table for dialogue was similar. Nine papers were presented, Scott's being one of them.

Governor Shapp received criticism for spending state money to host a conference, but he weathered the attacks well by noting that black lung disease was costing Pennsylvania millions of dollars in lost production, lost wages, workmen's compensation, and treatment costs—it was time to look beyond the norm. Governor Shapp clearly stated, "I am not saying that chiropractic has the answers. We deserve to have their input, along with that of every other health discipline, so as to get this disease eradicated, or at least under control, just as quickly as possible."[19]

The conference was labeled as "far out" by those wishing to discredit the governor's action, but presentations would dictate otherwise. Dr. Sion Kaftari explained the "Functional Anatomy and Histology of Peripheral Points of the Bronchial Tree and Aeveolar Region." Dr. Josefa M. Cubina established "Physiological Considerations." Dr. Ronald Modest gave "Pathological Considerations." Dr. Alan H. Adams presented "Clinical Laboratory Considerations." Dr. James F. Winterstein gave "Roentgenological Findings." Dr. Henry G. West, Jr. proposed "Physical Examination Procedures for a Pilot Research Project." Dr. Joseph Janse presented "Chiropractic Management

[18] Bracy, Marilyn, "Chiropractic: Black Lung Cure?" *Today's Post*, Wednesday, December 1, 1975, pg. 5.
[19] Ligas, Christine, "State Labor Secretary Urges Chiropractic Aid." *Times Herald*. December 2, 1975.

Rational."

Dr. Scott Haldeman outlined "Considerations of Methodology for Chiropractic Clinical Trials." He noted the following:

> Questions of the type which are being asked at this conference are becoming increasingly common. The recognition of chiropractic as a health profession is forcing chiropractors to meet the same level of justification for their claims of therapeutic success as is required from other professions, such as medicine, surgery and dentistry.[20]

Shapp urged the participation of chiropractors at a federally-funded Johnstown Rehabilitation Center, ignoring the fact that federal funds could not be used to employ chiropractors at that time. Dr. West had recommended the hiring of chiropractors to serve in eight state clinics that treat patients with black lung disease.

The conference closed with the words of its moderator and organizer, Dr.Sportelli:

> We've been overlooked for a long time. People think we just take care of backaches and headaches, and we do that, but there are much broader dimensions...It's time to cast aside some preconceived prejudices and explore new solutions. There's so little money for drugless research generally. All the emphasis in our society is on chemical cures.[21]

Scott reminisced many years later that this was one of the first conferences following the NINCDS conference that brought chiropractic research-minded individuals together. Nothing of note was ever done to eradicate black lung disease, but the chiropractic research community had begun to form itself, and Scott continued his hope of establishing his International Society for Chiropractic Research.

Governor Shapp promised a $50,000 grant for chiropractic research. Dr. Sportelli sent a letter to every college in the USA suggesting that they undertake a research project on this issue and told

---

[20] *Action Digest*. American Chiropractic Association. January, 1977. Copy in the Haldeman Collection.
[21] Ibid.

National College of Chiropractic graduation, 1976. (l to r): Governor Milton J. Schapp, Drs. Joseph Janse and Louis Sportelli—the motivating force behind the Black Lung Disease Conference in 1976.

them the money would be there. Dr. Sportelli relates that when he contacted Drs. Janse and Napolitano, the presidents of National College of Chiropractic and New York College of Chiropractic, they were enthusiastic, concerned, anxious, guarded, and reserved, but encouraged him to continue. All the colleges declined the offer due to insufficient staff and other related problems. This was an eye opener as it showed the level at which the chiropractic colleges were deficient in qualified research staff. Dr. Sportelli went to the Governor's Bureau of Labor and told them that the current priority in the colleges was spinal research and not pneumoconiosis and that perhaps on another day the profession could use the money for research but now was not the time. It broke Dr. Sportelli's heart because $50,000 in 1975 was a lot of money. The post conference publicity and press was fabulous for the chiropractic profession. It essentially silenced the critics considerably on this issue. The surge of press, because of the governor's participation and the secretary of labor's participation in the conference, gave an impetus to the profession that carried it to a few more political victories in the next few years.[22]

NEW ZEALAND COMMISSION OF INQUIRY ON CHIROPRACTIC

Chiropractic came under the critical eye of the New Zealand Medical Association (NZMA) in the late 1960s when editorials and letters about it began to appear in their profession's journal. The tone of the commentaries became even more critical in the 1970s. When the New Zealand House of Representatives received a petition with 94,210 signatures in 1975 requesting amendments to the Social Securities Act of 1964 and the Accident Compensation Act of 1972 to allow payment for chiropractic services, the discussion about chiropractic became quite heated. Subsequently, according to the report of Kevin Dew, the New Zealand Medical Association passed an amendment to its bylaws stating the NZMA "...cannot cooperate with a body of people who believe that all diseases are partly or wholly caused by displacement of the spine."[23]

This intractable position by medicine coupled with a massive plea from the public spurred the government to form a Commission of Inquiry into Chiropractic in July 1976. The order to appoint commissioners and to define the terms of reference was made in January 1978. The delay was in the negotiation of the terms of reference between the Ministry of Health, the New Zealand Chiropractic Association (NZCA), the New Zealand Medical Association (NZMA), and the New Zealand Society of Physiotherapists (NZSP). According to David Chapman-Smith, "...the NZCA wanted to keep the terms of reference as narrow as possible...to avoid a broad medical attack in areas such as philosophy and education..."[24] The NZMA wanted the

---

[22] Personal communication with Dr. Sportelli via e-mail 23 March 2009.
[23] Dew, Kevin. "Apostasy to orthodoxy: debates before a Commission of Inquiry into chiropractic." *Sociology of Health & Illness*, Vol. 22, No. 3, 2000, pg.313.
[24] Chapman-Smith, DA. "The New Zealand Commission of Inquiry: Its Significance in Chiropractic History." Chiropractic History, Vol. 3, No. 1, 1983, pg. 33.

terms of reference to be wide open, and they won this initial struggle. Chiropractic was to be examined on "...anything of possible relevance to the practice of chiropractic..."[25]

As a result of the open terms of reference, it became clear that this was going to be a long and expensive battle, that overseas experts would be summoned for witnesses, that chiropractic was not just being challenged on its ability to provide benefits through patient care, and that medicine looked at the process as an opportunity to "... expose and eliminate the New Zealand chiropractic profession."[26]

The Commission of Inquiry into Chiropractic (CIC) issued a final report in October 1979. At the outset, three commissioners—Professor Inglis, barrister and Queen's Counsel, Miss Betty Fraser, former head mistress of Wellington Girls' School, and Professor Penfold, professor of chemistry at the University of Christchurch—decided, "...evidence would be: (1) public; (2) on oath; (3) subject to generous cross-examination on behalf of all interested parties; (4) given orally, but in accordance with a written submission filed with the Commission and available to the principal parties at least 30 days beforehand... and; (5) recorded verbatim."[27]

The Commission was charged to consider:

1) The practice and philosophy of chiropractic, its scientific and educational basis, and whether it constitutes a separate and distinct healing art;

2) The contribution chiropractic could make to the health services of New Zealand;

3) Any other matters that may be thought by you to be relevant to the general objects of the inquiry.[28]

In a report by Kevin Dew:

There were 136 formal submissions made to the Commission,

---

[25] Ibid.
[26] Chapman-Smith, DA. "The New Zealand Commission of Inquiry: Its Significance in Chiropractic History." *Chiropractic History*, Vol. 3, No. 1, 1983, pg. 34.
[27] Ibid.
[28] Commission of Inquiry into Chiropractic. (1979) *Chiropractic in New Zealand: Report of the Commission of Inquiry.* Wellington: Government Printer.

coming to more than 2300 pages. Oral evidence amounted to 3658 pages of transcript presented over a period of 78 days (CIC 179: 15). In addition, the Commission received nearly 13,000 completed questionnaire forms from chiropractic patients...The Commission visited the medical schools at Otago and Auckland and the schools of physiotherapy in Auckland and Dunedin. In addition, chiropractic colleges were inspected in Australia, England, Canada and the United States.

The submissions to the inquiry polarized into two camps. On the one side, there was the medical profession and its allies: the physiotherapists, the Department of Health and the New Zealand Consumer Council. On the other were the chiropractors and their allies—the thousands of patients who sent in letters and survey forms expounding the virtues of chiropractic, and groups representing workers, such as the Federation of Labour.

Chiropractors were criticized for their lack of training, particularly as they acted as a first point of contact for patients...The medical profession argued that the systems of medicine and chiropractic were incompatible, and that as chiropractic was an unproven treatment directed at an unlimited range of disorders it would be absurd for chiropractic to be recognized by the state. Chiropractors responded to the issue of training by suggesting that medically-trained manipulators were inadequately trained, and that chiropractic training programmes were the only ones 'designed to prepare the graduates adequately to practice manipulative therapy as primary contact practitioners.'

The medical profession also attacked chiropractic for creating unnecessary markets. Chiropractors defended themselves...claiming that they would save the state money by reducing spending on pharmaceuticals and returning people quickly to productive work.[29]

Mr. David Chapman-Smith, LLB, was legal counsel for the New Zealand Chiropractic Association. As a first-hand witness of the entire proceedings and subsequently an advocate of chiropractic, he

---

[29] Dew, Kevin. "Apostasy to orthodoxy: debates before a Commission of Inquiry into chiropractic." *Sociology of Health & Illness*, Vol. 22, No. 3, 2000, pg.314-315.

shares his insight into the Commission of Inquiry into Chiropractic:

> By the end of 1978 the Commissioners had a very positive view of chiropractic, and one could sense they wanted to write a report generally endorsing the profession. However, although they had heard from patients, practicing chiropractors and educationalists such as Dr. Andries Kleynhans and Dr. Terry Yochum from the Philip Institute of Technology, International College of Chiropractic in Australia, they had not heard from an expert witness on the scientific basis of chiropractic, and relevant published research. They needed a highly credible and convincing witness if they were to make findings opposing the evidence of the medical experts who had denigrated chiropractic principles, science and the whole field of the manipulative arts.
>
> It was under these circumstances that the NZ Chiropractors Association (NZCA) called Dr. Scott Haldeman as its foremost scientific expert in Wellington, New Zealand in February 1979. The lawyers for the Association knew that Dr. Haldeman DC, MD, PhD, who was a neurology resident at the University of California at Irvine, had the academic qualifications, and placed great hope upon him. However they had not met him until his arrival in New Zealand a few days before, knew his testimony would be crucial to the whole Inquiry, and had therefore awaited his arrival in a mood of considerable suspense.
>
> According to the procedure of the Inquiry, Dr. Haldeman had already provided a written brief of his evidence. During his first hour before the Commission he read this and then answered questions from NZCA counsel Mr. David Chapman-Smith—on key subjects before the Commission including the definition and nature of subluxation.
>
> Then, for most of the rest of the day, Dr. Haldeman responded to questions from opposing legal counsel and the three Commissioners themselves. He triumphed beyond all expectations. Here was a sharp and informed young mind, and a person who clearly knew far more about the relevant basic and clinical sciences, and the state of the research evidence, than any witness produced by the NZ Medical Association. More than that, the Commission had before it a gifted and enthusiastic teacher. It was clearly very impressed, and

that day the Commission finally and fully had the hook to hang its hat on in finding that the fundamental theories and principles of chiropractic were sound.

Some two months later, legal counsel for the NZCA had to prepare final written submissions to present to the Commission. In the area of the scientific basis of chiropractic, the submission merely and confidently stated that "the NZCA accepts the evidence of Dr. Haldeman in its entirety." The Commission did so in its subsequent report.[30]

Scott's *Brief* submitted to the Commission of Inquiry into Chiropractic (CIC), referred to by Chapman-Smith, was organized into a logical progression of the development of spinal manipulation without focusing on chiropractic. The strategy used by Scott was to divert the focus of attention away from chiropractic and its lack of scientific substantiation and direct it to a procedure, spinal manipulation, that has an historical presence that dated back to Hippocrates and had an ever-growing literature base founded in scientific research. Convincing the Commission of the value of spinal manipulation was much less onerous than convincing them of the value of chiropractic care—although in the final analysis, the two were similar. Scott was referenced twenty-eight times in Appendix I of the report, far more than any other literature source used by the Commission.[31]

Scott also submitted an Addendum to his *Brief*, a tome of 189 pages. The Addendum contained all the supportive information referenced in his *Brief* and was divided into ten sections as follows:

A. Curriculum vita of Scott Haldeman

B. History of Spinal Manipulation and Chiropractic

C. The Utilization of Spinal Manipulation and Chiropractic

D. Spinal Manipulation in the Treatment of Spinal Pain Disorders

E. Spinal Manipulation in Visceral Disorders (articles from medical and osteopathic journals)

[30] Personal Communication with Mr. David Chapman-Smith via e-mail 23 Mar 2008. Haldeman Collection.
[31] Commission of Inquiry into Chiropractic. (1979) *Chiropractic in New Zealand: Report of the Commission of Inquiry.* Wellington: Government Printer. Appendix I.

F. The Theoretical Basis for Spinal Manipulative Therapy

G. Training in Spinal Manipulative Therapy

H. Topics Studied by Chiropractors

I. Medicaid and Chiropractic

J. Medicine and Chiropractic

The outcome of the most intensive investigation into chiropractic, up to that point in time, was quite favorable for chiropractic. The NZCA had recommended,

> ...that chiropractors should be able to write certificates that would allow payments under...the sickness benefit; that the NZMA ethical ruling be rescinded; that tertiary benefits be payable for approved chiropractic colleges; that the practice of spinal manipulation be restricted to chiropractors, specialist medical practitioners, and those medical practitioners and physiotherapists who had passed a course in spinal manipulative therapy as prescribed by the Chiropractic Board...and that chiropractors should not be excluded from hospitals. The Commission agreed on all counts.

> ...the Commission leveled a number of criticisms at the medical profession and rejected the case that it made. The Commission found that chiropractors were the only health practitioners who were necessarily equipped by their education and training to carry out spinal manipulative therapy...It recommended that chiropractic gain access to state health benefits that were available to medical doctors for the treatment of back problems (CIC 1979: 3).[32]

The actual CIC report made additional recommendations on the relationship between chiropractic and medicine, the need to restructure the laws governing the practice of chiropractic in New Zealand, the need for more research and better education for those doing spinal manipulation although the chiropractic program in Preston Institute in Australia was recognized as an institution with "...a high standard, and the need to allow chiropractors into New Zealand hospitals."[33]

---

[32] Dew, Kevin. "Apostasy to orthodoxy: debates before a Commission of Inquiry into chiropractic." *Sociology of Health & Illness*, Vol. 22, No. 3, 2000, pg.321-22.
[33] Commission of Inquiry into Chiropractic. (1979) *Chiropractic in New Zealand: Report of the Commission of Inquiry.* Wellington: Government Printer, p. 5.

The published proceedings of the CIC were distributed world-wide and became the main documentation in support of chiropractic legitimization for many years. In Chapman-Smith's words, "... the success of the chiropractic case in New Zealand resulted from Dr. Haldeman [testimony and submitted materials] more than any other single individual."[34]

HALDEMAN RESEARCH CONFERENCES & BOOKS

The residency program in neurology at UCI kept Scott occupied and challenged but did not fulfill all his dreams and ambitions. He knew this was just another step in his preparation to enter onto the world stage as an individual with a unique perspective on spinal research and care. Opportunity would not let Scott alone, nor would he allow himself to languish in the role of the average. He had to be doing something more than what was typical to fulfill his residency program requirements.

His dream, the International Society for the Advancement of Clinical Chiropractic and Spinal Research, was showing promise, and this further encouraged his efforts to nurture the budding idea. The mission of the Society was to inform and instruct the doctor in practice on the latest research information that related to practice. Organized as small sub-chapters dispersed over a wide geographic area—on every continent—it was near impossible to reach everyone with timely information as it became available.

Why not bring field practitioners into the research community and teach them in a conference setting? It was a brilliant idea but not an easy sell to anyone in chiropractic. Holding a conference dedicated to research and not practice building was a novel idea. Having scientists as the main speakers presenting their latest research was challenged on the basis that there was not enough research or research individuals to fill a conference, at least not in chiropractic in the late 1970s. Certainly no medical research person would consider participating in a chiropractic research conference, even if the AMA had recently

34 Chapman-Smith, DA. "The New Zealand Commission of Inquiry: Its Significance in Chiropractic History." *Chiropractic History*, Vol. 3, No. 1, 1983, pg. 38.

altered the "code of ethics" to allow association with chiropractors. The idea of an international, inter-disciplinary conference on spinal research appeared doomed to destruction before being born—an academic abortion.

But the idea had merit, so Scott reached deep into his personal resolve to succeed—maybe drawing on some of his old piano sales experiences. The first hurdle was to convince potential conference supporters—the national chiropractic organizations—that such an adventure would not be a financial loss. From the examples of successful practice building types of seminars in the profession, Scott realized that attendance was only a part of what was necessary for an adequate financial return. He needed a product to sell as a result of the conference as well. Thus the idea of a textbook on modern-day chiropractic—something not available but badly needed—was conceived. He would use the presentations at the conference as material for the textbook.

Without success, Scott had been attempting to convince the International Chiropractic Association (ICA) and then the American Chiropractic Association (ACA) to underwrite his efforts to publish an Annual Yearbook on chiropractic since he moved to California in 1977. This annual publication was intended to compile the latest research along with commentary by Scott with the intent to bring out practical applications of the new research. He was never able to convince either body to support this effort, so the concept of publishing conference proceedings of his latest "International Society" brainchild seemed a logical alternative.

In the late 1970s, Dr. Joe Mazzarelli was elected president of the International Chiropractor's Association, and Jerry McAndrews, one of Scott's instructors from Palmer College, had accepted the position of executive vice-president of the ICA. Scott had interacted with these two chiropractic leaders in their support of the research at the University of Colorado at Boulder under the direction of Dr. Chung Ha Suh. It did not take long for Scott to persuade the ICA of the importance of an international, interprofessional conference and the possibility of publishing a textbook with an interdisciplinary list of authors. Scott asked the ICA to underwrite the conference and the textbook. The ICA eventually agreed to do so but only if Scott did not take any compensation for organizing the meeting and was willing to sign over all royalties from the book that come out of the conference to the ICA.

1979 CONFERENCE ON THE MODERN DEVELOPMENTS IN THE PRINCIPLES AND PRACTICE OF CHIROPRACTIC—Anaheim, CA, February 1979

The NINCDS Conference and similar conferences subsequently held at UC Irvine and the University of Michigan focused on Spinal Manipulative Therapy (SMT). The conference Scott proposed and hosted was the first inter-disciplinary scientific conference with the central theme on chiropractic, placing SMT in a secondary light. Scott justified this change of focus in the preface of the resulting textbook, *Modern Developments in the Principles and Practice of Chiropractic*:

> Over the past ten years there has been a rapid increase in sociological, experimental, and clinical research that is relevant to chiropractic. This, in turn, has resulted in the development of a rational approach to the theory and practice of chiropractic. This volume is a product of the work of leading authorities in the fields of history, sociology, neurophysiology, spinal biomechanics, and clinical chiropractic.[35]

Scott concluded the preface with special recognition of Dr. Joseph Mazzarelli and the Board of Control of the International Chiropractors Association (ICA), Dr. Jerry McAndrews, executive vice-president of the ICA and former faculty member at Palmer when Scott was a student, his wife, Joan, and several others.

The conference presenters represented a true international, multi-disciplinary collection of famous people:

Leon R.Coelho, DC, PhD	Bundoora, Victoria, Australia
John H. Coote, PhD	Birmingham, England
H.F. Farfan, MD, CM, FRCS (C)	Montreal, Canada
Richard A. Gerren, PhD	Irvine, California

[35] Haldeman, *Modern Developments in the Principles and Practice of Chiropractic*. Appleton-Century-Crofts, 1980, preface.

375

Russell W. Gibbons, BA	Pittsburgh, Pennsylvania
Ronald Gitelman, DC, FCCS (C)	Toronto, Canada
Adrian S. Grice, DC, FCCS (C)	Toronto, Canada
Scott Haldeman, DC, PhD, MD	Irvine California
Andries M. Kleynhans, DC	Bundoora, Victoria, Australia
Marvin W. Luttges, PhD	Boulder, Colorado
Reed B. Phillips, DC, DACBR	Salt Lake City, Utah
Aiko Sato, MD	Tokyo, Japan
Chung Ha Suh, PhD	Boulder, Colorado
Sydney Sunderland, MD, DSc.	Melbourne, Australia
John J. Triano, DC	Boulder, Colorado
Walter I. Wardwell, PhD	Storrs, Connecticut
Henry G. West, Jr. DC, FICC	Glendale, California.

The program (and the book) was divided into three main sections dealing with 1) the social aspects of chiropractic, 2) the principles of chiropractic, and 3) the practice of chiropractic. The conference, held at the Disneyland Hotel, was a success with people attending from around the globe. In a March 1980 letter to George Davidson, editor of *The Digest for Chiropractic Economics*, Scott expressed his excitement regarding the Anaheim conference with more than 520 chiropractors in attendance and granted Davidson permission to publish all papers from the conference once proper copyright had been obtained.

While there is a story about Scott's personal relationship with each invited presenter, three will provide examples of how only Scott could have successfully pulled off such a conference:

Russell Gibbons

Russell Gibbons was known in chiropractic circles for his historical writings about chiropractic. Russ had an interest in the history of the Haldemans in chiropractic, and as early as October 1976, Scott sent Russ material on his grandmother, a copy of a paper, "Chiropractic – a dying cult in a growing profession" published in the *Medical Undergraduates Society Journal* at the University of British Columbia, and expressed his concern that "mixers" through the ACA were becoming stronger. Scott shared his belief with Russ that chiropractic should be more "...like a dentist, i.e. a limited health care practitioner with expertise in a particular field."[36]

As kindred spirits, both Russ and Scott were sons of "straight" chiropractors, Russ acquainted Scott with the social-historical part of chiropractic. He sent Scott two of his own papers, *Chiropractic: The Survival of an American Heresy and Chiropractic in America: The Historical Conflicts of Cultism and Science*, and also introduced Scott to Walter Wardwell, PhD and noted sociologist at the University of Connecticut. Wardwell had written on chiropractors in the early 1950s, labeling them as "marginal practitioners" in his paper, *Social Factors in the Survival of Chiropractic: A comparative View.*

Because of the relationship between Scott and Russ and due to Russ's historical academic writings, Scott invited Russ to give the opening address, *The History of Chiropractic*, at the ICA Conference.

Harry Farfan, MD

In Scott's invitation to H.F. Farfan, MD and world-renowned orthopedic surgeon from Montreal specializing in back pain, he attempted to bring an international and interdisciplinary flavor to the research conference. It is conceivable that a double motive was behind the invitation since Scott had also applied for membership to the International Society for the Study of the Lumbar Spine (ISSLS) and had sought Dr. Farfan's endorsement for membership. Farfan agreed to recommend Scott for membership to ISSLS and also agreed to present a paper, *Biomechanical Disorders of the Spine*. Scott was pleased with his contribution to the conference and noted the amount of interest by conference attendees in Farfan's own book. Farfan was able to complete his chapter for Scott's book in due order, and the two of them built a stronger relationship as a result of Farfan's conference participation. In fact, in 1981 Dr. Farfan invited Scott to join him on a project to study the nerve supply to the periosteum[37] and its ability to be biomechanically stimulated. Scott was unable to accept his invitation, however.

---

[36] Personal letter to Russell Gibbons from Scott, dated 15 Oct 1976. Letter is in the Haldeman Collection.
[37] A sensitive membrane covering bone tissue containing a rich nerve and blood supply.

Sir Sydney Sunderland

Scott had done research on nerve compression for his master's thesis and published the papers in the *South African Medical Journal*. He was excited when the most authoritative scientist on nerve injuries, Sir Sydney Sunderland from Australia, referenced Scott's articles in his textbook, *Nerves and Nerve Injuries*. Scott felt that this topic was too important to leave out of a conference and book on chiropractic and asked Dr. Sunderland if he would be willing to travel to California for the meeting and write a chapter for the text. It was one of Scott's hopes that he could meet Sir Sydney and was excited when he recognized Scott's name from his articles and accepted the invitation.

POST-CONFERENCE EXPERIENCES

The conference was a major step towards Scott's dream of developing the International Society for the Advancement of Clinical Chiropractic and Spinal Research. He was charged and excited and ready to start planning the next one. However, the experience was not without its political consequences as seen in the following correspondences.

Alan Adams, DC

In February 1978, Scott extended an invitation to Dr. Alan Adams, VP for Chiropractic Education at Los Angeles College of Chiropractic and former dean of CMCC, to present a paper at the upcoming Haldeman Conference on the role of laboratory examinations in chiropractic practice. In April, Scott had to send a retraction to Dr. Adams. Apparently the ICA Board of Control would not allow Dr. Adams to be on the program because of his political involvement in Michigan against the ICA, who was opposed to the use of laboratory examinations in a chiropractic office. Since the ICA was sponsoring the conference, Scott was obligated to follow their wishes. The more interesting point is that Scott invited Dr. Adams to speak at the conference on laboratory examinations in chiropractic practice—though contrary to ICA held policy. Scott was a long-time adherent to the ICA, but continued to feel that chiropractic was a primary contact profession and maintained a position that practicing chiropractors needed to be able to screen out seriously ill patients even if it required the use of laboratory medicine.

Henry G. West, Jr., DC

In April 1978, Scott wrote a letter to Dr. West, past president of the American Chiropractic Association (ACA), advising him that the ICA Board of Control had denied him the privilege of being on the program. "They felt that your intense involvement in chiropractic political affairs over the years made it inappropriate for you to participate in a purely academic conference of this type...I disagree with their decision...If this were not the case I would not have invited you in the first place...the ICA is the sponsoring organization and I have no option but to comply..."[38] Dr. West was eventually put back on the program, however.

The success of the Anaheim conference had bittersweet consequences. As Scott matured intellectually, the intra-professional feuding within chiropractic must have discouraged him at times. He did his best to stay above the political fracas as exemplified above and in the exchange of letters with his friend, Dr. Sportelli.

Lou Sportelli, DC

Following the Black Lung Conference in Pennsylvania, Dr. Sportelli and Scott developed a friendship and continued to correspond with each other. After the Anaheim Research Conference, Dr. Sportelli submitted a report to the FCER board. His report was a scathing chastisement of the board's actions (or inactions) on several programs, not the least of which was the Anaheim conference:

> The ICA conference in Anaheim was a resounding success and the ICA not only gained in prestige throughout the world, but also made considerable amount of money. For those of you who do not know it, that program was offered to ACA (who did not accept it) and also to FCER. Apparently, the leadership in FCER did not choose to be a party to such action. This conference, having to do

---

[38] Personal letter to Henry West, Jr., DC from Scott dated 26 Apr 1978. Letter is in the Haldeman Collection.

with research, should have been FCER's and gained stature for <u>our</u> Foundation.[39]

Ralph Guenthner, DC and chair of the ACA Board of Governors, responded to Dr. Sportelli's accusation of the ACA and FCER not accepting Scott's offer to host the conference and asked for his source of information. Sportelli responded to Guenthner telling him that Scott had told him personally of the ACA and FCER refusal of support. Sportelli then shared this correspondence with Scott who responded to Sportelli quite strongly:

> It appears that there is now another misunderstanding making the circuit which I believe is destructive to the future of chiropractic research. It appears that I am the originator and you are the perpetuator of a story which has left the impression that ACA and FCER refused to support the Anaheim conference. I am extremely distressed that this discussion is taking place and would like to stop it now to prevent a very positive experience in the history of chiropractic being used as a weapon against any segment of the profession.
>
> The facts are as follows: following the NINCDS conference and the subsequent conferences on manipulation in Irvine and Michigan, I repeatedly stressed the importance of the chiropractic profession sponsoring a similar scientific conference of this type. I discussed the feasibility and desirability of such a conference as well as its potential cost with executives of the ACA, FCER, ICA, Palmer College, Canadian Chiropractic Association, and anyone else who would listen, including yourself. All such approaches were made verbally and no formal presentation was made to any group. The Canadian Chiropractic Association was the first association to ask me to help organize a major scientific conference in 1976. I invited eight scientists and clinicians to that conference and each speaker presented a paper which was later published in the CCA Journal... The ICA was the second association to approach me to organize a conference. This was done following the same type of non-specific discussion I had had with ACA officers...I agreed to organize the

---

[39] Report to FCER Board of Trustees by fellow Trustee, Louis Sportelli, DC, dated 28 Feb. 1978. Report is in the Haldeman Collection.

conference...About six months later I addressed the ACA and FCER boards in San Diego. I cannot remember specifically discussing a conference with the ACA board, but I do remember encouraging the FCER board to begin thinking about similar conferences. The ACA board then requested that they be permitted to co-sponsor the conference.

I made formal recommendations to the ICA board for such a co-sponsorship, but they felt that they had already made a com-mitment and had advanced the organization of the conference to a point where a co-sponsorship was not necessary. The ACA has, since that time acted, in my opinion, in a completely honorable and professional manner in giving moral support to the conference.

The conference was a success for chiropractic science and education. It was not and should not be considered an ICA success any more than the 1976 conference was a Canadian success. The people who benefit from high standard conferences are chiropractic patients. I will not tolerate that a success of this type be used by you, the ICA, ACA, FCER or any other faction to belittle or point a finger at another organization or individual. The success of the conference should be one which every chiropractor should be proud of irre-spective of his association, affiliation or method of practice. There must be and I believe will be many bigger and better conferences of this type in the profession, provided such conferences are not used as political weapons.

For this reason, I am formally, via this letter, expressing an apology to the ACA and FCER for any statements which I might have inad-vertently made which could have suggested that these organizations in any way rejected or refused to interact in the organization of this conference.[40]

MODERN DEVELOPMENTS IN THE PRINCIPLES AND PRACTICE OF CHIROPRACTIC

The book, a compilation of the presentations at the conference, was also a success but slow coming to pass. Apparently it was much

[40] Personal letter to Louis Sportelli, DC from Scott, dated 27 Mar. 1979. Letter is in the Haldeman Collection.

easier to stand before a group, show a set of slides, and pontificate on the work one has done than to carefully and clearly write what one said using correct grammar and correct references. It took Scott the better part of a year to get everyone's material submitted, in good order, for the book to be published in 1980. This was the first major textbook on chiropractic to be published by a large medical publishing company. The company was not sure that chiropractors would purchase sufficient copies to make the venture profitable and were also concerned that the publication of a chiropractic text would alienate some of their medical audiences. When the ICA guaranteed to purchase sufficient books to eliminate the possibility of a financial loss, Appleton-Century-Croft agreed to publish the book. The greater challenge seemed to be with his chiropractic participants, who had never prepared material for scientific publications. Scott explained his efforts to the chiropractic college presidents at a Denver meeting in 1980:

> I had the privilege of editing, and where necessary, referring specific chapters back to the authors for rewriting or correction. Most of the chapters were rewritten 2 or 3 times by the authors. I personally read every chapter a minimum of 4 times (some as many as 8 times.) In addition, the editorial staff at Appleton-Century-Crofts read each chapter a minimum of 4 times (perhaps more than that)! Each reading was for content, flow accuracy, grammar, spelling and typographical errors. With a total of at least 10 critical readings of each chapter written originally by the highest authorities on this subject, it is in my opinion that the final product is the highest quality education textbook ever to be produced by or for the chiropractic profession.[41]

The following is an example of the struggle Scott experienced with one of the authors in getting this book, *Modern Developments in the Principles and Practice of Chiropractic*, to press:

Leon Coelho DC, PhD

Leon Coelho was a faculty member at Palmer College of Chiropractic and fellow South African who received an invitation from Scott in

[41] Haldeman, Scott. Address to the Chiropractic College Presidents, Denver, CO., 20 June 1980.

May 1978 to prepare and present a chapter on "Spinal Radiographic Techniques and Radiation Protection." Coelho was humbled and accepted and then rescinded his acceptance due to personal reasons, including accepting a position to teach at the International College of Chiropractic in Australia. Scott was able to convince Coelho to remain on the program and began the same kind of correspondence that he had with many of the other chiropractic authors, teaching them the proper format to follow when writing a scientific paper and how to appropriately include scientific references. In January 1979, a month before the conference, Scott was still correcting Coelho's submission and sent him an outline of Dr. Sunderland's chapter as an example to follow. Even after the conference was over, Scott was still working with Coelho to complete his chapter for the book. In a letter as late as March, Scott states that the second draft was an improvement over the first but far from a finished copy. Coelho then moved to Australia, which further complicated the difficulty of getting galley proofs to him for finalization of his chapter so the book could be published in 1980.

1980 HALDEMAN INTER-PROFESSIONAL CONFERENCE ON THE SPINE

With the momentum of the Anaheim conference pushing him, Scott decided scientific conferences were the pathway to bring science to the practitioner. With the help of Dr. Herb Vear, a friend from CMCC and president of Western States Chiropractic College (WSCC), a second major scientific conference was planned for October 3-5, 1980. The Foundation for the Advancement of Chiropractic Tenets and Sciences (FACTS) also helped sponsor the program. The venue was moved to the Dunes Hotel in Las Vegas, thinking it would be a good city to attract attendees, and WSCC was enlisted for organizational support and for obtaining continuing education (CE) credits for the attendees. The conference title, "A Comprehensive, Interdisciplinary Approach to the Management of Spinal Disorders" was an expansion on the theme of the Anaheim conference with an appeal to clinicians dealing with spinal disorders beyond the chiropractic community. The major societies, however, were not able to provide financial support for this meeting, so Scott and Joan decided to finance the conference themselves in the hope that it would generate funds for the international society.

Scott arranged for the following speakers:

> John Mennell, MD – physical medicine and rehabilitation
> Hamilton Hall, MD – orthopedic surgery
> Scott Haldeman, DC, PhD, MD – neurology
> Joan Haldeman, RPT – physical therapy
> John Triano, DC, MA – chiropractor, biomechanics
> Dennis Lindsey, PhD – clinical psychology

The program was divided into three sections: 1) The Pathophysiology of the Spine, 2) The Examination of the Spine, and 3) The Conservative Management of the Spine. In addition to the special guest speakers, there was a paper session scheduled for Sunday afternoon. Submitted abstracts were to be reviewed by Reed Phillips, Roy Hildebrandt, Herb Vear, Barry Davis, and Jerry McAndrews. A total of 31 free papers were presented on the afternoon of the third day of the conference. This conference received moral and promotional support from 22 different chiropractic-related individuals, institutions, and organizations across all political boundaries.

Attendance was considerably less than the Anaheim meeting with approximately 150 attendees, and the conference netted a weak but positive balance sheet. No book was to be produced from the proceedings of the conference and, therefore, post-conference follow-up for Scott was much less cumbersome than the Anaheim conference. The response from the people who attended was enthusiastic, and the speakers expressed their enjoyment interacting with practicing chiropractors.

1981 HALDEMAN INTER-PROFESSIONAL CONFERENCE ON THE SPINE

The third conference was held in Los Angeles with non-financial support from the Cleveland College of Chiropractic that gave continuing education credits. Still encouraged that scientific conferences were the right thing to promote, Scott felt that with perhaps more marketing, more time between conferences, and with duo sponsorship from both national associations the attendance could be increased and make the next scientific conference an even greater success than the Las Vegas conference.

National association support was waning. This third conference was not marketed well, and Los Angeles was not the best draw for a large conference attendance, but it was close to home for Scott and Cleveland College. While Scott was still able to entice his world-renowned colleagues to come and speak, attendance fell precipitously to less than 100 attendees. This may not have been so difficult to deal with, but in the adjoining ballroom in the Bonaventure Hotel was another chiropractic seminar on practice building that had over 250 attendees. Scott learned later that he was also in competition with a practice building seminar held in Vancouver that same weekend that drew more than 500 attendees.

Co-sponsor Cleveland College proposed starting the Haldeman Spinal Research Trust at their school in LA with the excess proceeds from the conference—an idea Scott had considered for chiropractic schools in other cities that helped host future conferences. Unfortunately, the conference was not financially viable enough to put any funds toward starting a trust. A fourth conference already planned for St. Louis in 1982 was cancelled along with plans for any future conferences.

Scott and Joan were devastated not only over the decline in attendance but because they believed so strongly in the value of what they were trying to achieve for chiropractic. They had invested a considerable amount of their own funds to carry the conference in LA. The financial losses nearly put them under. Scott expressed his disappointment:

> I did feel some frustration in getting the message across that research was the only manner in which chiropractic could survive. This was a bit of a mission on my part for a few years and I traveled extensively carrying the message. There was also no real understanding that chiropractic was an international profession and what happened in one country would influence chiropractic

around the world. This changed somewhat after the NINCDS conference and the New Zealand Commission of E(I)nquiry became widely discussed and debated. There, however, still was too little global or even national thinking in the profession. This was illustrated by the failure of any attempt to organize a large national scientific conference.[42]

In a letter to Doug Branvold, DC, in Vancouver in October 1981 shortly after the failure of the Los Angeles conference, Scott is a little more explicit regarding his efforts to bring chiropractic into the scientific community and science into the chiropractic community:

> I cannot stop the fear or growth of opinion (of chiropractors regarding my medical affiliations). I have essentially been deprived of all resources and tangible support by chiropractors. I do not have the financial ability or time to launch a campaign against people who feel the way Dr. Rheinhardt[43] does.
>
> I remain a third generation chiropractor with the longest heritage in chiropractic than anyone I am aware of since Palmer died. My grandmother was the first chiropractor in Canada (according to Russ Gibbons) and my heart is still with the profession.
>
> My support for research, facilities and food for my family is, however, coming from medicine and, in the absence of any chiropractic support I am and probably will continue to be more active in medical circles than in chiropractic circles.
>
> If chiropractic support develops at any time I will be more than pleased to become more active in chiropractic research.
>
> The decision for what I do in the future is no longer mine. It is up to the leaders and practitioners of chiropractic to decide whether they can utilize and pay for my skills and training or whether they prefer to ostracize and thereby force me to work exclusively in medical institutions.[44]

---

[42] Personal communication with Scott, January 2009.
[43] Dr. Rheinhardt was a chiropractor who adamantly opposed chiropractic association with anything medical.
[44] Letter to Doug Branvould, DC, from Scott dated 19 Oct 1981. Letter is in the Haldeman Collection.

Joan also shared her disappointment in a letter to "Mom" –her mother-in-law:

Well, I don't think I have told you about the conference in February [1981]. Such a Disappointment! You know it's not just the one conference (2 if one counts the conference planned for Oct.), but for 10 years he's been travelling the states & Canada, and giving his time,

Scott Haldeman, DC, PhD, MD, circa 1980

energy, expertise (& money) to try & get across the importance of research & an academic approach if the chiro's want to be accepted as a respected profession.

Well, we're $6,000 in debt for this conference. And finally, Scott has seen reality and accepted that the chiropractic profession is just not going to support anything which isn't a money-making type of movement. He's not putting on any more seminars. In fact he cancelled all his commitments to the chiropractors. He's tired of receiving no returns for all his efforts. My heart ached for him. You know he carried this ideal of helping the chiropractic profession all his life—got it from Dad. It's hard to see a dream shattered.

Anyway, now he's concentrating on building a practice, passing the nine exams he has to do to get all the high-level boards he wants— here and in Canada & working on his own research at the university on eletrodiagnosis. I was sad that it turned out as it did (for him) but you know, I've seen it for years and so I'm very relieved to see that behind us. But now! Groan—the work load for me has quadrupled! Never can win, can we.

In all the confusion of a change in direction, we've done absolutely nothing about finalizing the plans for the house. So I'm just living one day at a time, and expecting to do so for a year or so yet.[45]

In Scott's entire career, this was probably a low point in his support for his chiropractic profession. Circumstances were driving him away from his roots and he was unable to prevent it from happening. Fortunately for chiropractic, like the Phoenix that rises from the ashes, Scott would rekindle his efforts for the credibility of chiropractic, but in a fashion that reduced his dependence on chiropractic venues, something that caused a few to complain that he was a medical doctor using chiropractic techniques. This disparate few never knew the inner workings of Scott's intent, as he never lost his attachment to the heritage left to him by his father and grandmother.

---

[45] Personal letter from Joan Haldeman to "Mom", her mother-in-law, dated April 17, 1981. Letter has been partially modified with Joan's approval.

PRINCIPLES AND PRACTICE OF CHIROPRACTIC

The book that emanated from the Anaheim conference, *Modern Developments in the Principles and Practice of Chiropractic*, served as a classroom text for chiropractic students for the decade of the 80s. In the preface of the 2nd Edition Scott explains the need for the 2nd Edition:

> The past decade...has seen the greatest change in chiropractic science, clinical approach, and acceptance in the almost 100 years of this profession's history. Chiropractors are no longer isolated in their private practice or excluded from government and privately funded health care institutions and facilities. Chiropractors are increasingly included within large multidisciplinary clinics with medical and osteopathic physicians, surgeons, and specialists. They are included in Medicare, Medicaid and other government-funded health care systems and participate in health maintenance organizations (HMOs) and preferred provider organizations (PPOs). Increasing numbers of chiropractors have hospital privileges and all now have access to medical specialist consultations.
>
> This change in the status of chiropractic has made it necessary for chiropractors to understand and keep up with the scientific and clinical developments that influence their practice. Chiropractors must now be able to present their positions, theories, philosophy, and justification for treatment in terms that are understood and accepted by the other health care professionals.[46]

This 2nd Edition was written for both the chiropractic student and the doctor in practice. It was divided into four sections (32 chapters; 59 contributors of which 14 were chiropractors with graduate degrees) with two appendices as follows:

> The first section includes those topics which are commonly taught in the first year principle and philosophy courses at a chiropractic college.
>
> The second section is dedicated to the major scientific and

---

[46] Haldeman, Scott. *Principles and Practice of Chiropractic*, 2nd Edition. Appleton & Lange, Norwalk, CT. 1992, pg. xi.

physiological principles which form the basis of chiropractic theory...Two fields are covered in depth: spinal biomechanics and neurophysiology.

The third section of this text reviews, in detail, the examination methods that a chiropractic student is expected to master. The radiologic chapters review the importance of x-rays and other imaging studies for pathology recognition and biomechanical analysis. In addition there are chapters on history taking, the physical, and orthopedic and neurologic examination as well as the use of laboratory studies and instruments to measure spinal function.

The fourth section of this text is an in-depth presentation of the major chiropractic adjusting techniques with a review of the rationale behind each of the different methods of spinal adjusting and manipulation. There is...discussion of the soft tissue techniques and rehabilitation that are becoming an integral part of chiropractic practice. The last two chapters review the potential complications of manipulation and the increasing importance of defined standards of care.

Appendix A is a review of the status of chiropractic in different countries around the world and Appendix B is a glossary of terms commonly used within the chiropractic profession.[47]

The 2nd Edition became the mainstay for chiropractic students and practitioners until the appearance of the 3rd Edition in 2005. With the passage of yet another decade, the advancement of chiropractic science and the chiropractic profession justified the new edition in its expanded format, with Scott serving now as the editor-in-chief. In his preface Scott again writes:

...it is again time to reflect upon the position gained by the chiropractic profession over the past decade. Bolstered by the endorsement of spinal manipulation for low back pain and neck pain by several interdisciplinary guidelines both in the US and worldwide, chiropractic has developed a significant presence in the musculoskeletal literature of the 1990s. During this period, the

[47] Haldeman, Scott. *Principles and Practice of Chiropractic*, 2nd Edition. Appleton & Lange, Norwalk, CT. 1992, xi, xii.

focus slowly shifted from defending the practice of chiropractic to studying its appropriateness for a number of specific conditions. Helping this effort is a growing number of chiropractors who have gone on to obtain Masters and PhD degrees in various fields of research related to chiropractic. Their efforts have served to greatly increase the quality of the science on which chiropractic theory and practice are based and to develop new and increasingly interesting theories to explain the results observed in chiropractic clinical studies.[48]

Because of the expanded size of the 3rd edition (1,180 pages compared to the 384 in the first edition and 641 pages in the second edition), Scott needed to divide the work between an Associate Editor, Simon Dagenais, DC, and five Section Editors: Brian Budgell, DC, MSc; Niels Grunnet-Nilsson, DC, MD, PhD; Paul D. Hooper, DC, MPH; Dipl Erg; William C. Meeker, DC, MPH; and John Triano, DC, PhD.

There were 58 chapters with 78 contributors of which 34 were chiropractors with graduate degrees. This edition was divided into five sections with the first four divided in a fashion similar to the 2nd Edition. The fifth section of the 3rd Edition was:

...an attempt to integrate the prior

1980	1992	2005
384 pages	641 pages	1180 pages

[48] Haldeman, Scott, Editor-in-Chief. *Principles and Practice of Chiropractic*, 3rd Edition. McGraw-Hill, New York, 2005, pg. xvii-xviii.

chapters into a logical clinical approach to the most common conditions seen by chiropractors in practice. The majority of patients
who seek chiropractic care do so for low back pain, thoracic pain,
neck pain and headaches. There are also, however, a small percentage of patients who seek care for non-musculoskeletal symptoms
and a discussion of some of the research on these conditions is
necessary to put recommendations on these conditions in context.
There are also unique characteristics in the pediatric and geriatric
patient populations that can impact management that warrant
specific chapters on these topics. There is no treatment approach
that is without some risk. Although the risk of the most commonly used chiropractic treatment approaches is very small, it is
nonetheless important that those rare complications be discussed.
It is for this reason that two chapters were devoted to these issues.
The final chapter in this tes[x]t is devoted to the integration of
chiropractic into interdisciplinary spinal clinics. It is probable that
a fourth edition of this text will devote considerable more time on
the integration of chiropractic into mainstream health care.[49]

As clearly stated by Scott, a 4th Edition is "probable" but with the
3rd Edition less than a decade old, there is some time to consider the
future.

The International Society proposed by Scott to advance chiropractic research had not yet developed into what Scott originally
conceived. The Haldeman Research Conferences came before the
profession was capable of embracing them and, as a result, faltered.
The textbook, *Principles and Practice of Chiropractic*, was a success
beyond Scott's expectations. Despite his financial frustrations associated with the scientific conferences, Scott never left chiropractic. It
was chiropractic that was having difficulty keeping pace with Scott
Haldeman.

WILK vs. AMA TRIAL

Caustic relations between chiropractic and medicine have existed
almost since the beginning of chiropractic in 1895. The battle waxed
and waned over the years but never disappeared. In 1963 the Ameri-

---

[49] Ibid. xviii-xix.

can Medical Association (AMA) triggered a new intensity in this rivalry by organizing its internal Committee on Quackery with the explicit purpose to contain and eventually eliminate the chiropractic profession. The anti-chiropractic campaign enrolled state medical societies and included:

> ...suppressing research favorable to chiropractic; undermining chiropractic colleges and postgraduate education programs; using new ethical rulings to prevent cooperation between MDs and chiropractors in education, research and practice; subverting a 1967 United States government inquiry into the merits of chiropractic; and basing an extensive misinformation campaign against chiropractic on the calculating portrayal of chiropractors as "unscientific," "cultist," and having a philosophy incompatible with western scientific medicine.[50]

From the research writings of Joseph Keating, PhD, we find just how extensively this campaign had permeated the U.S. government:

> Wilbur J. Cohen, secretary of the U.S. Department of Health, Education and Welfare (DHEW), was directed by Congress in 1967 to prepare a report on the inclusion of chiropractic and other non allopathic, independent health care providers in the Medicare health care reimbursement program. Sociologist Walter Wardwell, PhD, was a participant in the sham investigation conducted by the surgeon general of the U.S. Public Health Service (USPHS), a division of DHEW. Early on, Dr. Wardwell recognized that the 22-member committee of scholars, professionals and businessmen assembled by the federal agency would have no actual voice in the final report, which had already been prepared by staff members of the USPHS (Wardwell 1992, p. 165). Secretary Cohen's 1968 report, *Independent Practitioners Under Medicare*, dealt a serious blow to chiropractors, who were excluded from the Medicare program until 1973.[51]

The dastardly work carried out by the AMA came to light when William Trever published *In the Public Interest* (1972). His book con-

---

[50] Chapman-Smith D. The Wilk case. *Journal of Manipulative and Physiological Therapeutics* 1989 (Apr); 12(2): 142-6.
[51] Keating, J. *Chiropractic History: A Primer*. Association of Chiropractic History, 2004, pg. 33.

tained extensive evidence through photocopied documents secretly copied from the AMA files detailing the plan to destroy the chiropractic profession.[52] The AMA carried its battle to the point where they made it "unethical" for their members to associate with, teach, accept referrals from or make referrals to, or in any way associate with chiropractors. Those MDs not belonging to the AMA were forced to comply with the anti-chiropractic campaign of the AMA or lose their hospital privileges when the Joint Commission on Accreditation of Hospitals (JCAH) adopted the same ethical restraints as the AMA.[53]

The zenith of the inter-professional feud occurred when five chiropractors under the representation of attorney George McAndrews filed suit against the AMA and eleven other medical organizations and four medical doctors for violation of the Sherman Anti-Trust laws in 1976.[54, 55] In 1980 the AMA was suffering from the expense associated with the legal action filed by the chiropractors and made a strategic policy change to avoid total collapse. In the August 1980 ICA newsletter, a report is given on the AMA revamp of its code of ethics:

> ...the American Medical Association has approved a new version of its Principles of Medical Ethics that will allow medical doctors to work with chiropractors.
>
> The lawsuits are costing the association more than $1 million per year to defend...the AMA would lose all four pending chiropractic suits (New Jersey, Pennsylvania, Chicago, New York) it..."would be bankrupt."
>
> The key change in the code is really an omission, since the new language does not forbid consorting with chiropractors. Instead, physicians are "free to choose whom to serve, with whom to associate, and the environment in which to provide medical services." Scrapped from the old code is the statement that "a physician

---

[52] Trever W. *In the Public Interest*. Los Angeles: Scriptures Unlimited, 1972.
[53] Pedigo, M. "Wilk vs. AMA: Was It Worth the Fight?" *Dynamic Chiropractic*, Vol. 16, Issue 15, 13 July 1998.
[54] Wardwell, W. *Chiropractic: History and Evolution of a New Profession*. St. Louis, Mosby, 1992.
[55] First page of the actual civil action filed under Judge Kirkland wherein the defendants and the plaintiffs or listed.

should practice a method of healing founded on a scientific basis; and he should not voluntarily associate professionally with anyone who violates this principle."[56]

In October 1976, when the Wilk vs. AMA legal action was filed, Scott was in his last year of medical school at the University of British Columbia and was only peripherally aware of what was happening in the U.S. courts. By the time he arrived at UC Irvine in July 1977, court proceedings were less than a year in duration and had not become much of an issue.

In November 1978, a letter went out from the American College of Physicians (ACP) informing its members of what was happening with the chiropractic lawsuit of which the ACP had been named as a co-defendant with the AMA. Excerpts from the letter are as follows:

> ...the common thread of these suits [the AMA and co-defendants] is that they charge conspiracy in restraint of trade by organizational and individual representatives of the medical care system of this country, and seek access to the radiologic facilities and clinical laboratories of the involved hospitals.

> Our concern about these suits does not relate to their merit; indeed, we feel strongly that they have no merit whatever, and that potential hazards to the health of the population are posed by systems which purport to render health care, and in doing so may produce delays in proper diagnostic and treatment efforts...This issue has been discussed on a number of occasions by the Board of Regents, and also by the Board of Governors...and all have agreed that the issue...is paramount to the health of the population of this country, and that the only ethical position for the College to take in relation to these efforts by the chiropractors is to resist them as strongly as possible.[57]

The ACP letter was distributed to ALL CONCERNED at the UC Irvine Medical Center by Edward J. Tomsovic, MD, Medical Director. In his cover letter he stated, "Should the chiropractors carry the day

---

[56] ICA Newsletter, August 1980. Vol. 17, No. 3. Pg. 1. Copy is in the Haldeman Collection.
[57] Barondess, J. Letter to the membership of the American College of Physicians, 10 November 1978. Letter is in the Haldeman Collection.

they will apparently have access to clinical pathology, radiology and other physician services. Denial of such access may be attacked as restraint of trade. You are invited to consider how your faculty and staff might wish to respond to this changing situation."[58]

By January 1981, the trial had grown to a point where Scott was called to testify as a witness for the plaintiff. Counsel for the plaintiffs, George P. McAndrews, needed witnesses who had credibility in the eyes of the jury, as not one of the jury members had ever been a chiropractic patient. Counsel for the defendants would not allow someone who had been treated by a chiropractor to be selected for the jury.

Scott's MD and PhD brought credibility to the witness stand for the plaintiffs, and McAndrews established Scott as an expert witness in the area of spinal manipulation. He brought in Scott's testimony from the New Zealand Commission on Inquiry into Chiropractic. McAndrews queried Scott on issues related to chiropractic education and training and research relating to the use of spinal manipulation by chiropractors. Defense counsel, as would be expected, attempted to undermine Scott's credibility by pointing out that he had only been licensed as a medical doctor for three years, had never practiced chiropractic in the United States, and lacked research evidence supporting spinal manipulative therapy. There were fourteen people representing nine medical organizations in the courtroom from the defense side representing the American Medical Association, American Hospital Association, American College of Surgeons, American College of Physicians, Joint Commission on Accreditation of Hospitals, American College of Radiology, American Academy of Orthopedic Surgeons, Illinois State Medical Society, and the Chicago Medical Society.[59]

After his court appearance and a meeting with Dr. Van den Noort, his residency supervisor, Scott sent Dr. Van den Noort a letter thanking him for the recent meeting they had and expressed apologies for any distress he may have caused as a result of his association with chi-

[58] Tomsovic, E. Letter to the UCI Medical Center staff, dated 21 Nov. 1978. Letter is in the Haldeman Collection.
[59] Court Proceedings of the *Trial Testimony of Dr. Scott Haldeman*, Wilk I Trial, January 15-16, 1981.

ropractic. Scott also expressed regret that they vigorously disagreed in their opinions on the topic and he hoped that his actions had not caused the university or the Manipulation Project any embarrassment. Scott was on staff at a number of hospitals in California and a young researcher in a fellowship at the VA. Any association with chiropractors was technically against medical ethics at the time. Scott was told that it would not be in his best interest to testify at the second trial and had to send his apologies to George McAndrews.

It wasn't until August 1987 and a second trial that the battle on paper had come to an end and federal Judge Susan Getzendanner ruled in favor of the chiropractors:

> ...Although the conspiracy ended in 1980, there are lingering effects of the illegal boycott and conspiracy which require an injunction. Some medical physicians' individual decisions on whether or not to professionally associate with chiropractors are still affected by the boycott. The injury to chiropractors' reputations which resulted from the boycott have not been repaired. Chiropractors suffer current economic injury as a result of the boycott. The AMA has never affirmatively acknowledged that there are and should be no collective impediments to professional association and cooperation between chiropractors and medical physicians, except as provided by law. Instead, the AMA has consistently argued that its conduct has not violated the anti-trust laws...An injunction is necessary to assure that the AMA does not interfere with the right of a physician, hospital, or other institution to make an individual decision on the question of professional association...[60]

While not a seminal event in Scott's life, the trial and its victory was a seminal event for chiropractic and its future relations with the AMA and other related organizations. A major barrier had been broken and patient care for spinal problems would never be quite the same. It was the credibility brought to the witness stand by Scott and his previous testimony in the New Zealand Commission of Inquiry in the first trial that convinced the judge that chiropractic was "in the right." Since it was a jury trial, chiropractic was not successful in the first trial because

[60] Getzendanner S. Untitled. Journal of the American Medical Association 1988 (Jan 1); 259(1): 81-2.

the jury had been persuaded by the plaintiff's attorneys that the plaintiffs were attempting to protect the health of the American public by the actions they had taken. Judge Kirkland was not so persuaded and helped convince Mr. McAndrews that their cause was worthy of an appeal. The defendants attempted to stop the appeal, which made its way to the Supreme Court of the United States where it was refused a hearing and remanded back to the Court of Appeals of the District Court for Northern Illinois—Judge Getzendanner's court—where in the eyes of chiropractic, justice finally prevailed. Without Scott's testimony, the whole process could have ended with the first trial and injustices could have continued to this day. Scott made a difference.[61]

THE MERCY CONFERENCE

In the 1980s and 1990s, research was demonstrating variations in the medical care received by similar patients in differing geographic areas, or between the same patient seeing different providers in the same city, or even between the same patient seeing the same provider at two different points in time. Chiropractic suffered from the same dilemma. The development of patient care guidelines by a variety of interested parties including third-party payers became the accepted thing to do. The objective was to clearly define, based on evidence and expert opinion, the best patient care protocols for a specified diagnosis or to lay out preferred practice parameters for a particular group of practitioners. The Mercy Conference was chiropractic's effort to establish its own practice parameters.

By the end of the 1980s, the need for a consensus within the chiropractic profession on guidelines for practice and quality assurance had become critical. The federal government was putting pressure on other health professions to develop guidelines within a two-year time frame. In August of 1989 the American Chiropractic Association had convened a "think tank" in Chicago "to identify, adopt, and implement standards of practice maximizing quality of care."[62] The California Chiropractic Association with the Consortium for Chiropractic

---

[61] Personal communication with Mr. George McAndrews, April, 2009.
[62] Editor. *Journal of the American Chiropractic Association.* Vol. 26, No. 10, Oct. 1989. Pg. 20-24.

Research established a joint committee in 1987 to study standards of care. Standards of care documents were being produced in a number of states including California, Georgia, and Ohio. The Canadian Chiropractic Association and the Australian Chiropractors Association had developed committees to establish practice guidelines. The attempt to establish practice guidelines in North America had the potential of setting a standard of care that could be recognized internationally.

In 1989, the Department of Health and Human Services through the United States Public Health Service created the Agency for Health Care Policy and Research (AHCPR). Its mission, "...is to improve the quality, appropriateness, and effectiveness of health care, and to improve access to health services."[63] Within AHCPR was the Office of the Forum for Quality and Effectiveness in Health Care ('the Forum'). This Forum was responsible for facilitating the development, review, and updating of clinically relevant guidelines, as well as standards of quality, performance measures, and medical review criteria. The Forum defined guidelines as, "systematically developed statements to assist practitioner and patient decisions about appropriate health care for specific clinical circumstances."[64] The decision to develop guidelines was based on four criteria:

1. High risks or potentially large benefits for large numbers of persons

2. Wide variations among different treatment options and outcomes

3. Costly services and procedures

4. Evaluation data that are readily available or that can be readily developed

The Forum identified sixteen topics for guideline development by 1992, and low back pain was on the list. The process used to develop guidelines was through the use of expert panels either convened by the Forum or contracted out to nonprofit organizations. The founda-

[63] AHCPR Fact Sheet. March 1992.
[64] AHCPR Fact Sheet, January 1992.

tion of the methodological process for the development of guidelines was explicitness and scientific evidence. All scientific evidence was to be considered, but recommendations were to be based on well-designed studies to the extent possible. When scientific evidence was lacking, consensus of expert opinion was the accepted methodology. Finally, it was felt the guideline development process would help identify areas where scientific evidence was missing and outcome research was needed.

The suggestion was made that a national consensus conference should be convened by the chiropractic profession for the purpose of establishing patient care guidelines. Dr. Haldeman was approached with the idea and he felt it would be impossible: "The divisions within the profession seemed to be large, and prior attempts to achieve agreement on how chiropractic should be practiced had often led to bitter argument which often became personal."[65]

The support of all the major organizations in the profession gave an indication that such a conference might be possible if, "...convened by a neutral sponsoring agency and governed by a completely independent Steering Committee."[66] The Congress of Chiropractic State Associations became that agency, and the Steering Committee was granted the independence required to put on a consensus conference. To be a success financially and otherwise it became necessary to obtain the support of the other major organizations in the chiropractic profession. The following endorsements were granted:

> The board of the Congress of Chiropractic State Associations enthusiastically endorses your concept of a chiropractic summit meeting. Brad M. Hayes, DC, President of COCSA, April 1989.

> I am enthusiastic about the idea of interested parties coming together and discussing, in a constructive fashion, the needs of the profession and our patients. Kenneth L. Luedtke, DC, FICC, President ACA, April, 1989.

---

[65] Haldeman, S., Chapman-Smith, D. and Petersen, D., (eds.), *Guidelines for Chiropractic Quality Assurance and Practice Parameters*. Aspen Publishers, Maryland, 1993. Preface.
[66] Ibid.

We agree that a meeting of the organizational leaders of the profession would be constructive and that professional facilitators should be utilized at such a conference. Fred H. Barge, DC, PhD, President ICA, April 1989.

We are in agreement with a summit conference which encourages communication between the factions in chiropractic. Douglas Gates, DC, President, and Joseph Donofrio, DC, Chairman FSCO, April, 1989.

The Canadian Chiropractic Association, the Association of Chiropractic Colleges, the Foundation for Chiropractic Education and Research and the Federation of Chiropractic Licensing Boards were also co-sponsors. [67]

While widespread political endorsement and financial support was present, it was the Steering Committee that made the decisions on the consensus process and those who were to participate. The Steering Committee was composed of the following:

Scott Haldeman, DC, MD, PhD, Chair of the Steering Committee
Chairman, Research Council, World Federation of Chiropractic Associate Clinical Professor, Department of Neurology, University of California, Irvine

Alan Adams, DC, MS
Vice President of Chiropractic Education, Los Angeles College of Chiropractic

Gerard W. Clum, DC
President, Life Chiropractic College West
President, Association of Chiropractic Colleges

Daniel T. Hansen, DC
Postgraduate faculty, Los Angeles College of Chiropractic, Private Practice

William Meeker, DC, MPH
Dean of Research, Palmer College of Chiropractic West

[67] Haldeman, S., Chapman-Smith, D. and Peterson, D., (eds.), *Guidelines for Chiropractic Quality Assurance and Practice Parameters.* Aspen Publishers, Maryland, 1993.

President, Consortium for Chiropractic Research

Reed Phillips, DC, PhD
President, Los Angeles College of Chiropractic
Vice President, Association of Chiropractic Colleges

John J. Triano, DC, MA
Director, Joint Ergonomics and Research Laboratory, National
College of Chiropractic

David Chapman-Smith, Counsel/Editor
Secretary-General, World Federation of Chiropractic
Editor/Publisher, *The Chiropractic Report*

Donald M. Petersen, Jr., BS, Secretary/Editor
Editor/Publisher, *Dynamic Chiropractic*

The Committee members were chosen on the basis of their understanding of the consensus process, their representation of different points of view, and their ability to encourage the most appropriate members of the profession to participate in the Commission—the body that would represent the profession in the actual work of establishing guidelines.

The Steering Committee met on three occasions during 1990 and had a number of conference calls as it developed the process. Discussion was held with professional facilitators. Intense discussion and consultation took place with multiple individuals within chiropractic colleges, state and national organizations, and the practicing profession.

Ten professional organizations and ten organizations from industry put up $2,500 each to raise $50,000 to support the consensus conference—a minimum budgeted amount. Participants paid their own expenses or were sponsored by their respective institutions. None of the participants were compensated for their efforts.

The Steering Committee initially identified thirty members of the Commission but that number was later revised to thirty-five to give better representation to certain groups felt to be underrepresented. All members of the Commission were graduate chiropractors. Twenty-three were from private practice in fourteen states. Eight members were full-time at a chiropractic college. Twelve came with some research experience. Eighteen were either currently or past senior officers in national or state chiropractic organizations.

A year was spent preparing a document composed of fifteen chapters each relating to a specific area of chiropractic practice. Committees directed by a captain were organized from members of the Commission and assigned specific chapters with the task of developing topic specific consensus statements. The captains were to conduct a literature search and complete an outline by May 1991. A meeting between the captains and the Steering Committee took place at the World Federation of Chiropractic in Toronto in May. Outlines were reviewed, and a final format for the guidelines document was decided. Initially twelve chapters were to be included:

History and Physical Examination
X-ray and Other Imaging
Instrumentation
Clinical Laboratory
Initial Documentation and Patient Consents
Clinical Impression
Modes of Care
Frequency of Care
Reassessment
Record Keeping
Outcome Assessment
Collaborative Care

The captains were instructed to complete a first draft by August, and they were instructed to use consultants outside the Commission members if necessary. Once the first draft was completed, it was to be submitted to experts for review and comment, and a second draft incorporating this feedback was to be completed by October. Second drafts were referred to seven appointed members of the Commission for critical review. A third draft was to be completed by 24 December 1991. The third draft of each chapter was sent to all thirty-five members of the Commission to review the entire document with special emphasis on the recommendations constructed by each team. Minority opinions were welcomed where significant difference of opinions existed. This was the final opportunity for input from the profession as a whole before the Commission met to make final decisions on the document.

The Commission, Steering Committee, and interested observers came together at the Mercy Conference Center in Burlingame, California, a 40-acre Catholic convent and retreat facility (http://www. mercy-center.org/) for five days (25-30 Jan. 1992). There were two key introductory speakers, Paul Shekelle, MD, MPH, and Herve Guillain, MD, MPH, who set the stage for the importance of what we were about to undertake. Staff support, computers, word processing, and editors were readily available. Each day lasted between 16 and 20 hours with time for an on-site meal. No one had the time or the energy to leave the facility, as spartan as it was.

Sleeping quarters were sparse at best. An 8' x 10' room with a single bed, small wash basin, medicine cabinet with mirrored sliding doors, 2' wide closet, and a small wooden desk, chair, and rocker. Above the head of the bed was a small night lamp, and hanging next to the bed was a religious picture.

For the first three days of the conference, the Commission was divided into fifteen committees, one for each chapter; however, it was decided to combine two chapters into one chapter during the conference. Ultimately, each person was on three different committees. Each captain presented their chapter to the other members of their committee. Deliberations lasted up to three hours on each chapter, and each committee had to come to a consensus on the recommendations made in the chapter under review. Any two members could oppose the opinion of the other committee members and render a minority opinion. Once the final vote had been taken in each of the committees on each of the recommendations in every chapter, it was time to bring the whole document before the entire Commission. It was Dr. Haldeman who served to facilitate this process. The changes made in the latest committee sessions were put on overhead transparencies and projected on a screen for the Commission to view. Each recommendation was taken in order and voted on by the Commission members. If there was any dissenting vote, the recommendation was opened to amendment. Only formal amendments were accepted and had to be supported by five members of the Commission for further discussion. Each amendment was then voted on and a majority of the members (18) was necessary for changes to the recommendation to be included as part of the majority opinion. Any amendment that was not accepted by the majority could then be submitted at any time during the conference by 25% (nine members) of the Commission.

No chapter was closed until the final discussion on the fourth day when each chapter was summarized and a table of all recommendations was presented to the Commission. The members were then asked to vote that the chapter, with all recommendations as amended and any minority opinion, accurately reflected the consensus of the Commission on that chapter. All Chapters were unanimously accepted by the Commission. The final draft recommendations or guidelines in each chapter as accepted had to be signed off by the committee captains as being accurate.

During the four day conference, the culmination of nearly three years of work, the panel of thirty-five voted on a total of 306 distinct guidelines on chiropractic practice. Of the 306 guidelines, these are the consensus results:

> 296 guidelines (96.7%) were rated Consensus Level 1
> (full agreement—over 85% of the panel in favor)
> Three guidelines (1%) were rated Consensus Level 2
> (consensus established—70%-84% of the panel in favor)
> Five guidelines (1.6%) were rated Consensus Level 3
> (majority/minority opinions—51%-69% of the panel in favor)

Of the five guidelines that received Consensus Level 3 ratings, only four (1.3%) had minority opinions. For chiropractic guidelines to be established by a representative group from the profession with only eight guidelines (3.4%) not receiving full agreement is incredible. Indeed, the vast majority of the Consensus Level 1 guidelines were unanimous.

There has probably never been a time in the history of the profession when there has been this close to full chiropractic consensus.

When all debate was complete, all chapters had been closed by unanimous vote, and all captains had signed off on their chapters, the conference was adjourned. Many commented afterwards that this was one of the most intense and grueling experiences of their lives. There was an air of satisfaction from the fact that the chiropractic profession had finally come together to produce something that we could all agree upon. This was a monumental project not yet undertaken by any other health care profession. Without the leadership and tenacity of Scott Haldeman, this event would have never been a success.

A hard-bound copy of the guidelines, published by Aspen publishers, was mailed to every known member of the chiropractic profession in the United States, over 50,000 copies, thanks to donations from the following:

> *Activator Methods*
> *California Chiropractic Association*
> *Foot Levelers, Inc.*
> *Leander Health Technologies*
> *Motion Palpation Institute*
> *National Upper Cervical Chiropractic Association*
> *NCMIC*
> *Nutri-West*
> *OUM Group*
> *Parker Chiropractic Resource Foundation*
> *The Practice Resource Group*
> *SuperFeet*
> *Synergy*
> *Visual Odyssey*
> *World-Wide Chiropractic Placement Service (WCPS)*

The American Chiropractic Association, California Chiropractic Association, Florida Chiropractic Association, Federation of Chiropractic Licensing Boards, and others endorsed the guidelines. The Mercy Guidelines were submitted at a public hearing to the AHCPR's low back pain panel prior to the panel publishing their low back pain guidelines and probably played a significant role in the formation of the Low Back Pain Guidelines produced by the AHCPR.

In his closing remarks, Rick Flaherty, CEO of the Leander Corporation at the time and a non-chiropractic observer at the conference, said:

> It took courage, understanding, and an unwavering commitment to the chiropractic profession for each of the members to prevail in their individual beliefs, yet so often as it was, to step back, listen to another opinion, and yield to another point of view, without compromising ethics, morals, standards or beliefs, and settling on the establishment of guidelines that all within the profession could live with. In the end, it was their love for the profession and a personal caring and love for each other that prevailed.

RAND & APPROPRIATENESS OF SPINAL MANIPULATION

The 90s was a decade when spinal manipulation came under intense scrutiny. It had finally become a subject worthy of scientific investigation. Because of the increased interest in musculoskeletal disorders, most especially back pain, the 90s became the forerunner of the Decade of the Bone and Joint that followed in 2000. With this new level of acceptance of spinal manipulation, there arose an army of practitioners, physical therapists, physiatrists, orthopedists, and osteopaths claiming the right to be recognized as "specialists" in spinal manipulation. Chiropractic, however, was still considered marginal.

One event that helped turn the tide of public and professional opinion toward spinal manipulation was the study undertaken by the RAND Corporation in Santa Monica, California, in 1990. RAND is an acronym for Research And Development and it was established during World War II as a think tank and research organization designed to advance the role of science, first in the war effort and thereafter in improved daily living. Today, RAND provides leadership and research development in many areas, not the least of which is health care.

In the late 1980s, the medical literature contained an increasing number of articles demonstrating wide variations in medical care for common conditions across geographic areas. This disturbing information became more alarming when the major causative factor identified was the number of physicians in the area. In other words, the more heart surgeons in a specific geographic area, the greater the number of heart surgeries.

This kind of information helped spur the establishment of a new government agency, the Agency for Health Care Policy and Research (AHCPR). This agency began to fund a variety of projects focused on learning more about practice variations for specific conditions and eventually to develop practice guidelines consistent with the latest scientific evidence for each condition. (There will be more to come on AHCPR.)

While federal research had not focused on the variations in chiropractic care, it was beginning to have concerns over variations in the treatment of back pain. It was only a matter of time before chiropractic would become wrapped into this movement.

Not wanting to be caught unprepared, the Pacific Consortium for Chiropractic Research (PCCR)[68] organized a committee on practice guidelines and assigned its co-chairs, Dr. Alan Adams and Dr. Reed Phillips from the Los Angeles College of Chiropractic (LACC), to investigate ways in which the PCCR could become involved.

It was probably no small coincidence that Dr. Ian Coulter was also at LACC as a faculty member in the research department. Coulter had a cross appointment with RAND. Robert Brook, MD, chaired the medical division at RAND. He had been quite prolific in advocating utilization research and implementation of practice guidelines for the medical profession but had met considerable resistance to his advocacy position. A third player was Paul Shekelle, MD, a resident in internal medicine at UCLA and also cross-appointed to RAND.

Knowing Dr. Brook's publication record and recognizing the prestige of RAND, Adams and Phillips paid Brook a visit, the purpose being to enlist his support in developing practice guidelines for chiropractic. The CCA was prepared to fund this effort. Brook fell out of his chair when the idea was presented. After gaining his composure, he explained the resistance he had received from the medical profession when he suggested they develop their own practice guidelines and now here were two chiropractors offering to pay him to help them do the same thing.

It didn't take long to formulate a plan that actually addressed a more fundamental issue than practice guidelines. It was first necessary to establish whether spinal manipulation was even an appropriate form of care and for what conditions. The combination of Drs. Phillips and Adams from LACC, Dr. Coulter, and Dr. Shekelle moved the work forward.

Ultimately nine experts were selected to evaluate the use of any

---

[68] The PCCR was an organization of research directors from the five chiropractic colleges on the west coast and the California Chiropractic Association.

particular medical procedure. In the case of chiropractic, the procedure was spinal manipulation.

This new methodology of bringing nine qualified individuals from areas related to the procedure of spinal manipulation—those who managed back pain—was no simple task. They could not fill all nine seats with medical surgeons anymore than they could fill all nine seats with chiropractors and expect an unbiased outcome. They were required to seek a balance, and thus the makeup of the group consisted of four chiropractors, an osteopath, a chiropractor/neurologist (Scott Haldeman), an internist, and two orthopedic medical doctors.

Before the group ever met, they were presented with an extensive literature review regarding the procedure under scrutiny—in this case, spinal manipulation for the treatment of low back pain. There were a total of 78 articles, 42 of which were controlled clinical trials in the literature review provided by Dr. Shekelle and assisted by Dr. Eric Hurwitz (LACC graduate 1988, and masters student at UCLA in epidemiology at that time). The nine participants were to become familiar with all the literature and be prepared to discuss it at a joint meeting of the group at a later date. They were also provided with a list of 17 definitions upon which they could either agree or offer possible alternative definitions that the group could agree upon when they met as a group.

In addition to becoming familiar with the literature, each participant was also given a questionnaire listing all the possible clinical scenarios where spinal manipulation could be applied to the back pain patient. Each of the 147 scenarios was further subdivided into four segments based on whether the patient in the scenario had never received spinal manipulation, had a favorable response to previous spinal manipulation, had an equivocal response, or had an unfavorable response or no response. In each of the 588 options, a nine (9) point scale was provided with a range from number one (1) indicating the risk of doing spinal manipulation exceeded the benefits, to number nine (9) indicating benefits greatly exceed risks. There was a second part of the questionnaire where 36 scenarios were presented and the participants were asked to estimate what they felt would be the expected average number of visits and the expected maximum number of visits for each scenario.

Each of the nine participants were to individually work through the questionnaire marking each of the 588 scenarios, based on their professional opinion, as to whether they felt the use of spinal manipulation would be appropriate treatment for the back pain scenario presented. Once the questionnaires were completed and submitted to Shekelle, they were compiled and sent back to the participants so they could compare their individual opinion to an average of the group.

The final step was to bring the group of nine to RAND for a face-to-face meeting and an opportunity to once again go through the questionnaire marking process, but this time raise questions and have discussion with the group. In summary, the group found consensus for the appropriate use of spinal manipulation for acute low back pain in the absence of significant risk factors such as trauma, infection, or cancer. The consensus was less on the appropriate use of spinal manipulation when radiating leg pain was present with back pain. [69]

The results, challenged by the chiropractic community, indicated more conditions were determined to be inappropriate for spinal manipulation than appropriate. At first blush, these results were a disappointment to the chiropractic community, but the actual numbers told a different story. Those cases deemed appropriate for spinal manipulation represented the vast majority of back pain cases and were typically seen in a chiropractic practice.

To address the concerns of the chiropractic community, RAND agreed to conduct a second study involving all doctors of chiropractic, of which only four were in full time chiropractic practice. Meticulously following the same procedures, the results from the all chiropractic panel favored a broader range of cases appropriate for manipulation than the previous mixed group. The area of appropriate spinal manipulation for the care of patients with back pain and leg pain was the point of the greatest discrepancy between the two groups.

[69] Shekelle, PG, AH Adams, MR Chassin, EL Hurwitz, RE Park, RB Phillips, et al. *The Appropriateness of Spinal Manipulation for Low-back Pain: Indications and Ratings by a Multidisciplinary Expert Panel.* R-4025/2-CCR/FCER. Santa Monica, CA. RAND, 1992.

Both groups attempted to determine the appropriate length of care for simple acute low back pain. Agreement was reached on the recommendation of two weeks of care, after which, if no change had occurred, another manipulative procedure should be considered. After four weeks, if no change had occurred, spinal manipulation was probably an inappropriate form of care.[70]

From this study, a meta-analysis was published in the *Annals of Internal Medicine*.[71] This article would be the first to be published in the journal that was co-authored by doctors of chiropractic and doctors of medicine. It was widely cited and became a significant document when the Agency for Health Care Policy and Research (AHCPR) developed the *Guidelines for Acute Low Back Pain in Adults*.[72]

As the 90s wore on, chiropractic received attention from the work at RAND and other research accomplishments. But for whatever reason, the funding sources from FCER, NCMIC, and even federal funding dwindled. Some within chiropractic expressed dissatisfaction of positions taken by Dr. Shekelle regarding the research findings. RAND people were chagrined at statements getting into the press that misrepresented what RAND had done as being supportive of the chiropractic profession. A relationship between LACC and RAND remained strong and work continued, but the absence of national level funding curtailed the maximization of results.

While Scott did not play a pivotal role in the organization of the RAND studies, he was a bridge between the chiropractors and medical doctors that facilitated open discussion and professional expression of opinions. His mediating presence prevented the construction of unnecessary barriers and his depth of knowledge in spinal ailments and manipulation was a key to the outcomes obtained.

---

[70] Shekelle, PG, AH Adams, MR Chassin, EL Hurwitz, RE Park, RB Phillips, et al. *The Appropriateness of Spinal Manipulation for Low Back Pain: Indications and Ratings by an All-Chiropractic Expert Panel*. R-4025/3-CCR/FCER. Santa Monica, CA, RAND, 1992.
[71] Shekelle, PG, AH Adams, MR Chassin, EL Hurwitz, RH Brook. "Spinal Manipulation for Low-Back Pain." Annals of Int. Med, Vol. 117, No. 7, 1 Oct. 1992, pp.590-598.
[72] US Dept Health & Human Services, Public Health Service, Agency for Health Care Policy & Research. Acute Low Back Problems in Adults: Assessment and Treatment. Number 14. Clinical Practice Guidelines, AHCPR Publication No. 95-0643, Dec. 1994.

The true value of the RAND appropriateness studies was that they served as the precursor of future AHCPR activities by providing a literature synthesis and adding credibility to the role of spinal manipulation. Scott would become more extensively involved and be a participant in the activities that led to the publication of national guidelines on the treatment of acute low back pain.

AGENCY FOR HEALTH CARE POLICY AND RESEARCH (AHCPR)
Back pain Outcome Assessment Team (BOAT)

In 1989, the Agency for Health Care Policy and Research (AHCPR) was established within the Public Health Service (PHS) of the United States. Its mission was, "...to improve the quality, appropriateness and effectiveness of health care, and improve access to health services."[73] To accomplish the mission, the agency involved itself in *Patient Outcome Research* and the development of *Clinical Practice Guidelines*. Patient Outcome Research Teams (PORT) were funded for five-year studies to determine what worked best for whom and how much it was costing. PORTs were established for a number of conditions such as diabetes, pneumonia, heart attack, stroke prevention, prostate disorders, and cesarean sections. Clinical Practice Guidelines were established by consensus panels composed of consumers and health care experts including physicians, nurses, and allied health professionals. The guidelines produced were to reflect current scientific knowledge and best professional judgment to prevent, diagnose, treat, or manage diseases and disorders.[74]

A PORT was funded to study low back pain at the University of Washington in Seattle. The team chair was Richard Deyo, MD, the internist who served on the RAND appropriateness study and a prolific author and researcher on low back pain. The team received a multi-million dollar grant. They were called the Back Pain Outcome Assessment Team (BOAT). Their charge was to study the increasing problem of surgery for low back pain in the Medicare population. The

---

[73] AHCPR *Fact Sheet*. March 1992.
[74] Ibid. January 1992.

team hosted an annual conference to report on the progress of their first year's work and invited members of their advisory committee to attend. Reed Phillips, DC, and Dan Hansen, DC, were the chiropractic representatives on this team.

At this first advisory committee meeting, the team reported concerns regarding the increasing rate of low back surgery in an aging population. They also reported a significant variation in the rate of back pain surgery based on geographic variation. The strongest correlating factor to the rate of surgery was the number of surgeons present in the same geographic area.

Alf Nachemsen, MD, orthopedic surgeon from Sweden and Gordon Waddell, MD, orthopedic surgeon from Scotland were also members of the advisory committee. At this first meeting, Dr. Nachemsen complained that surgery was occurring in the older population because too many people with back pain at a younger age were not being cared for adequately. He emphasized the need to provide good conservative care to prevent early acute back pain from becoming chronic back pain. Dr. Waddell responded to his concern by pulling a copy of the *London Times* from his briefcase and noting the report of a study in England that demonstrated chiropractic care to be more effective than hospital physical therapy care for the treatment of low back pain.[75]

From this interesting first meeting, the focus of BOAT turned from the study of chronic back pain in the Medicare population to the onset of back pain in a younger population and the importance of conservative management. While Scott did not participate on the BOAT team activities, he was close to many members of the team and it was the work of the team that led to the creation of the Clinical Practice Guideline Panel and Scott's participation.

Clinical Practice Guideline Panel

The work of BOAT served as the foundation for the low back pain

[75] Meade, TW, S Dyer, W Browne, J Townsend, AO Frank. "Low Back Pain of Mechanical Origin: Randomised Comparison of Chiropractic and Hospital Out Patient Treatment." Brit. Med. J., Vol. 300, pp. 1431-7, 1990.

practice guideline panel formed and funded by AHCPR. John Triano, MA, DC, and Scott Haldeman, DC, MD, PhD, were the two chiropractic members of this expanded twenty-three member panel. Stanley Bigos MD, an orthopedic surgeon from the University of Washington in Seattle, was appointed chairman. Both had served on the RAND appropriateness panels. The remainder of the panel was composed of eleven medical doctors, two osteopaths, two nurses, two physical therapists, a reverend, an occupational therapist and two PhDs. A staff of epidemiologists, who assisted in culling the literature and preparing evidence tables from relevant research articles, was provided. The goal of the guidelines was to reduce the number of persons disabled by low back problems by improving treatment of acute symptoms.[76]

This panel reviewed all literature regarding back pain, held public hearings, and entertained written submissions regarding their work. At the conclusion of two years, AHCPR published Clinical Practice Guideline Number 14, *Acute Low Back Problems in Adults*. In this guideline, spinal manipulation was the clinical procedure that received the strongest recommendation from the panel for the treatment of acute low back pain.[77]

The panel met twice per year, struggling in iterative rounds with fundamental questions that most clinicians, at the time, took for granted. To illustrate the complexity of the questions, such as identifying evidence supporting the validity of the most simple physical examination maneuvers commonly used for back pain patients, a spontaneous round-table debate arose that lasted half of one day. The contention was over the appropriate performance and interpretation of the single most valid maneuver, the straight leg raise test.

Even for this interdisciplinary panel, coming to grips with the extensive void in the evidence for care administered to patients was difficult. While all participants each offered the best information available within the discipline they represented, they understood

[76] HHS News Release, 20 Apr 1992.
[77] US Dept Health & Human Services, Public Health Service, Agency for Health Care Policy & Research. Acute Low Back Problems in Adults: Assessment and Treatment. Number 14. Clinical Practice Guidelines, AHCPR Publication No. 95-0643, Dec. 1994.

the risks of this process. As the focus of attention turned to surgery, the surgeon members attempted to exempt this therapy on the basis that surgery was too complex a procedure for such evaluation as a single randomized trial. The effort failed, recognizing that the overall state of the literature was far more fragile than desired. Of interest is that subsequent to the AHCPR conclusions, the number of randomized trials involving surgical approaches to back pain have increased significantly.

Initially the panel was openly skeptical of chiropractic participation; however, a courtesy copy of the Mercy Center guidelines had been provided to each member on the first day of the group's initial meeting. By the second day, Claire Bombardier, MD, a noted clinical epidemiologist, had read the guideline and offered a highly favorable report back to the group. Subsequently, the tone and reception of chiropractic input was significantly changed. On this foundation, the involvement of the chiropractic participants became much stronger.

This first governmental process to evaluate the strength of evidence for treatment of spine patients heralded intense discussion and debate. By the final meeting at the end of two years, the consensus process had collapsed into dispute and doubt, and Stanley Bigos, chairman of the panel, left the meeting in frustration. The potential failure to provide a final statement summarizing the preponderance of evidence concerned the organizers. With the experience in the large group consensus process underlying the Mercy Center document, Drs. Haldeman and Triano were approached by the organizers with a request that they briefly assume a co-chairing role managing the meeting process. With concurrence of the group, Dr. Bigos returned to the chairmanship, the AHCPR consensus panel was reengaged, and the document completed for publication.

The release of the Clinical Practice Guideline #14 resulted in an attack on the agency by those who received a very low recommendation or were not recommended at all in the guideline (i.e., the spinal surgeons). As a result of political pressure, the agency's funding was significantly reduced and their programs steered away from guideline development. In an April 30, 1996 statement before the House Labor-

HHS-Education Appropriations Subcommittee, AHCPR Clinton R. Gaus, ScD, announced a major restructuring of the Agency's clinical practice guideline program to meet the changing of the health care system:

> The world of medical care in 1996 is far different from the one that existed in 1989 when AHCPR was created...staff has consulted extensively with public—and private—sector guideline users...they are seeking the scientific foundation from which they can develop their own high-quality, evidence-based guidelines.

> In response, AHCPR has decided not to develop clinical practice guidelines in Fiscal Year 1997. Instead the Agency will serve as a "science partner" with private- and public-sector organizations—provider societies, health plans, purchasing groups, states, and others—by producing the scientific foundation for them to use in their efforts to improve clinical practice.[78]

The decision not to publish any more clinical practice guidelines resulted in the suppression of a guideline for conservative treatment for neck pain that was ready to be released by a different panel based out of Duke University. Dr. Triano served on this panel as well. Scott served as an external reviewer for this panel. The neck pain guideline recommended a conservative approach to the management of neck pain that included spinal manipulation. While AHCPR fulfilled its role as a "science partner" to private and public entities, the production of national guidelines essentially ceased. The reluctance of the medical profession to develop guidelines encountered by Robert Brook, MD, at RAND a decade earlier once again prevailed and public benefit slipped to subservience to professional protectionism.

QUEBEC COMMISSION ON INQUIRY
Expert Witness in Quebec

At the beginning of the twenty-first century, the pattern of having an "official" government-appointed commission investigate and report on the efficacy of chiropractic was happening in Quebec, Canada. Scott was a veteran of many such investigations, either in person

---

[78] HHS 'Statement for Public Release.' Dated 2 May 1996.

or by correspondence, and he defended the rights of the profession with the weight of his three degrees and with his clinical and professional experience. His written testimony to the Quebec Commission opens a window into the Scott Haldeman of 2002, showing how he matured in his position regarding chiropractic practice and became a seasoned warrior against those falsely accusing the profession of shortcomings. Louise Taché-Piette, advocate and legal advisor to the Quebec Order of Chiropractors, provided some helpful insights into that period in Scott's life:

> Around the year 2000, certain Québec government agencies and their legal advisors had begun to write opinions stating that Québec chiropractors did not have the right to establish a diagnosis or to prescribe laboratory analyses. After several efforts to convince these government agencies of the contrary, the Québec Order of Chiropractors decided to file a motion for declaratory judgement before the Québec Superior Court requesting a clear interpretation of the Québec Chiropractic Act.

> At the request of the Québec Order of Chiropractors, Dr. Scott Haldeman, DC, wrote two expert reports dated February 20, 2002 and May 31, 2002 that were filed before the Superior Court. Another expert witness, Dr. Pierre Boucher, DC, also wrote two expert reports.

> Drs. Scott Haldeman and Pierre Boucher both testified before the Superior Court with respect to the chiropractor's duty to diagnose and on the importance of laboratory analyses in the diagnosis process. Superior Court Judge Gilles Blanchet rendered his judgement on February 25, 2003 denying the right of Québec chiropractors to diagnose and to prescribe laboratory analyses.[79]

In Scott's written testimony submitted February 20, 2002, addressed to Mr. Decary, he outlined his qualifications, expressed his special interest in spinal disorders, stood firm in his belief that patients deserve the right to choose their provider, and believed those providers who are available should be licensed and held to the highest

---

[79] Personal e-mail from Louise Taché-Piette, advocate and legal advisor to the Quebec Order of Chiropractic, dated 26 March 2009. Copy in the Haldeman Collection.

quality of care possible. From this foundation he provides his opinion on several aspects of chiropractic under investigation. Extracts from his written testimony:

REGARDING THE CHIROPRACTOR'S RIGHT TO DIAGNOSE

1. ...Irrespective of the actual word used, the process of making a diagnosis or a decision as to what is wrong with a patient is an inherent part of the clinical skills necessary for all primary health care practitioners.

2. ...The act of making a decision as to what pathology or biomechanical abnormality is causing a patient's symptoms and the exact condition, sometimes referred to as a subluxation or spinal lesion, to which a treatment is applied, is the process of making a diagnosis. It is therefore not possible for a chiropractor to practice appropriately without making a diagnosis.

3. Chiropractors are required to make three forms of decisions or diagnoses prior to administering a treatment...The first...is to rule out those conditions which are contraindications to the care offered by the practitioner...The second...be capable of determining when a patient requires, in addition to chiropractic treatment, treatment from other health care providers or specialists...The third...be capable of determining the nature of the lesion likely to respond to his or her form of treatment. This requires the chiropractor to do the appropriate physical, clinical and radiological examinations to reach a diagnosis.

4. Chiropractors are trained in the course of their education...to reach diagnostic conclusions regarding the nature and extent of a patient's problem.

5. Without the ability to make a differential diagnosis...a chiropractor would be unable to practice, and the patient's safety would be seriously compromised.

6. If a chiropractor was denied the right to make a diagnosis, the patient seeking chiropractic care could not possibly be appropriately treated.

THE RECOURSE TO LABORATORY TESTS

1. Chiropractors...would order laboratory tests...when there is a suspected disorder that could require referral to a specialist or be a contraindication to chiropractic care.

2. Basic pathology, physical diagnosis, and the use of laboratory testing are taught in the curriculum of chiropractic colleges...

3. Examples of underlying disease that a chiropractor might identify with laboratory testing would include: Urinary tract infection, rheumatologic diseases, and metabolic disorders...a chiropractor, given the right to make a diagnosis, will make a more rapid and more accurate referral to the appropriate medical provider. A lengthy list of appropriate laboratory tests is included with his testimony.

CONCLUSIONS

It is my opinion that chiropractors are unable to practice appropriately and assure the safety of their patients if they cannot perform basic diagnostic procedures that lead to a differential diagnosis and conclusion. The privilege of ordering these tests by a chiropractor is included in the licensure of most state and provincial agencies in North America. Given this right, a significant number of chiropractors will utilize laboratory tests and x-rays, as well as a physical examination, to reach a diagnosis, but there does not appear to be abuse of the privilege of ordering expensive laboratory tests.[80]

Since the right to diagnose was denied, the Quebec Order of Chiropractors decided to appeal judgement, before the Quebec Court of Appeal. The expert reports of Drs. Haldeman and Boucher were re-filed before the Court of Appeal and referred to in the Order's factum. Louise Taché-Piette had the privilege of representing the Order before the Court of Appeal, which rendered the following judgment on February 25, 2005:

(13) [...] It would be illogic to authorize a chiropractor, who is an independent health professional, to perform a chiropractic treat-

---

[80] Testimony of Scott Haldeman presented to Michel Decary of the Quebec Commission of Inquiry, 20 Feb 2002. Testimony is in the Haldeman Collection.

ment on a human being without having first diagnosed the problem that may be solved by such treatment.

(23) [...] The Chiropractic Act authorizes chiropractors to establish diagnoses within the field of their competence such as outlined in Section 6 of that Act, on the basis of clinical and radiological examinations, such as provided in Section 7 of the said Act.[81]

The Court of Appeal ruled the Chiropractic Act did not authorize chiropractors to prescribe laboratory analyses. However, the fact that they were officially recognized as being entitled to establish diagnoses would give way, in the near future, to amendments that would authorize them to prescribe laboratory analyses. Ms. Tache-Piette and the Quebec Order of Chiropractic were pleased with the outcome and grateful for Scott's timely help.[82]

BONE AND JOINT DECADE 2000 – 2010
Neck Pain Task Force

Scott's drive for research and his quest for greater understanding naturally led him down the path of setting standards and developing clinical care guidelines. Who better to take on this responsibility than the one most familiar with or actually producing current information? We have already seen his involvement with the Mercy Guidelines for chiropractic care and the AHCPR Guidelines for the treatment of acute low back pain. He had also been responsible for initiating, as president, and then serving on a guidelines committee established by the North American Spine Society.

Scott also served as a member of the American Academy of Neurology's Quality Standards Subcommittee. This subcommittee was conceived by Dr. Michael Greenberg to set standards for the treatment of low back pain, and it was he who invited Scott to participate (1991). Current low back pain guidelines produced by the American College of Rheumatology and the American Academy of Orthopedic Surgery were deemed inadequate, and the American College of Phy-

---

81 Personal e-mail from Louise Taché-Piette, advocate and legal advisor to the Quebec Order of Chiropractic, dated 26 March 2009. Copy in the Haldeman Collection.
82 Ibid.

sicians was still developing their guidelines. It was Greenberg's idea to host a multispecialty conference that would include representation from the American Academy of Family Practice, American Academy of Orthopedic Surgeons, American Academy of Physical Medicine and Rehabilitation, American Association of Neurological Surgeons, American College of Physicians, American College of Rheumatology, and the North American Spine Society.[83] Scott had also been asked to serve as facilitator of a committee for the American Academy of Neurology Therapeutics and Technology Assessment Subcommittee on "Neurological Evaluation of Male Sexual Dysfunction." This was based on the research he had done at the Long Beach Veterans Administration Medical Center with Dr. Bill Bradley.

The Quebec Task Force on Spinal Disorders had published the most important review of the medical literature in 1995 where they had presented their recommendations.[84] However, neck pain in the general population and in the occupational setting was not considered, and the amount of research available for their recommendations was weak. The QTF had recommended that a second task force be established by the year 2000. Since the publication of the QTF there had been a marked increase in both the quantity and quality of published studies on neck pain and it was clear that understanding of neck pain had advanced considerably in the ten years since its publication. It was time for another task force on neck pain.

Neck Pain and Chiropractic

Previously cast off as quackery and unscientific cultism, spinal manipulation and chiropractic grew in both social and scientific acceptance during the decades of the 1970s and 1980s. This heightening profile also brought into focus the potentially harmful consequences of spinal manipulation, stroke being the most serious and newsworthy. Scott had been in Toronto in 1970 when the first public case of a stroke believed to be caused by a chiropractic manipulation

[83] Memo from Michael Greenberg, MD, to Jay Rosenberg, MD and Chair of the AAN Quality Standards Subcommittee, dated March 22, 1991.
[84] Spitzer, WO, et al. "Scientific Approach to the Assessment and Management of Activity-Related Spinal Disorders: A Monograph for Clinicians. *Spine*, 1987: 12:S1-S59.

came to trial in Canada. He and Dr. Grice had testified that the likelihood of a stroke occurring from a spinal manipulation was "one in a million treatments" based on calculations they did in preparation for the hearing. (See Chapter 5.)

Periodic reports of strokes occurring as a result of a spinal manipulation continued to pepper the medical literature, becoming more frequent in the 1980s, usually implicating a chiropractor as the culprit. The National Chiropractic Mutual Insurance Company (NCMIC), the major malpractice provider for chiropractic professionals in the United States, had concern regarding the supposed relationship between the occurrence of strokes and stroke-like conditions and manipulation of the neck.

Scott submitted a proposal to NCMIC in August 1991 to study the complications of chiropractic care with an emphasis on cerebrovascular accidents. The essence of the proposal was to do an in-depth analysis of the roughly forty cases in Scott's files that he had collected from around the country where a claim had been made that a patient had suffered a cerebrovascular accident (CVA) as the result of a chiropractic manipulation. The requested budget was $150,000 for two years with no compensation allotted to Scott as the supervisor of the project or for the use of his office space and personnel. The funds primarily supported the research assistants, students from the Los Angeles College of Chiropractic, who were doing the data collection. The proposal was accepted by NCMIC.[85]

In July 1994, Scott sent a report to the newly elected president of NCMIC, Arnold Cianciulli, DC, regarding the project. The number of cases being reviewed had grown to fifty and the work was to be submitted for publication within two months. The remainder of the report was a recommendation on how better information could be gathered in the future by implementing a more exacting protocol for the doctors in practice reporting CVA cases. NCMIC accepted Scott's

---

[85] Haldeman, Scott. *Complications of chiropractic care with an emphasis on cerebrovascular accidents.* A Research Proposal submitted to NCMIC, August 1991. Proposal is in the Haldeman Collection.

recommendations, and the "Vertebrobasilar Artery Stroke Project" continued.[86]

As is typically the case, imposing more rigorous "information collection" procedures on busy clinicians is fraught with potential failure. Such was the case in this project. In Scott's January 1996 report to NCMIC he stated, "...practicing chiropractors did not cooperate in sufficient number to make for a valid study." This lack of acceptance of a more rigorous data collection process in clinical practice settings prevented the collection of data necessary to prepare a report worthy of presentation at the highest levels of medicine, but the project did continue. Scott predicted the project would be completed by the end of 1996 with "...three to five papers and presentation of three to four papers at various meetings, as well as a significantly greater understanding of the risk factors, precipitating factors, frequency of occurrence, other causes of vertebrobasilar artery dissections, and whether certain adjustments create a particular risk for this complication."[87] The result of this research was published in a series of papers and presented at meetings of the American Academy of Neurology, the North American Spine Society, and multiple chiropractic meetings.

Expansion of the Project

The fact that strokes and related disorders were becoming a weapon of fear by forces in opposition to manipulation and chiropractic, the work Scott was doing with NCMIC began to take on greater dimensions. Every time someone claimed a stroke-related injury due to a chiropractic adjustment, the public media and the medical literature clamored for justice and the prohibition of any further chiropractic treatment of neck pain.

In March 1998, J. David Cassidy, DC, PhD, circulated a memo to David Chapman-Smith and Drs. Scott Haldeman, Paul Carey, Louis Sportelli, Paul Peloso, and John Sweaney suggesting the need for a Task Force on Cervical Manipulation. David had served on the Que-

---

[86] Letter to Arnold Cianciulli, DC, from Scott dated 8 July 1994. Letter is in the Haldeman Collection.
[87] Haldeman, Scott. *Report to the NCMIC Board on the Vertebrobasilar Artery Stroke Project.* 30 January 1996. Report is in the Haldeman Collection.

bec Task Force on Whiplash Associated Disorders and was currently serving as the Scientific Secretary for the World Health Organization (WHO) Collaborating Center Task Force on Mild Brain Injuries. David proposed three primary components of this task force:

1. Comprehensively and systematically reviewing the literature on the benefits and side effects of cervical manipulation

2. Developing a decision analytic model for the treatment of neck pain

3. Identifying the importance of cervical manipulation as a risk factor for stroke[88]

David's proposal was quickly endorsed, and Scott proposed they hold a meeting in Washington, DC in conjunction with the next Research Agenda Conference (RAC) on March 18th.[89]

On June 18, 1998, J. David Cassidy, DC, PhD; Scott Haldeman, DC, MD, PhD; Paul Peloso, MD, MSc; Paul Carey, DC, president of the Canadian Chiropractic Protective Association (CCPA); Lou Sportelli, DC and president of the National Chiropractic Mutual Insurance Company (NCMIC); and David Chapman-Smith, LLB and secretary-general of the World Federation of Chiropractic (WFC) met together at the Washington National Airport Hilton in Crystal City, VA. The purpose of the meeting was to discuss the proposed formation of a WFC Task Force on Cervical Manipulation. It was projected that it would take a year and $100,000 to prepare a proposal for the formation of the task force and that an additional $3 million would be necessary to carry on the work. NCMIC and the CCPA (Canadian Chiropractic Protective Association) agreed to provide the initial $100,000.

The Neck Pain Task Force, as it was now called, met in Saskatoon at the Institute for Health and Outcomes Research (IHOR), affiliated with the University of Saskatchewan, and the Population Health and Policy Planning Branch of Saskatchewan Health on September 14-16.

[88] Cassidy, J. David. *Memorandum for the Development of a Task Force on Cervical Manipulation.* 20 March 1998.
[89] There is some confusion, as the date proposed of March 18th was clearly in 1998 since the Task Force continued to meet in 1998, but Scott's letter is dated March 30th and was stamped as having been faxed on March 31st of 1998.

Attendance at this meeting included David Cassidy, DC, PhD, director of IHOR; Paul Peloso, MD, MS; and Pierre Côté, DC, PhD. Also in attendance were Linda Carroll, PhD, IHOR's clinical health psychologist; Rein Lepnurm, PhD, IHOR's health economist; and Emma Bartfay, PhD, IHOR biostatistician. Scott was selected to serve as the president of the task force, although he only attended the meeting by conference call on that day. David Cassidy was selected to be the Scientific Secretary.

Scott's first priority was to expand the scope of the task force beyond the interests in the chiropractic profession to include all aspects of neck pain, to ensure that the task force was multidisciplinary and international, to conduct original research, and to ensure that biases be reduced by expanding the support base. The group agreed and changed the original objectives laid out by David Cassidy in his earlier memo to include:

1. A systematic literature review on the benefit and harm of the most common treatments for non-specific neck pain

2. Original research to determine risk of adverse reactions to chiropractic manipulation and non-steroidal, anti-inflammatory drugs (NSAIDs)

3. A decision analytic study of patient preference for treatment of non-specific neck pain

4. A multicentre randomized controlled trial on treatment for non-specific neck pain

Several electronic databases, registries, and collaborative centers were identified as rich sources for the proposed literature and data gathering. Several names were mentioned as potential additional members to the task force and to an advisory board. Funding sources were considered and future meetings were planned for October in Toronto and November in Calgary.[90]

The minutes of the October 26-27, 1998, meeting of the task force

[90] Minutes of the September 14-16 1998, Task Force on Neck Pain prepared by David Cassidy, DC, PhD, Secretary of the Task Force, distributed to members of the Task Force via Fax 20 October 1998.

held in Toronto were distributed to the members along with the agenda for the meeting on November 10, 1998. Drs. Eric Hurwitz, DC, PhD from UCLA and Professor Ake Nygren, DDS, MD, Dr Med Sc, from the Karolinska Institute in Stockholm, expressed an interest of serving on the Scientific Secretariat making the Task Force an international initiative.

There was discussion regarding the approach to reviewing the literature, and they decided to use the "best evidence synthesis" methodology. A critical review software program was examined along with papers from the *Annals of Internal Medicine* on how to conduct systematic reviews of the literature. The Secretariat was informed on the "case control study" methodology, "decision analytic study" methodology, and "randomized controlled trial" methodology. Composition of the Secretariat and the Advisory Board were discussed and more potential names were put forth. David Chapman-Smith, secretary general of the World Federation of Chiropractic (WFC), met with the group and recommended the task force be associated with the World Health Organization. He was prepared to make appropriate connections. Finally, there was a meeting with Searle-Monsanto of Canada to solicit financial support. The response was positive enough to encourage the task force to prepare more detailed documentation on proposed plans and to propose a budget of between $2 and $4 million dollars to support their work.[91]

The minutes of the Calgary meeting (November 15-16, 1998) were faxed out on December 22, 1998. Scott reported the reaffirmation of support from NCMIC and the CCPA, indicated the acceptance of Chapman-Smith recommendations, and emphasized the need to get the task force aligned with an acceptable international body. More discussions regarding the methodologies to be used in the studies as well as membership of the Advisory Board took place. The next meeting was planned for February 1999 in conjunction with the Whiplash Associated Disorders conference in Vancouver, since four members

---

[91] Minutes of the October 26-27, 1998 Task Force on Neck Pain prepared by David Cassidy, DC, PhD, Scientific Secretary of the Task Force, distributed to members of the Task Force via Fax 10 November 1998.

of the task force were on the program.[92]

It must be remembered that this "proposed" task force had already hosted a series of meetings, had invited more people to participate, and had launched several projects. In the minutes of the February 12-13, 1999 meeting, in addition to a review of the work in progress, a mission statement was crafted:

> To review current knowledge about the epidemiology, treatment and economic costs of neck pain and related symptoms, and add new knowledge, incorporating patient preferences and values, in order to inform patients, clinicians, insurers and health policy-makers about this public health problem.[93]

The initial membership of the Secretariat[94] included Scott Haldeman as president, J. David Cassidy as scientific secretary, Ake Nygren, Linda Carroll, Eric Hurwitz, Pierre Côté, and Paul Peloso. Additional members were under consideration. However, funding continued to be a primary concern.

Chapman-Smith circulated a memo on June 14, 1999, asking for a meeting with Haldeman, Cassidy, Carey, and Sportelli to update them on the proposal for the task force. He noted in the memo that Searle-Monsanto would not fund the task force but State Farm Insurance was interested. UCLA and Karolinska Institute and possibly the University of New York had interest in becoming major centers for the task force.[95]

Information regarding the work of the task force is sketchy between June 1999 and November 2000. In December 1999, Cassidy left the University of Saskatchewan, having accepted an invitation from Dr. Tom Noseworthy, head of the Public Health Science Program at the

---

[92] Minutes of the November 15-16, 1998 Task Force on Neck Pain prepared by David Cassidy, DC, PhD, Scientific Secretary of the Task Force, distributed to members of the Task Force via Fax 22 December 1998.

[93] Minutes of the February 12-13, 1999 Task Force on Neck Pain prepared by David Cassidy, DC, PhD, Scientific Secretary of the Task Force, distributed to members of the Task Force via Fax 18 March 1999.

[94] The term Secretariat was applied to the center core of the Task Force on Neck Pain. The Advisory Board (later called a committee) was an adjunct group set up to advise and review the work of the Scientific Secretariat. See *Spine*, Vol. 33, No. 4S, February 15, 2008.

[95] Memo from David Chapman-Smith to Drs. Paul Carey and Louis Sportelli, dated 14 Jun 1999.

University of Alberta in Edmonton to join the faculty in the Department of Epidemiology. He was also cross appointed to the Department of Rheumatology and worked with Tony Russell, MD. Linda Carroll also accepted a position in the Department of Epidemiology at the University of Alberta. The University of Saskatchewan took months to transfer the research funds to the University of Alberta, preventing support for additional meetings. The task force held some telephone meetings, but the lack of access to funds did impact the progress of the task force. In 2003, Cassidy left the University of Alberta for a position at the University of Toronto. Linda Carroll remained at the University of Alberta and became the principle investigator (PI) of the project and was appointed co-scientific secretary of the task force. Carroll managed the bulk of the grant. Cassidy remained as co-scientific secretary and focused on the original research studies (which were taking place in Toronto). Carroll then focused on the literature review and best evidence synthesis.

Cassidy invited Dr. Sheilah Hogg-Johnson, biostatistician from the Institute for Work and Health in Toronto, to join the Science Secretariat in November 2000. She accepted the invitation. The task force assumed an official WHO designation when Ake Nygren joined. His department at Karolinska Institute had status as a WHO Collaborating Centre, and he was able to deliver the WHO designation.[96]

It is interesting that as the task force was gaining momentum, Scott was invited to testify as an expert witness on a second high profile case of a stroke related death following a chiropractic encounter in Ontario, Canada. In his legal brief Scott stated, "There is only speculation regarding any relationship between the chiropractic treatment and the subsequent stroke, based solely on a weak temporal relationship."[97] His testimony was part of a large inquest on the death of this patient that captured worldwide attention. At this inquest there was an intense discussion of the risks and benefits of all treatments for neck pain, and it became clear that there were many areas that required

[96] Letter to Dr. Sheilah Hogg-Johnson from Dr. Cassidy dated 28 November 2000.
[97] Letter to Tom Schneider, Counsel to the Chief Coroner of Ontario from Scott dated 1 February 2001.

better research and understanding. This was a further stimulation to hasten the work of the task force.

The committee now calling itself the WHO Collaborating Centre Task Force on Neck Pain and its Associated Disorders, held its next meeting in Edmonton, Alberta, Canada on March 31st and April 1st. Added to the usual list of attendees was Lori Giles, MLIS; Margareta Nordin, PT, Dr Med Sc; and Jon Schubert, CMA. The minutes of the meeting show the formation of three subcommittees: 1) WHO affiliation, 2) financing, and 3) Cochrane collaboration. As president of the task force, Scott was an ex-officio member of these three subcommittees. Numerous tasks were assigned out to individuals relating to financing future activities, specific research projects, additional membership, relationship with the WHO, and management of funds with the University of Alberta. The next meeting was set for December 2001 with the intervening time focused on literature reviews. Several conference calls did occur with the various subcommittees during the time between full meetings.

The December 2001 meeting was held in Toronto and was broken up into a two-day meeting of the Scientific Secretariat and a two-day meeting with the full task force (i.e., to include the Advisory Committee and observers). The focus of discussion was on the various research projects and literature reviews. Some change in the research protocols and priorities took place as a result of the work accomplished up to that time.

2001

Scott submitted a report to the primary financial sponsors in January 2002. The report listed support from the two original sponsors, NCMIC and CCPA along with the Lansforsakringer Wass from Sweden, Jalan Pacific, Inc. from Brazil, Flinn Foundation from Arizona, and the Ontario Ministry of Health and Long-Term Care from Canada. The task force was now taking on an international dimension. The report listed ten organizations that had recognized the importance of the task force to include UCLA School of Public Health, University of Alberta, and the Bone and Joint Decade 2001-2010.

The task force membership had grown and was now divided into the Advisory Committee, the Scientific Secretariat, and the Administrative Committee. In year one, the task force screened 32,621 papers or abstracts and culled them down to 5,644 papers to be reviewed for placement in the evidence tables. The first full meeting of the "official" task force occurred in Toronto in December 2001. Four research projects were reviewed at this meeting: 1) the Decision Analysis project, 2) the Risk of Stroke after Chiropractic Treatment project, funded by the Ontario Ministry of Health and Long-Term Care, 3) the Risk of GI Complications after NSAID project, and 4) the Occupational Neck Pain study funded by the Ontario Ministry of Health and Long-Term Care. Expenses for the first year of the task force was just over $400,000 CAN and were within $2,000 of the original budget. The total budgeted for the five-year project was $2.8 million dollars.[98]

2002

In 1999, probably the most important world initiative for the advancement of research into musculoskeletal disorders—the Decade of the Bone and Joint—was proposed for the period 2000-2010. This initiative was endorsed by the United Nations on November 30, 1999. It was formally launched at the WHO headquarters on January 13, 2000, in Geneva and had its headquarters in Lund, Sweden. Since then, national networks have been established in 97 countries. The initiative has been endorsed by the governments of 61 countries, and there are hundreds of participating professional organizations including the major spine research and chiropractic associations. Scott was appointed one of the early 31 (since expanded to 49) International Ambassadors for the Bone and Joint Decade 2000-2010. It became obvious to Scott that the ideal association for the task force would be the Bone and Joint Decade, as it was truly international and would greatly enhance the visibility and prestige of the task force and serve as a watchdog to ensure that bias was minimized.

In February 2003, Scott submitted the second annual report (2002)

---

[98] Report of the Task Force on Neck Pain and Associated Disorders dated 15 January 2002 was submitted by Scott to Drs. Sportelli and Carey of the NCMIC and CCPA respectively.

of the task force. By this time the task force had received formal recognition of the United Nations' Bone & Joint Decade 2000-2010 initiative and was becoming one of the leading bodies of research related to neck pain problems. Scott's cover letter to sponsors of the task force dated February 28, 2003, begins with a statement about the growth and credibility of the task force:

> The Task Force is entering its fourth year and is no longer simply another Task Force on the topic of neck or back pain. It has become the most highly visible and well-recognized Task Force currently in existence on this topic and is being followed closely by people interested in this problem.[99]

Linda Carroll and David Cassidy had received the Alberta Heritage Foundation for Medical research Health Scholar Awards that helped to pay their salaries. Lena Holm, Dr Med Sc and sociologist at the Karolinska Institute in Stockholm, Sweden, and Stephen Newman, MD, MS epidemiologist from the University of Alberta joined the Scientific Secretariat. Sam Cheng, MLIS from UCLA, replaced Lori Giles-Smith as librarian. Scott had been appointed a Bone and Joint Decade Ambassador and had also been appointed as an adjunct faculty member in the Department of Epidemiology, UCLA School of Public Health. Pierre Côté completed his PhD in May 2002. Gabrielle van der Velde, DC, PhD (candidate), joined the Scientific Secretariat as a student member in 2002 and finished her PhD before the task force had completed their work. Gabrielle's thesis was the decision analysis that was published in the final report.

Each research project was reviewed. The participants on the literature review study started having three hour conference calls every two to three weeks and sorted through 10,783 abstracts from Medline. The Occupational Neck Pain Study was underway. The Risk of Stroke following Manipulation was changed to include a case cross-over design in addition to the case-control design. The Risk of Complications from NSAID was having difficulty obtaining useful information

---

[99] Report of The Bone and Joint Decade 2000-2010 Task Force on Neck Pain and Its Associated Disorders to Drs. Carey and Sportelli of the CCPA and NCMIC respectively. Scott's cover letter.

on over the counter use of NSAID. The Decision Analysis Study of Neck Treatments was progressing. The budget was on target.[100]

2003

The task force met at the end of March in 2003. At the meeting there was information shared about the interests of the American Physical Therapy Association and the Japanese Spine Research Society becoming part of the task force advisory committee. Discussions ensued on how to make the literature review process more efficient and exclusion/inclusion criteria for papers to be reviewed were modified. Updates on the NSAIDS study and the stroke study were presented. Plans for the final report were proposed for the Scientific Secretariat to consider. A proposal to present at the Combined Spine Convention, the largest spine meeting ever to be held in the world to that date, in Porto, Portugal was also presented.[101]

There was a meeting of the task force administrative committee held in September 2003. Linda Carroll was approved as a member of the administrative committee. This was necessary as Cassidy had moved to Toronto leaving Carroll to manage the grant funds at the University of Alberta. They served jointly as principle investigators, which worked well since work was taking place both in Alberta and Toronto. It was decided to inform the sponsors that an additional year would be needed to complete the work of the task force. Plans for the next full Secretariat meeting in Bordeaux, France, were presented along with the proposed presentations at the combined spine meeting in Porto.[102]

2004

In February 2005, Scott produced the progress report for year four of the task force. The final product was beginning to formulate and plans for publication were taking place with the *Spine* journal and the

---

[100] Report of The Bone and Joint Decade 2000-2010 Task Force on Neck Pain and Its Associated Disorders to Drs. Carey and Sportelli of the CCPA and NCMIC respectively from Scott dated 24 February 2003.
[101] Meeting minutes of the Neck Pain Task Force Scientific Secretariat held March 27-30, 2003.
[102] Meeting minutes of the Neck Pain Task Force administrative committee, September 7, 2003.

European Spine Journal. The North American Spine Society (NASS) and the European Spine Society endorsed the work being done and recognized the need to revisit their own guidelines on the care of neck pain. Members of the task force were being invited to speak about their work in Canada, Sweden, Portugal, and Australia. The full task force met in Bordeaux, France, in June. Two surgeons, Bill Watters, MD, and Brian Freeman, DM, were added to the Advisory Committee. An increase in quality scientific publications on the spine increased the workload of the Secretariat in reviewing the new publications. Nicholas Walsh, MD, from the steering committee of the Bone and Joint Decade, attended as an observer.

There was a formal proposal to the Ontario and the Saskatchewan governments to access their databases to undertake the Stroke Study. The Decision Analysis project was collecting data from patients in Los Angeles and Toronto and was on target for completion. The NSAID study was impacted by the publication of risks from taking Vioxx, and a large number of randomized controlled studies on the use of Cox-2 drugs produced data that overshadowed the observational study proposed by the task force. The task force decided to limit the study of NSAIDs to a literature review on the effects of these medications on an otherwise healthy population of low back pain sufferers.

Due to the increase in publications and the modifications in certain research designs, Scott proposed to extend the work of the task force for an additional year, concluding their work by December 2006. The actual costs came to $3,267, 576 CAD. CCPA and NCMIC both agreed to fund the project in the amount of $1,092,000.[103] The task force pursued additional funding from other organizations and they obtained an unconditional grant of $400,000 from the State Farm insurance Company. The Stroke study was being funded by the Ontario government. The task force cut costs by reducing the number of face-to-face meetings, acquiring funding from organizations sponsoring someone on the Advisory Committee, and changing protocol in the NSAID study.[104]

[103] NCMIC actually paid $1,085,000. Personal communication with Dr. Sportelli 27 Apr 2009.
[104] Report of *The Bone and Joint Decade 200-2010 Task Force on Neck Pain and Its Associated Disorders* submitted to all sponsors by Scott dated 20 February 2005.

2005

In the February 2006 report to their sponsors, the task force was in its final year of its six-year history. The intensity of the work had not lessened with the members of the Secretariat meeting every two weeks for a three-hour consensus review of the literature. Only two meetings of the Secretariat were held in Toronto, and no meetings of the full task force were held as a budget saving measure. Completion date for submission of all chapters for publication was January 2007. Supplements of the *Spine* and the *European Spine Journal* were to be simultaneously published. Translations of the report into Spanish and Portuguese had been proposed.

The literature review and best synthesis had now screened more than 35,000 abstracts and completed critical reviews on 600 articles. Evidence tables were being completed. The Stroke Study received funding from the Ontario Ministry of Health and Long-Term Care, which allowed the project to meet its completion date. The NSAID's project was progressing well with assistance from Dr. Claire Bombardier. Papers were being completed on the Occupational Neck Pain Study and were ready for submission. The Decision Analysis on patients with Acute Whiplash was on schedule. With efforts of the task force members, additional funding had been obtained that would carry the task force through to the completion of their work.[105]

2006-2007

With the task force in a frenzy to complete its work and beginning to write up its findings, Scott and other members of the task force were receiving invitations to make presentations around the world. The results of the task force would be presented at Major Congresses specifically organized for this purpose in Bern, Switzerland, Los Angeles, and Regina, Canada. Symposia on the task force were presented at multiple professional conferences including the North American Spine Society and the American Academy of Physical Medicine and Rehabilitation. Members of the task force had also been asked

---

[105] Report of *The Bone and Joint Decade 200-2010 Task Force on Neck Pain and Its Associated Disorders* submitted to all sponsors by Scott dated 20 February 2006.

to present the findings in Sweden, Germany, and Australia. In May 2007 Scott reported to the World Federation of Chiropractic at their biennial meeting in Vilamoura, Portugal. He listed the objectives of the task force, the membership, sponsors (institutional, professional, and financial), the table of contents for the publication in *Spine*, and concluded his presentation with a statement of likely impact:

A Dissemination Strategy has been proposed to:

• Facilitate best practices in the diagnosis and management of neck pain including these symptoms that are associated with occupation factors and whiplash-associated disorders utilizing the evidence-based findings of the Bone and Joint Decade on Neck Pain.

• Identify and propose initiatives to enable the adoption of evidence-based best practices in prevention and management.

• Identify policy changes that may impact the incidence of neck pain and its disability.

• Create research and program evaluation initiatives and partnerships to further evaluate the causes of neck pain and its management.

The findings of the task force should increase the general understanding by the public and clinicians of the risk, prognosis, assessment, and management of patients with neck pain.

It will likely re-define how clinicians, patients, government, and insurance carriers view neck pain and its associated disorders. Through this process it will hopefully help reduce the cost and suffering associated with this disorder.

Chiropractors and other clinicians will be required to become aware of the latest research and its meaning if they are to practice in an evidence based practice world. They will have to be aware of the scientific evidence for their education of patients and recommended treatments rather than rely on opinion if they are to empower their patients to make decisions about their care.

The results of the task force will hopefully help fulfill an important knowledge gap and allow patients and their clinicians to understand and manage neck pain more effectively.[106]

In Scott's Executive Summary of the work of the task force he makes the following statements:

Over its lifespan, the task force consisted of a 5-member Executive Committee, a 13-member Scientific Secretariat, a 17-member Advisory Committee, and 18 research associates and graduate students. Committee members originated from 9 countries and represented 19 clinical and scientific disciplines or specialties. The task force was affiliated with 8 collaborating universities and research institutes in 4 countries, and 11 professional organizations agreed to become nonfinancial sponsors.

This supplement contains the results of a systematic review of the literature and best evidence synthesis. A total of 31,878 citations were screened, and 1,203 relevant articles were accepted for review. Ultimately, some 552 scientific papers were deemed to be scientifically admissible for the best evidence synthesis.

The Executive Summary goes on to list key factors from the task force relating to the epidemiology and risk factors associated with neck pain, a new classification system for neck pain, prognosis, assessment, and treatments for neck pain, and the significant finding that the relationship between chiropractic care and vertebrobasilar stroke is no different than the relationship between the same condition and care from a general practitioner.[107]

The work of the task force has certainly laid the groundwork for future research. Not only was it published as a supplement to *Spine* and the *European Spine Journal*, but it has since been reprinted in its entirety in the prominent chiropractic scientific publications *Journal of Manipulative and Physiological Therapeutics (JMPT)*, Vol. 32, No. 25, February 2009. The NCMIC purchased an additional 20,000 cop-

---

[106] Report by Scott to the World Federation of Chiropractic at Vilamoura, Portugal, 17 May 2007 on the Bone and Joint Decade 2000-2010 Task Force.
[107] Haldeman, Scott. "The Bone and Joint Decade 200-2010 Task Force on Neck Pain and its Associated Disorders. Executive Summary". *Spine*, Vol. 33, No. 4S, February 2008, pg. S5-S7.

ies of the Spine Supplement and sent a copy to every neurologist in the United States and Canada.

The monumental work of this task force has been disseminated worldwide to all the relevant recipients that treat neck pain. The impact of this work is something Scott never imagined in 1970 when he and Dr. Grice were dealing with the first public case of stroke and chiropractic care. His work on stroke cases in the early 90s and his participation in multiple guideline committees was a preparation for the task force. The forward thinking of the NCMIC and the CCPA with Scott and David Cassidy in 1998 laid the ground work, and the Bone and Joint Decade Task Force provided the vehicle for the Task

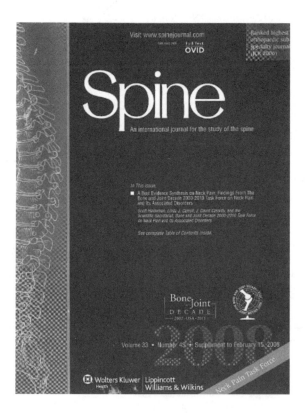

Force to become the most authoritative treatise of the subject to be published. Of the thirteen members of the Scientific Secretariat, five were chiropractors with PhD degrees. Scott also experienced a partial fulfillment of his life-long pursuit of seeing researchers with chiropractic degrees participate at the highest level of scientific investigation.

The meetings of the task force were not without their moments of personal experience. The following was submitted by Eric Hurwitz, DC, PhD:

> One experience at a task force meeting that comes to mind is when we were in Edmonton in March 2003. I don't know whose idea it was (one of the Canadians, no doubt), but one evening (March 29) a bunch of us (including Scott) went curling at the local curling rink (I'm not sure what the technical name is for the sheet of ice that curling is played on). Someone suggested that the novice from sunny California (yours truly) go first. So I went. Sliding down the ice with the "rock" in hand, releasing it as instructed, and ... splat! I slipped on the ice and fell smack dab on my very unpadded right hip. I couldn't get up and I knew something very bad had happened.
>
> Somehow Scott and the others carried me to the car and Scott drove me to the University of Alberta Hospital emergency room. He waited several hours until I finally saw a doctor and had x-rays taken of the hip. The ER doctor on duty read the x-ray and declared no fracture. Scott did not see the radiograph. I was sent back to the hotel with crutches and a prescription for ketoralac, which Scott filled for me. Scott stayed with me and comforted me the whole evening until I was safely in my room. It was well past midnight.

I could not put any weight on the leg without excruciating pain. After an unbearable flight back to LA using a wheelchair to get off and on the two planes needed to make the trip, I had the leg re-x-rayed. A clear hip fracture with displacement was found. I had surgery the next day. A little over a year later, I had another surgery to have the plate and screws removed. Except for a shorter right leg now and loss of some ROM, I have had good outcome over all.[108]

---

[108] Personal communication with Dr. Hurwitz. 2009

Pierre Côté shared the following comment:

> What really impressed me during the years of the task force was Scott's relentless commitment to make this body of work relevant to clinicians and patients. According to Scott, the task force research would be more than an academic exercise, "it would change the way people saw neck pain and empower patients to manage their pain." In the seven years of the task force, Scott never deviated from his goal. In fact, he made a point of reminding us of this goal at every meeting. For Scott, research must serve the greater good. His dedication to this goal was central to our work.[109]

J. David Cassidy expressed his gratitude for the opportunity to be a part of the task force as follows:

> The task force provided me with the opportunity to fulfill two of my lifelong professional goals. The first was to work with Scott Haldeman, who is a pioneer in chiropractic research and a world leader in spine research. The second was to organize an international task force on neck pain with chiropractic and medical scientists working together. Scott was the perfect president for our task force as he has spent his entire career building bridges between professions and perusing the highest level of research.

CONCLUSION

From the forgoing discussion, Scott was in the right place at the right time to participate and lead these landmark events. But being in the right place at the right time is not enough. Opportunities cannot be embraced if proper preparation had not preceded the option. Scott prepared well and when the door opened he was ready to step through.

The rest of the Scott Haldeman Legacy resides in the future. Predictions of what is to come and how Scott will be involved are just that—predictions. It is unknown at this time exactly what doors of opportunities are yet to open. In the concluding section we will take the liberty of a little speculating.

---

[109] Personal communication with Dr. Cote. 2009

SECTION IV

THE FUTURE

Chapter 16

On Becoming a Legacy

The chronicle of Scott Haldeman's life, detailed in the preceding pages, provides ample evidence of the maturation of a person, a student, a doctor of spinal care, a researcher, a writer and speaker, a leader in state, national, and international arenas, a teacher and mentor, also a husband and father. Scott has defined and determined his own legacy, and in so doing has influenced the lives of his associates and the professions that make up the spinal care world. It takes a lifetime to establish a legacy, and no legacy is ever established without years of toil mixed with times of tempest, turbidity, and tameness.

When I first met Scott, he was well down the road of life—married with two young children in tow, a resident in neurology at UC Irvine, already established as a recognized authority in spinal care because of his multiple degrees, along with his participation in the 1976 NINCDS conference. It was because of his reputation and achievement that I sought his counsel when pondering my own life's course of action. *Should I pursue a graduate degree after completing my chiropractic training?* His encouragement helped sway my decision to continue formal education. But I was neither the first nor the last to be guided along such a path. Part of Scott's legacy is evidenced by the trail of chiropractors who have become scholars and researchers, following his pioneering achievements in the academic world.

When Scott emerged onto the neurology clinical scene in the early 1980s, the chiropractic world was less than a hundred years old, and medical intrusion into spinal care was primarily focused on treatment for scoliosis or surgery, for repair of the classical herniated disc. Just one decade earlier the AMA Committee on Quackery was in full swing, attempting to convince the American public that chiropractic—lacking scientific evidence to support its existence—was nothing more than a fraudulent folk art practiced by the uneducated. As a result, it was a threat to the health of the nation and should be eliminated. The NINCDS conference had demonstrated that the world of spinal manipulation was unexplored and mapped mostly with anecdotal experiences and testimonials of health benefits, some bordering on the unbelievable. If ever there was a turf in need of tilling, the world of spinal care was it—ripe for cultivation and development. Scott, perhaps by design from a higher power, coupled with his own diligence, stepped out from his formal training with a shiny new plow hitched to three fresh horses—chiropractic, medicine, and research.

One of Scott's challenges as he transitioned from student to practitioner was more "what to be" than "where to be." Returning to South Africa was not an option, and while returning to British Columbia was a consideration, the family was well-rooted in Southern California by the time he finished his residency at UCI and his fellowship at Long Beach Memorial Hospital. But should Scott be a chiropractor practicing with a medical license, a medical doctor practicing with chiropractic expertise, or a university faculty member doing research? Given Scott's proclivity to work, he managed to embrace all three options into one frenetic life.

He was unable to practice under a chiropractic license in California due to his difficulty with the California Chiropractic Board of Examiners and issues related to his medical malpractice insurance. But there was no reason why Scott could not practice chiropractic under the auspices of his medical license, and in fact, he did. His practice was an eclectic mixture of neurology, physical therapy, and chiropractic—and probably one of the first interdisciplinary practices in spinal care that included specialties outside of recognized medical care. While novel at the time, the introduction of interdisciplinary spinal care in a clinical setting established a precedence that has become acceptable and routine even in military and veteran's health care facilities throughout the U.S.—another part of the man's legacy.

As Scott worked through his training, in both Canada and California, he was a tireless advocate for research in chiropractic—partially as a means of financial support, but more particularly with the desire to improve the chiropractic profession, and to scientifically support a premise deemed cultist by medicine.

Scott thoroughly investigated the scientific literature—no small task in the days before computer-assisted retrieval systems—and provided relevant articles with commentary to all of the major chiropractic organizations in North America and South Africa. He organized a journal club and helped establish advanced training for graduating chiropractors in research and teaching (at CMCC). As a result of his efforts, the first retrievable literature collection and the first clinical science residency program became and remain a part of the fiber of CMCC, and they are part of other chiropractic educational institutions as well. He has served, at times without compensation, as an adjunct faculty member to the Los Angeles College of Chiropractic (now Southern California University of Health Sciences), and in an advisory capacity to other chiropractic programs around the world. He has guided all the major chiropractic associations and has led actual work projects with the Foundation for Chiropractic Education and Research. He helped form the World Federation of Chiropractic and has chaired its Research Council since its inception in 1988. He has encouraged and mentored numerous fellow chiropractors, helping them become recognized research scientists on their own merit. He has published articles in scientific journals and has published seminal chiropractic textbooks. Scott has lectured to chiropractic audiences ranging from small gatherings in his home to huge international conferences boasting more than 1,000 attendees in places from Beijing, China, to Montreal, Canada, always advocating the value and importance of education and research.

The harvest of Scott's years of cultivation in chiropractic research is now bearing fruit. He will be recognized for generations as a pioneer in the development of chiropractic research. His legacy in the chiropractic world is unparalleled.

When Scott entered the medical field of spinal care, he found a world dominated by orthopedic surgeons practicing the best art of the day—aggressive, brutal surgical procedures that often created as much damage as repair. Mild, remitting back pain was left to the care of pill pushers and other alternative practitioners, thought to be little more than weeds in the highly cultivated fields of spine surgery. There were no spine specialty organizations. There were no peer-reviewed medical journals publishing scientific literature focused on spine care. There were no spine care training programs, and there were few spine care treatment centers. Surgery was the treatment of choice, and there was very little research into the efficacy of care, cost of care, or the outcomes of care. There were no treatment guidelines, no standards of care, and early research was showing that the frequency of surgery for spinal problems was more directly related to the number of surgeons than to any perceived clinical needs. In short, the field of medical care for spinal problems was in disarray.

Once again the combination of destiny and diligence placed Scott in a position to influence the treatment methods of spinal care, while he also matured in his own understanding through continued research and clinical practice. He learned what was needed to improve patient care, advance knowledge and understanding, and bring order and prestige to back care. Scott was involved, often from inception, in every spinal care-related medical organization. He served on most executive committees in each of these organizations, frequently becoming the president—an accomplishment never dreamed possible for a chiropractor. He lobbied aggressively to tear down the fences separating the medical world from the non-medical world of spinal care, and he became the most influential "bridge-builder" ever to emerge from either profession. His research-based perspective on the approach to spinal care, coupled with his conservative chiropractic background, made Scott unique on both sides of a political fence that divided medicine from chiropractic. There was no other person who so fully comprehended what each side had to offer, no one who practiced on both sides, and no one who carried the academic credentials into a bimodal clinical setting. His insight, research, teaching, mentoring, and leadership in the medical spinal care world matured a young, ambitious chiropractor into a world-renowned authority among all related types of practitioners. While Scott matured in thought, deed, and action, so did the spinal care world mature in quality patient care based on sound research initiated and inspired by Scott. The legacy of Scott Haldeman in the medical world of spinal care and research is only now being appreciated by his colleagues and the patients they serve.

Whether known as a "barrier buster" or "bridge builder," with finesse rather than force, Scott has done more to bring together the many factions in the world of spinal care than any other single individual in the last half-century. Whether by his physical stature, his impressive array of degrees and accomplishments, his intellect, or his ability to gently persuade, Scott's impact is immeasurable. From his early beginnings at Palmer College and while under the tutelage of his father in South Africa, he had no idea that his scope of influence would be as dramatic as it was in the ensuing years. Expecting to return to South Africa and a life in private practice—the alternate reality of international fame and travel based from a comfortable Southern California home was not even a remote possibility. When he left his home in Pretoria, South Africa, Scott was on track to change the world of spinal care and the relationship between two warring professions.

Few people start life focused on greatness. Few with the capacity to become great achieve their fullest potential. Few who become great remain respectful of their roots and committed to the fundamental causes that started them on that road. Scott's achievements have placed him in the latter category of men. Even so, he was not spared difficulties and disappointment, and everything he attempted did not succeed as he had originally planned. His International Society for Chiropractic Research and Postgraduate Education never came into existence, but served as a template for the organization of the

World Federation of Chiropractic. His chiropractic research conferences nearly caused him financial ruin. His attempts to gain entry for chiropractic into the North American Academy for Manipulative Medicine failed, but similar attempts to gain chiropractic acceptance into the North American Spine Society succeeded. Not every person Scott brought under his wing turned into a world-class researcher with a PhD and grant support rivaling those in the medical community. Scott labored assiduously to achieve his goals and assist others, but opposition or apathy became insurmountable at times.

There is possibly a tinge of disappointment that the "Haldeman" legacy in chiropractic will lapse, as neither of Scott's two boys, Reeve and Keatly, have selected a career in chiropractic or even health care. Blessed with talents of their own and well on paths leading to their own success, with college degrees and successful private business ventures, the fourth generation of Haldemans will not be making a mark in chiropractic. While Scott and Joan are fully accepting of the decisions of their two children, it is the chiropractic profession that will feel the loss of the Haldeman name, touch and vision.

As Scott and Joan transition into the "retirement" phase of their lives, it will not be in Scott's nature to sit back and do nothing. He talks of benevolent service in needy areas (most likely in Southern Africa), international travel and lecturing, and continued writing of scientific articles and sage treatises to inspire future generations. Scott will continually be sought as a consultant by all types of persons involved in spinal care. He will continue to serve on editorial boards of scientific journals, and he will continue to participate in numerous organizations albeit with reduced intensity.

Scott will serve the professions that have served him, even as he takes on his latest role and responsibility of grandfather. Scott and Joan will turn some of their attention toward the fifth Haldeman generation and assist in the inculcation of the family vision and drive to achieve whatever goal is worthy. A wise sage once said, "You don't know how good of a parent you are until you see how your grandchildren turn out." May success bless their posterity as it has Joan and Scott.

Chapter 17

Looking Forward

Scott Haldeman

Shortly after I went into practice, Joan gave me a music box for my office that played the tune, "Dream the Impossible Dream," the unforgettable song from *The Man from La Mancha*, a film based on my favorite book in high school, *Don Quixote*. I still, on occasion, enjoy winding it up and listening to the simple melody. And each time I do, I am reminded of the two messages from this story that have echoed through my head whenever I have considered the next step in my career: first, it is always possible to focus on the best in anyone, regardless of their position or opinion, and second, it is entirely honorable to strive towards seemingly impossible goals in an effort to achieve a better world. These messages that I found early in life have guided my approach to the problems I encountered throughout my career. What has been rewarding is that many, though not all, of the seemingly impossible changes that appeared necessary to improve spine care actually materialized. As a result, I believe we are in a better place in our understanding of spinal disorders than we were 45 years ago when I first began my own quest to contribute to the improvement of spine care.

During the early half of my career it was evident that a major problem in dealing with spinal disorders was the failure of the different professions and specialties to communicate with each other and share research. It seemed impossible to ever change these severely antagonistic attitudes. The dream at that time, in brief, was that if the barriers which prevented communication were broken down, it would be possible to take the best from each of the professions and develop the perfect model for helping patients with spinal pain. This vision of the future suggested that by developing strong interdisciplinary cooperation we could create one happy professional family, take the best from each profession, and together we could solve the problems of spine care based on research and mutual respect. It took many years of battling the unreasonable medical ethics rules and the scientific naiveté of the chiropractors, but eventually these barriers were broken down and the professions began formal dialogue. As interprofessional dialogue increased and some of the prejudices were breaking down, it became clear that none of the professions had the answer to the management of spinal disorders. A change in the vision was therefore required. The new vision was that, with sufficient research, the cause of spinal pain would soon be discovered, and by treating the cause of spinal pain, a cure would be found to control or abolish the pain. A great deal of effort was invested in developing diagnostic testing to achieve this goal. The professions spent a considerable amount of time and money trying to prove the concept that treatments aimed at specific pain generators in the spine would be an effective means of reducing the symptoms and disability of patients. This led to the development of more than 200 treatment approaches for back and neck pain, which were often very innovative and exotic. Unfortunately, this vision has proved to be as elusive as the first. Not only does the cause and cure remain unknown, but this approach has resulted in escalating costs to society and, if anything, there has been an increase in the disability associated with spinal pain.

THE NEW VISION FOR SPINE CARE

The effort to break down communication barriers and increase the breadth and scope of research that resulted from interdisciplinary cooperation, however, was not wasted. In fact, the process was an important evolutionary step that resulted in a marked increase in our understanding of the factors associated with spinal pain, the accuracy and value of available tests, and the impact of various treatments on patients. The volume of research that has been published over the past 20 years is the foundation for a new vision of how spinal pain should be managed.

The change in our approach to spinal disorders is gaining momentum in an environment where health care policy in virtually every country in the world is undergoing major restructuring and rethinking. Nowhere is this more evident than in the United States, where the debate on national healthcare is intense. The reason for this debate is that the cost of healthcare has exceeded the ability of society to pay for it, and a large percentage of the population in the USA and in developing countries has limited access to healthcare. It is now generally agreed that one solution to this problem is to provide healthcare that has research support for effectiveness and to limit or exclude ineffective treatment approaches.

There is no area of healthcare that is more controversial and challenging than the management of spinal pain. In recent discussions with the government, the AMA listed the management of back pain as one of the areas where there is room for significant reduction in costs. This has been one of the justifications for multiple task forces and committees that have produced guidelines for the management of back and neck pain. The review of the worldwide research literature by these task forces has led to a growing consensus that we need a new model for looking at spine care. This was most evident in the deliberations by the Bone and Joint Decade Task Force on Neck Pain and Its Associated Disorders.

A new vision for the delivery of spine care is based on the results and discussion of the task force and other scientific review and guideline committees. Here is a look at the points they are currently discussing:

- A new conceptual model needs to be understood and accepted by everyone involved in spine care, especially patients, clinicians, and policy makers.

• Guidelines based on the most up-to-date research must be accepted, adapted to the different health care systems, and then implemented into these systems.

• Patients must be educated to understand the factors that influence back and neck pain. They must have a reasonable expectation of treatment and be empowered to participate in their care.

• There must be a primary spine care specialty with practitioners who are readily accessible to patients and who will offer advice, relieve symptoms, and coordinate care.

• Clinicians and professions must establish what their specific role should be in the management of spinal disorders. As the primary spine care specialist develops clinicians who wish to provide specific treatments (rehabilitation, surgery, or advanced injections) and medical management will be freed to perfect their skills and focus attention on those patients who are most likely to benefit from their treatment approaches.

• It is important to make high quality spine care available to patients throughout the world in both developed and developing countries.

In order to understand how these six concepts will influence the delivery of care to patients with spinal disorders in the future, it is necessary to expand briefly on their basic principles.

The New Conceptual Model for Spinal Pain

Synthesis of the research to date suggests that the new model for spinal pain must include the following basic concepts:

1.   Spinal pain is not due to an identifiable disease but instead is an inevitable result of being alive. At any point in time, everyone either has back or neck pain or is at risk of developing these symptoms in the future. Pain significantly interferes with normal activities in about 5% of the population. However, people who have spinal pain due to serious pathology, identified by so-called "red flag symptoms," make up only 1-2% of all cases.

2.   Spinal pain is a chronic condition in many people and follows a variable pattern throughout one's life. At times there may be very

little or no pain. At other times it may interfere with activity and sometimes it may become incapacitating. In most people, the pain fluctuates between these states.

3.   There is no cure for spinal pain. Long term follow-up of people with spinal pain suggests that 50% will continue to have pain two, three, and five years later, irrespective of any specific treatment they may receive.

4.   There is no treatment that can prevent this normal fluctuation of symptoms throughout one's life. No procedure has been shown to influence the long-term prognosis for future pain. There are, however, a number of treatment approaches that can bring about short-term improvement in symptoms and disability.

5.   There are multiple work, sporting, recreational, and trauma-related activities that increase the likelihood of developing spinal pain or causing the pain to become debilitating.

6.   There are a number of factors that can have a positive or negative impact on spinal pain. This is true for both individual patients and specific patient populations. These include exercise, work and sports activities, co-morbidities, smoking, psychological stress, etc.

7.   There are multiple social, psychological, medical, and legal policy situations that have significant influence over the manner in which a person responds to pain.

This model will considerably affect the way clinicians and policy makers view patients. In the future, spinal pain will be managed, rather than treated, and will require a clinician who has a high level of knowledge and experience in all components of the model, and who stays abreast of the ever expanding research on the topic. Future research is likely to add to our understanding of these principles rather than change the basic concepts.

Implementing Universal Guidelines

At this point, the treatment a patient is likely to receive depends more on the training and experience of the clinician than on a generally agreed upon approach based on the available research and the new scientific conceptual model. With more than 200 available treatment options, I have likened the frustration of patients to that of shopping in a supermarket when one is hungry while at the same time not being able to read the labels on the products. It is clear that this is not a sustainable or acceptable situation.

One of the promises of a uniform, high quality spine care delivery system is that it will offer all patients a well thought out and researched protocol for treatment, and a consistent, easily understood explanation for their symptoms. Until recently, many professions have attempted to establish guidelines on the use of their particular treatment approach but they rarely addressed the overall management of patients with spinal disorders. This is changing rapidly as government agencies, academic committees, task forces, and private insurance programs implement general guidelines. These guidelines are being developed by interdisciplinary groups of scientists and clinicians and carry a great deal of authority.

Producing these guidelines, however, is the easy part of the process. Implementing the guidelines to the satisfaction of patients and their doctors poses the greater challenge. The manner in which the current health care delivery system is set up, the payment priorities for treatment, the resistance of clinicians to a new way of thinking, and the misunderstanding of patients as to what causes spinal pain and what they can expect, are some of the barriers to incorporating the guideline approach into the management of spinal disorders.

The new vision is to implement these universal guidelines in order to improve care of patients with spinal disorders and at the same time reduce the costs of care. Incorporating such guidelines has proved possible when managing other disorders such as cancer, hypertension, and stroke, and there does not appear to be any reason why it cannot be become part of the management of spinal pain.

Empowering Patients

It is increasingly clear that treatments offered by clinicians to patients with spinal disorders have had limited impact on pain and disability. It is also clear that we will not be able to improve the care without the active cooperation and input from patients. The day when a patient went to a doctor and passively accepted the treatment recommendation is gone—primarily because it has not worked.

Many of the factors that impact symptoms and disability require the patients' active participation. To maximize the effect of treatment, it is crucial to continually educate patients about how they can modify factors such as exercise, stress, fear, excessive treatment, and legal claims to markedly increase or decrease their symptoms.

The fact that there are a number of treatment approaches that can give relief but none that stand out as a panacea is empowering patients to be active in their care decisions. We can expect the spine care clinician to increasingly offer patients a choice of treatment options and allow the patient to choose the treatment they believe will be the most beneficial—this should lead to more effective outcomes.

The Primary Spine Care Specialist

Implementing the new conceptual model and treatment guidelines will require significant changes in the way clinicians manage patients with spinal disorders. Clinicians must understand in detail all aspects of spine care, not only the treatment approach that they offer. The reality is that, irrespective of the clinical discipline, most clinicians offer a limited number of treatments and rarely consider the greater picture of spinal pain care that is emerging from the literature. For example, the surgeon commonly offers only surgery, the medical or pain specialist often limits their recommendations to medication or injections, physical therapists focus on exercise or physical modalities, and chiropractors on manipulation or adjustments.

The only reasonable alternative to help patients who are confused as to which doctor to consult and which treatment is the most likely to be successful for them, is to create a "Primary Spine Care Specialist" position. This clinician would focus on the management of spinal pain in the same way a dentist focuses on the teeth or a neurologist on the nervous system.

The primary spine care specialist must be able to do the following:

1. Examine a patient and screen for serious diseases. When serious pathology is present or suspected, the primary spine care specialist would be able to refer the patient to the appropriate medical or surgical clinician.

2. Offer a number of common non-invasive, inexpensive, and effective treatments, and refer appropriately when more expensive or invasive approaches are necessary.

3. Discuss with the patient the risks, benefits, and the research basis for all treatments for spinal pain, and help him or her decide which treatment to choose when options have similar likely outcomes.

4. Assess the impact of treatment on the patient and recommend discontinuing any treatment that is not effective. Guide the patient to alternative treatments until the best approach is identified.

5. Inform and educate the patient on personal habits, work, and recreational activities that are likely to increase or decrease levels of pain or disability.

6. Invest adequate time to establish the confidence of patients—this will make the patient open to discussing social and psychological factors that may influence their symptoms and disability. The primary spine care specialist should then be able to give simple advice and counseling and make appropriate referrals after identifying risk factors for chronic incapacity due to psychological factors.

7. Navigate the very complex social systems which can markedly increase patient stress and hinder their response to treatment—these include the worker's compensation system, personal injury claims, personal and government disability claims, and medical insurance programs that can be so very difficult for claimants to negotiate.

This is not simply theory or hopeful thinking. There are a number of clinicians from different backgrounds who already have the necessary knowledge and skills to practice as primary spine care specialists. It is not unusual to meet a chiropractor who is working as the primary clinician in a multidisciplinary spine care clinic or hospital, or a trained orthopedic surgeon who has focused on general spine care rather than surgery, or a family or occupational physician who has a special interest in spinal disorders. At this point, however, there is no cohesion between individuals who have migrated to the role of primary spine care specialist, nor is there any professional forum where they can interact.

The Roles of Different Spine Care Clinicians

The primary spine care specialist will not function in isolation but will work with other professionals and specialists who are trained in advanced diagnostic techniques, skilled treatment methods, or complex rehabilitation systems—this will require greater interdisciplinary cooperation and communication. The primary spine care specialist will function in a manner similar to a family physician and will follow a patient throughout his or her life, be available at short notice, and have ready access to specialist care. This, in turn, will free up those specialists who provide highly skilled services to focus on improving and perfecting their skills without the responsibility of the day to day management of a patient's spinal problems.

The role of many spine care subspecialists is established. There are already spine surgery fellowships that provide advanced training in spine surgery, above and beyond the training of general orthopedic and neurosurgery. Rheumatologists have assumed the authority to deal with inflammatory joint diseases, and neurologists already are trained to manage primary neurological disorders that affect the spinal cord and peripheral nervous system. Chiropractors have focused on manipulation or adjustments, and physical therapists on rehabilitation (although there is some overlap and territorial dispute between the latter two professions).

The position of primary spine care specialist, however, is vacant. The reward to the clinician who assumes this role is substantial since he or she will be considered the cultural authority on spinal disorders in all of its ramifications. To achieve this goal, a clinician will need to spend considerable time increasing his or her knowledge of current research on the spine and its different treatment approaches. He or she will also need to participate in spine research meetings, attend courses, and listen to original scientific papers that discuss all approaches to spine care. Currently, it is common at scientific meetings for surgeons to exit the convention hall when non-surgery topics are discussed and the non-surgeons to act similarly when the discussion is primarily on surgery. The primary spine care specialist will be expected to have an interest in all forms of spinal care and, therefore, participate in discussions irrespective of the topic.

I anticipate that there will be some competition between professions to become the cultural authority for spinal disorders–chiropractors, family physicians, physical therapists, and nurse practitioners are potential candidates for the role of primary spine care clinician. This competition is healthy and should increase the general standard of care for patients. For a profession to achieve this goal, however, there will have to be a group decision to strive towards excellence. This will require a commitment by the professional associations and educational facilities to this end.

An alternative option is that no single profession will assume the authority in this field. Clinicians of different backgrounds and training may get together and develop a new specialty under the umbrella of one of the multidisciplinary associations, such as the North American Spine Society. There is some discussion about establishing postgraduate programs specifically to train primary spine care specialists, incorporating members with different professional backgrounds.

The Future Role of Chiropractic

Chiropractors have many historical and training advantages that would qualify them to accept the role of the primary spine care specialist. They are the only clinicians whose training, over a period of four years, focuses primarily on the spine—and they have the advantage of being identified by the public as doctors who primarily treat spinal disorders. With more than 60,000 chiropractors licensed in the U.S., there are sufficient numbers of practitioners to assume this role in America. Chiropractors currently practice in more than 80 countries, and in many countries they have already decided to work towards this goal. Furthermore, chiropractors are trained as primary contact physicians and practice out of offices that are readily accessible to patients. Chiropractors routinely see patients on an "as needed" basis, which is necessary when managing a recurring condition, and they have been forced to learn the different insurance and social systems that govern payment for services. They have the skills to offer manual therapies, exercise, and other non-invasive treatments that offer relief to patients. They also have an historical philosophical approach to health that emphasizes the importance of exercise, diet, good psychological health, and the body's natural ability to heal itself. These are all factors that have been shown to influence the prognosis of patients with back and neck pain.

However, at this time, it is by no means certain that chiropractors have the desire or the ability to take up the position of primary spine care specialist. The alternative is for them to maintain and expand their position as a subspecialist or special skills practitioner, working closely with the primary spine care specialist, and focusing on non-invasive, drugless treatment methods such as manipulation or spinal adjustment.

If, on the other hand, chiropractors do wish to rise to the challenge and claim the position of primary spine care specialist, they will have to change many aspects of their culture. For example, they will have to work harder to understand the principles of the new conceptual model for spinal pain and incorporate them into their practices. As primary spine care specialists, they will have to gain the respect of all other clinicians who offer care to patients—medical and surgical specialists, physical therapists, and acupuncturists—and understand the role each serves in spine care management. They must interact closely with all the spine subspecialists in their communities and be able to make informed referrals when necessary. Furthermore, they will need to attend research meetings and postgraduate courses that focus on the latest general knowledge about spine care, and not only on manipulation skills. They will also need to subscribe to spine journals where the latest research is presented to be sure that they are abreast of current research trends.

More than anything else, however, chiropractors must realize that it requires considerable effort to be the most knowledgeable clinician in a field. Chiropractic associations, educational institutions, and leaders will need to make a collective decision that this position is both desirable and possible. Educational institutions at both the undergraduate and graduate level will need to commit resources to courses that prepare practitioners to assume this role. Individual practitioners will need to support their professional associations, colleges, and research organizations in greater numbers.

Spine Care in Underserved Communities and Developing Countries

The problem of spinal pain and disability is not confined to developed nations and urban communities. If anything, the problem is even more devastating for people in developing nations. There is increasing evidence that musculoskeletal disorders have become one of the major causes of disability and reduced productivity in underdeveloped rural communities. One of the contributing factors may be the total lack of any clinician in these areas with expertise and training to treat these disorders. Despite the emphasis placed on the problem by the Bone and Joint Decade Initiative of the World Health Organization, there have been relatively few programs that have studied spinal disorders in developing nations, and virtually no programs that provide effective care.

The same problem applies to care in rural communities within developed nations. There are many areas where the only available clinician is a family physician and perhaps a dentist. The family physician is likely to be overwhelmed with general internal and infectious disorders and is unlikely to have more than superficial knowledge and interest in spinal disorders. Most likely, any chiropractors practicing in small towns limit their practices to spinal manipulation and have limited understanding of the alternative treatment approaches to spine care. In the absence of a primary spine care specialist to assume the management of patients with spinal disorders in the same manner that the dentist assumes control over the treatment of dental disorders, it is likely that these patients are not being provided the optimum available care.

LOOKING FORWARD

Spine care has entered what is probably the most intriguing phase of its evolution to date. The level of knowledge is growing exponentially, and our understanding of spinal disorders, although a long way from perfect is sufficient for improving many of the shortcomings of treatment in the current system. I believe a primary spine care specialist will emerge and that patients will have greater responsibility for their own health and more influence over the care they receive.

The next decade should increase our ability to overcome difficulties associated with implementing evidence-based practice in both developed and developing communities. At the same time, we will learn whether this approach can reduce morbidity and disability caused by spinal disorders. I expect this field will mature into a well-disciplined, scientifically valid and effective international and interdisciplinary health care delivery system that patients and the public can understand and benefit from.

One of my current interests and goals is to see if it is possible to incorporate guidelines in the management of spinal pain into the many different health care systems without corrupting the basic principles developed from the available research. I am currently involved as a consultant to projects in three different major health care systems, which represent examples of the changes currently being considered within different systems of delivery of care to patients with spinal disorders:

1. Government initiatives. The "Back to Work Project, reducing time lost to occupational injuries to the back, neck, and shoulders among VA staff." This is a project established as collaboration between the Veteran's Administration New York Harbor Healthcare System and New York Universities' Occupational and Industrial Orthopedic Center (OIOC).

2. Worker's compensation systems. The California Medical Evidence Evaluation and Advisory Committee of the Department of Industrial Relations. In California, legislation has been passed that requires the department to institute evidence-based guidelines for treatment.

3.   Private health care industry. At least one medical health care management company hopes to develop a spine care protocol that can be used in the private sector.

The objectives of the three projects are very similar:

•   To guide the care being provided to patients with spinal pain and ensure that it is effective, readily available, and affordable.

•   To ensure that all patients are treated in a similar manner irrespective of the training and qualifications of the clinician they consult.

•   To avoid delays in initiating treatment. If the initial recommendations of the clinician fall within guidelines, the clinician will not need to wait for insurance authorization or delay treatment.

•   To ensure that care is effective if it is to continue. Patients who seek spinal care from a clinician will be asked to submit forms describing their level of symptoms and disability when they first seek care and at regular intervals during their care. If a treatment approach is not resulting in an expected positive outcome, it will be discontinued.

•   To be flexible if treatment considerations are outside of the guidelines. If a recommended treatment falls outside the guidelines, the clinician and patient should be given the reason why it is not compliant with the guidelines, the opportunity to explain why the treatment is being recommended, and provide the research basis for reconsideration of the approach to care.

•   To monitor the outcome of treatment. As the treatment progresses and the patient supplies follow-up information on its effect, modification in the treatment protocol can be recommended.

•   Education. All health care systems require that there be close cooperation between the clinician, patient, and the insurance company or government agency. Success depends on each group being aware of the basis for the guidelines and the mechanism of their implementation.

The major challenge is changing the current culture within the different health care delivery systems. In the VA system, there is no designated primary spine care specialist and patients can leave the system whenever they are unhappy. In the California Worker's Compensation system, the decisions are now frequently made by insurance companies or by the legal system in an arbitrary and inconsistent manner. In the private sector, almost all utilization review is treatment-specific rather than for the management of spinal pain in its broader context.

There is one point that is common to all three systems that inhibits the implementation of guidelines: payment currently is greater for procedures than for patient management. This policy has made it more lucrative for clinicians to advocate a test or procedure rather than educate and monitor the effectiveness of specific treatments and make appropriate changes. This approach will have to change if we hope to improve the way patients are managed. There has to be adequate reimbursement for patient education and the management of their care.

A New International Initiative

I am also turning my attention to introducing evidence-based spine care to underserved communities in developing countries. I have decided to spearhead, with Joan as my partner, an initiative to develop a model of treatment for people with spinal disorders in rural underdeveloped communities. Together with a number of colleagues and friends from around the world, a non-profit foundation called "WORLD SPINE CARE" has been established to serve as the vehicle to achieve this goal.

The model that World Spine Care hopes to implement is to invite chiropractors or physical therapists to participate as primary spine care specialists. They will be asked to volunteer in clinics that are established as spine care centers. These clinicians will work closely with and instruct traditional healers, local nurse practitioners, and available medical personnel to ensure that there is basic screening for serious pathology and to administer what can be considered spinal first aid. The primary spine care specialists will practice according to current evidence-based guidelines within the limitations of the available resources. They will perform detailed clinical examinations to rule out red flags for serious pathology and provide care, including manipulation, exercise, education, and perhaps acupuncture. They could offer mild analgesics that have been shown to reduce symptoms and increase productivity. When serious pathology is documented, surgeons and specialists—such as rheumatologists and neurologists with specific skills—will be invited to come to the country on a volunteer basis to treat these conditions.

The first country where we anticipate this program to be tested is Botswana, where there are no neurologists or spine surgeons, and no programs for the management of spinal disorders. The second country where we have developed contacts is India. Physicians at a medical clinic in a rural community in India have identified spinal disorders as a major health concern and source of disability in the population they serve. They are requesting help to establish an appropriate treatment program.

This program will provide a tremendous educational experience to those clinicians who volunteer time in these communities. The primary spine care specialist will see more patients with serious diseases in a few months than they are likely see in years of private practice in a developed country. They will learn how to assume primary responsibility for patients and how to work within other cultures and with multiple clinicians of different backgrounds.

CONCLUSION

The messages I took from *Ingenious Hidalgo Don Quixote de la Mancha* remain the primary basis for some of the new projects I am involved in. I continue to believe that all players in the spine care arena are honorable and desire to help patients. This includes clinicians of all specialties and professions, the government and private payers of health care, patients, and individual philanthropic organizations. The challenge, at least in the programs in which I am involved, is to implement guidelines into the U.S. system of healthcare, facilitate spine care programs in developing nations through *World Spine Care*, and conduct research to monitor these changes. This has the potential to greatly reduce the discomfort and disability of people with spine pain. It is a large windmill to attack, but one whose rewards to society could be far-reaching.

Appendix A

Genealogy Pedigree Chart

Pedigree Chart

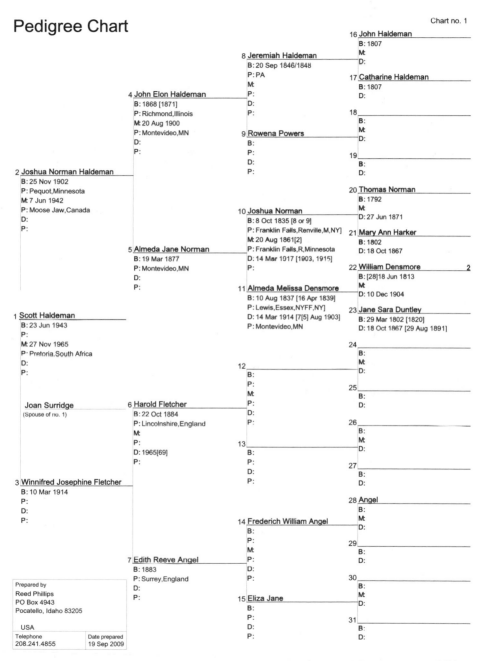

16 John Haldeman
B: 1807
M:
D:

8 Jeremiah Haldeman
B: 20 Sep 1846/1848
P: PA
M:
P:
D:
P:

17 Catharine Haldeman
B: 1807
D:

4 John Elon Haldeman
B: 1868 [1871]
P: Richmond,Illinois
M: 20 Aug 1900
P: Montevideo,MN
D:
P:

18
B:
M:
D:

9 Rowena Powers
B:
P:
D:
P:

19
B:
D:

2 Joshua Norman Haldeman
B: 25 Nov 1902
P: Pequot,Minnesota
M: 7 Jun 1942
P: Moose Jaw,Canada
D:
P:

20 Thomas Norman
B: 1792
M:
D: 27 Jun 1871

10 Joshua Norman
B: 8 Oct 1835 [8 or 9]
P: Franklin Falls,Renville,M,NY]
M: 20 Aug 1861[2]
P: Franklin Falls,R,Minnesota
D: 14 Mar 1917 [1903, 1915]
P:

21 Mary Ann Harker
B: 1802
D: 18 Oct 1867

5 Almeda Jane Norman
B: 19 Mar 1877
P: Montevideo,MN
D:
P:

22 William Densmore   2
B: [28]18 Jun 1813
M:
D: 10 Dec 1904

11 Almeda Melissa Densmore
B: 10 Aug 1837 [16 Apr 1839]
P: Lewis,Essex,NYFF,NY]
D: 14 Mar 1914 [7[5] Aug 1903]
P: Montevideo,MN

23 Jane Sara Duntley
B: 29 Mar 1802 [1820]
D: 18 Oct 1867 [29 Aug 1891]

1 Scott Haldeman
B: 23 Jun 1943
P:
M: 27 Nov 1965
P: Pretoria,South Africa
D:
P:

24
B:
M:
D:

12
B:
P:
M:
P:
D:
P:

25
B:
D:

Joan Surridge
(Spouse of no. 1)

6 Harold Fletcher
B: 22 Oct 1884
P: Lincolnshire,England
M:
P:
D: 1965[69]
P:

26
B:
M:
D:

13
B:
P:
D:
P:

27
B:
D:

3 Winnifred Josephine Fletcher
B: 10 Mar 1914
P:
D:
P:

28 Angel
B:
M:
D:

14 Frederich William Angel
B:
P:
M:
P:
D:
P:

29
B:
D:

7 Edith Reeve Angel
B: 1883
P: Surrey,England
D:
P:

30
B:
M:
D:

15 Eliza Jane
B:
P:
D:
P:

31
B:
D:

Prepared by
Reed Phillips
PO Box 4943
Pocatello, Idaho 83205

USA

Telephone	Date prepared
208.241.4855	19 Sep 2009

Scott Haldeman's Professional Travel and Speaking Schedule 1967–2009

Date	EVENT and Title of Talk or Purpose of Meeting	Location
1967	Annual Cape Chiropractic Congress	Cape Town
	Physiology of the nerves/Joan on the qualifications of a physiotherapist	
1968		
18 Feb	SACA Educational Conference	Pretorious Clinic SA
	Physiology of the nerves	
1971		
Sep	British Columbia Chiropractic Convention	Vancouver
	The Experimental Basis for the Philosophy of Chiropractic	
Nov	26th Annual Convention of the Industrial First Aid Assoc	British Columbia
	Chiropractic and Back Pain	
1972		
Nov	27th Annual Convention of the Industrial First Aid Assoc	British Columbia
	Chiropractic and Back Pain	
1973		
14 May-Jun 8	Association of Straight Chiropractors	Pretoria
	Speaker	
15 Aug	Palmer College Homecoming	Davenport
	Speaker	
1974		
17 Jun	NINDS Planning Meeting	Bethesda
	Committee member	
29 Jul	NINDS Planning Meeting	Bethesda
	Committee member	

Date	EVENT and Title of Talk or Purpose of Meeting	Location
1975		
3-5 Feb	NINCDS Conference	Bethesda, MD
	Status of Spinal Manipulative Therapy	
18 Feb	Vancouver Medical Association	Vancouver
	Chiropractic	
24 Jun	Vancouver General Hospital	Vancouver
	Back Pain Special Interest Group	
15 Jul	Vancouver General Hospital	Vancouver
	Back Pain Special Interest Group	
25-27 Jul	Washington Chiropractic Association	Orcas Is., Washington
	Neurophysiology/ NINCDS Conference	
27-30 Sep	UC Irvine Conference on Manipulation	Irvine
18 Oct	Western States Chiropractic College Commencement	Portland
	Commencement Speaker	
4 Nov	Vancouver General Hospital	Vancouver
	Back Pain Special Interest Group	
1976		
29-31 Jan	Chiropractic Society of Washington	Seattle
	Research, Professionalism and Chiropractic/Somatovisceral Reflexes & Philosophy	
	UCI Faculty of Physical Med	
	Vancouver Medical Society	
	St. Paul's Medical Staff	
25 May	Vancouver Medical Clinic Rounds	Vancouver
	Back Pain Special Interest Group	
5-6 Jun	ICAC Re-Licensure Seminar	Los Angeles
	Current Concepts in Chiro Theory and Practice	

Date	EVENT and Title of Talk or Purpose of Meeting	Location
Sep	65th Annual Wisconsin Chiropractic Association Conv. Speaker	Milwaukee
25 Sep	Oregon Chiropractic Associstion Annual Convention	Portland
4 Aug	Vancouver General Hospital Low Back Pain Special Interest Group	Vancouver
Nov	Alabama Chiropractic Association? License Renewal Seminar	Alabama
30 Nov	Vancouver General Hospital Back Pain Special Interest Group	Vancouver
1-2 Dec	Pneumoconiosis Conf	Pennsylvania
1977		
22-23 Jan	ICAC-Relicensure Seminar Current Concepts in Chiro Theory and Principles	Los Angeles
22-23 Feb	ICAC-Relicensure Seminar Current Concepts in Chiro Theory and Principles	Sacramento
Mar	Parker Seminar	Lubbock, TX
21-23 Apr	UBC Seminar on Low Back Pain Spinal Manipulation	Vancouver
Jun	?	Seattle
13-17 Jul	Parker Seminar	Los Angeles
22-23 Oct	Spinal Research Symposium Importance of Research/Aberant Flexion Atlanto-Occipital Subluxation	Troy, MI
23-26 Oct	Conf. Neurobiological Mechanisms of Spinal Manip. Clinical Observations and Emerging Questions	U of Michigan
28-31 Oct	Australian Chiropractic Association	Gold Coast, Queenslnd

Date	EVENT and Title of Talk or Purpose of Meeting	Location
18-19 Nov	Chiropractic Research Commission	Bloomington, MN
	The following are from a summary invoice	
	Tokyo, Birmingham,AL, Salt Lake City, Denver,	
	Hartford, Pittsburgh, Montreal, Toronto	
1978		
Feb	COCSA?	Denver
	?	
17-18 Mar	Chiropractic ResearchCommission	Houston
	Oversight and comments regarding the CRC	
13-15 Apr	University of Saskatchewan Hospital	Saskatoon
	SMT and LBP/Neurophysiology of Neck Pain/Somatovisceral Reflexes	
24-29 Apr	American Academy of Neurology	Los Angeles
	Attendee	
May	New Zealand Royal Commission of Inquiry	New Zealand
	Presentation	
6-7 May	Florida Chiropractic Society	Orlando
7 Jun	Australian Chiropractic Association	
8 Jun	Canadian Chiropractic Association	Quebec
	Neurophysiology of Back Pain	
21 June	ACA Annual Convention	New Orleans
	Report to the House of Delegates as their Research Consultant	
9-10 Sep	ICAC Re-Licensure Seminar	Los Angeles
	Neurophysiology of Back Pain	

471

Date	EVENT and Title of Talk or Purpose of Meeting	Location
Sep	American Academy of Manipulative Medicine	Dearborn, MI
8-9 Sep	Chiropractic ResearchCommission	Vancouver
21-24 Sep	British Columbia Chiropractic Associatin	
1 Oct	LACC Students	Glendale
4-5 Nov	LACC License Renewal Seminar	Glendale
	Neurophsiologic Approach to Low Back Pain	
1979		
23-25 Feb	Anaheim Research Conference	Anaheim
	Modern Developments in the Principles & Practice of Chiropractic	
22 Mar	LACC	Glendale
	Update on ICA Research Symposium, Workshop on Neurological Exam	
Apr	American Academy of Neurology	Chicago
May	CMCC Alumni Convention	British Columbia
	Presenter	
17 May	Bay Area Chiropractic Research Society	Oakland
	Neurophysiology Research	
June	California Chiropractic Association	Monterey
	Spinal Pain, Manipulative Research	
8-9 Jun	Western Canada Chiropractic Convention	Saskatoon
	The Need for a Scientific Approach, Res. USA	
9 Jun	University of Saskatchewan Hospital	Saskatoon
	Electrodiagnosis	
June	Texas Chiropractic Association	
	Presenter	
2 Jul-29 Aug	Round the World Trip with Joan and Kids	
	London, Johannesburg, Sydney, Aukland	

Date	EVENT and Title of Talk or Purpose of Meeting	Location
27-29 Jul	Foundation for the Advancement of Chiropractic Eesearch	Cumberland, WI
	The Importance of Research in the Principles and Practice of Chiropractic	
21-23 Sep	Colorado Chiropractic Fall Convention	Denver
	Pain Mechanisms	
24 Oct	NAAMM	Calgary
	Executive Council	
3-4 Nov	Minnesota Chiropractic Association	Minneapolis
9-2? Dec	New Zealand Commission on Inquiry	New Zealand
16 Dec	LACC Commencement Program	Los Angeles
	Greetings, Presentation of Candidates, Farewell	
1980		
10 Jan	Kaiser Foundation Hospital	San Diego
	Neurophysiology of spinal Pain/What is Manipulation	
22 Jan	Verdugo Hills Chiropractic Society	Verdugo Hills, CA
	Chiropractic Research	
19 Feb	Southwest LA Chiropractic Society	Los Angeles
21 Mar	Western States Chiropractic College Commencement	Portland
	Commencement Speaker	
	American Academy of Neurology	New Orleans
25-28 May	ISSLS	New Orleans
	The Electrodiagnostic Evaluation of Spinal Cord Function	
1 Jun	Neurology Conference	Los Angeles
	Spinal Neurology Part II	
8 Jun	Neurology Conference	San Francisco
	Spinal Neurology Part II	
Jun	California Chiropractic Convention	San Diego

Date	EVENT and Title of Talk or Purpose of Meeting	Location
14 Jun	Logan College Homecoming Spinal Neurology	St. Louis
24 Jun	Fund Raiser for Reseaerch	Pasadena
21-27 Jun	Pettibon Conference on Spinal Bio-MechanicsXXXX The Significance of Biomechanics in Spinal Neurology (Withdrew from Conf)	Portland
Jul		South Africa/New Zealand
12-13 Jul	Australian Chiropractic Association/PIT Spinal Neurology	Sydney
29 Aug	Pasadea College of Chiropractic Student lecture	Pasadena
8-10 Sep	Micigan State University Manual Medicine for German Physicians	Lansing
13 Sep	Northern California College of Chiropractic	Sunnyvale, CA
Sep	Ontario Chiropractic Assoc.	Toronto
Sep	British Pain Society	London
Sep	AECC	London
Sep	Wisconsin Chiropractic Associaton	Lake Lawn Lodge
3-5 Oct	Haldeman Interprofessional Conference on the Spine Neurological Examination of the Spine/Spinal Manipulative Therapy	Las Vegas
15-18 Oct	NAAMM Executive Council, Annual Mtg	Sanibel Is., FL

Date	EVENT and Title of Talk or Purpose of Meeting	Location
1981		
5 Jan	Palmer Faculty Workshop	Davenport
	Presenter	
17-18 Jan	Western States Chiropractic College	Portland
	Spinal Neurology Seminar	
13-15 Feb	Haldeman Interprofessional Conf on the Spine/ICA/Cleveland	Los Angeles
	Theoretical Mechanisms Where Manipulations May Cause Non-Spinal Symptoms	
22 Feb-1 Mar	Scandinavia, Denmark, Norway, Sweden	Oslo
	Norwegian Commission of Inquiry/Scandinavian Chiro Conv	
7 Mar	NAAMM	Chicago
	Executive Council	
15 Mar	California Medical Association	Los Angeles
	Spinal Manipulative Therapy, Joan on program	
9 Apr	Holistic Health Association	
21 Apr	American Board of Psychiatry and Neurology	Toronto
	Board Exam Part I	
25-26 Apr	CMCC Homecoming?	Toronto
	Cervical Syndromes	
27 Apr-2 May	American Academy of Neurology	Paris
	Pudendal Somatoesory Evoked Responses	
16-23 May	ISSLS	Los Angeles
	Electrodiagnostic Evaluation of Sacral Nerve Function/Symposium on Manipulation	
5 Jun	UCLA/Harbor Orthopedic Alumni Day	Long Beach
	Manipulative Medicine	
6 Jun	Long Beach Area Multiple Sclerosis Patient Group	Lake Tahoe
	Bladder, Bowel and Sexual Dysfunction	
24-27 June	American Medical Electroencephalographic Assoc.	Lake Tahoe
	Participant	
28 June	American Board of Electroencephalography	
	Board Exam	

475

Date	EVENT and Title of Talk or Purpose of Meeting	Location
30-31 Jul	Southwest Regional Medical Education/VA Applications of Evoked Potentials in Clinical Medicine	Wadsworth, CA
3 Sep	UCLA/Pain Mgt Ctr Spinal Manipulative Therapy in Modern Medicine	Los Angeles
9-11 Sep	Royal College of Physicians and Surgeons Canada Written Exams	Vancouver
19 Sep	5th International Conf on Human Functioning, U KS Neurophysiology of spinal pain and manipulation	Wichita
9 Oct	American Board in Qualification in Electroenchpalography Board Exam Part I	Westwood
23-25 Oct	California Chiropractic Association/Chiropractic 81 Pre Manipulation Neurological Exam	Anaheim
7-8 Nov	UC San Francisco Clinical Application of Evoked Potentials	San Francisco
11-14 Nov	North American Academy of Manipulative Medicine Elected President for next year/Electrodiagnosis of Sacral Nerve Function/Complications of Cervical Manipulation	San Antonio
2 Dec	Royal College of Physicians and Surgeons Canada Oral Exams	Toronto
1982		
15 Feb	American Physical Therapy Association Current Status of Spinal Manipulative Therapy	San Diego
6 Mar	NAAMM Executive Committee/Chair	Chicago
1-4 Apr	American Medical Electroencephalographic Assoc Attendee	Santa Fe, NM
25 Apr-1 May	American Academy of Neurology Clinical Electromyography	Washington
17-21 May	Hour Magazine - KTLA Back Problems–It's a Real Pain	Los Angeles

Date	EVENT and Title of Talk or Purpose of Meeting	Location
6-10 June	ISSLS The Importance of Electro-diagnostice Tests in the DX of Nerve Root Dysfunction	Toronto
7 Jun	TV Ontario Television Interview	Toronto
12 Jun	Palmer West College of Chiropractic Commencement Symp Speaker	Sunnyvale St. Thomas
1-4 Apr	Annual Mtg American Medical Electroencephalographic A. Evoked Potentials From Lower Extremities and Plevic Organs	Santa Fe, NM
9 Apr	American Board in Qualification in Electroencephalography Board Exam Part I	Santa Fe, NM
18-20 Apr	American Board of Psychiatry and Neurology Board Exam Part II	Seattle
6-10 Jun	ISSLS The Importance of Electro-diagnostic Tests in the DX of Nerve Root Dysfunction	Toronto
15 Jul	USC Dept Orthopedics Electrodiagnosis of Spinal Disorders	Los Angeles
9-11 Sep	UBC Low Back Pain Conf Manipulative Techniques	Vancouver
15 Sep	Orange County Chiropractic Society Vertebral Artery Occlusion	Orange County
27 Sep?	CMCC 4th year students/Ontario Chiropractic Association Neurologic Causes of Bowel. Bladder and Sexual Dysfunction	Toronto
29 Sep-2 Oct	NASS Manipulative Techniques	Ontario
5-9 Oct	British Back Pain Society/Colt Fdt Internatioinal Symposim Spinal Manipulation	London
10 Oct	AECC Electrodiagnosis of Spinal Nerve Function	Bournmoth
8-10 Nov	State of Science in EEG - 1982 Participant	Phoenix?

Date	EVENT and Title of Talk or Purpose of Meeting	Location
10-13 Nov	Annual Mtg American Electroencephalographic Society	Phoenix
	Participant	
14 Nov	American Board in Qualification in Electroencephalography	Phoenix
	Board Exam Part II (Oral Exam)	
18 Nov	Orange County Neurological Society	Orange County
	Pudendal Evoked Response	
29 Nov-1 Dec	Harvard Medical School	Boston
	Manipulation of the Lumbar Spine/Manipulation Techniques	
8-10 Dec	Challenge of the Lumbar Spine	San Francisco
	Electrodiagnostic Tests/Overview of Schools of Manipulation/Manipulation Tech.	
1983		
12-13 Feb	Personal Injury Seminar	Orlando
	Examination and Evaluation of Traumatic Injuries with Utilization of Med. Specialty	
19-11 Feb	Palmer College Facutly Workshop	Davenport
	Presenter	
12 Mar	California Chiropractic Association	Sacramento
	Evaluating Neurological Deficit	
19 Mar	North American Academy of Manipulative Medicine	Chicago
	Executive Committee	
5-9 Apr	ISSLS	Cambridge, Eng
	Electrodiagnosis of Nerve Root Dysfunction	
16 Apr	LACC Commencement	Anaheim
	Speaker	
24-27 Apr	American Academy of Neurology	San Diego
	Poster/Paper:Evoked Response Testing in Neuro-Urology	
30 Apr	American Board in Qualification in Electroencephalography	San Diego
	Board Exam Part II (Oral Exam)	
18 May	White Memorial Medical Ctr - Resident's Conf	Los Angeles
	Rationale for Manipulation	
21 May	Santa Monica Hospital Med. Ctr	Santa Monica
	Spinal Manipulation	

Date	EVENT and Title of Talk or Purpose of Meeting	Location
8-12 Jun	American Medical EMG Society	Orlando
	The Use of Pudendal Somatosensory Evoked Potentials in the DX of Sexual Dysfunc.	
22-26 Jun	2nd National Industrial Back Pain Symposium	Greenbrier, West VA
	Spinal Manipulative Therapy/Electrodiagnostic Evaluation of Spinal Disorders	
7-11 Sep	International Federation of Manipulative Medicine	Zurich
	Electrodiagnostic Testing of Spinal Disorders/Workshop on Standards & Terms	
Oct	ACA Council on Technique "Conference on Fundamentals	
	Presenter	
1-2 Oct	International Chiropractors Association of CA	Torrance
	Scientific Basis for Spinal Manipulation	
13 Oct	Harbor-UCLA Medical Ctr	Los Angeles
	Current Status of Clinical Research in Spinal Manipulative Therapy	
19-20 Oct	North American Academy of Manipulative Medicine	Alexandria, VA
	Current Status of Clinical Research in Spinal Manipulative Therapy	
27 Oct	Orange County Neurological Society	Orange
	Attendee	
27 Oct	Aetna Commercial Insurance Division	Orange
	Evolution of Treatment Procedures in Low Back Pain	
5 Nov	Tri County Orthopedic Surgeons & Stark County Hospital	Stark County, OH
	Neurological Explanation of Low Back Pain	
9 Nov	Workers' Compensation Claims Association	Burbank, CA
	The Role of Neurology in Workers' Compensation	
13-14 Nov	Harvard Medical School	Boston
	Spinal Manipulative Therapy in the Management of Low Back Pain	
12-15 Dec	Challenge of the Lumbar Spine	San Antonio
	Electrodiagnosis of Lumbosacral radiculopathy/Manipulation	

Date	EVENT and Title of Talk or Purpose of Meeting	Location
1984		
14 Feb	Orange County Neurological Society / Attendee	Orange
10 Mar	Personal Injury Symposium / Efficacy of Spinal Manipulation/Explanation oand Significance of Diagnostic Tests	Orlando
29-31 Mar	American Society for Evoked Response Society Annual Mtg / Pudendal Evoked Responses	Washington, DC
7-8 Apr	Palmer West Chiropractic College/Conf on Back Pain / Neurophysiology of Spinal Pain Syndrome/ EMG: A Diagnostic Tool	San Jose
10-11 Apr	American Academy of Neurology / Poster: Dissociatoin Between Posterior Tibial and Pudendal Somatosensory Evoked	Boston
24 Apr	Orange County Neurological Society / Attendee	Orange
25 Apr	UCI Dept of Orthopedic Surgery / Grand Rounds	Orange
8 May	Orange County Neurological Society / Evaluation of Low Back Pain	Orange
9 May	UCI Dept Neurology / Controversies in Low Back Pain	Orange
17 May	Industrial Indemnity / Evolution of Treatment Procedures for Low Back Pain	Orange
18 May	Pain Mgt Panel of RACC / Organizational Meeting	San Francisco
22 May	CMA Committee on Health / Discussion on Chiropractic	Orange
22 May	Orange County Pain Society / Organizational Meeting	Montreal
6-7 Jun	ISSLS / A Prospective Study of 2000 Patients Attending a Chiropractic College Clinic	Vail
26-29 Jul	NASS / Moderator/Evaluation of Bowel Motility, Bladder Dysfunction in Spinal Injury	

Date	EVENT and Title of Talk or Purpose of Meeting	Location
Aug	Claims Administration System Inc. Electrodiagnosis in Back Pain	Stanton, CA
6-7 Sep	Back Pain Monitor Pain: Practical Management Strategies for the 80s/Neurophysiology of Pain/SMT	Atlanta
20 Sep	Orange County Pain Society Attendee	Orange
28-29 Sep	U of Iowa College of Medicine Low Back Pain: A Course for Primary Care Physicians	Iowa City
22 Oct	CMA Committee on Health Discussion on Chiropractic	Los Angeles
23 Oct	Orange County Neurological Society Attendee	Orange
13 Nov	Orange County Neurological Society Attendee	Orange
15-17 Nov	North American Academy of Manipulative Med Updae on Research/Therapeutics of Lumbar Problems	San Diego
26-28 Nov	Harvard Med School Low Back Seminar Evoked Potentials/Techniques on Manipulation	Boston
30 Nov-2 Dec	Challenge of the Lumbar Spine A Scientific Basis for spinal Manipulation	New Orleans
4 Dec	Orange County Neurological Society Attendee	Orange
18 Dec	Orange County Worker's Compensation Bar Speaker	Orange
1985		
8 Jan	Orange County Neurological Society Attendee	Orange
26-28 Jan	UCI 8th Annual Workshop On Evoked Potentials Pudendal Evoked Potentials	Irvine
7 Feb	Orange County Pain Society Attendee	Orange

Date	EVENT and Title of Talk or Purpose of Meeting	Location
9 Feb	St. Joseph Hospital - Physical Rehab Dept Manipulative Therapy/Flexion vs. Extension Exercises	Orange
19 Feb	Orange County Neurological Society Attendee	Orange
22 Feb	Western Neurological Hospital Rehabilitation Nurses Post-Concussive Syndroms	Orange
1-28 Feb (3 days/wk)	UCI Neurology Dept Ward Rounds	Orange
8 Mar	General Telephone Head Injuries	Santa Monica
15-17 Mar	British Columbia Chiropractic Assoc Low Back Symposium-Chr/ Back Pain in Society/Spinal Pain Syndrome/ Overview	Vancouver
29 Mar	Fireman's Fund Adjuster's Mtg Manipulation, chiropractors, electrodiagnosis, NMR	Tustin
2 Apr	LACC site visit by CMA Committee on Health Evaluation of Facilities.	Whittier
14-20 Apr	ISSLS Attendee	Sydney
3-5May	WSCC Homecoming Cervical Spine Pain Syndrome - Diagnosis and Treatment	Portland
9 May	Orange County Pain Society Attendee	Orange
16 May	Los Angeles College of Chiropractic Lecture	Whittier
30 May	San Bernadino Med Ctr - Grand Rounds Manipulative Therapy in the Outpatient Setting.	San Bernardino
30 May	Los Angeles College of Chiropractic Lecture	Whittier

Date	EVENT and Title of Talk or Purpose of Meeting	Location
1-2 Jun	4th International Conf on LBP @ CMCC / Clinical Evaluation of Neurovisceral Function	Toronto
20 Jun	Los Angeles College of Chiropractic / Lecture	Whittier
27 Jun	Orange Co. Worker's Comp Carriers & Defense Counsel / Low Back Pain - A Real Pathology or A Doctor's Bonanza	Santa Ana
24-27 Jul	2nd Annual North American Lumbar Spine Association / Comprehensive Eval of Lumbar Neurological Lesions Utilizing EMG	Laguna Niguel
16-18 Aug	Washington Chiropractic Association / Neurology and Chiropractic	Coeur d' Alene, ID
18 Sep	Northwestern College of Chiropractic / All Student Convocation	Minneapolis
19-21 Sep	7th Annual Challenge of the Lumbar Spine / Thermography for Musculoskeletal Disorders/Workshop on Manipulation	Minneapolis
27 Sep	Cedars-Sinai Med Center - Pain and Ethics in the Emerg Dpt / Back Pain	Los Angeles
4 Oct	ABS One Day Symposium on Back Pain (failed to attend) / Spinal Manipulation, Conservative Treatment of Spinal Pain	San Francisco
5 Oct	ABS Committee on Manipulative Medicine / Chair of Committee	San Francisco
12-17 Oct	International Seminar for Manual Medicine (to ill to attend) / Attendee	Baden-Baden, W. Ger
1-3 Nov	Nordisk Spesialgruppe for Manuell Terapi / Scientific Basis for Manipulation/Various Theories of SMT	Oslo
4-8 Nov	1st International Congress on Low Back Pain / Objections to Conservative TX/Clinical Neuroanatomy/Future Back Pain Research	Vienna
Dec	Personal	South Africa

Date	EVENT and Title of Talk or Purpose of Meeting	Location
1986		
24-26 Jan	UC Irvine/Dept Neurology Evoked Potential, EEG Wrkshp Pudendal Evoked Responses-Techniques and Applications	UCI
Mar	Ward Rounds UCI 2nd and 4th Wednesday 8-9 AM Attending Neurologist	Irvine
27 Apr-3 May	American Academy of Neurology Participant?	New Orleans
9-10 May	American Back Society Symposium on Back Pain Instructor/ Manipulation of the Spine	Anaheim
13 May	Orange County Neurological Society Attendee	Orange, CA
15 May	CMA Committee on Health Discussion on Chiropractic	Los Angles
28 May-2 Jun	ISSLS CT, Electrodiagnostic and Clinical Findings in Chronic Workers' Comp Patients	Dallas
20 Jul	NASS Executive Comm Attendee	Boston Landing, NY
20-23 Jul	NASS Interaoperative Use of Dermatomal Somatosensory Evoked Potentials	Boston Landing, NY
8-9 Aug	UBC Class of 76 Reunion Attendee	Vancouver
17-22 Aug	7th AOA Symposium - Frontiers in Low Back Pain Electrodiagnosis of Spinal Neurologic Lesions/Spinal Manip Thrpy	Chicago
29 Aug-Sep 1	Association for Holistic Health Annual Conference Modern Treatment of Back Disorders	San Francisco
17-20 Sep	North American Academy of Manipulative Medicine Complications of Manipulation	Philidelphia
2-4 Oct	Worker's Comp Board of British Columbia and UBC The Role of Manipulation, EMG's are they Helpful	Vancouver
6-8 Oct	Rocky Mountain Ctr for Occupational and Environmental Electrodiagnosis of Spinal Neurologic Lesions/Spinal Manip Thrpy	Salt Lake City

Date	EVENT and Title of Talk or Purpose of Meeting	Location
6-9 Nov	Challenge of the Lumbar Spine	San Francisco
	Problems Facing the Spine Specialist/ Overtreatment/ Electrodiagnosis	
4-6 Dec	American Back Society Symposium on Back Pain	San Francisco
	Spinal Manipulations Therapy in Sports Medicine	
19 Dec	Palmer West College of Chiropractic Commencement	Sunnyvale
	Commencement Speaker	
1987		
20 Jan	NASS Ex. Comm	San Francisco
	Western Regional Representative	
7 Feb	NASS Ex. Comm	Atlanta
	Scott is VP	
11-16 Feb	Alaska Worker's Comp	Anchorage
	IME's	
7-9 Apr	American Academy of Neurology 39th Annual Mtg	New York City
29 Apr-2 May	American Back Society	Anaheim
	Short Term Trial of Chiropractic Adjustments for the Relief of CLBP	
2-28 May	ISSLS	Rome
	Impairment and Disability Rating of Patients with Low Back Pain	
6-7 Jun	LACC First Interdisciplinary Symposium	Whittier
	Research Challenges Facing Manipulative Therapy	
25 Jun	CHART	Banff
	Medical Advisory Board	
25 Jun	NASS Ex. Comm	Banff
	Executive Committee	
25 -28 Jun	NASS 2nd Annual Meeting	Banff
	The Correlation Between CT Scanning, Electrodiagnostic Studies & Clinical Findings	
21-23 Aug	Brisbane Spinal Study Group	Brisbane
	Speaking on Manipulation and Electordiagnosis of Spine Problems	
8 Sep	Orange County Neurological Society	Orange, CA
	Meeting and Dinner	

Date	EVENT and Title of Talk or Purpose of Meeting	Location
24-26 Sep	ICC Conference	London
	Clinical Neurophysiology and Neuropathology of the Spinal Motor Unit	
28-30 Sep	7th Annual Occupational Low Back Pain Conf	Louisville
	Problems with Disability Ratings/Electrodiagnostic Studies/Manipulation	
7-10 Oct	Challenge of the Lumbar Spine	New York City
	Soft Tissue Technique/Diagnostic Panel	
28-31 Oct	North American Academy of Manipulative Medicine	Las Vegas
	The Role of Manipulation in Sports Medicine	
18-22 Nov	CHART	Napa Valley, CA
	Medical Advisory Board	
2-5 Dec	ABS Fall Symposium on Back Pain	San Francisco
	Electrodiagnostic Studies/ Objective of Conservative Management of Back Pain	
7 Dec	Orange County Pain Society	Orange, CA
	Meeting and Dinner	
1988		
29 Jan	CA Work Comp Low Back Disability Workshop	Los Angeles
7 Feb	NASS Ex Comm/Membership Comm	Atlanta
	Scott Chaired the Membership Comm. Reed Phillips was applying	
19 Feb	Orange County Medical Society	Orange, CA
	Valid Measurements of Disability	
18 Mar	CA Work Comp Low Back Disability Workshop	San Francisco
26 Mar	Washington Chiropractic Advisory Committee	Seattle
	Validation of Chiropractic Necessity by Neurologic Methods	
9-10 Apr	ICA Hospital Privileges	Los Angeles
	Presenter	
13-17 Apr	ISSLS	Miami
	Attended	

Date	EVENT and Title of Talk or Purpose of Meeting	Location
17-23 Apr	American Academy of Neurology Not sure he attended?	Cincinnati
4-6 May	2nd European Congress on Back Pain Manipulation and Acute Back Pain	Montreux, Switzerland
12-14 May	American Back Society CT, Electrodiagnostic and Clinical Findings in Chronic Work Comp Pts	Orlando
31 May	Orange County Neurological Society Meeting and Dinner	Orange, CA
21 Jun	Orange County Neurological Society Meeting and Dinner	Orange, CA
24-27 Jun	NASS Ex Comm/3rd Annual Meeting Vice President	Colorado Springs
15-17 Jul	ICA Annual Convention How to make DC-MD Relations Work in the Future	Monterey, CA
24 Jul	NASS Executive Committee Scott reports on his role as liaison with Am. Academy of Neurology	Colorado Springs
17-19 Aug	North American Academy of Musculoskeletal Med.	Quebec City
15-17 Sep	Industrial Musculoskeletal Health:Sports Med Manipulation/ Mgt of Disabled Workers/ CA system of Impairment Rating	Dallas
30 Sep-2 Oct	Physical Medicine Research Foundation Conservative Management of Low Back Pain	Toronto
16-19 Oct	Occupational Low Back Pain Conference Back Impairment Rating/Electrodiagnostic Studies/ Manipulation Theory	Hilton Head, SC
8 Nov	Orange County Neurological Society Meeting and Dinner	Orange, CA
9-13 Nov	Challenge of the Lumbar Spine 99 Non-specific LBP Panel/Disability Rating Panel	San Antonio, TX
30 Nov	ABS Board of Directors Director	San Francisco
1-3 Dec	ABS Fall Symposium on Back Pain Clinical Spinal NeuralAnatomy and Physiology	San Francisco

Date	EVENT and Title of Talk or Purpose of Meeting	Location
1989		
11 Feb	NASS Executive Committee	Las Vegas
	President	
16-19 Feb	Sociedad Cientifico Quiropractica de Mexico	Mexico City
	Conservative Tx of the Spinal Column/Electrodiagnosis of the Spine	
3-8 Mar	CMA Western Scientific Assembly - Lumbago	Anaheim
	Conservative Tx: Objectives, Choices, Results	
11 Apr	Palmer College of Chiropractic	Davenport
	Scientific Research into the Principles and Practice of Chiropractic	
12 Apr	ABS Board of Directors	Cambridge, MA
	Board of Directors	
13-15 Apr	ABS Spring Symposium on Back Pain	Cambridge, MA
	Clinical Neurophysiological Evaluation of the Spine	
3-6 May	9th Annual Conf on Evoked Potentials	San Francisco
	Evoked Responses in Clinical Neuro-Urology	
15-19 May	ISSLS	Kyoto, Japan
	Participant	
29 Jun	NASS Executive Committee	Quebec
	President	
30 Jun-2 Jul	NASS 4th Annual Metting	Quebec
	President	
2 Jul	NASS Executive Committee	Quebec
	President	
19-20 Aug	ACA "Think Tank" Session for Long Range Planning	Chicago
	Participant	
12-16 Sep	1st Annual Multidisciplinary Symposium-Cervical Spine	Long Island
	Master of Ceremonies/Defining Spinal Manipulation/Complications of Cervical Ma.	
16-18 Sep	International Rheumatologic Mtg	Rio de Janeiro
	Physiotherapy and Manipulation in the Management of Back Pain	
24-26 Sep	Congresso Internacional Sobre Coluna Vertebral	Sao Paulo
	Physiotherapy and Manipulation in the Management of Back Pain	

Date	EVENT and Title of Talk or Purpose of Meeting	Location
18-21 Oct	10th Annual Occupational Low Back Pain Conf Course Chair/Acute vs Chronic Pain/Electrodiagnosis/Rating Systems/Manipulation	Long Beach
2-5 Nov	Challenge of the Lumbar Spine Differential Diagnosis of Low Back Pain/Social and Legal Aspects	San Francisco
30 Nov-3 Dec	ABS Fall Symposium on Back Pain Board of Directors/Complications of Cervical Spine Manipulation/Low Back Pain	Las Vegas
1990		
2-4 Feb	UCI Dept Neurology 13th Annual Evoked Potential Wrkshp Bladder and Genital SEPs	Costa Mesa
8-13 Feb	AOA 57th Annual Meeting Attendee	New Orleans
12 Feb	NASS Executive Committee Member & Liaison with American Academy of Neurology	New Orleans
25 Feb-3 Mar	MPI Advanced Seminar Malpractice, Research, Conservative Approaches	Maui
15 Mar	Workers' Comp Seminar on Orthopedic Injuries Electrodiagnostic Studies in Orthopedic Injuries	Santa Ana
16-17 Mar	U of Colorado Back Pain in the Nineties Scope of Back Pain Problems	Denver
22-23 Mar	UCI Dept Neurology A Wester View of Multiple Sclerosis? Attendee	Irvine
1 Apr	Orange County Chiropractic Society Diagnosis and Primary Care for the Chiropractic Professional	Orange County
20 Apr	RAND Corporation Consensus Panel Member	Santa Monica
21 Apr	Chiropractic Quality Assurance Conference Organizing Committee Mtg	Santa Monica
3-6 May	ABS Spring Symposium on Back Pain	Chicago
6-9 Jun	ACA Convention Philosophy and the Future of Chiropractic	Anchorage

Date	EVENT and Title of Talk or Purpose of Meeting	Location
13-17 Jun	ISSLS	Boston
	Prospective RCT of Manipulation, Corset, Massage and Transcutaneous Muscle Stim	
8 Aug	NASS Executive Committee	Monterey
	Conservatice Care Comm. Chr	
8-11 Aug	NASS 5th Annual Meeting	Monterey
	Prospective Short and Long Term Comparative Trial of Medical and Chiro Care?	
14-16 Sep	American Academy of Pain Mgt	Stockton
	Spinal Manipulation	
25 Aug	San Diego Chiropractic Society	San Diego
	Speaker	
20 Oct	Washington State Dept of Labor and Industries	Seattle
	Continuing Ed Symposium for Chiropractors and Consultants	
18-21 Oct	Palmer College of Chiropractic West Homecoming	San Jose
	Failure of the Medical Pathology Model to Explain Back Pain	
29-30 Oct	U of Michigan 11th Annual Low Back Pain Conference	Ypsilanti, MI
	Acute and Chronic Low Back Pain Impairment Rating Systems	
8-10 Nov	North American Academy of Musculoskeletal Medicine	Tucson
	Failure of the Medical Pathology Model to Explain Back Pain	
6-9 Dec	ABS Fall Symposium on Back Pain	San Francisco
	What Can We Expect from the Next Decade in the Mgt. of Back Pain	
9 Dec	NYCC Commencement	Long Island
	Commencement Speaker	
1991		
6-12 Jan	Osler Institute-Neurology & Neurosurgical Review Course	Los Angeles
	Electrodiagnosis of Spinal Disorders/Low Back Pain	
26-27 Jan	Mercy Conference Planning Mtg	Los Angeles
	Chair	
1 Feb	Therapeutics & Technology Assessment Subcommittee?	Chicago
	Assessment of Techniques Associated with the Diagnosis and Mgt of Sleep Disorder	

Date	EVENT and Title of Talk or Purpose of Meeting	Location
8-12 Mar	AOA Annual Mtg Indications and Results for Manipulative Treatment of Low Back Pain	Anaheim
11 Mar	NASS Executive Committee Conservative Care Comm Chr	Anaheim
25 Mar	Reliance Insurance Company Medical Coordination of Workers' Comp Claims/Dx Testing and Pain Mgt	Irvine
1 May	ABS Board of Directors Board Member	Toronto
1-5 May	ABS Spring Symposium on Back Pain Clinical Evaluation of Patients with Neurovisceral Disorders/Counsultation Clinic	Toronto
2-5 May	World Federation of Chiropractic Congress Chair/Evolution and Importance of Spinal and Chiropractic Research	Toronto
12-16 May	ISSLS Functional and Palpatory Examination/ Panel on Conservative Care	Heidelberg
6-9 Jun	Back Pain: Current Concepts & Recent Advances Neurophysiological Basis for Back Pain/Neurophysiological Assessment/Manipulat.	Sydney
31 Jul	NASS Executive Committee Conservative Care Comm. Chr	Keystone, CO
31 Jul-3 Aug	NASS 6th Annual Mtg Blue Collar Worker with Disabling Lumbar Disc Disease - Blue Ribbon Panel	Keystone, CO
22-24 Sep	Occupational Spinal Disorders: Prevention, Dx, Tx PRIDE Pain/Conservative Treatment Options/California Disability Evaluations	Chicago
27-28 Sep	Workers' Comp Advisor How to Wrtie a Winning Report	San Diego
27-29 Sep	Physical Med Research Fdt Manipulation/Failure of the Pathology Model to Predict Back Pain	Toronto
27-28 Sep	American Association of Electrodiagnostic Med? Attendee	Vancouver
18-19 Oct	Workers' Comp Advisor How to Wrtie a Winning Report/Apportionment in Physical Disabilities	Los Angeles

Date	EVENT and Title of Talk or Purpose of Meeting	Location
25-26 Oct	Workers' Comp Advisor? How to Wrtie a Winning Report	San Francisco
1-2 Nov	NCMIC Legal Counsel Seminar CVA/ Lumbar Case Studies	San Diego
8-9 Nov	NCMIC Legal Counsel Seminar CVA/ Lumbar Case Studies	Tampa
9-10 Nov	AHCPR Low Back Pain Guidelines Create Back Pain Guidelines for Treatment	Denver
14-15 Nov	Scientific Chiropractic Symposium The Evolution of Chiropractic: A Personal Perspective	Calgary
11 Dec	ABS Executive Committee Board Member	San Francisco
11-15 Dec	ABS Fall Symposium on Back Pain Current Status of Functional and Palpatory Evaluation of the Spine/Moderator	San Francisco
15 Dec	Peace Officer Standards and Training Neck/Spine Panel	San Diego
1992		
19 Jan	Peace Officer Standards and Training? Was not able to attend.	San Francisco
25-30 Jan	Mercy Conference Chaired and Moderated the Meeting	Burlingame
22 Feb	National Back Injury Network Advisory Comm Panel Member	Washington, DC
24 Feb	NASS Executive Committee Report on Public Relations	Washington, DC
24-27 Feb	Occupational Ergonomics Conservative Mgt LBP/Failure of Pathology to Explain Low Back Pain	San Diego
27-1 Feb/Mar	British Columbia/CMCC Alumni Mtg Failure of Pathology to Explain LBP/Practical Applications of Spinal Pain Physiology	Vancouver

Date	EVENT and Title of Talk or Purpose of Meeting	Location
13-18 Mar	California Medical Assoc. Scientific Assembly Role of Chiropractic Manipulation/Role of Electrical Studies in Eval of Surgical Pts.	Anaheim
21 Mar	Cal State Northridge Sports Medicine Seminar Evaluation of Indications and Effectiveness of Spinal Manipulation	Northridge, CA
3-5 Apr	NFL Physician's Society The Role of Manipulation and Mobilization	San Francisco
29-30 Apr	House Armed Services Subcommittee Statement on Chiropractic	Washington, DC
3-9 May	American Academy of Neurology	San Diego
18-20 May	AHCPR Low Back Pain Guidelines Create Back Pain Guidelines for Treatment	Chicago
20-24 May	ISSLS Paraspinal Muscle Evoked Cerebral Potentials in Muscle Spasm/Dr. Y. Zhu	Chicago
27-31 May	Canadian Chiropractic Association Neurological Assessment	Regina, Saskatchewan
1-5 Jun	International Federation of Ortho. Manipulative Therp Chiropractic Research-Past and Present/Chiropractic-Let's Cooperate	Vail
7 Jul	NASS Executive Committee Report on Public Relations	Boston
9-11 Jul	NASS 7th Annual Meeting Measurement of Magnetic Evoked Somatosensory Cortical Potentials…	Boston
16-18 Sep	AHCPR Low Back Pain Guidelines Panel Member	Washington, DC
28-30 Sep	Value Health-Laminectomy/Fusion Panel Member	Santa Monica
1-3 Oct	Occupatonal Spinal disorders Classification and Diagnostic Testing for Low Back Pain	Dallas
16 Oct	Palmer Graduation Commencement Speaker	Davenport

493

Date	EVENT and Title of Talk or Purpose of Meeting	Location
24-25 Oct	Puerto Rico Chiropractic Association	Puerto Rico
	Etiology of Back Pain/Spinal Neuroanatomy/Modern Diagnostic Techniques…	
5-7 Dec	AHCPR Low Back Pain Guidelines	Denver
	Panel Member	
9-12 Dec	American Back Society	San Francisco
	Moderator/Taking an Effective Work Injury History	
1993		
22 Feb	Occupational Ergonomics	San Diego
	Failure of Pathology to Explain Low Back Pain/ Conservative Mgt of LBP	
6 Mar	Los Angeles College of Chiropractic	Whittier
	Neurological Mechanisms of Spinal Manipulation	
9 Mar	Orange County Chiropractic Society	Costa Mesa
	Electrodiagnostic Evaluation of Spinal Disorders	
	Chang Zheng Hospital, 2nd Military Medical University	Shanghai
	Back Pain	
25 Apr-1 May	American Academy of Neurology	New York
	Recent Advances in the Evaluation and Treatment of Back Pain/Magnetic Stimulation	
30 Apr	San Francisco Spine Institute	San Francisco
	Let's Call It What It Is & Electrodiagnostics: When are EMG, NCV, SSEP Useful?	
4-5 Oct	Occupational Spinal Disorders	Pittsburgh
	Anatomy and Physiology of Back Pain - What Do We Know?	
10-15 Oct	South Africa International Chiropractic Congress	Sun City, SA
	Failure of Pathology to Explain Low Back Pain/ Conservative Mgt of LBP	
1994		
11-13 Feb	UCI-The Neurologist and Back Pain:MSK DX & Mgt	New Port Beach
	The Problems with Back Pain/SMT as a Primary TX/Problem with Disability	
23 Feb	Occupational Ergonomics	San Diego
	Failure of Pathology to Explain Low Back Pain/Conservative Mgt of LBP	

494

Date	EVENT and Title of Talk or Purpose of Meeting	Location
18 Mar	CMA Course on Practical Neurology Multiple Views of Pain Management	Anaheim
6 May	American Academy of Neurology Recent Advances in the Evaluation and Treatment of Low Back Pain	Washington, DC
25-26 Sep	Occupational Spinal Disorders Spinal Manipulation: The Legitimization of a Treatment Procedure	Atlanta
30 Nov-2 Dec	ABS Back Pain Symposium Myths Concerning Strokes Following Cervical Manipulation	Los Angeles
1995		
27 Jan	Council on Chiropractic Education Convocation The Role of Chiropractic in an Integrated Health Care System	New Orleans
20-23 Feb	Occupational Ergonomics: Work Evaluation and Prevention Failure of the Pathology Model to Explain LBP/Conservative Mgt of LBP	San Diego
28 Apr	Netherlands Manual Therapy Association Conference Lumar and Cervical Spine	Irvine via Video
6-13 May	American Academy of Neurology Course Director: Recent Advances in the Treatment of Back Pain	Seattle
18-20 May	Texas Medical Association Spinal Manipulation for Low Back Pain	Dallas
23 May	International Workers' Compensation Foundation IABC The Legitimizatoin of a Treatment Procedure	Newport Beach
18-22 Jun	ISSLS Correlation of Palpable Muscle Spasm, Pain and Activity Scores and Evoked Potentials	Helsinki
5-7 Jul	Chiropractic Centennial Foundation/WFC One-Hundred Years of Chiropractic Research	Washington, DC
10-11 Sep	16th Annual Occupational spiral Disorders Conf How to Prescribe Optimal Manipulative Therapy/How to Handle the Legal Issues	Toronto
14-16 Sep	Chiropractic Centennial Foundation/WFC One-Hundred Years of Chiropractic Research/Workshop on Neurology	Davenport
18-19 Nove	Chiropractic Centennial Foundation/WFC One-Hundred Years of Chiropractic Research/Neurophysiological Theories	Tokyo

495

Date	EVENT and Title of Talk or Purpose of Meeting	Location
1996		
18-19 Jan		Trinidad
24 Feb	State Farm Mutual Insurance: Personal Injury Law Suit	Los Angles
	Spinal Manipulation and Chiropractic Treatment for Spinal Pain Symdromes	
28 Feb	Occupatonal Ergonomics: Work Evalation and Prevention	San Diego
	Failure of the Pathology Model to Wxplain Low Back Pain/Conservative Care	
16-18 May	European Chiropractic Union:Vertigo and Cervical Spine	Geneva
	Incidence, Risk Factors and Mechanisms of Vertebral Basilar Artery Ischemia	
14 Jun	Palmer College of Chiropractic West Convocation	Santa Clara
	Chiropractic is an Accepted Profession: What Do I Do Now?	
22 Jun	ISSLS	New York
	Indications for Clinical Neurophysiological Testing/Spinal Manipulation	
24 Jun	SPINE Grand Rounds with SUNY, Syracuse	Syracuse
	The Failure of the Pathological Model to Explain Back Pain & Its Consequences	
23 Jul	Chiropractic Managed Care: Successful Integration	Coronado, CA
	A New Proposal for Standardizing Health Care Providers	
15-16 Sep	17th Occupatonal Spinal Disorders Conference	Calgary
	Chiropractic: The Second Hundred Years/The Barrier of Research	
23 Oct	NASS Membership Committee	Vancouver
23-26 Oct	NASS 11th Annual Mtg	Vancouver
30 Oct	UniCare Insurance Co.	Santa Ana
	Medical Management of Workers' Comp Claims	
12-14 Dec	ABS Diagnosis and Treatment of Back Pain	San Francisco
	Credentialing of Health Care Providers to Qualify for Managed Care Panels	

Date	EVENT and Title of Talk or Purpose of Meeting	Location
1997		
14-16 Feb	Clinical Neurology in Chiropractic Practice	Sydney/Brisbane
6-8 Jun	WFC Congress Course lecturer on the clinical aspects of neurophysiology	Tokyo
18-19 Jun	Birch and Davis/DoD Mtg Course Chair: Cerebrovascular Complicatons of Manipulation//Future Research	Alexandria
20-22 Jun	AHCPR Consultant on the DoD Chiropractic Demonstration Project	Alexandria
18-21 Sep	American Academy of Pain Mgt 8th Annual AHCPR Guidelines Agency	Las Vegas
17-20	American Association of Electrodiagnostc Medicine Lower Back Pain: Finding Common Ground, Chiropractic Perspective	San Diego
3-4 Oct	NCMIC Defense Counsel Seminar Electrophysiologic Studies in Bowel and Bladder Problems and Sexual Dysfunction	Chicago
22 Oct	Alternatives in Patient Care Conference A New Look at Stroke: The Facts of an Exhaustive Study	New York City
25 Nov	UCLA-LACC Neck Pain Study Chiropractic: Clinical Effectiveness and Contraindications	Los Angeles
10-13 Dec	ABS Diagnosis and Treatment of Back and Neck Pain Advisory Committee	San Francisco
	Evidence That Muscles Play a Role in Back Pain	
1998		
4 Feb	Occupational Ergonomics: Work Evaluation	San Diego
11-13 Mar	7th Annual Worker's Comp & Occupational Med. Seminar Failure of Pathology to Explain Low Back Pain/Conservative Mgt of LBP	San Francisco
4 Apr	Hospital for Joint Diseases Spine Ctr Spinal Manip Scientific Update/LBP Risk Factors	New York City
27 Jun	California Chiropractic Association History and Physical: Red Flags/ International Advances in Chiropractic	San Diego
	Tug-a-War II, The Great Debate	

497

Date	EVENT and Title of Talk or Purpose of Meeting	Location
10 Sep	UCLA-LACC Neck Pain Study Advisory Committee	Los Angeles
30 Oct	NASS 13th Annual Mtg Non-surgical Back Pain Mgt	San Francisco
2 Nov	Orange County Bar/Workers' Comp Section Recent Findings in the Treatment of Spinal Injuries	Orange County
14-15 Nov	Consortium of Canadian Chiropractic Research Ctrs Evolution of Chiropractic Research/Strokes and Adjustments	Calgary, Alberta
11 Dec	Palmer College of Chiropractic West Convocation The Search for a Post-Graduate Mentor	San Jose
1999		
10-11 Feb	Relax The Back/ Medical Advisory Panal Advisory Council Meeting	Las Vegas
12-13 Feb	Cervical Task Force Mtg Planning Mtg	Vancouver
28 Feb-3 Mar	Harvard Medical School:Alternative Medicine Chiropractic: Clinical Practice and State of the Science	Boston
11 Mar	UCLA-LACC Neck Pain Study Advisory Committee	Los Angeles
17 Mar	Occupational Ergonomics Failure of Pathology to Explain LBP/ Conservative Mgt of LBP	San Diego
25 Mar	LACC How to Measure Muscle Spasm	Whittier
19-20 Mar	Occupational Ergonomics:Work Evaluation & Prevention Failure of Pathology to Explain Low Back Pain/Conservative Management	San Diego
9 Apr	SUNY Health Science Center Maniiulative Medicine	Syracuse
10-11 Apr	NYCC Commencement Commencement Speaker	Sennaca Falls

498

Date	EVENT and Title of Talk or Purpose of Meeting	Location
17-22 May	WFC 5th Biennial Congress Symposium Co-Chair/Invited Paper - Neuro Effects of the Adj/Neurological Exam	Auckland, NZ
9-14 Jun		Moscow
21-25 Jun	ISSLS Attendee/Reading for the Soul Group?	Hawaii
23-25 Jul	RAC IV: Chiropractic Research: Implications for Practice Mentorship in Chiropractic Research	Arlington Park, IL
25 Jul	WFC Committee Mtg Planning Mtg	Arlington Park, IL
26 Jul	Insurance Council of Canada Discussion on Neck Pain Task Force	Toronto
27 Jul	Insurance Council of British Columbia Discussion on Neck Pain Task Force	Vancouver
29 Jul	UCLA-LACC Neck Pain Study Advisory Committee	Los Angeles
28 Aug	Kaiser 1999 Physical Medicine Symposium Cervicogeic Headache/ Complications of Cervical Manipulations	Dana Point
1 Oct	Relax The Back/ Medical Advisory Panal Advisory Council Meeting	El Segundo, CA
20-24 Oct	NASS 14th Annual Mtg Committees: Research Fund,Spine Editorial Bd, Chiropractic Issues Task Force	Chicago
29 Oct	York University/CMCC Conference Conference on University Chiropractic Degree Studies	Toronto
3-4 Dec	NASA/Clayton Davis T.V. Interview "New Horizons in Helath"	Houston
6 Dec	UCLA-LACC Neck Pain Study Advisory Committee	Los Angeles
8-11 Dec	ABS Fall Symposium on Back Pain A Century of Progress in Spinal Care	Las Vegas

Date	EVENT and Title of Talk or Purpose of Meeting	Location
2000		
4-5 Feb	ASU Healthy Back Study Advisory Committee	Phoenix
12-13 Feb	Relax the Back Medical Advisory Panel	Anaheim
1 Mar	Occupatonal Ergonomics: Work Evaluation Failure of Pathology to Explain LBP/Conservative Mgt of LBP	Los Angeles
12-15 Mar	Alternative Med-State of Science-Harvard Med School Speaking on Chiropractic	Boston
31 Mar-1 Apr	AECC/BCA Joint Conf What is the Relationship Between Spinal Pain, Disability and Pathology	Bournemouth, Eng
5 May	CMCC 55th Convocation The Importance of a Mentor in Maximizing the Opportunities of a Graduate	Toronto
2 Jun	Osteopathic Physicians 8th Annual Seminar Guest Speaker	Dana Point, CA
29 Jun	UCLA-LACC Neck Pain Study Advisory Committee	Los Angeles
20 Jul	Michigan State U, College of Osteopathic Med The Evolution and Current Status of Research into Spinal Manipulation	Lansing
21-23 Jul	RAC V Evolution of Manipulation Research	Chicago
22-23 Sep	ICSM/NWCC Research Conf/ASU Advisory Comm Strengths and Weaknesses of Current Chiropractic Neurological Theories	Bloomington, MN
6-7 Oct	Defense Counsel Seminar NCMIC CVA: A Clinical Analysis	San Antonio
24-28 Oct	NASS 15th Annual Mtg	New Orleans
26 Oct	NASS Chiropractic Task Force Chiropractic Issues	New Orleans
10-11 Nov	ASU Healthy Back Study Committee Mtg	Phoenix

Date	EVENT and Title of Talk or Purpose of Meeting	Location
30 Nov-2 Dec	New York Medical Center	New York
	Back Pain and Disability, Unraveling the Puzzle	
7-9 Dec	ABS:Advance Diagnosis and Treatment	Vancouver
	Differential Diagnosis of Back Pain-Has It Changed?	
2001		
17-19 Jan	Israel Chiropractic Association	Tel Aviv
	The Neurological Examination in the Chiropractic Office/Chiropractic and SMT	
11-14 Feb	Harvard Med School: Complementary and Alternative Med	Boston
	Chiropractic: Clinical Practice and State of the Science	
16-17 Feb	ASU Healthy Back Study	Phoenix
	Committee Mtg	
27-28 Feb	AAOS Annual Mtg	San Francisco
	Complementary and Alternative Medcine (CAM) and the Orthopedic Surgeon	
12 Mar	Occupational Ergonomics: Work Evaluation and Prevention	Los Angeles
	Failure of Pathology to Explain LBP/Conservative Mgt of LBP	
29 Mar-3 Apr	Neck Pain Scientific Secretariat	Edmonton
	Scientific Meeting	
24-26 May	WFC Congress	Paris
	The Role of Chiropractic in the Management of Neck Pain, Back Pain and Headaches	
18-22 Jun	ISSLS 28th Annual Mtg	Edinburgh
	The Role of Provider Networks in the Management of Work-Related Back Pain	Turkey
27-29 Jul	RAC VI	Kansas City
	Chiropractic Theory Revisited: Lessons from the Break-Out Sessions/Moderator	
10-11 Aug	Florida Chiropractic Association	Orlando
	Benefits, Risks and Theoretical Basis for Cervical Manipulation	
21-23 Sep	NYCC Investiture	Senaca Falls, NY
	Frank Nicchi's Inaguration	
4-5 Oct	Spine Journal Editorial Board	Rosemont, IL
	Board Mtg	

Date	EVENT and Title of Talk or Purpose of Meeting	Location
31 Oct	NASS 16th Annual Metting Chiropractic Task Force	Seattle
2 Nov	NASS Executive Committee	Seattle
17 Nov	The Integration of Chiropractic Care and Spinal Manipulation ASU Healthy Back Study Advisory Committee Mtg	Phoenix
2002		
18-21 Feb	U of Michigan, Occupational Ergonomics Failure of Pathology in Explaining Low Back Pain	Los Angeles
23 Feb	Bone and Joint Decade Task Force Scientific Secretariat Meeting	
13-16 Mar	ACC/RAC VII Moderator/Past, Present and Future Chiropractic Educatoin and Research	New Orleans
13-20 Apr	American Academy of Neurology Chiropractic & Spinal Manipulation/Neck Manipulation & Stroke	Denver
4-5 May	Neurology Knowledge Expert Panel Panel on Fixed Theme Park Rides & Head Injuries/Neurological Events	Boston
14-18 May	ISSLS F Waves of Peroneal and Tibial Nerves	Cleveland
18 Jun	NCCAM Expert Panel Panel Member	Bethesda
14-15 Sep	U of AZ Back Study Advisory Committee Committee Member	Phoenix
19 Sep	Neck Pain Task Force Task Force Chair	Edmonton
26-29 Sep	Symptom, Diagnostic and Disability Validity Medication, Chiropractic, Surgery or a Pamphlet for Tx for Neck Pain: How to Choose	Toronto
30 Sep	Spine Journal Ex. Bd. Board Member	La Grange, IL

Date	EVENT and Title of Talk or Purpose of Meeting	Location
27-28 Oct	Palmer West	San Jose
	Research in the Legal Arena	
29 Oct- 2 Nov	NASS 17th Annual Meeting	Montreal
	The Role of Scientific Research in Legal and Policy Making Deliberations	
4-9 Dec	Bone and Joint Decade Task Force	Toronto
	Spinal Manipulation in Spine Care: Who? Why? When?	
	Task Force Chair	
2003		
30-31 Jan	Parker	Las Vegas
25 Feb	Occupational Ergonomics: Work Evaluatin and Preventionq	Los Angeles
	The Role of Scientific Research and its Impact on Chiropractic	
13-16 Mar	ACC/RAC VII	New Orleans
	Failure of Pathology to Explain LBP/Conservative Mgt of LBP	
3-7 Apr	Japanese Spinal Research Society	Fukuoka, Japan
	Moderator - Influencing Public Policy on Chiropractic	
27 Apr-3 May	WFC Congress	Orlando
	Non-Surgical and Surgical Approaches to Spinal Pain - What Does the Literature Say?	
1 May	FCLB Congress	Orlando
	Report on the Bone and Joint Decade Neck Pain Task Force	
13-17 May	ISSLS	Vancouver, Can
	Janse Lecture: Make Research the Friend of Chiropractic	
24-27 Sep	Chiropractic Congress of South Africa	Durban
	The Appropriateness of Common Treatments for Neck Pain	
3-4 Oct	NCMIC Defense Counsel Seminar	New York
	Neck Manipulation & Stroke/Appropriate Tx for Neck Pain/Neurological Exam	
21-25 Oct	NASS 18th Annual Mtg	San Diego
	Cervical Manipulation and Stroke: A Critical Review of the Literature	
6 Nov	UCI/Samueli Ctr	UCI Medical Ctr
	Examining the Sacro Iliac Joint/Chiropractic Approach to Spine Mgt	

Date	EVENT and Title of Talk or Purpose of Meeting	Location
13-15 Nov	American Back Society Current Status f the Research on Chiropractic and Spinal Manipulation Non-Surgical and Surgical Approaches to Spinal Pain - What Does the Literature Say?	Las Vegas
2004		
6-7 Feb	Arizona State University Back Study	Phoenix
25 Feb	Occupational Ergonomics: Work Evaluation and Prevention Committee Member	Los Angeles
26-28 Feb	WFC Identity Conf Failure of Pathology to Explain LBP/Conservative Mgt of LBP	Hayward, CA
12-14 Mar	ACC/RAC VIII Consultation on the Identity of the Chiropractic Profession	Las Vegas
25-26 Mar	Impact Medical Solutions Results and Clinical Relevance of Basic Science Research/ Panelist	Chicago
27-30 Mar	Neck Pain Task Force Scientific Secretariat MPR Advisory Board Mtgs	Toronto
21-24 Apr	American Academy of Orthopedic Med Secretariat Meeting	La Jolla
30 May-5 Jun	ISSLS The Lumbo Sacral Spine/The Feasibility of a Non-profit Back PainFoundation	Porto, Portugal
25-26 Jun	Canadian Chiropractic Protective Association Assessing the Effectiveness and Complicatons of Neck Pain Treatment Options	Toronto
14-16 Oct	WFC/ACC Educational Conf Countering the Myths: Stroke Research and Latest Evidence	Toronto
27-30 Oct	NASS 19th Annual Meeting	Chicago
11-14 Nov	British Columbia Chiropractic Association Multidisciplinary Approach to the Essentials of Spine Care	Vancouver
14-17 Nov	Neck Pain Task Force Scientific Secretariat Principles and Practice of Chiropractic: Current Research Status	Toronto

Date	EVENT and Title of Talk or Purpose of Meeting	Location
8-11 Dec	ABS Advanced Diagnosis and Treatment of Back Pain / Secretariat Meeting / President/ Panel Member	Las Vegas
2005		
28 Feb-3 Mar	Occupational Ergonomics: Work Evaluation and Prevention	Los Angeles
17-19 Mar	ACC/RAC IX / Failure of Pathology to Explain LBP/Conservative Mgt of LBP	Las Vegas
10-13 Apr	Neck Pain Task Force Scientific Secretariat / Results and Clinical Relevance of Basic Science Research/ Panelist	Toronto
13-14 Apr	State Farm Insurance Whiplash Conf / Secretariat Meeting	Bloomington, IN
Apr	Southern California University of Health Science / Controlling Health Care Through Evidence Based Guidelines	Whittier
5-7 May	European Chiropractic Union / Visiting Scholar	Lemesos, Cyprus
10-14 May	ISSLS / Chiropractic Manipulation: Treatment of Choice for Patients with Spinal Pain	New York
31 May	NASS	Chicago
16-18 Jun	WFC 8th Biennial Congress / Austr Debate: Grounding in Philosophy vs. Grounding in Science / Significance of the Neck Pain Task Force for Chiropractic	Sydney / Sydney
23-24 Jun	State Farm Insurance Mtg / Update on Research Methods	Bloomington, IN
17-19 Jul	Palmer College of Chiropractic / Planning Effective Interventoins	Davenport
22-23 Jul	Activator Methods Instructor's Conf / All-School Assembly	Phoenix
23 Sep	NCMIC Defense Counsel Seminar / Speaker	Des Moines

Date	EVENT and Title of Talk or Purpose of Meeting	Location
27 Sep - 1 Oct	NASS 20th Annual Meeting Speaker	Philadelphia
28-31 Oct	Neck Pain Task Force Scientific Secretariat	Toronto
16-19 Nov	ABS Advanced Diagnosis and Treatment for Back Pain Secretariat Meeting	San Francisco
8 Dec	Palmer College of Chiropractic West Graduation Clinical Application of the ACOEM Occupational Medicine Practice Guidelines Graduation Speaker: Future Direction and Challenges	San Jose
2006		
2-4 Feb	Northwestern Health Science University	Minneapolis
17 Feb	Chiropractic Strategic Planning for the Next 25 Years Changing Chiropractic Identity and Practice in the Era of Evidence Based Health Care	Lombard
22-25 Feb	American Academy of Pain Medicine 22nd Annual Mtg Moderator for Formal Consensus Session	San Diego
2-6 Mar	Neck Pain Task Force Scientific Secretariat Alternative Therapies for Treating Pain: An Evidence Based Approach/SMT Evidence	Toronto
15-18 Mar	ACC/RAC Secretariat Meeting	Washington, DC
1 Apr	Impact Medical Solutions Panel: Evidence for the Risk and Benefits of Spinal Manipulation	Orange County, CA
29-30 Apr	NYCC/New York Chiropractic Association/NY Chiro Council Medical Advisory Board	Elmhurst, NY
11-13 Aug	Chiropractic Strategic Planning for the Next 25 Years Surviving the Era of Evidenced Based Guidelines	Lombard
13-17 Jun	ISSLS Planning Meeting	Bergen, Norway
24-26 Aug	Florida Chiropractic Association	Orlando

Date	EVENT and Title of Talk or Purpose of Meeting	Location
27-30 Sep	NASS 21st Annual Meeting	Seattle
	Changing Chiropractic Identity and Practice in the Era of Evidence Based Health Care	
19-22 Oct	Neck Pain Task Force Scientific Secretariat	Thousand Oaks, CA
16-18 Nov	Canadian National Chiropractic Convention	Vancouver
	Secretariat Meeting	
13-16 Dec	ABS - Advanced Diagnosis and Treatment for Neck & Back	Las Vegas
	Changing Chiropractic Identity and Practice in the Era of Evidence Based Health Care	
	Patient Empowerment: The Newest Component I Decision Making	
2007		
12-15 Jan	Neck Pain Task Force Scientific Secretariat	Toronto
15-17 Mar	ACC/RAC	Phoenix
	President's Report and conduct the meeting	
17 Mar	ASH Research Advisory Committee	Phoenix
	Communicating & Understanding the Risk of Manipulation to Non-DCs	
19 Mar	CA Work Comp Medical Evidence Evaluation Advisory Com	San Francisco
	Advisory Board for ASH	
Apr	Canadian Institute for Relief of Pain and Disability	Vancouver
	Review of ACOEM's Treatment Guidelines	
16-19 Apr	Neck Pain Task Force Scientific Secretariat Mtg	Stockholm, Sweden
24-25 Apr	HLDI and Insurance Institute for Highway Safety (IIHS)	Charlottesville, VA
	President's Report and conduct the meeting	
13-19 May	WFC 9th Biennial Congress	Vilamoura, Portugal
	Presentation on the NPTF findings	
10-14 Jun	ISSLS	Hong Kong
	NPTF Report	
27-28 Jul	Physical Med & Rehab Pain Mgt Symposium (Kaiser)	Las Vegas
15-16 Aug	Palmer College of Chiropractic	Davenport
	Cervicogenic Headache/Chiropractic Controversy in the Treatement of Neck & Back	

Date	EVENT and Title of Talk or Purpose of Meeting	Location
17-18 Aug	Florida Chiropractic Association Presentation on the NPTF findings	Orlando
10-27 Sep	Presentation on the NPTF findings/Scientific Evidence and the Examination of Pt.	Bern
27-28 Sep	NPTF Annual Mtg	Bern
4-5 Oct	Palmer College of Chiropractic Chair/History, Composition, Process	Davenport
23 Oct	NASS Past President's Dinner/CAM Research Mtg Board Retreat	Austin
23-27 Oct	NASS 22nd Annual Mtg CAM Research with Simon and Jim?	Austin
13-17 Nov	100 Years of Chiropractic in Saskatchewan Managing Neck Conditions	Regina
4 Dec	Medical Evidence Evaluation Advisory Committee Banquet Speaker	Oakland
14 Dec	SCUHS Commencement Committee Member Speaker	Whittier
2008		
19-22 Jan	World Congress on Neck Pain	Los Angeles
26 Jan	Tribute Lunch to Reed Phillips NPTF Report	Whittier
Feb	CCA Annual Convention Representing WFC	Reno
13-15 Mar	ACC/RAC NPTF Report	Washington, DC
10-11 May	U of Rochester/Neuropathic Pain TX Consensus Mtg NPTF Report/Keynote Speaker	Tampa

Date	EVENT and Title of Talk or Purpose of Meeting	Location
15-18 May	California Orthopaedic Association	Newport Beach
	Consulting Meeting	
26-31 May	ISSLS	Geneva
	NPTF Report	
4 Jun	Medical Evidence Evaluation Advisory Committee	Oakland
18-20 Jun	ABS 25th Annual Mtg	Las Vegas
	Low Back Guidelines	
7-8 Aug	Palmer College of Chiropractic	Davenport
	Evidence Informed Management of LBP Without Surgery	
22-23 Aug	Florida Chiropractic Association	Orlando
	Homecoming Keynote speaker	
16 Aug	SCUHS/Extravaganza	Long Beach
	Speaker	
Sep-Oct	Private Excursion	South Africa
	Scott and Joan were tour guides.	
14-18 Oct	NASS 23rd Annual Mtg	Toronto
	Cultural Authority for Spine Disorders	
5-11 Nov	WHO/WFC Conf on Manual Methods of Health Care	Beijing
	Current State of the Art for Managing Chronic Low Back Pain	
20-23 Nov	American Academy of Physical Medicine and Rehab	San Diego
	Research Status of Western Manual Med	
Dec	American Academy of Physical Medicine and Rehab	
	NPTF: Implications for the Physiatrist	
	Speaker	

509

Date	EVENT and Title of Talk or Purpose of Meeting	Location
2009		
9 Jan	Palmer Board	Chicago
	Botswana Project	
13-15 Mar	ACC/RAC	Las Vegas
26-29 Mar	School of Naprapathy	Stockholm
30-31 Mar	Whiplash Associated Disorders Conf	Stockholm
	NPTF Report	
25 Apr-2 May	WFC 10th Biennial Congress	Montreal
	NPTF Report	

Summary of Scott's travels from 1980 to 2009

Year	# Trips/yr	# Overseas	Location
1980	20	2	London/Australia, New Zealand, South Africa
1981	22	2	Oslo/Paris
1982	21	2	St. Thomas/ London
1983	22	2	Cambridge/ Zurich
1984	27	0	
1985	30	5	Sydney/West Germany/Oslo/Vienna/South Africa
1986	16	0	
1987	17	3	Rome/Brisbane/London
1988	23	1	Switzerland
1989	15	3	Kyoto/Rio de Janeiro/Sao Paulo
			(Mexico City & Quebec are in NA)
1990	20	0	
1991	21	2	Heidelberg/Sydney
1992	21	1	Puerto Rico
1993	8	2	Shanghai/Xian/Beijing, Sun City South Africa
1994	6	0	
1995	11	2	Helsinki/Tokyo
1996	12	2	Trinidad/Geneva
1997	9	3	Sydney, Brisbane/Tokyo
1998	9	1	Moscow
1999	22	2	Auckland/Moscow
2000	16	1	Bournmouth
2001	15	3	Tel Aviv/Paris/Edinburgh, Turkey
2002	14	1	Spain and Portugal
2003	11	2	Fukuoka, Japan/Durbin, South Africa
2004	14	2	Porto, Portugal/Bordeaux, France
2005	17	2	Brazil and Argentina/Greece, Cyprus
2006	14	3	Ireland/Bergen, Norway/Jordan and Egypt
2007	17	4	Stockholm/Portugal, France, Italy/Hong Kong/
			Bern, Croatia
2008	17	3	Costa Rica/Southern Africa/Beijing
2009	6	3	Stockholm /Saint Petersburg/Belgium/Switzerland
Total	**493**	**59**	
Average	16	1.9	

511

Appendix C

Curriculum Vitae
and
Bibliography

SCOTT HALDEMAN
CURRICULUM VITAE
September, 2009

Date of Birth: June 23, 1943
Marital Status: Married
 Wife: Joan
 Sons: Reeve and Keatly

BASIC QUALIFICATIONS

Academic Degrees

D.C. Palmer College of Chiropractic, 1964

B.Sc. University of Pretoria, 1968 (Physiology, Physics)

M.Sc. University of Pretoria, 1970 (Neurophysiology)

Ph.D. University of British Columbia, 1973 (Neurophysiology)

M.D. University of British Columbia, 1976

Honorary Degrees

D.Sc. (hon) Western States College of Chiropractic, 1981.

D. Humanities (hon) Southern California University of Health Sciences, 2008.

Residency

Intern, Department of Internal Medicine, Vancouver General Hospital, 1976-1977

Resident, Department of Neurology, University of California, Irvine, 1977-1980

515

Fellow in Electrodiagnosis, Department of Neurology, Long Beach Veterans Administration

Medical Center, 1980-1981

Licensure Examinations

Iowa State Basic Science Board of Examiners, 1964

Canadian National Chiropractic Board of Examiners, 1970

Board of Directors of Chiropractic, Ontario Drugless Practitioners Act, 1970

National Board of Chiropractic Examiners (United States), 1978

Medical Council of Canada Examinations (L.M.C.C.), 1976

Federation of Licensing Examination Boards (FLEX) -- (United States), 1976

National Board of Medical Examiners (United States), 1976

Specialty Qualifications

FCCS(C) – Fellow of College of Chiropractic Sciences (Canada), 1975

FRCP(C) -- Fellow of the Royal College of Physicians (Canada), 1981

FAAN – Fellow of the American Academy of Neurology, 1985

Diplomate -- American Board of Psychiatry & Neurology, 1982

Diplomate -- American Board of Electroencephalography and Neurophysiology, 1981

Diplomate -- American Board of Clinical Neurophysiology, Inc., 1983

Diplomate -- American Board of Electrodiagnostic Medicine, 1982

ACADEMIC POSITIONS

1. Laboratory Assistant, University of Pretoria, 1968-1969

2. Student Academic Assistant, University of British Columbia, 1970-1971

3. Lecturer, Canadian Memorial Chiropractic College, 1970

4. Special Academic Staff, Chiropractic Sciences Division, Canadian Memorial Chiropractic College, 1976-1979

5. Assistant Clinical Professor, Department of Neurology, University of California, Irvine, 1984 to 1990

6. Associate Clinical Professor, Department of Neurology, University of California, Irvine, 1991 to 1998

7. Clinical Professor, Department of Neurology, University of California, Irvine, 1998 to Present.

8. Adjunct Professor, Research Department, Southern California University of Health Sciences (formerly known as Los Angeles Chiropractic College), 1985 to Present.

9. Adjunct Professor, Department of Epidemiology, School of Public Health, University of California, Los Angeles, 2002 to Present.

UNIVERSITY AND COLLEGE HONORS

1. Valedictorian, Class of January 1962, Palmer College

2. Pi Tau Delta, Honor Society, Palmer College, 1964

3. Captain of the Rugby Team (college letters), Palmer College, 1963

4. President, Student International Chiropractors Association, Palmer College, 1963

5. International Chiropractors Association Student Achievement Award, 1963

6. President, Palmer College Flying Club, 1962

7. B.Sc. distinction in physiology

8. M.Sc. with honors

9. South African Medical Research Council Overseas Study Bursary, 1972

10. Louis Lipsy Toohill Scholarship in Rheumatology, University of British Columbia, 1972, 1974, and 1975

11. The Northwest Association of Physical Medicine and Rehabilitation Award, 1975

12. The Vancouver General Hospital, Department of Psychiatry Attending Staff Prize, 1975

13. The British Columbia Anesthetists Society Prize, 1976

14. Dr. A.M. Agnew Memorial Scholarship for Obstetrics, University of British Columbia, 1976

15. Dr. Peter H. Spohn Memorial Prize for Gynecology, University of British Columbia, 1976

PROFESSIONAL HONORS

1. Certificate of Merit, South African Chiropractors Association, 1967

2. Chiropractor of the Year, South African Chiropractors Association, 1968

3. Palmer College Alumni Award, 1968

4. Research Fellowship, Foundation of Chiropractic Education and Research, 1975

5. Doctor of Science degree (honorary), Western States Chiropractic College, 1981

6. Researcher of the Year Award, American Chiropractic Association, 1990

7. Chiropractor of the Year, Dynamic Chiropractic, 1991

8. Outstanding Service Award, World Federation of Chiropractic, 1995

9. Honorary member of Canadian Memorial Chiropractic College, 1999

10. Presentation in Appreciation for Continued Unselfish, Outstanding and Dedicated Support of The American Back Society, December 2, 1998

11. Outstanding Achievement by Volunteer Faculty, University of California, Irvine, Department of Neurology, 1999

12. Michigan State University, College of Osteopathic Medicine. Patenge Distinguished Lecturer, Lansing, Michigan, July 20, 2000.

13. Researcher of the Year, Foundation for Chiropractic Education and Research, 2002

14. Ambassador for The Bone and Joint Decade 2000-2010, September 30, 2002.

15. The 13th Annual Joseph Janse Lecture Series Award, Federation of Chiropractic Licensing Boards, 2003

16. Outstanding Achievement by Volunteer Faculty, University of California, Irvine, Department of Neurology, 2003

17. David Selby Award, North American Spine Society - for individuals who have contributed greatly to the art and science of spinal disorder management through service to NASS, 2005.

18. Member, Canadian Memorial Chiropractic College, 2007

19. Doctor of Humanities Award (honorary), Southern California University of Health Sciences, 2008

CLINICAL EXPERIENCE

1. Private Practice, Chiropractic, 1964-1977

2. Internship, Medicine, June 1976-1977

3. Resident, Neurology, July 1977-June 1980

4. Fellow, Electrodiagnosis, Veterans Administration Medical Center, Long Beach, California, September 1980-August 1981

5. Private Practice, Neurology, January 1981-Present

HOSPITAL AFFILIATION

University of California, Irvine Medical Center, Orange, California

PROFESSIONAL ORGANIZATIONS

1. American Academy of Neurology, 1977- student, 1980-active, 1985-fellow

2. Orange County Medical Society, 1982- 2005

3. California Medical Association, 1984-2005

4. American Medical Association, 1982-2005

5. Royal College of Physicians of Canada, 1982

6. International Society for the Study of the Lumbar Spine, 1979, 2004 - Senior status

7. American Back Society, 1984-present

8. North American Spine Association, 1982-1984

9. North American Spine Society, 1984-Present

10. North American Academy of Manipulative Medicine, 1977-1995

Currently American Academy of Orthopedic Medicine

11. American Chiropractic Association, 1976- 2004

12. International Chiropractic Association, 1971-1990

13. College of Chiropractic Sciences (Canada), 1976-97 member, 1978 fellow

14. Federation Internationale de Medecine Manuell, 1981-1993

15. National Back Research Foundation, 1981-1985

16. Association for the History of Chiropractic, 1981-present

17. American Medical Electroencepholgraphic Association, 1982-1994

18. Orange County Neurological Society, 1982 – 2000

19. American Academy of Clinical Neurophysiology, 1988

20. American Academy of Spine Physicians - 2003

21. American Association of Electrodiagnosis and Electromyography - currently The American Academy of Neuromuscular and Electro-diagnostic Medicine, 1982-2002, 2002 – present - Emeritus status

22. North American Cervicogenic Headache Society, 1996-2002

Chiropractic Committees and Positions

1. Research Consultant, American Chiropractic Association, 1978-1979

2. Advisor Board, Canadian Foundation for Spinal Research, 1978

3. Consultant, Foundation for the Advancement of Chiropractic Research, 1979

4. Consultant, Foundation for Chiropractic Education and Research, 1979

5. Executive Member, South African Chiropractors Association, 1965-1969

6. Founding Committee, South African Chiropractic Research Foundation, 1968-1969

7. Canadian Chiropractic Association,
   a. Committee for a Definition of Chiropractic, 1970
   b. Research Consultant, 1973-1979
   c. Convention Organizing Committee, 1976

8. British Columbia Chiropractic Association
   a. Public Relations Committee, 1971-1972
   b. Committee to Investigate the Establishment of a Faculty of Chiropractic, 1974
   c. Committee on Continuing Education 1975-1976

9. "ICA Review," Technical Paper Review Committee, 1978-1979

10. Kentuckiana Chirdren's Center, National Advisory Board, 1980

11. Mississippi Association of Chiropractors, Committee on Research, 1979

12. American Chiropractic Association,
   a. Council of Neurology, 1974-1977
   b. ACA Consultant on Research, 1978

13. International Chiropractors Association,
   a. Student Advisory Board, 1963
   b. Research Consultant, 1973-1982
   c. Conference Committee, 1979

d. Inter-professional relations advisory committee, 1985

14. Guidelines for Chiropractic Quality Assurance and Standards of Practice, Chairman, 1990-1992

15. Advisory Panel for the Research Division, Anglo-European College of Chiropractic/British College of Chiropractic, 1997

16. National Workshop to Develop the Chiropractic Research Agenda. Member of Planning Committee and participant, 1995, 1996, 1997, 1998, 1999, 2000, 2001, 2002, 2003, 2004, 2005, 2006.

17. World Federation of Chiropractic, Chairman - Research Council, 1988 to Present.

Medical Committees and Positions

1. Vancouver General Hospital.
   a. Back Pain Special Interest Group, 1976-1977
2. North American Academy of Manipulative Medicine
   a. Counselor, 1975-1979
   b. Vice-President 1980
   c. President-Elect 1981
   d. President 1983
   e. Resident 3rd Vice-President 1986-1988
   f. Society Coordination Committee, 1988
   g. Conservative Care Fellowship Committee, 1990
3. University of California, Irvine.
   a. Manipulation Research Committee, 1978
   4. International Society for the Study of the Lumbar Spine
   a. Membership Committee 1980-1982
   b. Membership Committee - Chairman 1982
   c. Executive Committee 1992-1994
5. Physical Medicine Research Foundation, International Multidisciplinary committee – changed to The Canadian Institute for the Relief of Pain and Disability
   a. Medical Advisory Committee, 1986
   b. Chairman of the Multidisciplinary Board. 2002- 2006
6. National Back Foundation.
   National Advisory Committee

7. National Back Injury Network
Medical Advisory Board, 1992.

8. California Medical Association.
   a. Committee on Health Care, 1984-1986
   b. Advisory Panel on Neurology

9. American Back Society
   a. Chairman, Manipulation Committee, 1984
   b. Council of Advisors, 1984
   c. Board of Directors, 1988-present
   d. President, 2003-2008

10. North American Spine Society
    a. Executive Council 1984-1986
    b. Vice-President and President-Elect 1987
    c. President 1988-1989
    d. Parliamentarian 1989
    e. Public Relations Committee 1991
    f. Long Range Planning Committee 1992
    g. Membership Committee 1992-present
    h. Practice Guidelines Committee 1996
    i. Guidelines Committee, Advisory Panel 1997.
    j. NASS News Sub-Committee/Editorial Board, 1997
    k. Research Fund Management Committee 1999
    l. Member, Combined Task Forces of the North American Spine Society, American Society of Spine Radiology, and American Society of Neuroradiology - Nomenclature and Classification of Lumbar Disc Pathology. Published in *Spine*, Vol. 26., No. 5, 2001
    m. Task Force on Clinical Guidelines Work Group—Guideline Consultant, 2002 - 2008
    n. Recognition and Awards Committee 2003 – 2006, chairman 2007-2008.
    o. Governance Committee, 2009

11. Orange County Neurological Society.
    President 1988-1989

12. American Academy of Neurology
    a. Liaison with North American Spine Society, 1989-1995
    b. Quality Standards Subcommittee of the AAN on Low Back Pain, 1991

c. Facilitator - Assessment: The Neurological Evaluation of Male Sexual Dysfunction. Report of the Therapeutics and Technology Assessment Subcommittee, 1993-1995
d. Course Director: Recent changes in the treatment of back pain. AAN Annual Meeting, 1993, 1994, 1995

13. American Academy of Orthopedic Surgery
    a. Orthopedic Research Society. Panelist, Occupational Medical Science Study Group, 1995
    b. New Horizons in Low Back Pain. Workshop participant, 1995

14. Value Health Sciences.
    Panel member, "Laminectomy and Spinal Fusion," September, 1992

15. American Board of Independent Medical Examiners.
    Examination Committee, 1995-1996

16. North American Cervicogenic Headache Society.
    Member, Scientific Board, 1996

17. The American Academy of Spine Physicians.
    Council Member 2003

18. "The Bone and Joint Decade 2000-2010 Task Force on Neck Pain and Its Associated Disorders," President: 2001 to 2007.

19. Bone and Joint Decade 2000-2010, Ambassador 2002

20. American College of Occupational and Environmental Medicine. Occupational Practice Guidelines, second edition. Panel member, 2007-2008.

21. American Medical Society.
    a. Guides to the Evaluation of Permanent Impairment, Fifth Edition. Reviewer, 2000
    b. Guides to the Evaluation of Permanent Impairment, Sixth Edition. Reviewer, 2007-2008

Government Committees and Positions

1. National Institute of Neurological Diseases and Stroke:
   Committee to Establish a "Workshop on the Research Status of Spinal Manipulative Therapy" 1974-1975

2. State of California, Division of Industrial Accidents, Medical Bureau.

Committee on Chiropractic Standards, 1985-1986

3. U.S. Department of Health and Human Services, Agency for Health Care Policy and Research.

a. Panel member - "Clinical Practice Guidelines on Acute Low Back Problems in Adults," 1991-1994.

b. Peer Reviewer, "Headache Evidence Report Project," 1994-1997.

4. State of California, Commission on Peace Officer Standards and Training.

Member of Spine Specialist Panel 1992

5. State of California, Division of Industrial Relations,

a. Independent Medical Examiner, 1983 to Present

b. Qualified Medical Examiner, 1991 – present

c. Low Back Disability Schedule Committee 1986

d. Committee on Chiropractic Standards 1998

e. Medical Evidence Evaluation Advisory Committee 2007

6. U.S. Department of Defense, Chiropractic Demonstration Project.

Consultant, Birch & Davis, 1995 - 1997

7. National Center for Complementary and Alternative Medicine.

Expert Review Panel to Assess Centers Programs. June 18,2002. Bethesda.

8. U.S. Department of Health and Human Services. Public Health Service. Health Resources and Services Administration. Bureau of Health Professions. Division of State, Community and Public Health. Chiropractic Demonstration Project Peer Grant Reviewer. 2003.

9. National Advisory Council for Complementary and Alternative Medicine – discussant, 2008

Editorial Boards

1. Journal of Manipulative and Physiological Therapeutics. - Editorial Board, 1979-Present

2. North American Academy of Manipulative Medicine Newsletter. -Editor, 1980-1982

3. Australian Chiropractic Association - Editorial Board, 1983-Present

4. Journal of the Canadian Chiropractic Association. -, Editorial Board, 1985-Present

5. International Chiropractic Association. - Editorial Advisory Board, 1983

6. Manual Medicine. -Editorial Board, 1984-1992

7. Neuro-Orthopedics. -Editorial Board, 1986-1995

8. *Spine*, Associate Editor - 1988-Present

9. Back Pain Monitor, Editorial Advisory Board 1983-1989

10. Injury Data Corporation Newsletter. -, Founding Medical Advisory Board, 1996

11. Alternative Therapies in Health and Medicine. -, Editorial Board, 1991-2004

12. The Back Letter - Editorial Board, 1992-1994. 1998-Present

13. Spine Letter. - Editorial Board, 1994-1998

14. Journal of the Neuromusculoskeletal System, - Editor in Chief, 1992-2003.

15. Clinical Chiropractic. - International Advisory Board. 2002-Present

16. The Spine Journal, - Deputy editor 2000 - 2006. Editorial Board, 2006-Present

Commercial Advisory Committees

1. Chart Corporation, Medical Advisory Committee, 1986-1991

2. Birch and Davis. Independent contractor for the Department of Defense chiropractic health care demonstration project, 1998

3. Ergometrics Inc, Medical Advisory Board, 1999

4. Relax the Back, Medical Advisory Panel, 1999

5. Rodale Health Books, Board of Advisors, 1992-2002

6. Spine-Health.com, Medical Advisory Board, 2000-present

7. Impact Medical Solutions, iTech Medical Inc, Medical Advisory Board, 2000-presen

8. Palladian Health Care, Clinical Advisory Board - chairman, 2008 - present

INVITED LECTURES

1985

1. Lumbar Spine Seminar, sponsored by St. Joseph Hospital, Orange, California, February 9. "Manipulative Therapy"; "Flexion vs. Extension Exercises."

2. Back Pain Symposium, sponsored by British Columbia Chiropractic Association, March 15 - 16. "Spinal Pain Syndrome"; "An Overview of Trials of Manipulation"; "Neurophysiological Models", "Concluding Remarks."

3. Western States Chiropractic College's Homecoming '85, sponsored by Western States Chiropractic College, Portland, Oregon, May 3 - 5. "Cervical Spine Pain Syndrome - Diagnosis and Treatment."

4. San Bernardino County Medical Center Meeting, sponsored by Syntex Speaker's Bureau, San Bernardino, California, May 30. "Low Back Pain."

5. Fourth International Conference on Low Back Pain, sponsored by Canadian Memorial College, Toronto, Canada, June 1 - 2. "Clinical Evaluation of Neurovisceral Function."

6. Joint Orange County Workers' Compensation Carriers and Defense Counsel Association, sponsored by JOCWCCDCA, Santa Ana, California, June 27. Guest speaker. "Low Back Pain: A Real Pathology or a Doctor's Bonanza."

7. Second Annual Meeting, sponsored by North American Lumbar Spine Association, Laguna Niguel, California, July 24 - 27. Session Chairman on Clinical Neurophysiology. "The Comprehensive Evaluation of Lumbar Neurological Lesions Utilizing EMG, H-Reflexes, F-Responses, SEPs, BCR, Cystometry, and Colonometry."

8. Summer Convention and Educational Symposium, sponsored by Washington Chiropractors Association, Coeur d' Alene, Idaho, August 16 - 18. "Neurology and Chiropractic."

9. Seventh Annual Challenge of the Lumbar Spine '85, sponsored by Abbott Northwestern Hospital and its Rehabilitation Division, the Sister Kenny Institute, Minneapolis, Minnesota, September 19 - 21. "Thermography for Musculoskeletal Disorders: Real or Rip-off?" Moderator on low back pain.

10. Pain and Ethics in the Emergency Department, sponsored by Cedars-Sinai Medical Center, Department of Emergency Medicine, Los Angeles, California, September 27. "Low Back Pain."

11. Symposium on Back Pain, sponsored by the American Back Society, San Francisco, California, October 4. "Conservative Treatment of Spinal Pain"; "Electrodiagnostic Evaluation of Spinal Disorders"; "Spinal Manipulation."

12. First International Congress, Back Pain: Current Concepts and Recent Advances, Vienna, Austria, November 3 - 8. "Clinical Neuroanatomy of the Spine"; "What Are the Objectives of Conservative Treatment?"

1986

13. Ninth Annual Conference on Evoked Potential and Advances in Electroencephalography, sponsored by UCI Department of Neurology, Irvine, California, January 24 - 26. "Pudendal evoked Responses - Techniques and Applications."

14. Symposium on Back Pain, sponsored by the American Back Society, Anaheim, California, May 9 - 10. "Manipulation of the Spine."

15. Seventh Annual AOA International Symposium: Frontiers in

Low Back Pain, sponsored by American Orthopedic Association, Chicago, Illinois, August 17 - 22. "Electrodiagnosis of Spinal Neurologic Lesions"; "Spinal Manipulative Treatment."

16. Annual Conference 1986, sponsored by Association for Holistic Health, San Francisco, California, August 29 - September 1. "Modern Treatment of Back Disorders."

17. Low Back Pain: A Multidisciplinary Approach, sponsored by Workers' Compensation Board of British Columbia, Vancouver, B.C., October 2 - 4. "The Circuitry of Pain"; "The Role of Manipulation"; "EMGs: Are They Helpful?"

18. Occupational Low Back Pain Course, sponsored by University of Utah, Snowbird, Utah, October 6 - 8. "Electrodiagnostic Studies"; "Manipulation."

19. The Challenge of the Lumbar Spine '86, sponsored by St. Mary's Hospital and Medical Center, St. Mary's Spine Center, San Francisco, California, November 6 - 9. "Problems Facing the Spine Specialist as Viewed by the Neurologist"; "Over-treatment as Viewed by the Neurologist"; Moderator on topic: Electrodiagnosis and Thermography. Chairman of Thermography Panel.

20. Fall Symposium on Back Pain, sponsored by American Back Society, San Francisco, California, December 4 - 6. "Spinal Manipulative Therapy and Sports Medicine."

1987

21. Spring Symposium on Back Pain, sponsored by the American Back Society, Anaheim, California, April 29 - May 2. Position: Member of the Board of Directors. "Electrodiagnostic Studies: Indications and Techniques"; "Short-term Trial of Chiropractic Adjustments for the Relief of Chronic Low Back Pain."

22. North American Spine Society, Second Annual Meeting, sponsored by NASS, Banff, Alberta, Canada, June 25 - 28. "The Correlation Between CT Scanning, Electrodiagnostic Studies, and Clinical Findings in Workers' Compensation Patients with Back and Leg Pain."

23. Brisbane Spinal Study Group, Brisbane, Australia, August 21 - 23.

24. Role of Manipulation in Sports Medicine, sponsored by North American Academy of Manipulative Medicine, Las Vegas, Nevada, October 28 - 31. "The Role of Manipulation in Sports Medicine."

1988

25. Industrial Musculoskeletal Health: Sports Medicine for Working People, sponsored by Division of Orthopedic Surgery, Southwestern Medical School, the University of Texas, South Western Medical Center, Dallas, Texas, September 15 - 17. "Selecting Among Manipulation and Other Modalities"; "Office Management of Disabled Workers"; "Workman's Compensation: The California System of Evaluating Permanent and Partial Impairment."

26. Low Back Pain - A Changing Paradigm, sponsored by Physical Medical Research Foundation, Ontario, Canada, September 30 - October 2. "The Objectives of Conservative Management of Low Back Pain."

27. Occupational Low Back Pain Conference, sponsored by Rehabilitation Engineering Center, Department of Orthopedics and Rehabilitation, University of Vermont College of Medicine, Hilton Head, South Carolina, October 16 - 19. "Disability Ratings"; "Electrodiagnostic Studies"; "Manipulation: Theory, Practice, and Utilization."

28. The Challenge of the Lumbar Spine '88, sponsored by The Arthritis Foundation, San Antonio, Texas, November 9 - 13. "Non-specific Low Back Pain Syndrome -- What is it? Why does it happen?"

29. Fall Symposium on Back Pain, sponsored by American Back Society, San Francisco, California, December 1 - 3. "Clinical Spinal Neural Anatomy and Neurophysiology."

1989

30. Second International Interdisciplinary Chiropractic Seminar, sponsored by Sociedad Cientifico Quiropractica de Mexico, Mexico City, Mexico, February 16 - 19.

31. The 118th Annual Session and Western Scientific Assembly,

sponsored by California Medical Association, Anaheim, California, March 3 - 8. "Conservative Treatment: Objectives, Choices, Results."

32. Invited Lecture Series, sponsored by Palmer College of Chiropractic Graduate School, UCI, April 11. "Current and Future Clinical Research Status of the Chiropractic Adjustment."

33. Spring Symposium on Back Pain, sponsored by American Back Society, Cambridge, Massachusetts, April 13 - 15. "Differentiation of Acute and Chronic Back Pain."

34. The 9th Annual Conference on Evoked Potentials, sponsored by the American Society for Clinical Evoked Potentials, San Francisco, California, May 3 - 6. "Evaluation of Bowel, Bladder, and Sexual Disturbances by Electrophysiologic Methods"; "Evoked Responses in Clinical Neuro-Urology"; "Pudendal Nerve Evoked Spinal, Cortical, and Bulbocavernosus Reflex Responses: Methods and Applications"; "The Neurovisceral and Electrodiagnosis Evaluation of Patients with Thoracic Spinal Cord Injury."

35. The First Annual Multidisciplinary Symposium - Cervical Spine '89, sponsored by New York Chiropractic College, New York, September 12 - 16. Position: Master of Ceremonies. "Defining Spinal Manipulation"; "Complications of Cervical Manipulation."

36. XVIIth ILAR Congress of Rheumatology, sponsored by ILAR, Rio de Janeiro, Brazil, September 17 - 23. "Physiotherapy and Manipulation in the Management of Back Pain."

37. Congresso Internacional Sobre Coluna Vertebral, sponsored by Centro Brasileiro de Estudos de Coluna Vertebral Sao Paolo, September 24 - 26. "Physiotherapy and Manipulation in the Management of Back Pain"; "Defining Spinal Manipulation."

38. Tenth Annual National Occupational Low Back Pain Conference, sponsored by UCI Department of Neurology, Long Beach, California, October 18 - 21. "Acute versus Chronic Pain"; "Electrodiagnosis"; "Manipulation - Indications and Limitation"; "Rating Systems - Principles and Problems."

39. Perspectives on Pain - Low Back Pain: Mechanisms and Man-

agement. Sponsored by Challenge of the Lumbar Spine, San Francisco, California, November 2 - 5. "Differential Diagnosis of Low Back Pain"; "Social and Legal Aspects."

40. Fall Symposium on Back Pain, sponsored by the American Back Society, Las Vegas, Nevada, November 30 - December 2. "Complications of Cervical Spine Manipulation."

1990

41. Thirteenth Annual Evoked Potential and Electrodiagnostic Workshop, sponsored by UCI Department of Neurology, Irvine, California, February 2 - 4. "Bladder and Genital SEPs."

42. Advanced Seminar, sponsored by Motion Palpation Institute, Maui, Hawaii, February 25 - March 3. "Malpractice Suits: Reducing Frequency and Increasing Dependability"; "Research: Beneficial Response to Chiropractic"; "Relationship: Spinal Pathology, Patient Symptoms"; "Conservative Treatment and Approaches."

43. Back Pain in the Nineties: New Solutions to Old Problems, sponsored by University of Colorado Health Sciences Center, Denver, Colorado, March 16 - 17. "Scope of Back Pain Problems."

44. Primary Care and Diagnosis for the Chiropractic Profession, sponsored by the Orange County Chiropractic Association, Santa Ana, California, April 1. Position: Guest Speaker.

45. Bright Horizons for Chiropractic, sponsored by the American Chiropractic Association, Anchorage, Alaska, June 6 - 9. "Chiropractic Philosophy: The Relevance in the 90s."

46. Homecoming VI, "A Decade of Growth & Vision," sponsored by Palmer College of Chiropractic West, San Jose, California, October 18 - 21. "Failure of the Medical Pathology Model to Explain Back Pain."

47. Eleventh Annual Low Back Pain Conference, sponsored by University of Michigan Center for Occupational Health and Safety Engineering, Ann Arbor, Michigan, October 29 - 30. "Acute and Chronic Low Back Pain"; "Impairment Rating Systems."

48. The Many Faces of Pain conference, sponsored by the North

American Academy of Musculoskeletal Medicine, Tucson, Arizona, November 8 - 10. "The Failure of the Pathological Model to Explain the Presence of Back Pain"; "Advanced Seminar"; "Assessment of Craniocervical Dysfunction and Risk Factors for Chronic Pain: A Neurologist's View of the Role of Manual Medicine."

49. Fall Symposium on Back Pain, sponsored by the American Back Society, San Francisco, California, December 6 - 9. Course Chairman/Moderator.

1991

50. Neurology and Neurosurgery Review Courses, sponsored by Osler Institute, Los Angeles, California, January 6 - 12. "Electrodiagnosis of Spinal Disorders"; "Low Back Pain."

51. Fifty-eighth Annual Meeting, American Academy of Orthopedic Surgeons, Anaheim, California, March 7 - 12. "Indications and Results of Manipulative Treatment for Low Back Pain."

52. Medical Coordination of Workers' Compensation Claims Class, sponsored by Reliance Insurance Company, March 25. "Diagnostic testing and pain management."

53. Spring Symposium on Back Pain, sponsored by the American Back Society, Toronto, Canada, May 1 - 5. Course Director, Clinic Faculty. "The Clinical Evaluation of Patients with Neurovisceral Disorders."

54. World Chiropractic Congress 1991, sponsored by World Federation of Chiropractic, Toronto, Canada, May 4 - 5. Course chairman. "The Evolution and Importance of Spinal and Chiropractic Research."

55. Back Pain Current Concepts and Advances, 4th International Congress, sponsored by International Back Pain Society, Sydney, Australia, June 6 - 9. "The Neurophysiological Basis of Back Pain"; "Neurophysiological Assessment"; "Manipulation."

56. Occupational Spinal Disorders: Prevention, Diagnosis & Treatment, sponsored by University of Vermont, College of Medicine, Chicago, Illinois, September 22 - 24. "Pain"; "Conservative Treat-

ment Options"; "California Approaches to Disability Evaluation."

57. Fourth International Symposium, Physical Medicine Research Foundation, Toronto, Canada, September 27 - 29. "Manipulation"; "Failure of the Pathology Model to Predict Back Pain."

58. Report Writing Seminar, sponsored by Workers' Compensation Advisor and Stress Management Advisor, Los Angeles, California, October 19. "Apportionment in Physical Disabilities."

59. Fall Symposium on Back Pain, sponsored by American Back Society, San Francisco, California, December 11 - 15. "Current Status of Functional and Palpatory Diagnosis."

1992

60. Occupational Ergonomics: Work Evaluation and Prevention of Upper Limb and Back Disorders, sponsored by Workers' Evaluation and Rehabilitation Center: Department of Occupational Therapy, Loma Linda University, San Diego, California, February 24. "Failure of the Pathology Model to Explain Low Back Pain"; "Conservative Management of Low Back Pain."

61. Adjustment and Manipulation for Spinal Pain, sponsored by British Columbia College of Chiropractic, Vancouver, B.C., February 27 - March 1. "Failure of the Pathology Model to Explain Spinal Pain"; "Practical Applications of Spinal Pain Physiology"; "Acute vs. Chronic Pain."

62. Annual Session and Western Scientific Assembly, sponsored by California Medical Association, Anaheim, California, March 13 - 18. "The Role of Chiropractic Manipulation"; "The Role of Electrical Studies in Evaluation of Surgical Candidates."

63. Clinical Seminars in Sports Medicine, sponsored by Tarzana Regional Medical Center, Orthopedic Consultants Medical Group, and Cummings and Gillette Physical Therapy, Northridge, California, March 21. "Evaluation of Indications and Effectiveness of Spinal Manipulation."

64. National Football League Physicians Society Conference, sponsored by National Football League Physicians Society, San

Francisco, California, April 3 - 5. "The Role of Manipulation and Mobilization."

65. Canadian Chiropractic Association Convention '92, Regina, Saskatchewan, May 27 - 31. "Neurologic Assessment"; "Looking to the Twenty-First Century."

66. Fifth International Conference, sponsored by International Federation of Orthopaedic Manipulative Therapists, Vail, Colorado, June 1 - 5. "Chiropractic Research - Past and Present"; "Chiropractic - Let's Cooperate."

67. Seventh Annual Meeting, sponsored by North American Spine Society, Boston, Massachusetts, July 9 - 11. Moderator of session on Neurophysiology and Electrodiagnostics.

68. Occupational Spinal Disorders: Primary, Secondary, and Tertiary Care and Prevention, sponsored by Pride Research Foundation, University of Vermont, Dallas, Texas, October 1 - 3. Moderator on topic of Basic Science: "Classification and Diagnostic Tests for Back Pain"; "Structural Diagnostic Tests"; "Physical Therapy and Chiropractic Approaches to Secondary Prevention"; "Alternative Systems for Disability Evaluation."

69. Palmer College Graduating Class Commencement Address, Davenport, Iowa, October 16. Position: Keynote Speaker.

70. The Industrial Back, sponsored by the American Back Society, San Francisco, California, December 9 - 13. Moderator: "Taking an Effective Work Injury History."

1993

71. Occupational Ergonomics, February 22, San Diego, California. "Failure of Pathology to Explain Low Back Pain" and "Conservative Management of Low Back Pain."

72. Los Angeles College of Chiropractic 6th Annual Interdisciplinary Symposium - "Neurobiological Mechanisms of Spinal Manipulation." March 6, Whittier, California.

73. Orange County Chiropractic Society, March 9, Costa Mesa, California. "The Electrodiagnostic Evaluation of Spinal Disorders."

74. Chang Zheng Hospital, The Second Military Medical University of China, Shanghai Tang Du Hospital, The Fourth Military Medical University of China, Xian The Third Military Hospital, Beijing Medical University, Beijing, China. "Back Pain."

75. American Academy of Neurology Annual Meeting, April 25, New York City. Course Chairman. "Recent Advances in the Evaluation and Treatment of Back Pain."

76. San Francisco Spine Institute, April 30, San Francisco, California. "NASS Nomenclature/Chiropractic Language: Let's Call It What It Is" and "Electrodiagnostics: When Are EMG, NCV, SSEP Useful?"

77. Occupational Spinal Disorders, October 4 - 5, Pittsburgh, Pennsylvania. "The Anatomy and Physiology of Back Pain: What Do We Know?"

78. South Africa International Chiropractic Congress, October 10 - 15, Sun City, South Africa. "Failure of the Pathology Model to Explain Back Pain"; "Research Supporting the Efficacy of Chiropractic Manipulative Procedures."

1994

79. University of California, Irvine, February 11 - 13, Newport Beach, California. Course Chairman. "The Neurologist and Back Pain: Musculoskeletal Diagnosis and Management."

80. Occupational Ergonomics, February 23, San Diego, California. "Failure of Pathology to Explain Low Back Pain" and "Conservative Management of Low Back Pain."

81. California Medical Association, March 18, March 20, Anaheim, California. Course on Practical Neurology: The Old, and The New and Promising. "Multiple Views of Pain Management."

82. American Academy of Neurology, May 6, Washington, D.C. Course Chairman. "Recent Advances in the Evaluation and Treatment of Back Pain."

83. Occupational Spinal Disorders, September 25 - 26, Atlanta, Georgia. "Spinal Manipulation: The Legitimization of a Treatment Procedure."

84. American Back Society, November 30 - December 2, Los Angeles, California. "Guidelines for Managed Care of Low Back Pain" and "Myths Concerning Strokes Following Cervical Manipulation."

1995

85. Council on Chiropractic Education Convocation, New Orleans, Louisiana, January 27. "The Role of Chiropractic in an Integrated Health Care System."

86. Occupational Ergonomics: Work Evaluation and Prevention of Upper Limb and Back Disorders, sponsored by the University of Michigan, American Industrial Hygiene Association, San Diego Local Section, State Compensation Insurance Fund of California; San Diego, California, February 20 - 23. "Failure of the Pathology Model to Explain Low Back Pain"; "Conservative Management of Low Back Pain."

87. Netherlands Manual Therapy Association Conference, sponsored by NVMT, conducted via video at View Tech, Inc., Irvine, California, April 28. Topic: Lumbar and cervical spine.

88. Forty-seventh Annual Meeting, American Academy of Neurology, Seattle, May 6 - 13. Course Director. Topic: Recent Advances in the Treatment of Back Pain.

89. Texas Medical Association Spring Program, sponsored by University of Texas MD Anderson Cancer Center, Dallas, Texas, May 18 - 20. "Spinal Manipulation for Low Back Pain."

90. International Workers' Compensation Foundation Forum VII, sponsored by IABC, Newport Beach, California, May 23. "The Legitimization of a Treatment Procedure."

91. International Society for the Study of the Lumbar Spine 22nd Annual Meeting, Helsinki, Finland, June 18 - 22. "The correlation of palpable muscle spasm, pain, and activity scores and cerebral potentials evoked by the magnetic stimulation of paraspinal muscles." Session Chairman.

92. Chiropractic Centennial Foundation Convention, sponsored by World Federation of Chiropractic, Washington, D.C., July 5 - 7.

Co-Chair, Academic Program. "One Hundred Years of Chiropractic Research."

93. Sixteenth Annual Occupational Spinal Disorders Conference, sponsored by Canadian Back Institute, Toronto, Canada, September 10 - 11. "How to Prescribe Optimal Manipulative Therapy"; "How to Handle the Legal Implications of Aggressive Therapy."

94. Chiropractic Centennial Foundation Celebration, sponsored by World Federation of Chiropractic, Davenport, Iowa, September 14 - 16. "One Hundred years of Chiropractic Research." Workshop on spinal neurophysiology and somatovisceral reflexes.

95. Chiropractic Centennial Celebration, sponsored by Doctors of Chiropractic Liaison Council, Tokyo, Japan, November 18 - 19. "One Hundred Years of Chiropractic Research"; "Neurophysiological theories on which chiropractic in based"; "The clinical research which has established chiropractic as an accepted health care profession."

1996

96. Defending the Personal Injury Lawsuit, sponsored by State Farm Mutual Insurance Company, Los Angeles, California, February 24. "Spinal Manipulation and Chiropractic Treatment for Spinal Pain Syndromes."

97. Occupational Ergonomics: Work Evaluation and Prevention of Upper Limb and Back Disorders, sponsored by University of Michigan and State Compensation Insurance, San Diego, California, February 28. "Failure of Pathology to Explain Low Back Pain"; "Conservative Management of Low Back Pain."

98. The Puzzling Relationship of Vertigo and Cervical Spine, sponsored by the European Chiropractors' Union, Geneva, Switzerland, May 16 - 18. "Incidence, Risk Factors, and Mechanisms of Vertebral Basilar Artery Ischemia Following Cervical Manipulation"; "A Critical Analysis of Vertiginous Symptoms in the Practice of Chiropractic."

99. Palmer College of Chiropractic West, graduation ceremony, Santa Clara, California, June 14. Commencement Address: "Chiro-

practic is an Accepted Profession: What Do I Do Now?"

100. Recent Advances in the Treatment of Low Back Pain, 11th ISSLS Instructional Course, sponsored by Hospital for Joint Diseases,. "Indications for Clinical Neurophysiological Testing"; "Spinal Manipulation: When? How? Who?" New York City, June 22,1996.

101. SPINE Combined Grand Rounds, sponsored by the University of New York, Syracuse, Department of Physical Medicine and Research,. "The Failure of Pathological Model to Explain Back Pain and its Consequence in Guideline Development." June 24,1996.

102. Chiropractic Managed Care: Developing Successful Integration Strategies, sponsored by the National Managed Health Care Congress,. "A New Proposal for Standardizing Health Care Providers." Coronado, California, July 23, 1996.

103. 17th Annual Occupational Spinal Disorders Conference: Return to Work with Pain; Crossing the Barrier, sponsored by Canadian Back Institute, "Chiropractic: The second 100 years"; Session: The Barrier of Research. Topic: "Why should we look?" Calgary, Alberta, Canada, September 15 – 16,1996

104. American Back Society and Saint Mary's Spine Center. Diagnosis & Treatment of Back Pain - The Next Level, sponsored by "Credentialing of health care providers to qualify for managed care referral panels - including compliance with minimum standards and specific treatment protocols"; "Legitimization of manipulation - for who and how will you provide this treatment." San Francisco, California, December 12 – 14, 1996.

1997

105. Clinical Neurology in Chiropractic Practice, in Patients' Interest, sponsored by the International College of Australia, Ltd. and Chiropractors' Association of Australia,. Course lecturer on the clinical aspects of neurophysiology. Sydney and Brisbane, Australia, February 15 – 16, 1997.

106. 1997 World Chiropractic Congress, sponsored by World Federation of Chiropractic, The Chiropractic Council of Japan, and the

World Health Organization, - 8. Course chairman. "Cerebrovascular complications of manipulation - Our current level of understanding"; "The future of research into the role of manipulation in the treatment of the cervical spine." Tokyo, Japan, June 6, 1997.

107. American Academy of Pain Management 8th Annual Clinical Meeting. Workshop topic: "Lower back pain: Finding common ground - Chiropractic Perspective." Las Vegas, Nevada, September 18, 1997.

108. American Association of Electrodiagnostic Medicine 44th Annual Scientific Meeting, 20th Annual Courses and Workshops. Special Interest Group Session topic: "Electrophysiologic studies in bowel and bladder problems and sexual dysfunction." San Diego, California, September 18, 1997.

109. NCMIC 1997 Defense Counsel Seminar, presented by National Chiropractic Mutual Insurance Company. Lecture topic: "A new look at stroke: The facts of an exhaustive study." Chicago, Illinois, October 3 – 4, 1997.

110. The College of Physicians of Columbia University and Oxford Health Plans. Alternatives in Patient Care. Presentation: "Chiropractic: Clinical Effectiveness and Contraindications." New York City, October 22, 1997.

111. American Back Society and Stanford University, The Diagnosis and Treatment of Neck and Back Pain -- The Integrative Approach. "Evidence that muscles play a role in back pain." San Francisco, California, December 10 – 13, 1997.

1998

112. Occupational Ergonomics: Work Evaluation and Prevention of Upper Limb and Back Disorders, sponsored by University of Michigan, American Industrial Hygiene Association (San Diego Local Section), and State Compensation Insurance Fund, San Diego, California, February 4. Presentations: "Failure of Pathology to Explain Low Back Pain"; "Conservative Management of Low Back Pain."

113. Seventh Annual Workers' Compensation and Occupational Medicine Seminar, sponsored by SEAK, Inc., and The American

College of Occupational and Environmental Medicine, San Francisco, California, March 11. Presentations: "Spinal Manipulation: Scientific Update," "Low Back Pain Risk Factors."

114. Hospital for Joint Diseases Spine Center symposium: Management of Recalcitrant Back Disorders, sponsored by New York Chiropractic College, New York, New York, April 4. Presentations: "History and Physical: Red Flags," "International advances in chiropractic."

115. 1998 California Chiropractic Association Convention, Clinical Concepts Workshops and Tug-of-War II, The Great Debate. San Diego, California, June 27.

116. North American Spine Society 13th Annual Meeting. Presentation: "Sixty-four cases of CVAs following cervical spine manipulative therapy." Symposium: "Non-surgical Back Pain Management." San Francisco, California, October 30.

117. Canadian Heritage Conference, 1st Scientific Chiropractic Symposium, sponsored by the University of Calgary. Lecture: "The Evolution of Chiropractic Research: A Personal Perspective." Calgary, Alberta, November 15.

118. Palmer College of Chiropractic West, commencement speech at the graduation ceremony. "The Search for a Post-Graduate Mentor." San Jose, California, December 11.

1999

119. Alternative Medicine: Implications for Clinical Practice and State-of-the-Science Symposia, sponsored by Harvard Medical School, Department of Continuing Education. Lecture: "Chiropractic." Boston, Massachusetts, February 28 - March 2.

120. Occupational Ergonomics: Work Evaluation and Prevention of Upper Limb and Back Disorders, sponsored by University of Michigan Center for Occupational Health and Safety Engineering and by American College of Occupational and Environmental Medicine. Lectures: "Failure of Pathology to Explain Low Back Pain," "Conservative Management of Low Back Pain." San Diego, California, March 17.

121. World Federation of Chiropractic 5th WFC Congress and Conference. Lecture: "The Neurological Effects of the Adjustment." Auckland, New Zealand, May 20 - 22.

122. Advanced Diagnosis and Treatment of Neck and Back Pain: The Integrated Approach. Sponsored by American Back Society and St. Mary's Regional Medical Center. Lecture: "A Century of Progress in Spinal Care." Las Vegas, Nevada, December 9.

2000

123. Occupational Ergonomics: Work Evaluation and Prevention of Upper Limb and Back Disorders. Sponsored by University of Michigan. Lecture: "Failure of Pathology to Explain Low Back Pain" and "Conservative Management of Low Back Pain." Los Angeles, California, March 1.

124. Complementary and Alternative Medicine symposia. Sponsored by Harvard Medical School, Department of Continuing Education. Lecture: "Chiropractic." Boston, Massachusetts, March 12.

125. Anglo-European College of Chiropractic/British Chiropractic Association Joint Conference. Lecture: "What is the relationship between spinal pain, disability, and pathology?" "Cervicogenic headaches - what is our current level of understanding?" "Research and interprofessional cooperation as the basis for future understanding of neck pain." Bournemouth, England, March 31-April 1.

126. Canadian Memorial Chiropractic College, 55th Convocation. Speech: "The importance of a mentor in maximizing the opportunities of a graduating chiropractor." Toronto, Canada, May 5.

127. Osteopathic Physicians and Surgeons of California 8th Annual Seminar. Guest speaker. Dana Point, California, June 2.

128. Michigan State University, College of Osteopathic Medicine. Patenge Distinguished Lecturer. "Evolution of manipulation research." Lansing, Michigan, July 20.

129. International Conference on Spinal Manipulation, sponsored by Foundation for Chiropractic Education and Research, Minnesota Chiropractic Association, and Northwestern College of Chi-

ropractic. Keynote presentation: "Strengths and weaknesses of current chiropractic neurological theories." Bloomington, Michigan, September 23.

130. Defense Counsel Seminar, presented by NCMIC Insurance Company. Presentation: "CVA: A clinical analysis." San Antonio, Texas, October 6.

131. Advanced Diagnosis and Treatment for Neck and Back Pain 2000, sponsored by American Back Society and Allegheny General Hospital. Lecture: "Differential diagnosis of back pain - has it changed?" Vancouver, B.C., December 7.

2001

132. Chiropractic Neurology Seminar, sponsored by the Israel Chiropractic Association. Topics of discussion: Current status of neurologic theories of chiropractic; Differential diagnosis of patients with spinal pain; Modern models to explain spinal pain; Cervicogenic headaches; Grand rounds/presentation of cases. Lecture: "Chiropractic and Spinal Manipulation. Integration into Modern Health Care." Workshop: "The neurological examination in the chiropractic office." Tel Aviv, Israel, January 17 and 19.

133. Harvard Complimentary and Integrative Medicine Symposium, Harvard Medical School, Department of Continuing Education. Lecture: "Chiropractic. Clinical Practice and State of the Science." Boston, Massachusetts, February 11.

134. American Academy of Orthopedic Surgeons 68th Annual Meeting Scientific Program. Symposium: "Complementary and Alternative Medicine (CAM) and the Orthopedic Surgeon." San Francisco, California, February 28.

135. Occupational Ergonomics: Work Evaluation and Prevention of Upper Limb and Back Disorders. Sponsored by University of Michigan. Lecture: "Failure of pathology to explain low back pain." "Conservative management of low back pain." Los Angeles, California, March 12.

136. World Federation of Chiropractic 6th Biennial Congress. Lecture: "The role of chiropractic in the management of neck pain,

back pain, and headaches." Workshop: "The basic neurological examination." Paris, France, May 25.

137. Research Agenda Conference VI: Advancing the Science of Chiropractic. Co-sponsored by the U.S. Health Resources and Services Administration, Bureau of Health Professions, and the National Center for Complementary Alternative Medicine (NCCAM). Moderator: "Neurological Approaches to Researching the Subluxation and the Adjustment." Panelist "Chiropractic Theory Revisited: Lessons from the Break-Out Sessions." Kansas City, Missouri, July 28.

138. Florida Chiropractic Association Meeting National Convention and Expo. Lecture, "Benefits, Risks, and Theoretical Basis for Cervical Manipulation." Orlando, Florida, August 11.

2002

139. Occupational Ergonomics: Work Evaluation and Prevention of Upper Limb and Back Disorders. Sponsored by The University of Michigan. Lecture: "Failure of Pathology to Explain Low Back Pain." "Conservative Management of Low Back Pain." Los Angeles, California, February 18.

140. ACC/RACVII Conference 2002: Faculty and Personnel Development: The Power of Human Potential. Co-sponsored by the U.S. Health Resources and Services Administration, Bureau of Health Professions, and the National Center for Complementary and Alternative Medicine (NCCAM). Symposium: moderator on "State of the Art Presentations." Panelist on "Past, Present and Future Chiropractic Education and Research: Panel Discussion." New Orleans, Louisiana, March 14-16.

141. American Academy of Neurology 54th Annual Meeting. Course on: "Carotid and Vertebral Dissection." Lecture: "Neck Manipulation and Stroke". Denver, Colorado, April 14-17.

142. American Academy of Neurology 54th Annual Meeting. Course on: "Complementary and Alternative Medicine in Neurologic Disorders." Lecture: "Chiropractic and Spinal Manipulation." Denver, Colorado, April 14-17.

143. Physical Medicine and Research Foundation Symposium

on "Symptom, Diagnostic and Disability Validation: Improving Patients Outcomes". Presentation "Medication, Chiropractic, Surgery, or a Pamphlet for the Treatment of Neck and Back Pain. How do we Choose?" Toronto, Canada. September 26-29, 2002.

144. Palmer West College of Chiropractic All School Assembly. Invited Talk on "Research in the Legal Arena" San Jose, California. October 28, 2002.

145. North American Spine Society 17th Annual Meeting. Co-Chairman of symposium titled "Spinal Manipulation in Spine Care: Who? Why? When?" Title of presentation "The Status of Spinal Manipulation. Utilization, Clinical Trials, Guideline recommendations." and "Complications of Spinal Manipulation. Minor side effects, Disc Herniation, Arterial Dissections". Montreal, Canada. October 29-November 2, 2002.

2003

146. Occupational Ergonomics: Work Evaluation and Prevention of Upper Limb and Back Disorders. Sponsored by The University of Michigan. Lecture: "Failure of Pathology to Explain Low Back Pain." "Conservative Management of Low Back Pain." Los Angeles, California, February 25, 2003.

147. ACC/RAC VIII Research Agenda Conference. Co-sponsored by the U.S. Health Resources and Services Administration, Bureau of Health Professions, and the National Center for Complementary and Alternative Medicine (NCCAM). Symposium Moderator on "Influencing Public Policy on Chiropractic: How evidence impacts policy development, legislation and litigation". Presentation on "Overview of the role of research in chiropractic's hope for recognition". New Orleans, March 13-16, 2003

148. Japan Spine Research Society Annual Meeting. "Non-surgical approaches to the patient with spinal pain. Clinical research, theories and indications" Fukuoka Japan. April 2-7, 2003

149. World Federation of Chiropractic 7th Biennial Congress. Speaker "Appropriateness of Common Treatments in Neck Pain, The Bone and Joint Decade 2000-2010 Neck Pain Task Force".

150. Florida Chiropractic Association. Panel member "Risks of Neck Manipulation" Orlando, Florida, May 1-3, 2003.

151. Federation of Chiropractic Licensing Board 77th Annual Congress. 13th Annual Joseph Janse Lecture. " Make Research the Friend of Chiropractic. The Role of the Licensing Boards". Orlando Florida, May 1, 2003.

152. South African Chiropractic Congress. Presentation on "The Appropriateness of Common Treatments for Neck Pain" and Neck Manipulation and Stroke: A Clinician's View" Durban, South Africa. September 24-27, 2003

153. North American Spine Society 18th Annual meeting. Symposium co-chairman "My aching Sacroiliac" Presentation "Examination and Differential Diagnosis of Sacroiliac Syndrome"

154. Pre-Course on A Multidisciplinary Approach to the Essentials in Spine Care" Presentation topic "Chiropractic Approach to Spine Management". San Diego, October 21-25, 2003.

155. American Back Society Annual Meeting. "Advanced diagnosis and treatment for neck and back pain." Keynote Address titled " Non-surgical and surgical approaches to patients with spinal pain. What does the scientific literature tell us? Las Vegas, November 13-15, 2003.

2004

156. Occupational Ergonomics: Work Evaluation and Prevention of Upper Limb and Back Disorders. Sponsored by The University of Michigan. Lecture: "Failure of Pathology to Explain Low Back Pain." "Conservative Management of Low Back Pain." Los Angeles, California, February 25, 2004.

157. ACC/RAC VIII Research Agenda Conference. Co-sponsored by the U.S. Health Resources and Services Administration, Bureau of Health Professions, and the National Center for Complementary and Alternative Medicine (NCCAM). Symposium Moderator on "Results and clinical relevance of basic science research." Panelist and presenter – "Best Practices for Chiropractic: Policy Cure of Policy Disaster". Las Vegas March 12-14., 2004.

158. American Academy of Orthopedic Medicine. 21st Annual Conference and Scientific Seminar. "The Lumbo Sacral Spine." Presentation on "The Feasibility of a Non-profit Back Pain Foundation." La Jolla, CA. April 21-24, 2004.

159. International Society for the Study of the Lumbar Spine. Spineweek 2004. Symposium Chairman and Speaker – "Assessing the Effectiveness and Complications of Neck Pain Treatment Options." Porto Portugal. May 30, 2004.

160. American Back Society. "Are Your Treatments Evidence Based?" Las Vegas December 9, 2004.

2005

161. Occupational Ergonomics: Work Evaluation and Prevention of Upper Limb and Back Disorders. Sponsored by The University of Michigan. Lecture: "Failure of Pathology to Explain Low Back Pain." "Conservative Management of Low Back Pain." Los Angeles, California, February, 2005.

162. ACC/RAC IX Research Agenda Conference. Co-sponsored by the U.S. Health Resources and Services Administration, Bureau of Health Professions, and the National Center for Complementary and Alternative Medicine (NCCAM). Symposium Moderator on "Results and Clinical Relevance of Basic Science Research", and "Best Practices for Chiropractic: A Policy Cure or Policy Disaster" Las Vegas March 12-14.

163. Southern California University of Health Sciences, Whittier, CA – Visiting Scholar.

164. State Farm Insurance Meeting. "Controlling Health Care Through Evidence Based Guidelines." Bloomington, IL, April 14, 2005.

165. European Chiropractic Union, "Chiropractic Manipulation: Treatment of choice for patients with spinal pain" "A Search for the Identity of Chiropractic. A 40-year personal odyssey through association with chiropractic, non-chiropractic manipulation, and spine research societies." Cyprus, May 5-7, 2005

166. World Federation of Chiropractic. "The WHO Bone and Joint Decade Neck Pain Task Force: The significance of its research findings for the chiropractic profession." Sydney, Australia. June 16, 2005.

167. World Federation of Chiropractic. Debate on "A firm grounding in the philosophy of chiropractic is more important than a firm grounding in the scientific basis of chiropractic for practicing chiropractors." Sydney, Australia. June 16, 2005.

168. Australian Spine Research Foundation. "Update on Research Method. Basic Science Research." Sydney, Australia. June 18, 2005.

169. Palmer University, Davenport Iowa, Visiting Scholar presentation to students, July 17-19, 2005

170. NCMIC, "Update on Etiological Factors Associated With Cerebral Arterial Dissection." Des Moines Iowa, September 27-30, 2005

171. American Back Society San Francisco. "Clinical Application of the ACOEM Occupational and Environmental Medicine Practice Guidelines." November 16-19, 2005.

172. Palmer College West. Commencement Address. San Jose, CA, December 8, 2005

2006

173. Northwestern University of Health Sciences, Homecoming. "Changing Chiropractic Identity and Practice in the Era of Evidence-Based Health Care." Minneapolis, February 2-5, 2006.

174. Ad Hoc Chiropractic Strategic Planning Conference. Consensus Session I: The Preferred Future – Tangible objectives for professional credibility and cultural authority. Lombard, IL, February 17-19, 2006.

175. American Academy of Pain Management 22nd Annual Meeting. "Spinal Manipulation: Evidence-Based Applications." San Diego February 25-26, 2006

176. ACC/ Research Agenda Conference. Session Title: "Evidence

for the Risk and Benefits of Spinal Manipulation". Washington DC, March 15-18, 2006

177. New York State Chiropractic Association. "Surviving the Era of Evidence Based Guidelines." New York, April 29-30, 2006

178. Florida Chiropractic Association. "Changing Chiropractic Identity and Practice in the Era of Evidence Based Health Care." Kissimmee, Florida, August 25-26, 2006.

179. Canadian Chiropractic Association Convention. "Changing Chiropractic Identity and Practice in the Era of Evidence Based Healthcare." Vancouver, B.C., November 18, 2006.

180. Canadian Chiropractic Association Convention. "Changing Chiropractic Identity and Practice in the Era of Evidence Based Healthcare." Vancouver, B.C., November 18, 2006.

181. American Back Society. "Patient Empowerment: The Newest Component in the Decision Making Process" Las Vegas, December 13-15, 2006.

2007

182. ACC/Research Agenda Conference. "Understanding and Communicating the Risk of Manipulation to Non-DCs." Phoenix, Arizona, March 16, 2007.

183. World Federation of Chiropractic 9th Biennial Congress. "Bone and Joint Decade, Neck Pain Task Force Report". Vilamoura, Portugal, May 16, 2007.

184. Joint Physical Medicine & Rehabilitation Pain Management Symposium. "Chiropractic Controversy in the Treatment of Neck and Back Pain." Las Vegas, July 27-28, 2007.

185. Florida Chiropractic Association. Plenary: "Why do we need another Task Force on Neck Pain? Why should the results of the Task Force be considered?" "How does the Scientific Evidence advise us on the examination of patients and the documentation of patient response to treatment?" Kissimmee, Florida, August 17-18, 2007.

186. Swiss Spine Institute. International Symposium on the Task Force on Neck Pain and Its Associated Disorders. "History, Composition and Process of the Task Force", "The Expected Impact and Dissemination of the Task Force Findings". Bern, Switzerland. September 27-28, 2007.

187. Palmer College of Chiropractic. "Presentation on Neck Pain Task Force". Chicago, October 5, 2007.

188. North American Spine Society 22nd Annual Meeting. Symposium: "The Best Evidence Synthesis of the Bone and Joint Decade 2000-2010: Task Force on Neck Pain and its Associated Disorders". Austin, Texas, October 26, 2007.

189. Congress on Managing Neck Conditions. "Introduction and history of the Task Force", "Putting it All Together-What does it Mean". Regina, Saskatchewan. November 15-16,2007.

190. Chiropractor's Association of Saskatchewan. Banquet speaker. "Celebrating 100 years of Chiropractic in Saskatchewan and Canada". Regina, Saskatchewan. November 17, 2007.

2008

191. World Congress on Neck Pain. "Presentation on Bone & Joint Decade Neck Pain Task Force. Los Angeles". January 20-22, 2008.

192. California Chiropractic Association Annual Convention. "The Bone and Joint Decade 2000-2010: Task Force on Neck Pain and its Associated Disorders". Reno, Nevada, February 22, 2008.

193. Orange County Chiropractic Association. "The Bone and Joint Decade 2000-2010: Task Force on Neck Pain and its Associated Disorders". April 8, 2008.

194. California Orthopaedic Association Annual Meeting. Discussion: "New Spine Treatment Guidelines – Presentation on Bone and Joint Decade". Newport Beach, California, May 18, 2008.

195. American Back Society 25th Anniversary Meeting. Director: "Evidence Informed Management of Low Back Pain without Surgery". Session: "Findings and Impact of the Bone and Joint Decade 2000-2010 Task Force on Neck Pain and its Associated Disorders".

Las Vegas, June 18-19, 2008.

196. Palmer College of Chiropractic Homecoming. Presentation: "The Establishment of Cultural Authority on Spine Related Disorders". Davenport, Iowa, August 9, 2008.

197. Southern California University of Health Sciences. "Establishment of Cultural Authority on Spine Disorders". Long Beach, California, August 16, 2008.

198. Florida Chiropractic Association National Convention. "Evidence Informed Management of Chronic Low Back Pain without Surgery". Clearwater, Florida, August 23, 2008.

199. North American Spine Society 23rd Annual Meeting. "Current state of the art for managing chronic low back pain; Pain mechanisms and treatment principles". Toronto, Ontario, Canada, October 14, 2008.

200. WHO Congress on Traditional Medicine. Presentation: "The Research Status of Western Manual Health Care". Beijing, China, November 8, 2008.

201. American Academy of Physical Medicine and Research. Faculty Member: "The Bone and Joint Decade 2000-2010 Task Force on Neck Pain and Its Associated Disorders: Implications for the Physiatrist"; "Evidence-Informed Management of Chronic Low Back Pain Without Surgery, Part I; Evidence-Informed Management of Chronic Low Back Pain Without Surgery, Part II." San Diego, California, November 20-21, 2008.

2009

202. Karolinska Institute. Whiplash Conference. "Neck Pain Task Force, Introduction, Sponsorship, Process", "Treatment of Whiplash". Stockholm, Sweden. April 30, 2009.

203. Neprapathy Conference. Presentation: "Conceptual Model for Neck Pain"; "Current Status of the Delivery of Care to Patients with Low Back Pain". Stockholm, Sweden, March 27, 2009.

204. World Federation of Chiropractic 10th Biennial Congress. Presentation: "The Bone and Joint Decade Neck Pain Task Force

– New Model of Management of Neck Pain". Montreal, Quebec, Canada, April 30, 2009.

205. New York Chiropractic College. 50th Homecoming Celebration. "Cultural Authority through Education and Research". Seneca, New York. July 18, 2009.

206. D'Youville College. "Cultural Authority through Education and Research". Buffalo, New York. July 21, 2009.

BIBLIOGRAPHY
Scott Haldeman, DC, PhD, MD

THESES AND BOOKS

1. Haldeman, S: Changes in the structure and function of sciatic nerve caused by constriction. M.Sc. thesis (Physiology). Faculty of Mathematics and Natural Sciences, University of Pretoria, South Africa, November, 1969.

2. Haldeman, S: "Evidence in Favor of Glutamate as a Mediator of Synaptic Transmission." Ph.D. Thesis, Department of Physiology, University of British Columbia, Vancouver, B.C., Canada, January, 1973.

3. Haldeman, S (editor): *Modern Developments in the Principles and Practice of Chiropractic.* Appleton-Century Crofts, New York, 1980.

4. LeCorre, F, Haldeman, S: *La Chiropraxie* (French) 1986. Presses Universitaires de France, Paris, 1986.

5. Haldeman, S (editor): *Principles and Practice of Chiropractic.* Appleton & Lange, Connecticut, 1992.

6. Haldeman, S., Chapman-Smith, D., Petersen, D. (eds): *Guidelines for Chiropractic Quality Assurance and Practice Parameters.* Aspen Publishers, Maryland, 1993.

7. Haldeman, S (guest editor): *Neurologic Clinics. Lower Back Pain*, Volume 17, Number 1. W.B. Saunders Company, Philadelphia, 1999.

8. Haldeman, S, Kirkaldy-Willis, W, Bernard, T: *An Atlas of Back Pain*, Parthenon Publishing, New York, 2002.

9. Haldeman S (Editor in Chief) Principles and Practice of Chiropractic, Third Edition. McGraw-Hill (New York) 2005.

ARTICLES AND BOOK CHAPTERS

1. Haldeman, S: "The First Impressions of the Synchro-Therme as

a Skin Temperature Reading Instrument." *J. Can. Chiropr. Assn.* 14 (1): 7, 8, 22, 1970.

2. Haldeman, S: "Observations Made Under Test Conditions with the Synchro-Therme." *J. Can. Chiropr. Assn.* 14 (3): 9-12, 1970.

3. Haldeman, S, Hartwick, WG: "Chiropractic in British Columbia and its Relationship to Industrial First Aid." *The Industrial First Aid Attendant* 30 #6, 1971.

4. Haldeman, S, Drum, D: "The Compression Subluxation." *J. Clin. Chiropr. Arch.* 1: 10-21, 1971.

5. Haldeman, S, Hammerich, K: "The Evolution of Neurology and the Concept of Chiropractic." *J. Can. Chiropr. Assn.* 15 4: 20-25, 1971.

6. Haldeman, S: "The Interactions Between the Somatic and Visceral Nervous Systems." *Am. Chiropr. Assn.* J. 5: 57-64, 1971.

7. Haldeman, S, Meyer, BJ: "The Effect of Constriction on the Conduction of the Action Potential in the Sciatic Nerve." *S. Afr. Med. J.* 44: 902-906, 1970. Abstracted: Yearbook of Neurology and Neurosurgery, 1972.

8. Haldeman, S, Meyer, BJ: "The Effect of Experimental Constriction of the Structures of the Sciatic Nerve." *S. Afr. Med. J.* 44: 888-892, 1970. Abstracted: Yearbook of Neurology and Neurosurgery, 1972.

9. Haldeman, S, Huffman, RD, Marshall, KC, McLennan, H: "The Antagonism of the Glutamate-Induced and Synaptic Excitations of Thalamic Neurons." *Brain Research* 39: 419-425, 1972.

10. Haldeman, S, McLennan, H: "The Antagonistic Action of Glutamic Acid Diethylester Towards Amino Acid-Induced and Synaptic Excitations of Central Neurons." *Brain Research* 45: 393-400, 1972

11. Haldeman, S, McLennan, H: "The Actions of the Dimethyl and Diethyl Esters of Glutamic Acid on Glutamate Uptake by Brain Tissue." *J. Neurochem.* 20: 629-631, 1972

12. Haldeman, S: "Spinal and Paraspinal Receptors." *Am. Chiropr. Assn. J.* 6, 5: 25-31, 1972.

13. Haldeman, S: "Autoregulation of Renal Blood Flow and Glo-

merular Filtration Rate." *Internat. Rev. Chiropr.* 25 5: 17-19, 1972.

14. Haldeman, S: "Histamine: The Ultimate Stimulator of Gastric Acid Secretion?." *J. Can. Chiropr. Assn.* 16 3: 25-29, 1972.

15. Haldeman, S: "A Light and Electron Microscopic Study of the Sciatic Nerve of the South African Frog." *J. Clin. Chiropr. Arch.* 2: 50-62, 1972.

16. Haldeman, S: "Renal Function and the Nervous System." *Int. Chiropr. Assn. Rev.* 3: 4-7, 1972. (Reprinted in *J. Can. Chiropr. Assn.* 16 1: 22, March-April, 1972).

17. Haldeman, S, McLennan, H: "The Action of Two Inhibitors of Glutamic Acid Uptake Upon Amino Acid-Induced and Synaptic Excitations of Thalamic Neurons." *Brain Res.* 63: 123-129, 1973.

18. Haldeman, S: Address to the 27th Annual Convention of Industrial First Aid Attendants. "Interruption of Normal Peripheral Nerve Function." *The Industrial First Aid Attendant* 32 31: 5-7, 1973.

19. Haldeman, S: "The Safety-Pin Cycle Brought Up To-Date." *Int. Rev. Chiropr.* 26 5: 14-15, 1973.

20. Haldeman, S: "The Release from Abnormal Musculoskeletal Sensory Activity." Chapter 11. In Schwarts HS (ed) *Mental Health and Chiropractic*, New York, Session Publishers, 1973.

21. Haldeman, S: "Referred Pain-Extraspinal Symptoms of Spinal Origin." *J. Can. Chiropr. Assn.* 8-11, 1973.

22. Haldeman, S: "Neurophysiological Concepts of Importance to Chiropractors." *J. Can. Chiropr. Assn.* 18 2: 6, 1974.

23. Haldeman, S: "The Influence of Autonomic Nervous System on Cerebral Blood Flow." *J. Can. Chiropr. Assn.* 6-15, 1974.

24. Haldeman, S: "Importance of Record Keeping in Evaluation of Chiropractic Results." *A.C.A. J. of Chiropr.* Vol IX:S 108-114, 1975.

25. Haldeman, S, Gillies, J, Haldeman, J, Patterson, C: "Low Back Pain: A Study of Fifty Patients on a Group Exercise Program." *Physiotherapy Canada* 27: 71-77, 1975.

26. Haldeman, S: "The Importance of Neurophysiological Research into the Principles of Spinal Manipulation." In Goldstein, M. (3d) "The Research Status of Spinal Manipulative Therapy", NINCDS Monograph #15, HEW (Washington, D.C.), pp 183-187, 1975.

27. Haldeman, S: "The Pathophysiology of the Spinal Subluxation." In Goldstein, M. (ed) *The Research Status of Spinal Manipulative Therapy.* HEW (Washington, D.C.), pp 217-225, 1975. NINCDS Monograph #5.

28. Haldeman S: "Why Chiropractic Needs a Post-Graduate School." *J. Can. Chiropr. Assn.* 19, 3: 15, 37, 38, 1975.

29. Haldeman, S: "Why One Cause of Back Pain" in Buerger, A.A., Tobis, J.S., Thomas, C.C. (eds): *Approaches to the Validation of Manipulative Therapy.* Springfield, IL, pp 189-199, 1976.

30. Haldeman, S: "What is Meant by Manipulation." In Buerger, A.A., Tobis, J.S., Thomas, C.C. (eds): *Approaches to the Validation of Manipulative Therapy.* Springfield, IL, pp 301-304, 1976.

31. Haldeman, S: "The Importance of Neurophysiological Research into the Principles of Spinal Manipulation." *Europ. Chiropr. Union Bull.* 24, 1:10-18, 1976.

32. Haldeman, S: "A Profession Deserves a Professional Conference." *J. Can. Chiropr. Assn.* 20 1: 7, 1976.

33. Haldeman, S: "The Neurophysiologic Mechanism of Pain." *Am. Chiropr. Assn.* J. 10: 53-66, 1976.

34. Haldeman, S: "The Importance of Research in the Principles and Practice of Chiropractic." *J. Can. Chiropr. Assn.* 20, 3: 7-10, 1976.

35. Haldeman, S: "Chiropractic - A Dying Cult or a Growing Profession." *Musings Quarterly*, Journal of the Medical Undergraduate Society, University of British Columbia. 1 (11): 53-58, 1975. (Reprinted in: *International Review of Chiropractic*, March, 1976).

36. Haldeman, S: "The Intervertebrate Neuromuscular Junction. A Model for the Demonstration of the Principles of Neural Transmission Across the Synapse." *Int. Rev. Chiropr.* 31 4: 17-23, 1977.

37. Haldeman, S: "The Clinical Basis for Discussion of Mechanisms of Manipulative Therapy." In Korr IM (ed): *Neurobiologic Mechanisms in Manipulative Therapy*. New York, Plenum Press, pp 53-75, 1978.

38. Haldeman, S: "Basic Principles in Establishing a Chiropractic Clinical Trial." *Am. Chiropr. Assn. J.* 12: 33-37, 1978.

39. Haldeman, S: "Basic Concepts in Multiple Sclerosis." *Am. Chiropr. Assn. J.* 13: 37-47, 1979.

40. Haldeman, S: "Spinal Manipulative Therapy in the Management of Low Back Pain." In Finneson, B.E. (ed): *Low Back Pain*. Philadelphia, Lippencott, Co., 2nd Edition, p 245, 1980.

41. Greenland, S, Reisbord, LS, Haldeman, S, Buerger, AA: "Controlled Clinical Trials of Manipulation: A Review and a Proposal." *J. Occ. Med.* 22:10: 670-676, 1980.

42. Haldeman, S: "The Neurophysiology of Spinal Pain Syndromes." In Haldeman, S. (ed) *Modern Developments in the Principles of Chiropractic*. New York, Appleton-Century C Crofts, pp 119-141, 1980.

43. Haldeman, S: "Pain Physiology as a Neurologic Model for Manipulation." *Manuelle Medicine* 19, 1981.

44. Haldeman, S, Goldman, JW, Hyde, J, Pribram, HFW: "Progressive Supranuclear Palsy, Computed Tomography, and Response to Antiparkinsonian Drugs." *Neurology* 31: 442-445, 1981.

45. Bhatia, NN, Bradley, WE, Haldeman, S, Johnson, BK: "Continuous Urodynamic Monitoring." International Continence Society Proceedings, pp 39-41, Lund, Sweden, 1981.

46. Bhatia, NN, Bradley, WE, Haldeman, S, Johnson, BK: "Continuous Monitoring of Bladder and Urethral Pressures: New Technique." *Urology* 18: 207-210, 1981.

47. Haldeman, S: "Prospects for Research in a Faculty of Chiropractic." In *Arch. of the California Chiropractic Association*, Second Half, Volume 5, Number 2, 1981.

48. Haldeman, S, Glick, M., Bhatia, NN, Johnson, BK, Bradley, WE: "Colonometry, Cystometry and Evoked Potentials in Multiple Scle-

rosis." *Arch. Neurol.* 39: 698-701, 1982.

49. Bhatia, NN, Bradley, WE, Haldeman, S, Johnson, BK: "Continuous Ambulatory Urodynamic Monitoring." *Brit. J. Urology* 54: 357-359, 1982.

50. Haldeman, S, Bradley, WE, Bhatia, NN, Johnson, BK: "Pudendal Evoked Responses." *Arch. Neurol.* 39: 280-283, 1982.

51. Haldeman, S, Bradley, WE, Bhatia, NN: "Evoked Responses in Clinical Neuro-Urology." *Bull. L.A. Neuro. Soc.* 47: 76-90, 1982.

52. Haldeman, S, Bradley, WE, Bhatia, NN: "Evoked Responses from the Pudendal Nerve." *J. Urology* 128: 974-980, 1982.

53. Haldeman, S: "Spinal Manipulative Therapy." In Nelson M.Ed. *Low Back Pain and Industrial & Social Disablement.* Proceedings of an International Symposium. Back Pain Association. London, pp 68-71, October, 1982.

54. Bhatia, NN, Bradley, WE, Haldeman, S: (Editorial Comment by E.J. McGuire): Urodynamics: Continuous Monitoring. The Journal of Urology. 128(5): 963-968, November, 1982.

55. Glick, MD, Meshkinpour, H, Haldeman, S, Bhatia, NN, Bradley, WE: "Colonic Dysfunction in Multiple Sclerosis." *Gastroenterology* 82: 1002-1007, 1982.

56. Haldeman, S, Bradley, WE, Bhatia, NN, Glick, ME, Ek, A: "Neurologic Evaluation of Bladder, Bowel and Sexual Disturbances in Diabetic Men." In Goto, Y., Horiuchi, A., Kogure, K. (eds) *Diabetic Neurolopathy: Proceedings of the International Symposium on Diabetic Neuropathy and its Treatment.* Tokyo, Excerpta Medica, Amsterdam-Oxford-Princeton, pp 298-301, 1982.

57. Haldeman, S: "How to Refer a Patient." In Archives of the California Chiropractic Association, Vol. 6, #1, pp.31-34, 1982.

58. Haldeman, S, Fowler, GW, Ashwald, S, Schneider, S: "Acute Flaccid Neonatal Paraplegia: A Case Report." *Neurology* 33: 93-95, 1983.

59. Haldeman, S: "Evoked Response Testing in Neurology." American Academy of Neurology. Evoked Response Course, San Diego, 1983.

60. Haldeman, S: "Spinal Manipulative Therapy: A Status Report." *Clin. Orthop. Rel. Res.* 179: 62-70, 1983.

61. Haldeman, S, Bradley, WE, Bhatia, NN, Johnson, BK: "Cortical Evoked Potentials on Stimulation of Pudendal Nerve in Women." *Urology* 21: 590-593, 1983

62. Haldeman, S: "Almeda Haldeman, Canada's First Chiropractor: Pioneering the Prairie Provinces, 1907-1917." *Chiropractic History*, 3, 1: 65-67, 1983.

63. Glick, ME, Meshkinpour, H, Haldeman, S, Hoehler, F, Downey, N, Bradley, WE: "Colonic Dysfunction in Patients with Thoracic Spinal Cord Injury." *Gastroenterology* 86: 287-294, 1984.

64. Taylor, MC, Bradley, WE, Bhatia, N, Glick, M., Haldeman, S: "The Conus Demyelination Syndrome in Multiple Sclerosis." *Acta. Neurol. Scand.* 69: 80-89, 1984.

65. Haldeman, S: "The Electrodiagnostic Evaluation of Nerve Root Function." *Spine* 9, 1, 9: 42-48, 1984.

66. Haldeman, S: "Pain Physiology as a Neurological Model for Manipulation." In Greenman, P. (ed) *Neuromuscular Functions.* Springer-Verlag. Berlin, Heidelberg, New York, Tokyo, pp 9-18, 1984.

67. Haldeman, S, M.D., D.C. - Contributor. Manuelle Medizin 1984. Edited by Dvorak, J., Dvorak, A., and Schneider, W. Springer-Verlag, Berlin, 1984.

68. Haldeman, S: "Interprofessional Communication." *The Primer on Thermography.* H. Rein, publisher, Orlando, Florida, pp 23-1 - 23-6, 1984.

69. Chehrazi, B, Haldeman, S: "Adult Onset of Tethered Spinal Cord Syndrome due to Fibrous Diastematomyelia." *Neurology*, 16 5: 681-685, 1985.

70. Haldeman, S: "Pudendal Nerve Evoked Spinal and Cortical and Bulbocavernosus Reflex Responses -- Methods and Application." In *Evoked Potentials.* Edited by R. Cracco and I. Bodis-Wollner. Alan R. Liss, Inc., New York, 1986.

71. Haldeman, S: "Spinal Manipulative Therapy in Sports Medicine." *In Clinics in Sports Medicine*, 5, 2, pp 277-293, April, 1986.

72. Waagen, GN, Haldeman, S, Cook, G, Lopez, D, DeBoer, KF: "Short-Term Trial of Chiropractic Adjustments for the Relief of Chronic Low Back Pain." *Manual Medicine* 2: 63-67, 1986.

73. Glick, ME, Haldeman, S, Meshkinpour, H: "The Neurovisceral and Electrodiagnostic Evaluation of Patients with Spinal Cord Injury." In *Paraplegia* 24: 129-137, 1986.

74. Nyiendo, J, Haldeman, S: "A Critical Study of the Student Interns: Practice Activities in a Chiropractic College Teaching Clinic." *Journal of Manipulative and Physiological Therapeutics*, Vol. 9, #3, September, 1986.

75. Nyiendo, J, Haldeman, S: "A Prospective Study of 2,000 Patients Attending a Chiropractic College Teaching Clinic." *In Medical Care*, Vol. 25, #6, June, 1987.

76. Clark, W, Haldeman, S, Johnson, P, Morris, J, Schulenberger, C, Trauner, D, White, A: "Back Impairment and Disability Determination. Another Attempt at Objective Reliable Rating." *Spine*, 13 3: 332-341, 1988.

77. Haldeman, S, Robboy, S, Shouka, M: "Computed Tomography Electrodiagnostic and Clinical Findings in Chronic Workers' Compensation Patients with Back and Leg Pain." *Spine*, 13, 3: 345-350, 1988.

78. Haldeman, S: "How to Make DC/MD Relations Work After Antitrust." *ICA International Review of Chiropractic*, September/October 1988, pp 19-21.

79. Haldeman, S: "Manipulative Therapy." *In Pain Control in Emergency Medicine*. Edited by Paul Paris. Appleton-Century Crofts, Connecticut, 1988.

80. Haldeman, S: "Spinal Clinical Neurophysiology." In Cauthen, J.C. (editor), *Lumbar Spine Surgery*, 2nd Ed., Baltimore, Williams & Wilkins, 1988.

81. Haldeman, S: "Manipulation and Massage for the Relief of

Pain." *In Textbook of Pain*, 2nd Edition. Wall & Melzack (editors). Churchill Livingstone, London, 1989.

82. Haldeman, S: "Clinical Neurophysiology and Electrodiagnostic Testing in Low Back Pain." In Weinstein, J., and Wiesel, S., (eds), *The Lumbar Spine*. W.B. Saunders Company, Philadelphia, 1990.

83. Haldeman, S: "The Limitations of Single Journal Reading." *J. Manual Medicine*, Volume 5, Number 4, pg. 143-144, 1990. Also printed in: *JMPT*, Volume 14, Number 2, pg. 93-94, February, 1991; *Chiropractic Technique*, Volume 3, Number 1, pg. 3-4, February, 1991.

84. Haldeman, S: "Physical Therapies and Manipulation in the Management of Back Pain." In Jayson MIV, Swezey RL, Knoplich J, and Hubault A (editors), *Back Pain, Painful Syndromes and Muscle Spasms: Current Concepts and Recent Advances*. Parthenon Publishing Group, New Jersey, 1990.

85. Haldeman, S: "Failure of the Pathology Model to Predict Back Pain." *Spine*, Volume 15, Number 7, pg. 718-724, 1990.

86. Haldeman, S, Phillips, R: "Spinal Manipulative Therapy in the Management of Low Back Pain." In Frymoyer, J (ed), *The Adult Spine: Principles and Practice* Volume Two. Raven Press, New York, 1991.

87. Glantz, R, Haldeman, S: "Other Diagnostic Studies/Electro-diagnosis." In Frymoyer, J (ed), *The Adult Spine: Principles and Practice*. Volume One. Raven Press, New York, 1991.

88. Haldeman, S: "The Learned Spine Societies and Meetings." In Anderson, R, and White, A (eds), *Conservative Care of Low Back Pain*. Williams & Wilkins, Baltimore, 1991.

89. Haldeman, S: "The Chiropractic View of Acute Spinal Disorders." In Mayer, T, Mooney, V, and Gatchel, R (eds) *Contemporary Care for Painful Spinal Disorders*. Lea & Febiger, Philadelphia, 1991.

90. Frymoyer, J, Haldeman, S: "Evaluation of the Worker with Low Back Pain." Chapter 8 in Pope MH, Andersson GBJ, Frymoyer JW, Chaffin DB (editors), *Occupational Low Back Pain: Assessment,*

Treatment and Prevention. Mosby-Year Book, Inc., 1991.

91. Frymoyer JW, Haldeman S, Andersson GBJ: "Impairment Rating - The United States Perspective." Chapter 16 in Pope MH, Andersson GBJ, Frymoyer JW, Chaffin DB (editors), *Occupational Low Back Pain: Assessment, Treatment and Prevention.* Mosby-Year Book, Inc., 1991.

92. Haldeman, S: "The Evolution and Importance of Spinal and Chiropractic Research." *Journal of Manipulative and Physiological Therapeutics,* Volume 15, Number 1, 1992.

93. Haldeman, S, Rubinstein, S: "Compression Fractures in Patients Undergoing Spinal Manipulative Therapy." *Journal of Manipulative and Physiological Therapeutics,* Volume 15, Number 7, pg. 450-454, 1992.

94. Haldeman, S: "The Neurodiagnostic Evaluation of Spinal Stenosis." In Andersson, G, and McNeill, T (eds), *Spinal Stenosis.* Mosby-Year Book, Inc., 1992.

95. Haldeman, S: "The Neurophysiology of Spinal Pain." In Haldeman, S (editor) *Principles and Practice of Chiropractic, Second Edition.* Appleton & Lange, 1992.

96. Haldeman, S, Rubinstein, S: "Cauda Equina Syndrome Following Lumbar Spine Manipulation." *Spine,* Vol 17 (12):1469-1473, 1992.

97. Zhu, Y, Su, SH, Woodward, KG, Haldeman, S, Starr, A: "The H-Reflex to Magnetic Stimulation of Lower-Limb Nerves." *Archives of Neurology,* Volume 49, Number 1, pg. 66-71, 1992.

98. Haldeman, S, Rubinstein, S: "The Precipitation or Aggravation of Musculoskeletal Pain in Patients Receiving Spinal Manipulative Therapy." *Journal of Manipulative and Physiological Therapeutics,* Volume 16, No. 1, pg.47-50, January, 1993.

99. Haldeman S: "Evaluation of Total-Body Impairment." Chapter 7 in *Rehabilitation of the Spine - Science and Practice,* Hochschuler, Cotler and Guyer (Editors). Mosby-Year Book, Inc., St. Louis, 1993.

100. Zhu, Y, Haldeman, S, Starr, A, Seffinger, M.A, Su, SH: "Paraspinal Muscle Evoked Cerebral Potentials in Patients with Unilateral Low Back Pain." *SPINE,* Volume 18, No. 8, pg. 1096-1102, June, 1993.

101. Clark, W, Haldeman, S: "The Development of Guideline Factors for the Evaluation of Disability in Neck and Back Injuries." *Spine*, Volume 18, No. 13, pg. 1736-1745, October, 1993.

102. Haldeman, S: "Manipulation and Massage for the Relief of Back Pain." Chapter 68 in *Textbook of Pain, Third Edition*, Wall and Melzack (Editors). Churchill Livingston, 1994.

103. Pope, MH, Phillips, R, Haugh, L, Hsieh, CYJ, MacDonald, L, Haldeman, S: "A Prospective Randomized Three Week Trial of Spinal Manipulation, Transcutaneous Muscle Stimulation, Massage and Corset in the Treatment of Subacute Low Back Pain." *Spine* 19: 2571-2577, 1994.

104. Haldeman S: In Defense of the Independent Medical Examiner. *APS Journal* 3(3): 189-190, 1994.

105. Mootz, RD, Haldeman, S: The Evolving Role of Chiropractic Within Mainstream Health Care. Topics in Clinical Chiropractic 2(2):11-21, 1995.

106. Haldeman S, Lue T, Krane R, Shabsigh R, Bradley W: "Assessment: Neurological evaluation of male sexual dysfunction," *Neurology* 45: 2287-2292, 1995.

107. McGregor M, Haldeman S, Kohlbeck F: Vertebrobasilar Compromise Associated with Cervical Manipulation. *Topics in Clinical Chiropractic*, 2(3): 63-73, 1995.

108. Keating JC, Haldeman S: "Joshua N. Haldeman, D.C.: the Canadian Years, 1926-1950." *J Can Chiropr Assoc*, 39(3), 172-186, 1995.

109. Haldeman S: "Diagnostic Tests," Chapter 38 in *Disability Evaluation*, Demeter SL, Smith GM, Andersson GBJ (eds). Mosby-Year Book, 1996.

110. Haldeman S: "Diagnostic Tests for the Evaluation of Back and Neck Pain." *Neurologic Clinics*, 14(1): 103-117, 1996.

111. Haldeman S: "Spinal Manipulation: How did it get so accepted?" *Orthopedics Today*, pg 41-42, March 1996.

112. Flaherty R, Rashbaum R, Triano J, Hansen D, Mootz R, Coile R,

Haldeman S: "Healthcare Credentialing and Qualifications Commission: An Alternative to 'Any Willing Provider'?" *The American Journal of Managed Care*, II(5): 559-566, 1996.

113. Zhu Y, Starr A, Haldeman S, Fu HX, Wu PG: Magnetic Stimulation of Muscle Evoked Cerebral Potentials by Directly Activating Muscle Afferents: A Study During Muscle Paralysis. *Muscle & Nerve*, 19:1570-1575, 1996.

114. Haldeman S: "Indications for clinical neurophysiological testing." *Bulletin. Hospital for Joint Diseases*, 55(3): 122-124, 1996.

115. Haldeman S: "Spinal manipulation: when, how, and who?" *Bulletin. Hospital for Joint Diseases*, 55(3): 135-137, 1996.

116. Haldeman S, Dvorak J: "Clinical Neurophysiology and Electrodiagnostic Testing in Low Back Pain." Chapter 3 in *The Lumbar Spine, Volume 1*, Second Edition. The International Society for the Study of the Lumbar Spine Editorial Committee. W.B. Saunders Company, Philadelphia, 1996.

117. Haldeman S: Letter to the Editor, review of article by Lee et al. *Neurology* 46: 885, 1996.

118. Haldeman S: The Physician's Role in Disability Evaluation. Chapter 50 in *Musculoskeletal Disorders in the Workplace*, Nordin M, Andersson G, Pope M (eds). Mosby-Year Book, Inc., 1997.

119. Glantz R, Haldeman S: "Other Diagnostic Studies: Electrodiagnosis." Chapter 33 in The Adult Spine, Principles and Practice. Second Edition. Frymoyer JW (ed). Lippincott-Raven, Philadelphia, 1997.

120. Haldeman S, Hooper PD, Scaringe JG, Traina AB: "Spinal Manipulative Therapy." Chapter 86 in *The Adult Spine, Principles and Practice*. Second Edition. Frymoyer JW (ed). Lippincott-Raven Publishers, Philadelphia, 1997.

121. Fardon DF, Herzog RJ, Mink JH, Simmons JD, Kahanovitz N, Haldeman S: "Nomenclature of Lumbar Disc Disorders." *Orthopaedic Knowledge Update: Spine*, Garfin SF, Vacarro AR (eds), developed by North American Spine Society. Published by the

American Academy of Orthopaedic Surgeons, 1997.

122. Zhu Y, Starr A, Haldeman S, Chu JK, Sugerman RA: "Soleus H-Reflex to S1 Nerve Root Stimulation." *Electroencephalography and Clinical Neurophysiology*, 109: 10-14, 1998.

123. Haldeman S: "Low Back Pain. Current Physiologic Concepts." *Neurologic Clinics of North America*, Volume 17, No. 1. W.B. Saunders Company, Philadelphia, 1999.

124. Haldeman S: "Differential Diagnosis of Low Back Pain." Chapter 12 in *Managing Low Back Pain*, Fourth Edition. Kirkaldy-Willis WH, Bernard, Jr., TN (eds). Churchill Livingstone, Philadelphia, 1999.

125. Haldeman S, Kohlbeck FJ, McGregor M: "Risk Factors and Precipitating Neck Movements Causing Vertebrobasilar Artery Dissection After Cervical Trauma and Spinal Manipulation." *Spine*, Vol. 24, No. 8, 785-794, 1999.

126. Bronfort G, Haldeman S: "Spinal Manipulation in Patients with Lumbar Disc Disease." *Seminars in Spine Surgery*, Vol. 11, No. 2 (June), 97-108, 1999.

127. Haldeman S: "Neck and Back Pain." Chapter 2 in *Diagnostic Testing in Neurology*, Evans RW (ed). W.B. Saunders Company, Philadelphia, 1999.

128. Haldeman S, Hooper PD: "Mobilization, manipulation, massage and exercise for the relief of musculoskeletal pain." Chapter 61 in *Textbook of Pain*, 4th Edition, Wall and Melzack (eds), Churchill-Livingstone, London, 1999.

129. Zhu Y, Starr A, Haldeman S, Chu J.K., Weber, R: "Magnetic stimulation of muscles evokes cerebral potentials: Neurophysiological and clinical studies." Hashimoto and Kakigi (eds) "Recent Advances in Human Neurophysiology." Elsevier Science B.V., 1999.

130. Haldeman S, Hooper PD: "Manipulative Therapy for Post-acute Occupational Musculoskeletal Disorders." Chapter 25 in *Occupational Musculoskeletal Disorders. Function, Outcomes, and Evidence*, Mayer TG (ed). Lippincott Williams & Wilkins, Philadelphia, 2000.

131. Haldeman S: "Neurological Effects of the Adjustment." *JMPT*, Vol. 23, No. 2, 112-114, 2000.

132. Zhu Y, Haldeman S, Hsieh CJ, Wu P, Starr A: "Do Cerebral Potentials to Magnetic Stimulation of Paraspinal Muscles Reflect Changes in Palpable Muscle Spasm, Low Back Pain, and Activity Scores?" *JMPT*, Vol. 2, No. 7, 458-464, 2000.

133. Haldeman, S. Assisting Patients in their Choice of Treatment Options: A primary Goal of all Spine Care Clinicians. The Spine Journal 2001; 1:307-309.

134. Haldeman S: "The Evolution of Chiropractic–Science & Theory," excerpt from ICSM Keynote Presentation. *Advance*, Vol. 22, No. 1, Winter 2001. Published by the Foundation for Chiropractic Education and Research.

135. Haldeman S, Hooper P: "Chiropractic Approach to Neurologic Illness." Chapter 8 in *Alternative and Complementary Treatment in Neurologic Illness*, Weintraub M (ed). Churchill Livingstone, Philadelphia, 2001.

136. Haldeman S, Dagenais S: "Cervicogenic headaches: a critical review." *The Spine Journal*, 1, 31-46, 2001.

137. Haldeman S, Carey P, Townsend M, Papadopoulos C: "Arterial dissections following cervical manipulation: the chiropractic experience." *Canadian Medical Association Journal*, 2001; 165(7): 905-6.

138. Rubinstein S, Haldeman S: "Cervical manipulation to a patient with a history of traumatically induced dissection of the internal carotid artery: A case report and review of the literature on recurrent dissections." *JMPT*, Vol. 24, No. 8, 520-525, 2001.

139. Meeker W, Haldeman S.: "Chiropractic: A Profession at the Crossroads of Mainstream and Alternative Medicine." *Annals of Internal Medicine*, 2002; 136: 216-227.

140. Haldeman S, Kohlbeck F, McGregor M.: "Unpredictability of Cerebrovascular Ischemia Associate With Cervical Spine Manipulation Therapy." *Spine* 2002; 27:49-55

141. Dagenais S, Haldeman S: "Chiropractic." *Primary Care Clinic Office Practice*, 29(2002): 419-437.

142. Haldeman S, Kohlbeck F, McGregor M: "Stroke, cerebral artery dissection, and cervical spine manipulation therapy." Journal of Neurology, 2002; 249:1098-1104.

143. Meeker W, Mootz R, Haldeman S: "Back to Basics...The State of Chiropractic Research." *Topics in Clinical Chiropractic*, 2002; 9(1): 1-13.

144. Kohlbeck F, Haldeman S: "Medication-assisted Spinal Manipulation." The Spine Journal 2002; 2: 288-302.

145. Haldeman S, Carey P, Townsend M, Papadopoulos C: "Clinical perceptions of the risk of vertebral artery dissection after cervical manipulation: the effect of referral bias." The Spine Journal 2002; 2: 334-342.

146. Hooper PD, Haldeman S. Mobilization, manipulation, massage and exercise for the relief of musculoskeletal pain. Chapter 32 in R Melzack and PD Wall, editors. Handbook of pain management. A clinical companion to Wall and Melzack's Textbook of Pain. Churchill Livingstone, Edinburgh. 2003:485-501.

147. Haldeman S, Swenson RS. Neurologic Diagnostic Testing. Chapter 33 in Demeter SL and Andersson GBJ (editors). Disability Evaluation. American Medical Association. Mosby Publishers (St Louis) 2003.

148. Swenson R, Haldeman S. Spinal manipulative therapy for low back pain. J Am Acad Orthop Surg. 2003; 11:228-237.

149. Haldeman S, Gatchel RJ, Bogduk N. Difficulties inherent in the interpretation and performance of randomized controlled clinical trials. The Spine Journal 2004; 4: 241-247.

150. Haldeman S. Clinical Neurophysiology and Electrodiagnosis. Chapter 7 in Frymoyer JW and Wiesel SW (editors) *The Adult and Pediatric Spine*, Third Edition. Lippincott Williams and Wilkins. Philadelphia. 2004; 111-118.

151. Swenson RS, Haldeman S, Dagenais S. Complementary and

alternative medicine: treatment of back and neck pain. Chapter 14 in BS Oken (Editor) *Complementarry Therapies in Neurology. An Evidence Based Approach*. Parthenon, London. 2004; 243-263.

152. Dvorak J, Haldeman S. Clinical Neurophysiologic and Electro-diagnostic Testing in Disorders of the Spine. Chapter 10 in Herkovitz HN, Dvorak J, Bell G, Nordin M, Grob D. (Editors) *The Lumbar Spine, Third Edition*. Lippincott, Williams & Wilkins. Philadelphia. 2004; 113-119.

153. Dvorak J, Haldeman S, Gillar W. Manual Therapy in Patients with Low Back Pain. chapter 14 in Herkovitz HN, Dvorak J, Bell G, Nordin M, Grob D. (Editors) *The Lumbar Spine, Third Edition*. Lippincott, Williams & Wilkins. Philadelphia. 2004; 151-157.

154. Hurwitz EL, Haldeman S. Manual Therapy including Manipulation. Acute and Chronic Neck Pain. Chapter 7 in JS Fischgrund (Editor) *Neck Pain. American Academy of Orthopedic Surgeons Monograph series 27*. American Academy of Orthopaedic Surgeons, Rosemont IL. 2004; 65-78.

155. Dagenais S, Haldeman S. Headaches of Spinal Origin. Chapter 24 in Haldeman (Editor-in-Chief) Principles and Practice of Chiropractic, Third Edition. McGraw-Hill (New York) pp. 2005; 447-464.3.

156. Dagenais S, Haldeman S, Wooley JR. Intraligamentous injection of sclerosing solutions (Prolotherapy) for spinal pain: A critical review of the literature. The Spine Journal 2005; 5:310-328.

157. Rubinstein SM, Peerdeman SM; van Tulder MW; Riphagen I; Haldeman S. A systemic review of the risk factors for cervical artery dissection. Stroke 2005; 36:1575-580.

158. Dagenais S, Haldeman S, Polatin PB. It is time for physicians to embrace cost-effectiveness and cost utility analysis research in the treatment of spinal pain. The Spine Journal 2005; 5:357-360.

159. Kohlbeck FJ, Haldeman S, Hurwitz E, Dagenais S. Supplemental care with medication assisted manipulation versus spinal manipulation therapy alone for patients with chronic low back pain. L Manipulative Physiol. Ther. 2005:28:245-252.

160. Haldeman S, Herring SA, Pearson JK. When to consider spinal manipulation. Patient Care. August 2005: 32-37.

161. Dagenais, S., Haldeman, S., Wooley, J. Author's reply to Drs. Watson & Oppenheim. The Spine Journal, Vol. 6, Issue 1, Jan-Feb 2006, p.103.

162. Haldeman, S., Rosner, A., Chapman-Smith, D. The International Conference on Chiropractic Research: Promoting Excellence in Chiropractic Research Worldwide. J. Manipulative Physiol. Ther. 2006; 29:1-3

163. Rubinstein MS, Haldeman S, van Tulder MW. An etiologic model to help explain the pathogenesis of cervical artery dissection: Implications for cervical manipulation. J. Manipulative Physiol. Ther. 2006:29:336-338.

164. Dagenais S, Ogunseitan O, Haldeman S, Wooley JR, Zaldivar F, Kim RC. Acute toxicity pilot examination of Proliferol in rats and swine. International J. Toxicology 2006:25:171-181.

165. Dagenais S, Ogunseitan O, Haldeman S, Wooley JR, Newcomb, RL. Side Effects and Adverse Events Related to Intraligamentous Injection of Sclerosing Solutions (Prolotherapy) for Back and Neck Pain: A Survey of Practitioners. Arch Phys Med Rehabil July 2006:87:909-913.

166. Dagenais S, Caro JJ, Haldeman S. A systematic review of low back pain cost of illness studies in the united states and internationally, *Spine* J;2008;8(1): 8-20.

167. Dagenais S, Mayer J, Haldeman S, Borg-Stein J. Evidence informed management of chronic low back pain with prolotherapy, *Spine* J;2008;8(1):203-212.

168. Dagenais S, Mayer J, Wooley JR, Haldeman S. Evidence informed management of chronic low back pain with medicine assisted manipulation, *Spine* J;2008;8(1):142-149.

169. Haldeman S, Dagenais S. A supermarket approach to the evidence informed management of chronic low back pain, *Spine* J;2008;8(1):1-7.

170. Haldeman S, Dagenais S. What have we learned about the evidence informed management of chronic low back pain? *Spine* J;2008;8(1):266-277.

171. Dagenais S, Mayer J, Wooley J, Haldeman S, Hite M. Acute toxicity evaluation of Proliferol: a dose- escalating, placebo-controlled study in rats. Int J Toxicol 2007;26(5):451-463.

172. Haldeman S, Carroll LJ, Cassidy JD, Schubert J, Nygren Å. Executive summary: The Bone and Joint Decade 2000-2010 Task Force on Neck Pain and Its Associated Disorders. *Spine* 2008;33(4S): S5-S7.

173. Haldeman S, Carroll LJ, Cassidy JD. Introduction/Mandate: The empowerment of people with neck pain. The Bone and Joint Decade 2000-2010 Task Force on Neck Pain and Its Associated Disorders. *Spine* 2008;33(4S):S8-S13.

174. Guzman J, Hurwitz EL, Carroll LJ, Haldeman S, Côté P, Carragee EJ, Peloso PM, van der Velde G, Holm LW, Hogg-Johnson S, Nordin M, Cassidy JD. A conceptual model for the course and care of neck pain. Results of The Bone and Joint Decade 2000-2010 Task Force on Neck Pain and Its Associated Disorders. *Spine* 2008;33(4S): S14-S23.

175. Carroll LJ, Cassidy JD, Peloso PM, Giles-Smith L, Cheng CS, Greenhalgh S, Haldeman S, van der Velde G, Hurwitz EL, Côté P, Nordin M, Hogg-Johnson S, Holm LW, Guzman J, Carragee EJ. Methods for the best evidence synthesis on neck pain and its associated disorders. The Bone and Joint Decade 2000-2010 Task Force on Neck Pain and Its Associated Disorders. *Spine* 2008;33(4S): S33-S38.

176. Hogg-Johnson S, van der Velde G, Carroll LJ, Holm LW, Cassidy JD, Guzman J, Côté P, Haldeman S, Ammendolia C, Carragee EJ, Hurwitz E, Nordin M, Peloso PM. The burden and determinants of neck pain in the general population: Results of the Bone and Joint Decade 2000-2010 Task Force on Neck Pain and Its Associated Disorders. *Spine* 2008;33(4S):S39-S51.

177. Holm LW, Carroll LJ, Cassidy JD, Hogg-Johnson S, Côté P, Guzman J, Peloso PM, Nordin M, Hurwitz EL, van der Velde G,

Carragee EJ, Haldeman S. The burden and determinants of neck pain in whiplash-associated disorders after traffic collisions: Results of the Bone and Joint Decade 2000-2010 Task Force on Neck Pain and Its Associated Disorders. *Spine* 2008;33(4S):S52-S59.

178. Côté P, van der Velde G, Cassidy JD, Carroll LJ, Hogg-Johnson S, Holm LW, Carragee EJ, Haldeman S, Nordin M, Hurwitz EL, Guzman J, Peloso PM. The burden and determinants of neck pain in workers. Results of the Bone and Joint 2000-2010 Task Force on Neck Pain and Its Associated Disorders. *Spine* 2008;33(4S): S60-S74.

179. Carroll LJ, Hogg-Johnson S, van der Velde G, Haldeman S, Holm LW, Carragee EJ, Hurwitz EL, Côté P, Nordin M, Peloso PM, Cassidy JD, Guzman J. Course and prognostic factors for neck pain in the general population. Results of the Bone and Joint Decade 2000-2010 Task Force on Neck Pain and Its Associated Disorders. *Spine* 2008;33(4S):S75-S82.

180. Carroll LJ, Holm LW, Hogg-Johnson S, Côté P, Cassidy JD, Haldeman S, Nordin M, Hurwitz EL, Carragee EJ, van der Velde G, Peloso PM, Guzman J. Course and prognostic factors for neck pain in whiplash-associated disorders (WAD). Results of the Bone and Joint Decade 2000 2010 Task Force on Neck Pain and Its Associated Disorders. *Spine* 2008;33(4S):S83-S92.

181. Carroll LJ, Hogg-Johnson S, Côté P, van der Velde G, Holm LW, Carragee EJ, Hurwitz EL, Peloso PM, Cassidy JD, Guzman J, Nordin M, Haldeman S. Course and prognostic factors for neck pain in workers. Results of the Bone and Joint Decade 2000-2010 Task Force on Neck Pain and Its Associated Disorders. *Spine* 2008;33(4S):S93-S100.

182. Nordin M, Carragee EJ, Hogg-Johnson S, Schector-Weiner S, Hurwitz EL, Peloso PM, Guzman J, van der Velde G, Carroll LJ, Holm LW, Côté P, Cassidy JD, Haldeman S. Assessment of neck pain and its associated disorders. Results of the Bone and Joint Decade 2000-2010 Task Force on Neck Pain and Its Associated Disorders. *Spine* 2008;33(4S):S101-S122.

183. Hurwitz EL, Carragee EJ, van der Velde G, Carroll LJ, Nordin

M, Guzman J, Peloso PM, Holm LW, Côté P, Hogg-Johnson S, Côté P, Haldeman S. Treatment of neck pain: Non-invasive interventions. Results of the Bone and Joint Decade 2000-2010 Task Force on Neck Pain and its Associated Disorders. *Spine* 2008;33(4S):S123-S152.

184. Carragee EJ, Hurwitz EL, Cheng I, Carroll LJ, Nordin M, Guzman J, Peloso PM, Holm LW, Côté P, Hogg-Johnson S, van der Velde G, Cassidy JD, Haldeman S. Treatment of neck pain: Injections and surgical interventions. Results of the Bone and Joint Decade 2000-2010 Task Force on Neck Pain and its Associated Disorders. *Spine* 2008;33(4S):S153-S169.

185. Guzman J, Haldeman S, Carroll LJ, Carragee EJ, Hurwitz EL, Peloso PM, Nordin M, Cassidy JD, Holm LW, Côté P, van der Velde G, Hogg-Johnson S. Practice implications of the results of the Bone and Joint Decade 2000-2010 Task Force on Neck Pain and Its Associated Disorders: From concepts and findings to recommendations. *Spine* 2008;33(4S):S199-S213.

186. Carroll LJ, Hurwitz EL, Côté P, Hogg-Johnson S, Carragee EJ, Nordin M, Holm LW, van der Velde G, Cassidy JD, Guzman J, Peloso PM, Haldeman S. Research priorities and methodological implications. Results of the Bone and Joint Decade 2000-2010 Task Force on Neck Pain and Its Associated Disorders. *Spine* 2008;33(4S): S214-S220.

187. Haldeman, S, Carroll LJ, Cassidy JD. A Best Evidence Synthesis on Neck Pain: Findings from The Bone and Joint Decade 2000-2010 Task Force on Neck Pain and Its Associated Disorders. *Spine* 2008;33(4S). (Citation for complete report)

188. Reardon R, Haldeman S. Self-study of values, beliefs, and conflicts of interest: The Bone and Joint Decade 2000-2010 Task Force on Neck Pain and Its Associated Disorders. *Spine* 2008;33(4S)S24-S32.

189. Dagenais S, Roffey DM, Wai EK, Haldeman S, Caro J. Can cost utility evaluations inform decision making about interventions for low back pain? A systematic review. Accepted for publication in The Spine Journal, 2009.

ABSTRACTS

1. Haldeman, S: Chiropractic Needs Proper Diagnosis. Letter, *Canad Med Assn. J.* 116: 594-595, 1979.

2. Haldeman S: Manipulation (Epitome) *West J. Med* 131: 132, 1979.

3. Haldeman, S, Debernardi, D, Nudleman, K: The Electrodiagnostic Evaluation of the Spinal Cord Function. Proceedings: International Society for the Study of the Lumbar Spine. New Orleans, 1980.

4. Haldeman, S, Bradley, WE, Bhatia, N, Johnson, B: The Electrodiagnostic Evaluation of Sacral Nerve Function. Proceedings: International Society for the Study of the Lumbar Spine. Paris, 1981.

5. Haldeman, S: Spinal Manipulation. Terminology and Neurologic Implications. Proceedings: International Society for the Study of the Lumbar Spine. Paris, 1981.

6. Haldeman, S, Bradley, WE, Johnson, BK: Pudendal Somatosensory Evoked Potentials. Abstract: 33rd Annual Meeting of the American Academy of Neurology, 1981.

7. Bhatia, NN, Bradley, WE, Haldeman, S, Johnson, BK: Continuous Urodynamic Monitoring. Proceedings of the International Continence Society. Lund, Sweden, September 3-5, 1981.

8. Haldeman, S: The Electrodiagnostic of Nerve Root Dysfunction. Proceedings: The International Society for the Study of the Lumbar Spine. Toronto, 1982.

9. Haldeman, S, Bradley, WE, Bhatia, NN, Ek, A, Taylor, M, Johnson, BK: Pudendal Evoked Responses in Neurologic Disease. *Neurology* 32:2, 1982. 34th Annual Meeting of the American Academy of Neurology.

10. Haldeman, S: Review of "Sclerosant Therapy by Brian Pattinson." *Arch Calif Chiropr Assn.* 6: 15-17, 1982.

11. Haldeman, S, Bradley, WE, Bhatia, ND: Pudendal Evoked Responses. Proceedings of the Annual Neurological Society Meeting, July, 1982.

12. Glick, ME, Meshkinpour, H, Haldeman, S, Bhatia, NN: Colonic Dysfunction in Multiple Sclerosis. Proceedings of Gastroenterology Society, July, 1982.

13. Haldeman, S: "Spinal Manipulative Therapy." Proceedings of the International Symposium, Back Pain Association, London, October, 1982.

14. Haldeman, S: Electrodiagnostic Testing of Spinal Disorders. International Federation of *Manuelle Medicine*, Zurich, 1983. Manuelle Medizin 21: 84, 1983.

15. Nyiendo, J, Haldeman, S: A Prospective Trial of 2000 Patients Attending a Chiropractic College Clinic. Proceedings: International Society for the Study of the Lumbar Spine. Montreal, 1984. Refer to *Medical Care*, Vol. 25, No. 6, June, 1987.

16. Haldeman, S: Dissociation Between Posterior Tibial and Pudendal Somatosensory Evoked Responses: Possible Different Central Pathways. 35th Annual Meeting of the American Academy of Neurology. In *Neurology*, 34: 143, 1984.

17. Glick, M, Haldeman, S: The Electrodiagnostic and Neurovisceral Evaluation of Patients With Spinal Cord Injuries. 35th Annual Meeting of the American Academy of Neurology. In *Neurology*, 34: 209, 1984.

18. Haldeman, S: Reviewer's Comments: Manipulation Techniques. *Patient Care*, Vol. 18, No. 14: 187-189, August, 1984.

19. Glick, ME, Meshkinpour, H, Haldeman, S: Colonic Compliance and Motility in Patients with Spinal Cord Disease. XII and V International Gastroenterology and Endoscopy Congresses. Lisbon, 16-22. September, 1984.

20. Haldeman, S, Shouka, M, Robboy, S: Computerized Tomography, Electrodiagnostic and Clinical Findings in Chronic Workers' Compensation Patients with Back and Leg Pain. International Society for the Study of the Lumbar Spine. Rome, May 24-28, 1987. Refer to *Spine*, 13, 3: 345-350, 1988.

21. Haldeman, S, Shouka, M, Robboy, S: The Correlation Between

CT Scanning Electrodiagnostic Studies and Clinical Findings in Workers Compensation Patients with Back and Leg Pain. North American Spine Society. Banff, Canada, June 25-28, 1987.

22. Clark, WL, Haldeman, S, Johnson, P, Morris, J, Trauner, D, White, AH: Back Pain Impairment and Disability Determination. Another Attempt at Objective, Reliable Rating. North American Spine Society. Banff, Canada, June 25-28, 1987. Refer to *Spine*, 13, 3: 332-341, 1988.

23. Haldeman, S: How To Make DC/MD Relations Work After Antitrust. International Chiropractors Association, 62nd Annual Convention and Scientific Symposium on spinal Biomechanics. Monterey, California, July 15-17, 1988. Refer to *ICA International Review of Chiropractic*, September/October 1988, pg. 19-21.

24. Haldeman, S: Manipulation in Acute Back Pain. International Back Pain Society. Montreaux, Switzerland, May 4-6, 1988.

25. Haldeman, S: Indications and Limitations of Conservative Treatment of Back Pain. International Back Pain Society. Montreaux, Switzerland, May 4-6, 1988.

26. Haldeman, S: Workmans Compensation: The California System of Evaluating Permanent Partial Impairment. Industrial Musculoskeletal Health Seminar, Dallas, Texas, September 15-17, 1988.

27. Haldeman, S: Selecting Among Manipulation and Other Modalities. Industrial Musculoskeletal Health Seminar, Dallas, Texas, September 15-17, 1988.

28. Haldeman, S: Office Management of Disabled Workers. Industrial Musculoskeletal Health Seminar, Dallas, Texas, September, 15-17, 1988.

29. Haldeman, S: Failure of the Pathology Model to Predict Back Pain. Presidential address, North American Spine Society, Quebec City, 1989. (Printed in *Spine*, Vol. 15, No. 7, 1990.)

30. Haldeman, S: Physical Therapies and Manipulation in the Management of Back Pain. Back Pain. XVIIth ILAR Congress of Rheumatology, Rio de Janeiro, September, 1989. (Printed in Jay-

son, M.I.V., et. al (eds) *Back Pain, Painful Syndromes and Muscle Spasms: Current Concepts and Recent Advances.* Parthenon Publishing Group, New Jersey, 1990).

31. Haldeman, S: "Philosophy and the Future of Chiropractic." Keynote Address, American Chiropractic Association, Anchorage, Alaska, June 7, 1990. Printed in *ACA Journal of Chiropractic*, pg. 23-28, July, 1990.

32. Waagen, G, DeBoer, K, Hansen, J, McGee, D, Haldeman, S: A Prospective Comparative Trial of General Practice Medical Care, Chiropractic Manipulative Therapy and Sham Manipulation in the Management of Patients with Chronic or Repetitive Low Back Pain. International Society for the Study of the Lumbar Spine, Boston, Massachusetts, June 13-19, 1990.

33. Pope, MH, Phillips, RB, MacDonald, L, Haugh, L, Hsieh, J, Haldeman, S: A Prospective Randomized Trial of Manipulation, Corset, Massage, and Transcutaneous Muscle Stimulation. International Society for the Study of the Lumbar Spine, Boston, Massachusetts, June 13-19, 1990.

34. Zhu, Y, Su, SH, Woodward, KG, Haldeman, S, Starr, A: The Use of Peripheral Magnetic Stimulation in the Investigation of Sciatic and S1 Nerve Root Function. International Society for the Study of the Lumbar Spine, 18th Annual Meeting, Heidelberg, Germany, May 12-16, 1991.

35. Zhu, Y, Starr, A, Haldeman, S: Paraspinal Muscle Evoked Cerebral Potentials in Muscle Spasm. American Academy of Electrodiagnostic Medicine, Vancouver, B.C., Canada, September 25-28, 1991.

36. Haldeman, S: Current Status of Functional and Palpatory Evaluation of the Spine. American Back Society Fall Symposium, San Francisco, 1991.

37. Haldeman, S: The Evolution and Importance of Spinal and Chiropractic Research. World Federation of Chiropractic, Toronto, May 4-5, 1991. Refer to *Journal of Manipulative and Physiological Therapeutics*, Vol. 15, No. 1, January, 1992.

38. Zhu, Y, Haldeman, S, Seffinger, M, Su, SH, Claxton, R, Starr,

A: Paraspinal Muscle Evoked Cerebral Potentials in Muscle Spasm. International Society for the Study of the Lumbar Spine, Chicago, Illinois, May 20-24, 1992.

39. Zhu, Y, Starr, A, Claxton, R, Haldeman, S: Soleus H-M Interval from S-1 Root Stimulation. EMG-CN-IX, Jerusalem, Israel, June 8-12, 1992.

40. Haldeman, S, Zhu, Y, Claxton, R, Starr, A: The Measurement of Magnetic Evoked Somatosensory Cortical Potentials in Normal Subjects with Unilateral Low Back Pain and Paraspinal Muscle Spasm. North American Spine Society 7th Annual Meeting, Boston, Massachusetts, July 9-11, 1992.

41. Zhu, Y, Starr, A, Haldeman, S: Muscle Evoked Cerebral Potentials in Muscle Spasm. American Association of Osteopathic Medicine, Annual Scientific Research Conference, San Diego, California, October 3-7, 1992.

42. Zhu, Y, Starr, A, Haldeman, S: H-Reflexes of the Proximal Muscles in Lower Limb in Humans. American Association of Electrodiagnostic Medicine, Charleston, South Carolina, October 14-18, 1992.

43. Zhu, Y, Seffinger, MA, Haldeman, S, Su, SH, Starr, A: Cerebral Evoked Potentials in Somatic Dysfunction. American Osteopathic Association 36th Research Conference, San Diego, California, November 1-4, 1992.

44. Zhu, Y, Haldeman, S, Starr, A: Soleus H-M Interval from Percutaneous Electrical S1 root Stimulation in the Diagnosis of S1 radiculopathy. North American Spine Society Annual Scientific Meeting, San Diego, California, October 11-13, 1993.

45. Zhu, Y, Hsieh, J, Haldeman, S, Starr, A, Fu, HX: The Assessment of Muscle Spasm in Low Back Pain: A Quantitative Study of the Effect of Spinal Manipulation on Cerebral Potentials Evoked by Magnetic Stimulation to Paraspinal Muscles. The Fifth International Conference of Spinal Manipulation, Palm Springs, California, June 10-11, 1994.

46. Haldeman, S, Kohlbeck, F, McGregor, M: Cerebrovascular

577

Complications Following Cervical Spine Manipulation Therapy: A Review of 53 Cases. International Conference on Spinal Manipulation, Palm Springs, California, June 10-11, 1994.

47. Haldeman S, Kohlbeck FH, McGregor M: Trivial Trauma as a Cause of Vertebrobasilar Artery Occlusions: Review and Analysis of the Literature. International Conference on Spinal Manipulation, Palm Springs, California, June 10-11, 1994.

48. Zhu, Y, Starr, A, Haldeman, S, Heige, D, Sugerman, R: Quantitative Evaluation of the Somatic Dysfunction in Osteopathic Medicine with Muscle Afferent Somatosensory Evoked Potentials. American Association of Osteopathic Medicine, Annual Scientific Meeting, San Francisco, California, July 12-14, 1994.

49. Zhu, Y, Starr, A, Haldeman, S: Magnetic Stimulation of Muscle Evoked Cerebral Potentials: An Approach to the Spinal Cord Monitoring. The Third International Symposium of the Spinal Cord Monitoring, New York, May 23-29, 1995.

50. Zhu, Y, Starr, A, Haldeman, S, Cui, L: Central H-Reflex Latency from S1 Root Stimulation: I. Intraspinal Conduction Time of S1 Root. American Association of Electrodiagnostic Medicine 42nd Annual Scientific Meeting, Montreal, September 22-23, 1995.

50. Zhu, Y, Haldeman, S, Starr, A, Cui, L: Central H-Reflex Latency from S1 Root Stimulation: II. A Highly Sensitive Test for S1 radiculopathy. American Association of Electrodiagnostic Medicine 42nd Annual Scientific Meeting, Montreal, September 22-23, 1995.

51. Haldeman S, Kohlbeck F, McGregor M: Risk Factors for Vertebrobasilar Artery Dissection Following Cervical Spine Manipulation: A review of 60 cases. *Neurology* 46: A440, February 1996.

52. Zhu Y, Haldeman, S, Fredrickson B, Yuan H, Weber R: "Magnetic Stimulation of muscles evokes cerebral potentials: A new approach to spinal cord and nerve root monitoring.: International Society for the Study of the Lumbar Spine, 23 Annual Meeting, Burlimgton, June 25-29, 1996.

53. Zhu Y, Starr A, Haldeman S, Weber R: "Some new measures of Electrodiagnostic in chronic lumbosacral radiculopathy." North

American Spine Society, Spine Across the Sea '97, Honolulu, March 16-20, 1997.

54. Zhu Y, Starr A, Haldeman S, Weber R: "Magnetic stimulation of muscle evokes cerebral potentials by direct activation of nerve afferents." International society for the study of the Lumbar Spine, 24th Annual Meeting, Singapore, June 2-6, 1997.

55. Zhu Y, Starr A, Haldeman S, Weber R: "Magnetic stimulation of muscle evokes cerebral potentials by direct activation of nerve afferents: A study in S1 Radiculopathy." 14th International Conference of Electroencephalography and Clinical Neurophysiology, Florence, Italy, August 24-29, 1997.

56. Zhu Y, Starr A, Haldeman S, Ciu L, Chu J, Weber, R: "Magnetic stimulation of muscle evoked cerebral potentials: neurophysiological and clinical studies." *Recent Advances in Human Neurophysiology*. Proceedings of the 6th International Evoked Potentials Symposium, Okazaki, Japan, March 21-25, 1998, Elsevier Science.

57. Zhu Y, Haldeman S, Weber R, Yuan H.: "Complex repetitive discharges in the diagnosis of long term and active lumbosacral radiculopathy." International Society for the study of the Lumbar Spine, 25th Annual Meeting, Brussels, Belgium, June 12-17, 1998.

58. Zhu Y, Fang, X, Fredrickson B, Haldeman S.: "Evidence against the presence of the double crush syndrome in the lower extremities," International Society for the study of the Lumbar Spine, 28th Annual Meeting, Edinburgh, Scotland, June 20-25, 2001.

58. Tai Y, Zhu Y, Weber R, Haldeman S, Fredrickson B, Yuan H.: "Electrodiagnosis in low back pain patients with diabetic polyneuropathy." International Society for the study of the Lumbar Spine, 29th Annual Meeting, Cleveland, May 14-18, 2002.

59. Zhu Y, Weber R, Li J, Chu J, Haldeman S, Fredrickson B, Yuan H: "F waves of peroneal and tibial nerve provide unique information in ongoing L5 and S1 radiculopathies." International Society for the study of the Lumbar Spine, 29th Annual Meeting, Cleveland, May 14-18, 2002.

61. Kohlbeck F, Haldeman S, Dagenais S, Wooley J, Kemper C

Characteristics of patients who undergo medication-assisted manipulation compared to those receiving usual chiropractic care. Platform presentation at the ACC-RAC 2003 Conference, March 13-16, 2003, New Orleans, Louisiana.

62. Kohlbeck F, Haldeman S, Dagenais S, Wooley J, Kemper C. Medication-assisted manipulation for low back pain. International Society for the Study of the Lumbar Spine. Vancouver, Canada May 13-17, 2003.

63. Rubinstein SM, Peerdeman SM; van Tulder MW; Riphagen I; Haldeman S. Manipulation-Induced Stroke. Are We Any Closer to Identifying Who Is at Risk? A Systematic Review of the Risk Factors for Cervical Artery Dissection. European Chiropractic Union. Cyprus, May 6, 2005.

64. Rubinstein SM, Peerdeman SM; van Tulder MW; Riphagen I; Haldeman S. Is it possible to explain why cervical artery dissection is so rare and typically occurs in the young? A systematic review of the risk factors for cervical artery dissection. World Federation of Chiropractic. Sydney, Australia. Jun 16, 2005

65. Kawchuk G, Haldeman S, Hill M, Kohlbeck F. Distribution of vertebral artery injury location in cases associated with and without cervical manipulation. World Federation of Chiropractic. Sydney, Australia. June 16, 2005.

66. Haldeman, S. Spinal Manipulation: Evidence-Based Applications. American Academy of Pain Management. San Diego, California. February 25-26, 2006.

67 Dagenais S, Mayer J, Haldeman S, Wooley J. Dose-escalation, placebo-controlled acute toxicity evaluation of a drug commonly used in prolotherapy following spinal injection in rats. North American Spine Society 21st Annual meeting, Seattle, WA. September 26-30, 2006. The Spine Journal 6, 2006: 76S.

69. Dagenais S, Mayer J, Wooley J, Haldeman S. Safety and toxicity of prolotherapy for back pain, 6th Interdisciplinary World Congress on Low Back & Pelvic Pain, Barcelona, 2007.

70. Dagenais S, Caro J, Haldeman S. A systematic review of low back pain cost of illness studies in the United States and Internationally. ISPOR 13th Annual International Meeting, Toronto, May 3, 2008.

Index

About the Author

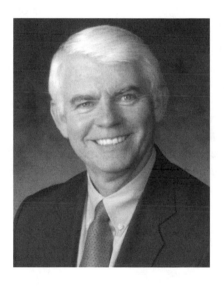

Reed Phillips attended National College of Chiropractic in Illinois, after completing an undergraduate degree in biology at The University of Utah. He was persuaded to extend his Chicago-land experience further, and finished a radiology program before returning to private practice in Salt Lake City. Concurrent with his 11 years in practice, he completed a master's of science degree in community medicine at the University of Utah, School of Medicine, followed by a PhD in medical sociology at the same institution.

When the invitation came to head the research department at the Los Angeles College of Chiropractic, it seemed a natural fit for his clinical and academic doctorates. With his wife Sandra, and their family of eight children, they relocated to beautiful LaHabra Heights—just north of Disneyland. This involved placing the children in all age levels of school, and building a custom home big enough to hold them all.

Ultimately, the move proved positive for the family and for Reed, allowing him to continue to develop professionally. After three years, he was offered the title of president at what would become known as Southern California University of Health Sciences. The position offered challenge, growth, and extensive world-wide travel with his family. It was seventeen years before he turned over the baton of the presidency, and headed north to cleaner air in the mountain country he'd always loved...southeast Idaho.

He and Sandra are currently building another custom home in Inkom, Idaho, and Reed is back in school, taking any class he hasn't already taught himself. He remains active in his LDS church, currently co-teaching a class in gospel doctrine with his wife. The couple has now been married over 40 years and will soon have 15 grandchildren.

Just since age sixty, Reed has scuba dived in Australia, climbed Mt. Kilamanjaro, toured Africa, taken up mountain biking, snow board-ing, pie baking, and learned how to drive a tractor. Retirement is not on the horizon for a man who is beginning his third historical book, consults with research organizations, and serves as director of the forthcoming *Don Aslett's Museum of Clean* in Pocatello, Idaho. As the director he is becoming knowledgeable in environmentally "green" buildings and an expert in the historical documentation of the social movement of clean.